D1430868

THE TREASURY OF MATHEMATICS

The Treasury of Mathematics

A COLLECTION OF SOURCE MATERIAL IN MATHEMATICS EDITED AND PRESENTED WITH INTRODUCTORY BIOGRAPHICAL AND HISTORICAL SKETCHES

Edited by

HENRIETTA O. MIDONICK

PHILOSOPHICAL LIBRARY

NEW YORK

15 East 40 Street, New York 16, New York.
Library of Congress Catalog Card No. 62-20873.

Printed in the United States of America

CONTENTS

FOREWORD

In this volume, I have collected significant contributions to the development of mathematics, selecting such as changed and influenced the course of human action, paying special attention to those whose lasting effect is discernible today. The form adopted for this publication is one which is, I believe, excellently suited to the task of making the landmarks of mathematical advance live again. Here we shall have not mere narration, nor simple paraphrasing, but the original master-words of the greatest inventive minds of the world, rendered easily accessible to student and layman.

There can be no easy or quick solution to the basic problem of selection in the preparation of such a work. The ablest and most profound mathematicians frequently prove to be prolific writers. Five volumes are required for the *Dialogues of Plato*, three for Euclid's *Elements* (the most famous of nine or ten works attributed to him). The collected papers of Charles S. Peirce appear in six volumes, those of James J. Sylvester in four, those of Arthur Cayley in thirteen. Moreover, for most mathematicians, complete collections have never been issued. Mathematical works containing vital, original contributions are, in general, widely scattered in books and professional periodicals over many lands. The essential part of the task of selection reduces to ascertaining where and how, in the prodigious, vastly extended outpouring of the human mind, where and how to seize a high moment of inspiration and inventiveness, a moment of passionate enthusiasm and vigorous creativeness, a moment whose fire forever fascinates.

The matter of translation in connection with an item to be included in the collection cannot by any means be regarded as one of secondary importance. Readers in English-speaking countries, apart from a comparatively small number of persons sufficiently trained in foreign languages, are dependent upon translations for a full view of what the world has accomplished in mathematics. Even in the case of English writers, the practice of writing scholarly works in Latin persisted for a long time. The works of Isaac Barrow published in the second half of the seventeenth century were in Latin. Newton's *Principia* was first translated into English from the Latin in 1729. Fortunately we possess superb translations of many works composed by the ancient Greek masters. The mysteries of mathematical inscriptions on clay, stone and papyrus are now dispelled by the combined forces of modern archeology, linguistics and mathematical science. Leading us step by step through the meanings of primitive symbols they join to transport us back in time to the great civilizations that flourished before Greece, there to observe examples of mathematics set down by ancient hands. In a translation, clearly, the search must be for one which not only reflects the author's thought and style, but also tends, through the subtleties of language, to minimize distance both in time and space.

Consideration along these lines entered basically into the choice of articles collected in the *Treasury of Mathematics.* The selections represent pivotal points in the advance and spread of mathematical knowledge from its earliest appearance to the rise of the fundamental notions of the calculus, mathematical philosophy and logic. To the justly famous treasures of Europe have been added valuable finds of recent discovery. These together with the mathematical works arising in the Far East, the Middle East and the Americas are dramatic evidence of the world-embracing grandeur of the progress of mathematics. Wherever possible, a selection is given under the name of the great innovator to whom we are indebted for it. Mathematics in many aspects will be found here: the exposition of the concept of number by Gottlob Frege, the so-called "Chinese remainder problem" first stated by Sun Tsu, the revelation by Archimedes of his way of thinking, the eloquent and effective plea by Simon Stevin for the adoption of the decimal system of notation, the shaded diagrams introduced in symbolic logic by John Venn, the algebra of Omar Khayyam, and so on. Where the evidences of mathematical knowledge and skill have lost all vestiges of individual contributions, source material has been drawn from the realm of the specialist's bookshelf. We turn, for example, to T. E. Peet for the analysis of Egyptian arithmetic and mensuration found in the Moscow Mathematical Papyrus, to C. P. Bowditch and S. G. Morley for an explanation of Mayan numeration and the amazingly accurate Mayan calendrical system, to L. L. Locke for a lucid account of the Peruvian *quipu,* to O. Neugebauer and A. Sachs for the results of recent researches on Babylonian mathematics. Occasion has been taken, too, to include the reproduction of some pages from rare old editions so that to the unhurried reader, the flavor of an old work and the personality of its author may be the more fully manifest.

Each of the fifty-four articles is preceded by a brief introductory essay in which I have sketched relevant biographical and historical details. The essays serve the purpose of general orientation. They also serve to indicate that the selections despite their wide variety, do not stand unrelated to one other or to world history, but are indeed prime instances of the continuity of the intellectual growth of mankind, and of the reality of the interplay of mathematical ideas with the economic, political and religious forces that shape men's lives.

HENRIETTA O. MIDONICK

arithmetic and mensuration found in the Moscow Mathematical Papyrus, to C. P. Bowditch and S. G. Morley for an explanation of Mayan numeration and the amazingly accurate Mayan calendrical system, to L. L. Locke for a lucid account of the Peruvian quipus, to O. Neugebauer and A. Sachs for the results of recent researches on Babylonian mathematics. Occasion has been taken, too, to include the reproduction of some pages from rare old editions so that to the unhurried reader, the flavor of an old work and the personality of its author may be the more fully manifest.

Each of the fifty-four articles is preceded by a brief introductory essay in which I have sketched relevant biographical and historical details. The essays serve the purpose of general orientation. They also serve to indicate that the selections despite their wide variety, do not stand unrelated to one other or to world history, but are indeed prime instances of the continuity of the intellectual growth of mankind, and of the reality of the interplay of mathematical ideas with the economic, political and religious forces that shape men's lives.

HENRIETTA O. MIDONICK

ACKNOWLEDGMENTS

Grateful acknowledgment and appreciation is extended to the publishers below, for their gracious consent to the use of the material listed:

APOLLONIUS OF PERGA.
Selections from Eutocius's **Commentary on Apollonius's Conics** and from Apollonius's **Conics.** Both from **Greek Mathematical Works,** Vol. II, translated by Ivor Thomas. Harvard University Press, Cambridge, Mass., 1941, repr. 1957. (Loeb Classical Library, No. 362).

ARCHIMEDES.
Selections from **On Spirals;** Selections from **The Method;** Selections from **The Quadrature of the Parabola.** All from **The Works of Archimedes, with The Method of Archimedes** edited by T. L. Heath, Dover Publications Inc., N. Y., an unabridged reissue of the Heath ed. of 1897, including the Supplement of 1912, by special arrangement with Cambridge U. Press.

ARYABHATA, THE ELDER.
Selections from **The Aryabhatiya of Aryabhata,** translated with notes by Walter Eugene Clark. University of Chicago Press, Chicago, Ill., 1930.

THE BABYLONIANS.
Selections from **The Exact Sciences in Antiquity,** Chaps. I and II, by Otto Neugebauer, Princeton University Press, Princeton, N. J., 1952; Selections from **Mathematical Cuneiform Texts,** edited by O. Neugebauer and A. Sachs. Published jointly by American Oriental Society and the American Schools of Oriental Research in the **American Oriental Series,** Vol. 29, New Haven, Conn., 1945.

THE BAKHSHALI MANUSCRIPT.
Selections from the article, **The Bakhshali Manuscript,** by Dr. A. F. Rudolf Hoernle, in **The Indian Antiquary,** a Journal of Oriental Research, Vol. XVII, February 1888.

ISAAC BARROW.
Selections from **Lecture X,** of the **Geometrical Lectures of Isaac Barrow,** translated with notes etc. by J. M. Child, Open Court Press Pub. Co., Chicago and London, 1916.

BHASCARA ACHARYA.
Selections from the **Sidd'hanta-siromani,** Chapters entitled, **Lilavati** and **Vija-Ganita;** these selections are from **Algebra with Arithmetic and Mensuration** from the Sanscrit of Brahmagupta and Bhascara, translated by Henry Thomas Colebrooke; published by John Murray, London, 1817.

IMMANUEL BEN JACOB BONFILS.
Selections from **Derekh Hilluq.** Translated, with notes, by Solomon Gandz. From an article by Solomon Gandz entitled, **The Invention of Decimal Fractions and the Application of the Exponential Calculus by Immanuel Bonfils of Tarascon, in ISIS,** vol. 25, 1936.

GEORGE BOOLE.
Selections from Boole's **The Mathematical Analysis of Logic,** Philosophical Libr., 1948 (reprint of 1847 publication). Selec. from Boole's **An Investigation of the Laws of Thought,** Walton and Maberly, London, Cambridge: Macmillan and Co., 1854.

BRAHMAGUPTA.
Selections from Chapters 12 and 18 of the **Brahma-sphuta-sidd'hanta;** these selections are from the **Algebra with Arithmetic and Mensuration** from the Sanscrit of Brahmagupta and Bhascara, translated by Henry Thomas Colebrooke, pub. by John Murray, London, 1817.

GEORG CANTOR.
Selections from Article I, publ. 1895 vol. xlvi pp. 481-512 in **Mathematische Annalen,** under the title **Beiträge zur Begrundüng der transfiniten Mengenlehre.** Translated by Philip E. B. Jourdain, and appearing **in Contributions to the Founding of the Theory of Transfinite Numbers by Georg Cantor,** translated with notes by Jourdain; reprint of 1915 edition published by Dover Publications Inc., N. Y.

ARTHUR CAYLEY.
Selections from **A Memoir on the Theory of Matrices,** from the **Collected Mathematical Papers of Arthur Cayley** Vol. II Cambridge University Press, 1889.

CHANG TSANG.
Excerpts from the "Arithmetical Rules of the Nine Sections" (Chinese title, **K'iu-ch'ang Suan-shu),** from the following: (1) **Chinese Researches,** by Alexander Wylie, Shanghai, 1897; (2) **The Development of Mathematics in China and Japan,** by Yoshio Mikami, which appears in **Abhandlungen zur Geschichte der Mathematischen Wissenschaften,** Leipzig, 1913, and Chelsea Publishing Co., N. Y.

GEOFFREY CHAUCER.
Pages 1-28, 114-115 and 118-119 from **Early Science in Oxford,** Vol. 5, **Chaucer and Messahallah on the Astrolabe** by Dr. R. T. Gunther, Fellow of Magdalen College, Oxford; Printed for Subscribers at the University Press, 1929; by courtesy of Mr. A. E. Gunther.

CH'IN CHIU-SHAO.
Selections from **Su-shu Chiu-chang ("Nine Sections of the Art of Numbers")**. From **Chinese Researches**, by Alexander Wylie, Shanghai, 1897.

CHOU KUNG.
Selections from the **Chou-Pi** (Chow-pi). From **Chinese Researches** by Alexander Wylie, Shanghai, 1897.

CHU CHI-CHIEH.
Excerpts from **Suan-hsiao Chi-meng**, from **A History of Japanese Mathematics** by D. E. Smith and Y. Mikami, Open Court Pub. Co., Chicago, 1914. Excerpts from **"Precious Mirror of the Four Origins"** from the following two sources: (1) **Chinese Researches**, Alexander Wylie, Shanghai, 1897; (2) **The Development of Mathematics in China and Japan**, Y. Mikami in **Abhandlungen zur Geschichte der Mathematischen Wissenschaften**, vol. XXX, 1913, Leipzig, and Chelsea Publishing Co., N. Y.

GABRIEL CRAMER.
Selections from **Introduction to the Analysis of Algebraic Curves**, translated especially for this publication by Henrietta O. Midonick, from the French **Introduction a l'Analyse des Lignes Courbes Algebriques**, published by Cramer Bros. and Cl. Philibert, Geneva, 1750.

AUGUSTUS DE MORGAN.
Selections from **On the Syllogism, No. III and On Logic in General**, Transactions of the Cambridge Philosophical Society, vol. X, 1864, Cambridge University Press, London.

RENÉ DESCARTES.
Selections from **Discourse on Method**, translated by John Veitch, published by L. Walter Dunne, London and Washington, 1901. Selections from **The Geometry of René Descartes**, translated from the French by D. E. Smith and M. L. Latham. Dover, 1954.

DIOPHANTUS.
Selections from the **Arithmetica**, taken from **Diophantus of Alexandria** by Sir Thomas L. Heath, Cambridge University Press, Second Edition, 1910.

ALBRECHT DÜRER.
Selections from **Four Books on Human Proportions**, and from **The Art of Mensuration**, in **The Writings of Albrecht Dürer**, translated by William Martin Conway, published by Peter Owen, Ltd., and later by Philosophical Library. Selections from **The Mathematics of Great Amateurs**, by Julian Lowell Coolidge, pub. by Oxford, Clarendon Press, 1949.

EUCLID OF ALEXANDRIA.
Selections from the **Elements.** Taken from **The Thirteen Books of Euclid's Elements**, translated from the text of Heiberg by Sir Thomas

L. Heath, second edition, vol. I, vol. II, Dover Publ. Inc., N. Y., 1956 reprint of the second ed., through special arrangement with Cambridge U. Press.

GOTTLOB FREGE.
Selections from **The Foundation of Arithmetic,** English translation by J. L. Austin from the German text **Die Grundlagen der Arithmetik,** Philosophical Library, 1953 reprint.

CARL FRIEDRICH GAUSS.
Selections from: (1) **Disquisitiones Arithmeticae,** translated from the Latin by Ralph G. Archibald, published in **A Source Book in Mathematics,** ed. by D. E. Smith, McGraw Hill, N. Y., 1929, and Harvard University Press; (2) **Theoria Motus,** translated from the Latin by Charles Henry Davis, pub. by Little, Brown & Co., 1857; (3) **The Foundations of Mathematics,** translated by G. Waldo Dunnington, Louisiana U. Press, Baton Rouge, 1937; (4) **Superficies Curvas,** translated from the Latin by J. C. Morehead and A. M. Hiltebeitel, Princeton U. Library, 1902.

HIPPOCRATES OF CHIOS.
Selections from Eudemus's **History of Geometry** taken from **Greek Geometry from Thales to Euclid,** by George J. Allman, Longmans, Green & Co., Lond., 1889.

HSIA-HOU YANG.
Excerpts from **Arithmetical Classic of Hsia-hou Yang,** by Pére Louis Vanhee, S. J., Brussels, taken from **The American Mathematical Monthly,** Vol. XXXI, 1924. Publ. by The Mathematical Association of America, Lancaster, Pa. and Ann Arbor, Mich.

MOHAMMED BEN MUSA AL-KHOWARIZMI.
Selections from **The Algebra of Mohammed ben Musa,** translated by Frederic Rosen, London: Printed for the Oriental Translation Fund, 1831.

GOTTFRIED WILHELM V. LEIBNIZ.
Selections from **Non inelegans specimen demonstrandi in abstractis,** translated from Gehrhardt's German translation into English by C. I. Lewis. The selections, **Scientia Generalis and Characteristica,** were taken from the Appendix to Lewis's book, entitled **A Survey of Symbolic Logic,** published by University of California Press, Berkeley, 1918.

LI YEH.
Extracts from **Tse-yuan Hai-ching** and from **I-ku Yen-tuan,** taken from **The Development of Mathematics in China and Japan** by Yoshio Mikami, in vol. XXX of **Abhandlungen zur Geschichte der Mathematischen Wissenschaften,** 1913, Chelsea Publishing Co., N. Y.

LIU HUI.

Extracts from the **Sea Island Arithmetic Classic,** taken from **The Development of Mathematics in China and Japan** by Yoshio Mikami, in vol. XXX of **Abhandlungen zur Geschichte der Mathematischen Wissenschaften,** 1913, Chelsea Publishing Co., N. Y.

THE MAYA CIVILIZATION.

Selections from: (1) **Mayan Numbers,** from **The Numeration, Calendar Systems and Astronomical Knowledge of the Mayas,** by Charles P. Bowditch, Cambridge, The U. Press, 1910; (2) **Table: Characteristics of Head-Variant Numerals,** from **An Introduction to the Study of the Maya Hieroglyphs,** by Sylvanus Morley, Washington Printing Office, 1915; (3) **The Maya Arithmetic and Chronology,** from **The Ancient Maya,** by Sylvanus G. Morley, Stanford U., Cal., 1947.

METRODORUS.

Selections from **Greek Anthology,** vol. 5, Bk. XIV, translated into English by W. R. Paton, Harvard U. Press, Cambridge, Mass., 1953.

THE MOSCOW PAPYRUS.

Selections: from **Four Geometrical Problems from the Moscow Mathematical Papyrus,** by Battiscombe Gunn and T. Eric Peet, published in the **Journal of Egyptian Archaeology,** vol. XV, parts III & IV Nov. 1929, by the Egyptian Exploration Society, London.

R. NEHEMIAH.

Selections from **The Mishnat ha-Middot,** translated into English by Solomon Gandz, published in **Quellen und Studien zur Geschichte der Mathematik, Astronomie und Physik,** Abteilung A, vol. 2, 1932, Julius Springer, Berlin.

SIR ISAAC NEWTON.

Selections: (1) from **Two Treatises (Of the Quadrature of Curves and Analysis by Equations of An Infinite Number of Terms)** translated into English by John Stewart, pub. by James Bettenham, London, 1745; (2) from **Mathematical Principles of Natural Philosophy and His System of the World.** Translated into English by Andrew Motte in 1729, revised by Florian Cajori, 1946, University of California Press, Berkeley, Cal.

NICOMACHUS OF GERASA.

Selections from the **Introduction to Arithmetic,** translated into English by Martin Luther D'Ooge, with studies in Greek Arithmetic by F. E. Robbins and L. C. Karpinski. Macmillan, N. Y., 1926. (Published in the University of Michigan Series, Humanistic Series, Vol. XVI.)

OMAR KHAYYAM.

Selections from **The Algebra of Omar Khayyam,** translated by Daoud S. Kasir, pub. by Bureau of Publications, Teachers College, Columbia University, N. Y., 1931.

PAPPUS.
Selections from **The Mathematical Collection,** translated into English by Ivor Thomas in **Greek Mathematical Works,** Vol. II. Harvard University Press, 1941, reprint 1957.

BENJAMIN PEIRCE.
Selections from **Linear Associative Algebra** with notes and addenda by C. S. Peirce, published in the **American Journal of Mathematics,** vol. IV, 1881. (Published under auspices of Johns Hopkins University, Balt., Md.)

CHARLES SANDERS PEIRCE.
Selections from the **Collected Papers of Charles Sanders Peirce,** Vol. III **(Exact Logic)** and Vol. IV **(The Simplest Mathematics).** Both volumes pub. by Harvard U. Press, 1933. (edited by Chas. Hartshorne and Paul Weiss.)

THE PERUVIAN QUIPU.
Selections from **The Ancient Quipu or Peruvian Knot Record** by Leslie Leland Locke, pub. by American Museum of Natural History, 1923.

PLATO.
Selection from **The Dialogues of Plato,** translated by B. Jowett, Second Edition, Oxford, Clarendon Press, 1875. Selections taken from: Vol. IV, Philebus, Theaetetus, Statesman; Vol. III, The Republic; Vol. II, Gorgias; Vol. V, Laws.

PROCLUS.
Selections from **Proclus's Summary** taken from his **Commentaries on Euclid, Bk. I,** translated into English by Ivor Thomas in **Greek Mathematical Works,** Vol. I. Harvard U. Press, 1939, reprint 1957. (Loeb Classical Library, No. 335).

ROBERT RECORDE.
Selections from **The Whetstone of Witte,** London 1557. On microfilm in Reading Room of N. Y. Public Library, 5th Ave. and 42nd Street, N. Y. This book is the 13th item on Reel 550, entitled **English Books Before 1640.** (Classmark *ZKC) The star is part of the classmark.

THE RHIND MATHEMATICAL PAPYRUS.
Selections from: (1) **The Rhind Mathematical Papyrus** by T. Eric Peet, pub., University Press of Liverpool, Ltd., Hodder and Stoughton, Ltd., London, 1923; (2) **The Rhind Mathematical Papyrus** by Arnold B. Chace and H. P. Manning, pub. by Mathematical Association of America, Vols. I & II, 1927, Oberlin, Ohio.

SIMON STEVIN.
Selections from **De Thiende in The Principal Works of Simon Stevin,** Vol. II, ed. by D. J. Struik, pub. by C. V. Swets and Zeitlinger, Amsterdam, 1958.

SUN-TSU.

Selections from the **Sun-Tsu Suan-ching** in **The Development of Mathematics in China and Japan** by Yoshio Mikami, pub. in **Abhandlungen zur Geschichte der Mathematischen Wissenschaften,** vol. XXX, 1913. Chelsea Publishing Co., N. Y.

JAMES JOSEPH SYLVESTER.

Selections from: (1) **Presidential Address to Section A of the British Association, 1869.** In the **Collected Mathematical Papers of James Joseph Sylvester,** Vol. II, Cambridge U. Press, 1908; (2) **Address on Commemoration Day at Johns Hopkins University,** Feb. 22, 1877. In the Collected Mathematical Papers etc., (as above in item (1)), Vol. III.

JOHN VENN.

Selections from **Symbolic Logic,** Second edition. Macmillan and Co., London & N. Y., 1894.

WAN WANG.

Selections from the **Yi King,** Part II of the **Texts of Confucianism,** translated by James Legge, published as Vol. XVI of **The Sacred Books of the East.** Oxford, At the Clarendon Press, 1882.

WANG HS'IAO-T'UNG.

Selections from the **Ch'i-ku Suan-ching** in **The Development of Mathematics in China and Japan** by Yoshio Mikami pub. in **Abhandlungen zur Geschichte der Mathematischen Wissenschaften,** vol XXX, 1913, Chelsea Publishing Co., N. Y.

CASPAR WESSEL.

Selections from **On the Analytic Representation of Direction,** translated into English by Martin A. Nordgaard in **A Source Book in Mathematics,** first ed., D. E. Smith. McGraw-Hill, N. Y., 1929, and Harvard University Press.

YANG HUI.

Selections from the **Analysis of the Nine Sections,** in **The Development of Mathematics in China and Japan** by Yoshio Mikami, pub. in **Abhandlungen zur Geschichte der Mathematischen Wissenschaften,** vol. XXX, 1913, Chelsea Publishing Co., N. Y.

THE TREASURY OF MATHEMATICS

APOLLONIUS OF PERGA

(Third Century B.C.)

Apollonius, an ancient mathematician of the great Alexandrian school, who was known to his contemporaries as "the Great Geometer," was born at Perga in Pamphylia a region in the south of Asia Minor. At least twenty-five years younger than Archimedes, he was at the height of his powers during the reign of Ptolemy Euergetes (247—221 B.C.) and Ptolemy Philopater (221—203 B.C.). Although it is believed by some that he appropriated a number of Archimedes' discoveries, he nevertheless has the unquestioned credit for having improved and advanced the theory of conics. Apollonius invented a generalized theory of conic sections in which he replaced the constructions of the conics proposed by Menaechmus (sections made by a plane perpendicular to an element of a right-angled, acute-angled and obtuse-angled cone for the parabola, ellipse and hyperbola, respectively) by constructions exhibiting all the conic sections on a single cone through the variation of the angle of the cutting plane. His detailed and well organized works swiftly became standard texts in ancient times, superseding previous writings, especially those on conics. Seven of the eight books of his great *Conics* have come down to us, the first four in Greek and the next three in Arabic. Only one treatise *(On the Cutting-off of a Ratio)* of the six Apollonian treatises mentioned by Pappus in his *Treasury of Analysis* has survived. We know from other commentaries that among his lost writings there are works on regular solids, on the theory of irrationals, on a number system, on properties of burning mirrors. Ptolemy credits Apollonius with a theory of epicycles and eccentric circles by which the latter sought to explain the movements of the planets.

Widespread interest in Apollonius's works was aroused by the Latin translation of Books I—IV of the *Conics* by Commanidinus (1566), an edition which also included the lemmas of Pappus and the commentaries of Eutocius. In 1710 a Latin translation of Books I—VII of the *Conics* begun by Gregory and completed by Halley was published. Offering a comprehensive treatment of the extant material of Books I—VII on a scale hitherto unknown, this publication was further distinguished by the addition of a restoration of Book VIII by Halley who based this part of the work on the accounts of its substance in the commentaries. Many attempts to restore the lost works of Apollonius were made by leading mathematicians, among them, Vieta, Snellius, Ghetaldus, Anderson, Schooten, Fermat, Simson, Horsely, Lawson and others. Indeed, the prodigious activity surrounding the study and reconstitution of his works effectively placed Apollonius in the direct line of the invention of analytic geometry and made him a powerful force in the modern development of mathematics.

THE CONIC SECTIONS

From

Selections Illustrating the History of Greek Mathematics
with an English Translation by Ivor Thomas

(i.) *Relation to Previous Works*

Eutocius, *Commentary on Apollonius's Conics*,
Apoll. Perg. ed. Heiberg ii. 168. 5-170. 26

Apollonius the geometer, my dear Anthemius, flourished at Perga in Pamphylia during the time of Ptolemy Euergetes, as is related in the life of Archimedes written by Heraclius,[b] who also says that Archimedes first conceived the theorems in conics and that Apollonius, finding they had been discovered by Archimedes but not published, appropriated them for himself, but in my opinion he errs. For in many places Archimedes appears to refer to the elements of conics as an older work, and moreover Apollonius does not claim to be giving his own discoveries; otherwise he would not have described his purpose as "to investigate these properties more fully and more generally than is done in the works of others." But what Geminus says is correct: defining a cone as the figure formed by the revolution of a right-angled triangle about one of the sides containing the right angle, the ancients naturally took all cones to be right with one section in each—in the right-angled cone the section now called the parabola, in the obtuse-angled the hyperbola, and in the acute-angled the ellipse; and in this may be found the reason for the names they gave to the sections. Just as the ancients, investigating each species of triangle separately, proved that there were two right angles first in the equilateral triangle, then in the isosceles, and finally in the scalene, whereas the more recent geometers have proved the general theorem, that *in any triangle the three internal angles are equal to*

[b] More probably Heraclides.

two right angles, so it has been with the sections of the cone; for the ancients investigated the so-called *section of a right-angled cone* in a right-angled cone only, cutting it by a plane perpendicular to one side of the cone, and they demonstrated the *section of an obtuse-angled cone* in an obtuse-angled cone and the *section of an acute-angled cone* in the acute-angled cone, in the cases of all the cones drawing the planes in the same way perpendicularly to one side of the cone; hence, it is clear, the ancient names of the curves. But later Apollonius of Perga proved generally that all the sections can be obtained in any cone, whether right or scalene, according to different relations of the plane to the cone. In admiration for this, and on account of the remarkable nature of the theorems in conics proved by him, his contemporaries called him the "Great Geometer." Geminus relates these details in the sixth book of his *Theory of Mathematics.*

(ii.) *Scope of the Work*

Apollonius, *Conics* i., Preface, Apoll. Perg. ed. Heiberg i. 2. 2-4. 28

Apollonius to Eudemus[b] greeting.

If you are in good health and matters are in other respects as you wish, it is well; I am pretty well too. During the time I spent with you at Pergamum, I noticed how eager you were to make acquaintance with my work in conics; I have therefore sent to you the first book, which I have revised, and I will send the remaining books when I am satisfied with them. I suppose you have not forgotten hearing me say that I took up this study at the request of Naucrates the geometer, at the time when he came to Alexandria and stayed with me, and that, when I had completed the investigation in

[b] Not, of course, the pupil of Aristotle who wrote the famous *History of Geometry,* unhappily lost.

eight books, I gave them to him at once, a little too hastily, because he was on the point of sailing, and so I was not able to correct them, but put down everything as it occurred to me, intending to make a revision at the end. Accordingly, as opportunity permits, I now publish on each occasion as much of the work as I have been able to correct. As certain other persons whom I have met have happened to get hold of the first and second books before they were corrected, do not be surprised if you come across them in a different form.

Of the eight books the first four form an elementary introduction. The first includes the methods of producing the three sections and the opposite branches [of the hyperbola] and their fundamental properties, which are investigated more fully and more generally than in the works of others. The second book includes the properties of the diameters and the axes of the sections as well the asymptotes, with other things generally and necessarily used in determining limits of possibility; and what I call diameters and axes you will learn from this book. The third book includes many remarkable theorems useful for the syntheses of solid loci and for determining limits of possibility; most of these theorems, and the most elegant, are new, and it was their discovery which made me realize that Euclid had not worked out the synthesis of the locus with respect to three and four lines, but only a chance portion of it, and that not successfully; for the synthesis could not be completed without the theorems discovered by me. The fourth book investigates how many times the sections of cones can meet one another and the circumference of a circle; in addition it contains other things, none of which have been discussed by previous writers, namely, in how many points a section of a cone or a circumference of a circle can meet [the opposite branches of hyperbolas].

The remaining books are thrown in by way of addition: one of them discusses fully *minima* and *maxima*, another deals with equal and similar sections of cones, another with theorems about the determinations of limits, and the last with determinate conic problems. When they are all published it will be possible for anyone who reads them to form his own judgement. Farewell.

(iii.) *Definitions*

Ibid., Definitions, Apoll. Perg. ed. Heiberg i. 6. 2-8. 20

If a straight line be drawn from a point to the circumference of a circle, which is not in the same plane with the point, and be produced in either direction, and if, while the point remains stationary, the straight line be made to move round the circumference of the circle until it returns to the point whence it set out, I call the surface described by the straight line *a conical surface*; it is composed of two surfaces lying vertically opposite to each other, of which each extends to infinity when the straight line which describes them is produced to infinity; I call the fixed point the vertex, and the straight line drawn through this point and the centre of the circle I call the *axis*.

The figure bounded by the circle and the conical surface between the vertex and the circumference of the circle I term a *cone*, and by the *vertex of the cone* I mean the point which is the vertex of the surface, and by the *axis* I mean the straight line drawn from the vertex to the centre of the circle, and by the *base* I mean the circle.

Of cones, I term those *right* which have their axes at right angles to their bases, and *scalene* those which have their axes not at right angles to their bases.

In any plane curve I mean by a *diameter* a straight line drawn from the curve which bisects all straight lines drawn in the curve parallel to a given straight line, and by the *vertex of the curve* I mean the extremity of the straight line on the curve, and I describe each of the parallels as being drawn *ordinatewise* to the diameter.

Similarly, in a pair of plane curves I mean by a *transverse diameter* a straight line which cuts the two curves and bisects all the straight lines drawn in either curve parallel to a given straight line, and by the *vertices of the curves* I mean the extremities of the diameter on the curves; and by an *erect diameter* I mean a straight line which lies between the two curves and bisects the portions cut off between the curves of all straight lines drawn parallel to a given straight line; and I describe each of the parallels as drawn *ordinate-wise to the diameter*.

By *conjugate diameters* in a curve or pair of curves I mean straight lines of which each, being a diameter, bisects parallels to the other.

By an *axis* of a curve or pair of curves I mean a straight line which, being a diameter of the curve or pair of curves, bisects the parallels at right angles.

By *conjugate axes* in a curve or pair of curves I mean straight lines which, being conjugate diameters, bisect at right angles the parallels to each other.

(v.) *Fundamental Properties*

Ibid., Props. 11-14, Apoll. Perg. ed. Heiberg i. 36. 26-58. 7

Prop. 11

Let a cone be cut by a plane through the axis, and let it be also cut by another plane cutting the base of the cone in a straight line perpendicular to the base of the axial triangle, and further let the diameter of the section be parallel to one side of the axial triangle; then if any straight line be drawn from the section of the cone parallel to the common section of the cutting plane and the base of the cone as far as the diameter of the section, its square will be equal to the rectangle bounded by the intercept made by it on the diameter in the direc-

tion of the vertex of the section and a certain other straight line; this straight line will bear the same ratio to the intercept between the angle of the cone and the vertex of the segment as the square on the base of the axial triangle bears to the rectangle bounded by the remaining two sides of the triangle; and let such a section be called a parabola.

For let there be a cone whose vertex is the point A and whose base is the circle ΒΓ, and let it be cut by a plane through the axis, and let the section so made be the triangle ΑΒΓ, and let it be cut by another plane cutting the base of the cone in the straight line ΔΕ perpendicular to ΒΓ, and let the section so made on the surface of the cone be ΔΖΕ, and let ΖΗ, the diameter of the section, be parallel to ΑΓ, one side of the axial triangle, and from the point Ζ let ΖΘ be drawn perpendicular to ΖΗ, and let $ΒΓ^2 : ΒΑ . ΑΓ = ΖΘ : ΖΑ$, and let any point Κ be taken at random on the section, and through Κ let ΚΛ be drawn parallel to ΔΕ. I say that $ΚΛ^2 = ΘΖ . ΖΛ$.

For let ΜΝ be drawn through Λ parallel to ΒΓ; but ΚΛ is parallel to ΔΕ; therefore the plane through ΚΛ,

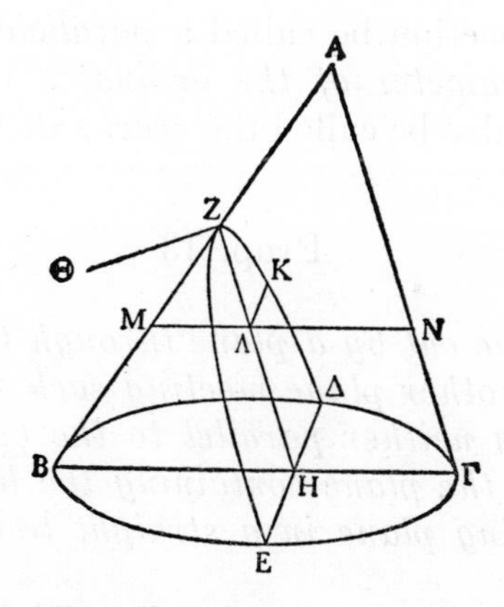

ΜΝ is parallel to the plane through ΒΓ, ΔΕ [Eucl. xi. 15], that is to the base of the cone. Therefore the plane

through $K\Lambda$, MN is a circle, whose diameter is MN [Prop. 4]. And $K\Lambda$ is perpendicular to MN, since ΔE is perpendicular to $B\Gamma$ [Eucl. xi. 10);

therefore $M\Lambda . \Lambda N = K\Lambda^2$.

And since $B\Gamma^2 : BA . 9\Gamma = \Theta Z : ZA$,

while $B\Gamma^2 : BA . A\Gamma = (B\Gamma : \Gamma A)(B\Gamma : BA)$,

therefore $\Theta Z : ZA = (B\Gamma : \Gamma A)(\Gamma B : BA)$.

But $B\Gamma : \Gamma A = MN : NA$

$= M\Lambda : \Lambda Z$, [Eucl. vi. 4

and $B\Gamma : BA = MN : MA$

$= \Lambda M : MZ$ [*ibid.*

$= N\Lambda : ZA$. [Eucl. vi. 2

Therefore $\Theta Z : ZA = (M\Lambda : \Lambda Z)(N\Lambda : ZA)$.

But $(M\Lambda : \Lambda Z)(\Lambda N : ZA) = M\Lambda . \Lambda N : \Lambda Z . ZA$.

Therefore $\Theta Z : ZA = M\Lambda . \Lambda N : \Lambda Z . ZA$.

But $\Theta Z : ZA = \Theta Z . Z\Lambda : \Lambda Z . ZA$,

by taking a common height $Z\Lambda$;

therefore $M\Lambda . \Lambda N : \Lambda Z . ZA = \Theta Z . Z\Lambda : \Lambda Z . ZA$.

Therefore $M\Lambda . \Lambda N = \Theta Z . Z\Lambda$. [Eucl. v. 9

But $M\Lambda . \Lambda N = K\Lambda^2$;

and therefore $K\Lambda^2 = \Theta Z . Z\Lambda$.

Let such a section be called a *parabola*, and let ΘZ be called the *parameter of the ordinates* to the diameter ZH, and let it also be called the *erect side* (*latus rectum*).[a]

Prop. 13

Let a cone be cut by a plane through the axis, and let it be cut by another plane meeting each side of the axial triangle, being neither parallel to the base nor subcontrary, and let the plane containing the base of the cone meet the cutting plane in a straight line perpendicular

[a] A *parabola* because the square on the ordinate $K\Lambda$ is *applied* to the parameter ΘZ in the form of the rectangle $\Theta Z . Z\Lambda$, and is exactly equal to this rectangle. It was Apollonius's most distinctive achievement to have based his treatment of the conic sections on the Pythagorean theory of the *application of areas*.

either to the base of the axial triangle or to the base produced; then if a straight line be drawn from any point of the section of the cone parallel to the common section of the planes as far as the diameter of the section, its square will be equal to an area applied to a certain straight line; this line is such that the diameter of the section will bear to it the same ratio as the square on the line drawn from the vertex of the cone parallel to the diameter of the section as far as the base of the triangle bears to the rectangle contained by the intercepts made by it on the sides of the triangle; the breadth of the applied figure will be the intercept made by it on the diameter in the direction of the vertex of the section; and the applied figure will be deficient by a figure similar and similarly situated to the rectangle bounded by the diameter and the parameter; and let such a section be called an ellipse.

Let there be a cone, whose vertex is the point Α and whose base is the circle ΒΓ, and let it be cut by a plane through the axis, and let the section so made be the tri-

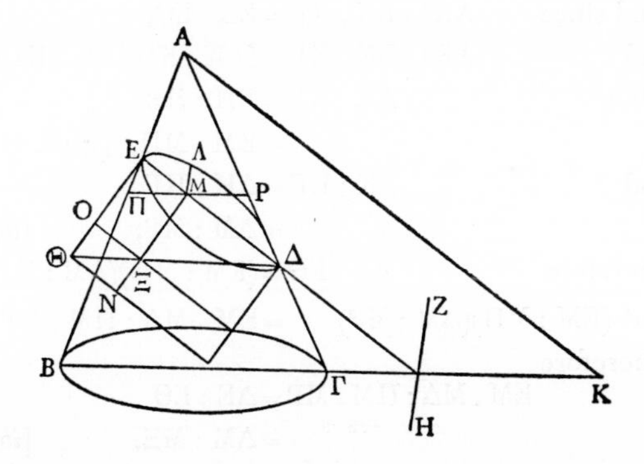

angle ΑΒΓ, and let it be cut by another plane meeting either side of the axial triangle, being drawn neither parallel to the base nor subcontrary, and let the section made on the surface of the cone be the curve ΔΕ; let the common section of the cutting plane and of that containing the base of the cone be ΖΗ, perpendicular to ΒΓ, and let the diameter of the section be ΕΔ, and from Ε let EΘ be drawn perpendicular to EΔ, and through A let AK be drawn parallel to EΔ, and let AK^2 : BK . KΓ = ΔE : EΘ, and let any point Λ be taken on the section, and through Λ let ΛM be drawn parallel to ZH. I say that the square on ΛM is equal to an area applied to the straight line EΘ, having EM for its breadth, and being deficient by a figure similar to the rectangle contained by ΔE, EΘ.

For let ΔΘ be joined, and through M let MΞN be drawn parallel to ΘE, and through Θ, Ξ, let ΘN, ΞO be drawn parallel to EM, and through M let ΠMP be drawn parallel to BΓ. Then since ΠP is parallel to BΓ, and ΛM is parallel to ZH, therefore the plane through ΛM, ΠP is parallel to the plane through ZH, BΓ [Eucl. xi. 15], that is to the base of the cone. If, therefore, the plane through ΛM, ΠP be produced, the section will be a circle with diameter ΠP [Prop. 4]. And ΛM is perpendicular to it; therefore

$$\Pi M \cdot MP = \Lambda M^2.$$

And since $AK^2 : BK \cdot K\Gamma = E\Delta : E\Theta$,

and $AK^2 : BK \cdot K\Gamma = (AK : KB)(AK : K\Gamma)$,

while $AK : KB = EH : HB$

$= EM : M\Pi$, [Eucl. vi. 4

and $AK : K\Gamma = \Delta H : H\Gamma$

$= \Delta M : MP$, [*ibid.*

therefore $\Delta E : E\Theta = (EM : M\Pi)(\Delta M : MP)$.

But $(EM : M\Pi)(\Delta M : MP) = EM \cdot M\Delta : \Pi M \cdot MP$.

Therefore

$EM \cdot M\Delta : \Pi M \cdot MP = \Delta E : E\Theta$

$= \Delta M : M\Xi$. [*ibid.*

But $\Delta M : M\Xi = \Delta M \cdot ME : \Xi M \cdot ME$,

by taking a common height ME.

Therefore $\Delta M \cdot ME : \Pi M \cdot MP = \Delta M \cdot ME : \Xi M \cdot ME$.

Therefore $\Pi M \cdot MP = \Xi M \cdot ME$. [Eucl. v. 9

But $\Pi M \cdot MP = \Lambda M^2$,

as was proved;

and therefore $\Xi M \cdot ME = \Lambda M^2$.

Therefore the square on ΛM is equal to MO, which is applied to ΘE, having EM for its breadth, and being deficient by the figure ON similar to the rectangle ΔE . EΘ. Let such a section be called an *ellipse,* let EΘ be called *the parameter to the ordinates* to ΔE, and let this line be called the *erect side* (*latus rectum*), and EΔ the *transverse side.*[a]

Prop. 14

If the vertically opposite surfaces [of a double cone] be cut by a plane not through the vertex, there will be

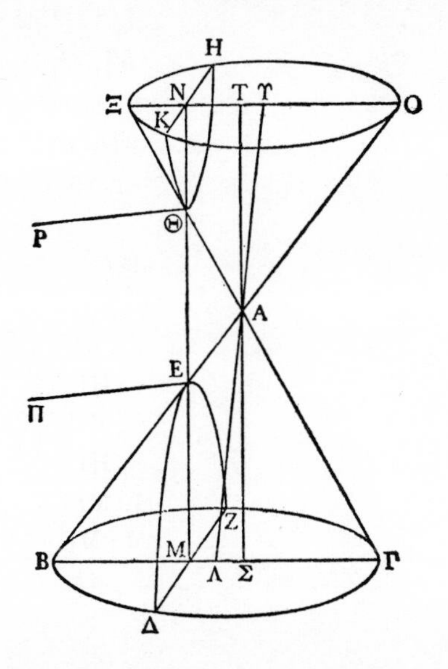

[a] Let p be the parameter of a conic section and d the corresponding diameter, and let the diameter of the section and the tangent at its extremity be taken as axes of co-ordinates (in general oblique). Then Props. 11-13 are equivalent to the Cartesian equations.

$$y^2 = px \qquad \text{(the parabola)},$$

and

$$y^2 = px \pm \frac{p}{q}x^2 \quad \text{(the hyperbola and ellipse respectively)}.$$

It is the essence of Apollonius's treatment to express the fundamental properties of the conics as equations between *areas,* whereas Archimedes had given the fundamental properties of the central conics as *proportions.*

formed on each of the surfaces the section called a hyperbola, and the diameter of both sections will be the same, and the parameter to the ordinates drawn parallel to the straight line in the base of the cone will be equal, and the transverse side of the figure will be common, being the straight line between the vertices of the sections; and let such sections be called opposite.

Let there be vertically opposite surfaces having the point A for vertex, and let them be cut by a plane not through the vertex, and let the sections so made on the surface be ΔEZ, HΘK. I say that each of the sections ΔEZ, HΘK is the so-called hyperbola.

ARCHIMEDES

(c. 287—212 B.C.)

Archimedes, mathematician, physicist and astronomer, the greatest universal intellect of ancient times, who was without a peer in breadth of knowledge and inventiveness for almost two thousand years, was born in Syracuse, a Greek settlement in Sicily, about 287 B.C. The son of Pheidias, an astronomer, he was a kinsman of King Hieron of Syracuse (260—216 B.C.), for whose benefit many of his discoveries in physical and mechanical science were made. The greatest part of Archimedes' life was spent in Syracuse, but it is known that he travelled to Egypt and that he studied for some time in Alexandria where the tradition of Euclid was still strong. Archimedes formed deep and lasting friendships with the mathematicians of Alexandria. His wide acquaintance among the scholars of his time and his personal attachment to some of them is shown in the prefaces written by him to his treatises, *On the Sphere and the Cylinder, On Spirals, The Method,* and others. Here Archimedes speaks with appreciation of Eratosthenes as "an earnest student, a man of considerable eminence in philosophy and an admirer of mathematical inquiry," and of Conon of Samos as a mathematician of "uncommon ability" and "extraordinary industry" by whose death he suffered the loss of an irreplaceable friend.

In the performance of many services for the king and for Syracuse, Archimedes acquired fame over the whole of the ancient world for his matchless originality in the fields of astronomy, mechanics, hydrostatics and optics as well as in mathematics. His test for determining the proportions of metals in a gold wreath consecrated by the king is well known. He was held in the highest esteem for his cochlias (Archimedean screw), his hydraulic organ, ballistic machines, cranes, burning mirrors, compound pulleys and the like. Nevertheless he regarded such inventions and contrivances as sordidly commercial, refusing to write on these subjects except in one instance *(On Sphere-making).* His published treatises were models of mathematical organization.

When Syracuse was attacked by the Roman forces under Marcellus, Archimedes actively participated in the defense of the city. Directing the use of systems of pulleys, levers, cranes and other devices which he had invented long before, as practical demonstrations of his theories, Archimedes forced the withdrawal of the Romans and was the principal factor in the three year delay of the fall of Syracuse. Details of Archimedes' death are variously told, but all accounts agree that he was killed at the age of seventy-five by a blundering soldier of the invading Roman army. Marcellus, overwhelmed with grief at the news of his death, attempted to make amends by protecting and even honoring any who could claim relationship to Archimedes. Cicero informs us that when he was quaestor in Sicily (75 B.C.) he saw Archimedes' tombstone which, though neglected, still showed the incised figure of a sphere inscribed in a cylinder. The theory epitomized by this figure was considered by Archimedes to be his greatest achievement.

The discovery by Heiberg in 1906 of a manuscript of Archimedes' treatise, *The Method,* believed until that time to be irretrievably lost, augmented the small portion of his published works which had come down to us. *The Method* is unusually informative for an ancient Greek mathematical work, in that it contains a discussion of the problem of the discovery of mathematical theorems as well as the construction of their proofs. Highly suggestive as Archimedes' works were to his contemporaries and to succeeding generations, it remained for mathematicians living almost two thousand years after him, to perceive the import of the form in which he preferred to state his mathematical problems, and his analyses of them. In the hands of seventeenth century scholars, Archimedes' writings were of prime influence in the evolution of the calculus.

ON SPIRALS[1]

"ARCHIMEDES to Dositheus greeting.

Of most of the theorems which I sent to Conon, and of which you ask me from time to time to send you the proofs, the demonstrations are already before you in the books brought to you by Heracleides; and some more are also contained in that which I now send you. Do not be surprised at my taking a considerable time before publishing these proofs. This has been owing to my desire to communicate them first to persons engaged in mathematical studies and anxious to investigate them. In fact, how many theorems in geometry which have seemed at first impracticable are in time successfully worked out!

[1] Extracts from *On Spirals, The Method* and *Quadrature of the Parabola* are taken from *The Works of Archimedes,* edited in modern notation by Sir Thomas L. Heath.

Now Conon died before he had sufficient time to investigate the theorems referred to; otherwise he would have discovered and made manifest all these things, and would have enriched geometry by many other discoveries besides. For I know well that it was no common ability that he brought to bear on mathematics, and that his industry was extraordinary. But, though many years have elapsed since Conon's death, I do not find that any one of the problems has been stirred by a single person. I wish now to put them in review one by one, particularly as it happens that there are two included among them which are impossible of realisation [and which may serve as a warning] how those who claim to discover everything but produce no proofs of the same may be confuted as having actually pretended to discover the impossible.

What are the problems I mean, and what are those of which you have already received the proofs, and those of which the proofs are contained in this book respectively, I think it proper to specify. The first of the problems was, Given a sphere, to find a plane area equal to the surface of the sphere; and this was first made manifest on the publication of the book concerning the sphere, for, when it is once proved that the surface of any sphere is four times the greatest circle in the sphere, it is clear that it is possible to find a plane area equal to the surface of the sphere. The second was, Given a cone or a cylinder, to find a sphere equal to the cone or cylinder; the third, To cut a given sphere by a plane so that the segments of it have to one another an assigned ratio; the fourth, To cut a given sphere by a plane so that the segments of the surface have to one another an assigned ratio; the fifth, To make a given segment of a sphere similar to a given segment of a sphere*; the sixth, Given two segments of either the same or different spheres, to

* **τὸ δοθὲν τμᾶμα σφαίρας τῷ δοθέντι τμάματι σφαίρας ὁμοιῶσαι, i.e. to make a segment of a sphere similar to one given segment and equal in content to another given segment. [Cf. *On the Sphere and Cylinder*, II. 5.]**

find a segment of a sphere which shall be similar to one of the segments and have its surface equal to the surface of the other segment. The seventh was, From a given sphere to cut off a segment by a plane so that the segment bears to the cone which has the same base as the segment and equal height an assigned ratio greater than that of three to two. Of all the propositions just enumerated Heracleides brought you the proofs. The proposition stated next after these was wrong, viz. that, if a sphere be cut by a plane into unequal parts, the greater segment will have to the less the duplicate ratio of that which the greater surface has to the less. That this is wrong is obvious by what I sent you before; for it included this proposition: If a sphere be cut into unequal parts by a plane at right angles to any diameter in the sphere, the greater segment of the surface will have to the less the same ratio as the greater segment of the diameter has to the less, while the greater segment of the sphere has to the less a ratio less than the duplicate ratio of that which the greater surface has to the less, but greater than the sesquialterate* of that ratio. The last of the problems was also wrong, viz. that, if the diameter of any sphere be cut so that the square on the greater segment is triple of the square on the lesser segment, and if through the point thus arrived at a plane be drawn at right angles to the diameter and cutting the sphere, the figure in such a form as is the greater segment of the sphere is the greatest of all the segments which have an equal surface. That this is wrong is also clear from the theorems which I before sent you. For it was there proved that the hemisphere is the greatest of all the segments of a sphere bounded by an equal surface.

After these theorems the following were propounded concerning the cone†. If a section of a right-angled cone [a parabola], in which the diameter [axis] remains fixed,

* (*λόγον*) *μείζονα ἢ ἡμιόλιον τοῦ, ὃν ἔχει κ.τ.λ.*, i.e. a ratio greater than (the ratio of the surfaces)$^{\frac{3}{2}}$. See *On the Sphere and Cylinder*, II. 8.

† This should be presumably 'the *conoid*,' not 'the cone.'

be made to revolve so that the diameter [axis] is the axis [of revolution], let the figure described by the section of the right-angled cone be called a *conoid.* And if a plane touch the conoidal figure and another plane drawn parallel to the tangent plane cut off a segment of the conoid, let the *base* of the segment cut off be defined as the cutting plane, and the *vertex* as the point in which the other plane touches the conoid. Now, if the said figure be cut by a plane at right angles to the axis, it is clear that the section will be a circle; but it needs to be proved that the segment cut off will be half as large again as the cone which has the same base as the segment and equal height. And if two segments be cut off from the conoid by planes drawn in any manner, it is clear that the sections will be sections of acute-angled cones [ellipses] if the cutting planes be not at right angles to the axis; but it needs to be proved that the segments will bear to one another the ratio of the squares on the lines drawn from their vertices parallel to the axis to meet the cutting planes. The proofs of these propositions are not yet sent to you.

After these came the following propositions about the *spiral,* which are as it were another sort of problem having nothing in common with the foregoing; and I have written out the proofs of them for you in this book. They are as follows. If a straight line of which one extremity remains fixed be made to revolve at a uniform rate in a plane until it returns to the position from which it started, and if, at the same time as the straight line revolves, a point move at a uniform rate along the straight line, starting from the fixed extremity, the point will describe a spiral in the plane. I say then that the area bounded by the spiral and the straight line which has returned to the position from which it started is a third part of the circle described with the fixed point as centre and with radius the length traversed by the point along the straight line during the one revolution. And, if a straight line touch the spiral at the extreme end of the spiral, and another straight line be drawn at right angles to the line which has revolved and resumed its position from the fixed extremity of it, so as to meet the tangent, I say that the straight line so drawn to meet it is equal to the circumference of the circle. Again, if the revolving line and the point moving along it make several revolutions and return to the position from which the straight line started, I say that the area added by the spiral in the third revolution will be double of that added in the second, that in the fourth three times, that in the fifth four times, and generally the areas added in the later revolutions will be multiples of that added in the second revolution according to the successive numbers, while the area bounded by the spiral in the first revolution is a sixth part of that added in the second revolution. Also, if on the spiral described in one revolution two points be taken and straight lines be drawn joining them to the fixed extremity of the revolving line, and if two circles be drawn with the fixed point as centre and radii the lines drawn to the fixed extremity of the straight line, and the shorter of the two lines be produced, I say that (1) the area bounded by the circumference of the greater circle in the direction of (the part of) the spiral included between the straight lines, the spiral (itself) and the produced straight line will bear to (2) the area bounded by the circumference of the lesser circle, the same (part of the) spiral and the straight line joining their extremities the ratio which (3) the radius of the lesser circle together with two thirds of the excess of the radius of the greater circle over the radius of the lesser bears to (4) the radius of the lesser circle together with one third of the said excess.

The proofs then of these theorems and others relating to the spiral are given in the present book. Prefixed to them, after the manner usual in other geometrical works, are the propositions necessary to the proofs of them. And here too, as in the books previously published, I assume the following lemma, that, if there be (two) unequal lines or (two) unequal areas, the excess by which the greater exceeds the less can, by being [continually] added to itself, be made to exceed any given magnitude among those which are comparable with [it and with] one another."

Proposition 1.

If a point move at a uniform rate along any line, and two lengths be taken on it, they will be proportional to the times of describing them.

Proposition 2.

If each of two points on different lines respectively move along them each at a uniform rate, and if lengths be taken, one on each line, forming pairs, such that each pair are described in equal times, the lengths will be proportionals.

Proposition 3.

Given any number of circles, it is possible to find a straight line greater than the sum of all their circumferences.

For we have only to describe polygons about each and then take a straight line equal to the sum of the perimeters of the polygons.

Proposition 4.

Given two unequal lines, viz. a straight line and the circumference of a circle, it is possible to find a straight line less than the greater of the two lines and greater than the less.

For, by the Lemma, the excess can, by being added a sufficient number of times to itself, be made to exceed the lesser line.

Thus e.g., if $c > l$ (where c is the circumference of the circle and l the length of the straight line), we can find a number n such that

$$n\,(c - l) > l.$$

Therefore $$c - l > \frac{l}{n},$$

and $$c > l + \frac{l}{n} > l.$$

Hence we have only to divide l into n equal parts and add one of them to l. The resulting line will satisfy the condition.

Proposition 5.

Given a circle with centre O, and the tangent to it at a point A, it is possible to draw from O a straight line OPF, meeting the circle in P and the tangent in F, such that, if c be the circumference of any given circle whatever,

$$FP : OP < (\text{arc } AP) : c.$$

Take a straight line, as D, greater than the circumference c. [Prop. 3]

Through O draw OH parallel to the given tangent, and draw through A a line APH, meeting the circle in P and

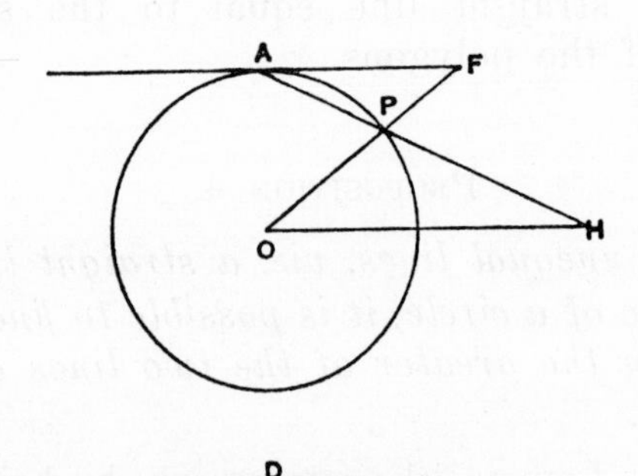

OH in H, such that the portion PH intercepted between the circle and the line OH may be equal to D. Join OP and produce it to meet the tangent in F.

Then $FP : OP = AP : PH$, by parallels,

$= AP : D$

$< (\text{arc } AP) : c.$

PROPOSITION 10.

If $A_1, A_2, A_3, \ldots A_n$ be n lines forming an ascending arithmetical progression in which the common difference is equal to A_1, the least term, then

$$(n+1) A_n^2 + A_1 (A_1 + A_3 + \ldots + A_n) = 3 (A_1^2 + A_2^2 + \ldots + A_n^2).$$

[Archimedes' result is equivalent to

$$1^2 + 2^2 + 3^2 + \ldots + n^2 = \frac{n(n+1)(2n+1)}{6}.]$$

COR. 1. *It follows from this proposition that*

$$n \cdot A_n^2 < 3 (A_1^2 + A_2^2 + \ldots + A_n^2),$$

and also that

$$n \cdot A_n^2 > 3 (A_1^2 + A_2^2 + \ldots + A_{n-1}^2).$$

COR. 2. *All the results will equally hold if similar figures are substituted for squares.*

DEFINITIONS.

1. If a straight line drawn in a plane revolve at a uniform rate about one extremity which remains fixed and return to the position from which it started, and if, at the same time as the line revolves, a point move at a uniform rate along the straight line beginning from the extremity which remains fixed, the point will describe a *spiral* (ἕλιξ) in the plane.

2. Let the extremity of the straight line which remains fixed while the straight line revolves be called the *origin** (ἀρχά) of the spiral.

3. And let the position of the line from which the straight line began to revolve be called the *initial line** in the revolution (ἀρχὰ τᾶς περιφορᾶς).

* The literal translation would of course be the "beginning of the spiral" and "the beginning of the revolution" respectively. But the modern names will be more suitable for use later on, and are therefore employed here.

4. Let the length which the point that moves along the straight line describes in one revolution be called the *first distance,* that which the same point describes in the second revolution the *second distance,* and similarly let the distances described in further revolutions be called after the number of the particular revolution.

5. Let the area bounded by the spiral described in the first revolution and the *first distance* be called the *first area,* that bounded by the spiral described in the second revolution and the *second distance* the *second area,* and similarly for the rest in order.

6. If from the origin of the spiral any straight line be drawn, let that side of it which is in the same direction as that of the revolution be called *forward* (*προαγουμενα*), and that which is in the other direction *backward* (*ἑπόμενα*).

7. Let the circle drawn with the *origin* as centre and the *first distance* as radius be called the *first circle,* that drawn with the same centre and twice the radius the *second circle,* and similarly for the succeeding circles.

Proposition 12.

If any number of straight lines drawn from the origin to meet the spiral make equal angles with one another, the lines will be in arithmetical progression.

Propositions 21, 22, 23.

Given an area bounded by any arc of a spiral and the lines joining the extremities of the arc to the origin, it is possible to circumscribe about the area one figure, and to inscribe in it another figure, each consisting of similar sectors of circles, and such that the circumscribed figure exceeds the inscribed by less than any assigned area.

For let BC be any arc of the spiral, O the origin. Draw the circle with centre O and radius OC, where C is the 'forward' end of the arc.

Then, by bisecting the angle BOC, bisecting the resulting angles, and so on continually, we shall ultimately arrive at an angle COr cutting off a sector of the circle less than any assigned area. Let COr be this sector.

Let the other lines dividing the angle BOC into equal parts meet the spiral in P, Q, and let Or meet it in R. With O as centre and radii OB, OP, OQ, OR respectively describe arcs of circles Bp', bBq', pQr', qRc', each meeting the adjacent radii as shown in the figure. In each case the arc in the 'forward' direction from each point will fall within, and the arc in the 'backward' direction outside, the spiral.

We have now a circumscribed figure and an inscribed figure each consisting of similar sectors of circles. To compare their areas, we take the successive sectors of each, beginning from OC, and compare them.

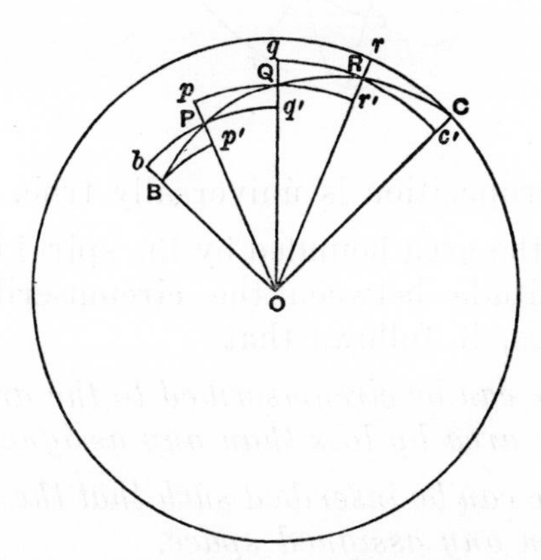

The sector OCr in the circumscribed figure stands alone.

And (sector ORq) = (sector ORc'),
(sector OQp) = (sector OQr'),
(sector OPb) = (sector OPq'),

while the sector OBp' in the inscribed figure stands alone.

Hence, if the equal sectors be taken away, the difference between the circumscribed and inscribed figures is equal to the difference between the sectors OCr and OBp'; and this difference is less than the sector OCr, which is itself less than any assigned area.

The proof is exactly the same whatever be the number of angles into which the angle BOC is divided, the only difference being that, when the arc begins from the origin, the smallest sectors OPb, OPq' in each figure are equal, and there is therefore no inscribed sector standing by itself, so that the difference between the circumscribed and inscribed figures is equal to the sector OCr itself.

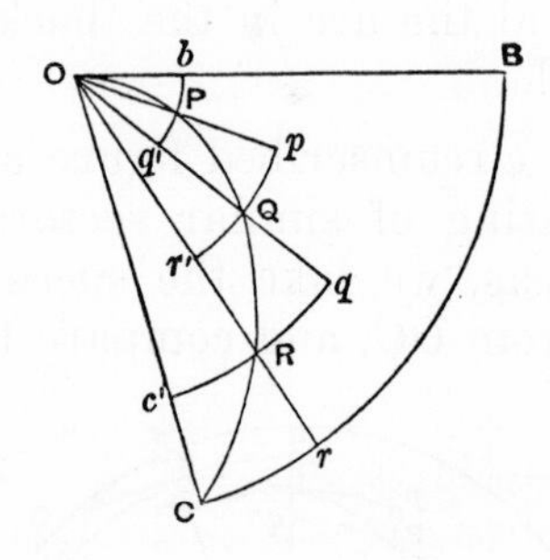

Thus the proposition is universally true.

Cor. Since the area bounded by the spiral is intermediate in magnitude between the circumscribed and inscribed figures, it follows that

(1) *a figure can be circumscribed to the area such that it exceeds the area by less than any assigned space,*

(2) *a figure can be inscribed such that the area exceeds it by less than any assigned space.*

Proposition 24.

The area bounded by the first turn of the spiral and the initial line is equal to one-third of the 'first circle' [$= \frac{1}{3}\pi(2\pi a)^2$, where the spiral is $r = a\theta$].

THE METHOD OF ARCHIMEDES TREATING OF MECHANICAL PROBLEMS

"Archimedes to Eratosthenes greeting.

I sent you on a former occasion some of the theorems discovered by me, merely writing out the enunciations and inviting you to discover the proofs, which at the moment I did not give. The enunciations of the theorems which I sent were as follows.

1. If in a right prism with parallelogrammic base a cylinder be inscribed which has its bases in the opposite parallelograms*, and its sides [i.e. four generators] on the remaining planes (faces) of the prism, and if through the centre of the circle which is the base of the cylinder and (through) one side of the square in the plane opposite to it a plane be drawn, the plane so drawn will cut off from the cylinder a segment which is bounded by two planes and the surface of the cylinder, one of the two planes being the plane which has been drawn and the other the plane in which the base of the cylinder is, and the surface being that which is between the said planes; and the segment cut off from the cylinder is one sixth part of the whole prism.

2. If in a cube a cylinder be inscribed which has its bases in the opposite parallelograms† and touches with its surface the remaining four planes (faces), and if there also be inscribed in the same cube another cylinder which has its bases in other parallelograms and touches with its surface the remaining four planes (faces), then the figure bounded by the surfaces of the cylinders, which is within both cylinders, is two-thirds of the whole cube.

Now these theorems differ in character from those communicated before; for we compared the figures then in question, conoids and spheroids and segments of them, in respect of size, with figures of cones and cylinders:

* The parallelograms are apparently *squares*.

† i.e. squares.

but none of those figures have yet been found to be equal to a solid figure bounded by planes; whereas each of the present figures bounded by two planes and surfaces of cylinders is found to be equal to one of the solid figures which are bounded by planes. The proofs then of these theorems I have written in this book and now send to you. Seeing moreover in you, as I say, an earnest student, a man of considerable eminence in philosophy, and an admirer [of mathematical inquiry], I thought fit to write out for you and explain in detail in the same book the peculiarity of a certain method, by which it will be possible for you to get a start to enable you to investigate some of the problems in mathematics by means of mechanics. This procedure is, I am persuaded, no less useful even for the proof of the theorems themselves; for certain things first became clear to me by a mechanical method, although they had to be demonstrated by geometry afterwards because their investigation by the said method did not furnish an actual demonstration. But it is of course easier, when we have previously acquired, by the method, some knowledge of the questions, to supply the proof than it is to find it without any previous knowledge. This is a reason why, in the case of the theorems the proof of which Eudoxus was the first to discover, namely that the cone is a third part of the cylinder, and the pyramid of the prism, having the same base and equal height, we should give no small share of the credit to Democritus who was the first to make the assertion with regard to the said figure though he did not prove it. I am myself in the position of having first made the discovery of the theorem now to be published [by the method indicated], and I deem it necessary to expound the method partly because I have already spoken of it† and I do not want to be thought to have uttered vain words, but equally because I am persuaded that it will be of no little service to mathematics; for I apprehend that some, either of my contemporaries or of my successors, will, by means of the method when

† Cf. Preface to *Quadrature of Parabola.*

once established, be able to discover other theorems in addition, which have not yet occurred to me.

First then I will set out the very first theorem which became known to me by means of mechanics, namely that

Any segment of a section of a right-angled cone (*i.e. a parabola*) *is four-thirds of the triangle which has the same base and equal height,*

and after this I will give each of the other theorems investigated by the same method. Then, at the end of the book, I will give the geometrical [proofs of the propositions] . . .

[I premise the following propositions which I shall use in the course of the work.]

1. If from [one magnitude another magnitude be subtracted which has not the same centre of gravity, the centre of gravity of the remainder is found by] producing [the straight line joining the centres of gravity of the whole magnitude and of the subtracted part in the direction of the centre of gravity of the whole] and cutting off from it a length which has to the distance between the said centres of gravity the ratio which the weight of the subtracted magnitude has to the weight of the remainder.

[*On the Equilibrium of Planes,* I. 8]

2. If the centres of gravity of any number of magnitudes whatever be on the same straight line, the centre of gravity of the magnitude made up of all of them will be on the same straight line. [Cf. *Ibid.* I. 5]

3. The centre of gravity of any straight line is the point of bisection of the straight line. [Cf. *Ibid.* I. 4]

4. The centre of gravity of any triangle is the point in which the straight lines drawn from the angular points of the triangle to the middle points of the (opposite) sides cut one another. [*Ibid.* I. 13, 14]

5. The centre of gravity of any parallelogram is the point in which the diagonals meet. [*Ibid.* I. 10]

6. The centre of gravity of a circle is the point which is also the centre [of the circle].

7. The centre of gravity of any cylinder is the point of bisection of the axis.

8. The centre of gravity of any cone is [the point which divides its axis so that] the portion [adjacent to the vertex is] triple [of the portion adjacent to the base].

[All these propositions have already been] proved*. [Besides these I require also the following proposition, which is easily proved:

If in two series of magnitudes those of the first series are, in order, proportional to those of the second series and further] the magnitudes [of the first series], either all or some of them, are in any ratio whatever [to those of a third series], and if the magnitudes of the second series are in the same ratio to the corresponding magnitudes [of a fourth series], then the sum of the magnitudes of the first series has to the sum of the selected magnitudes of the third series the same ratio which the sum of the magnitudes of the second series has to the sum of the (correspondingly) selected magnitudes of the fourth series. [*On Conoids and Spheroids*, Prop. 1.]"

Proposition 1.

Let *ABC* be a segment of a parabola bounded by the straight line *AC* and the parabola *ABC*, and let *D* be the middle point of *AC*. Draw the straight line *DBE* parallel to the axis of the parabola and join *AB*, *BC*.

Then shall the segment *ABC* be 4/3 of the triangle *ABC*.

From *A* draw *AKF* parallel to *DE*, and let the tangent to the parabola at *C* meet *DBE* in *E* and *AKF* in *F*.

* The problem of finding the centre of gravity of a cone is not solved in any extant work of Archimedes. It may have been solved either in a separate treatise [*On Balances* or *Levers*] which is lost, or perhaps in a larger mechanical work of which the extant books *On the Equilibrium of Planes* formed only a part.

Produce CB to meet AF in K, and again produce CK to H, making KH equal to CK.

Consider CH as the bar of a balance, K being its middle point.

Let MO be any straight line parallel to ED, and let it meet CF, CK, AC in M, N, O and the curve in P.

Now since CE is a tangent to the parabola and CD the semi-ordinate,

$$EB = BD;$$

"for this is proved in the Elements [of Conics]*."

Since FA, MO are parallel to ED, it follows that

$$FK = KA, MN = NO.$$

Now, by the property of the parabola, "proved in a lemma,"

$$MO : OP = CA : AO$$ [Cf. *Quadrature of Parabola*, Prop. 5]

$$= CK : KN$$ [Eucl. VI. 2]

$$= HK : KN.$$

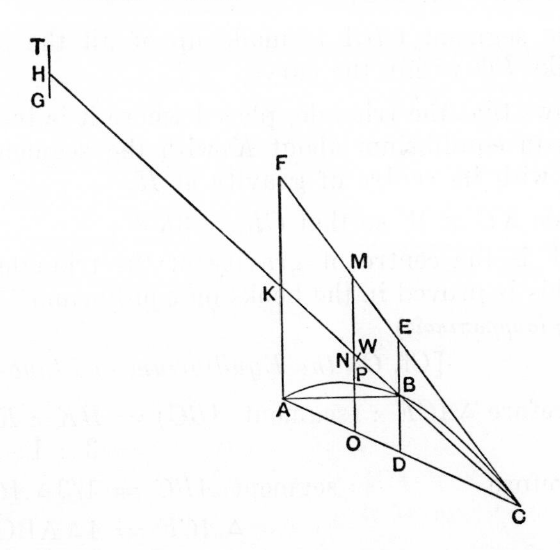

Take a straight line TG equal to OP, and place it with

* i.e. the works on conics by Aristaeus and Euclid.

its centre of gravity at H, so that $TH = HG$; then, since N is the centre of gravity of the straight line MO,

and $$MO : TG = HK : KN,$$

it follows that TG at H and MO at N will be in equilibrium about K. [*On the Equilibrium of Planes*, I. 6,7]

Similarly, for all other straight lines parallel to DE and meeting the arc of the parabola, (1) the portion intercepted between FC, AC with its middle point on KC and (2) a length equal to the intercept between the curve and AC placed with centre of gravity at H will be in equilibrium about K.

Therefore K is the centre of gravity of the whole system consisting (1) of all the straight lines as MO intercepted between FC, AC and placed as they actually are in the figure and (2) of all the straight lines placed at H equal to the straight lines as PO intercepted between the curve and AC.

And, since the triangle CFA is made up of all the parallel lines like MO,

and the segment CBA is made up of all the straight lines like PO within the curve,

it follows that the triangle, placed where it is in the figure, is in equilibrium about K with the segment CBA placed with its centre of gravity at H.

Divide KC at W so that $CK = 3KW$;

then W is the centre of gravity of the triangle ACF; "for this is proved in the books on equilibrium" (ἐν τοῖς ἰσορροπικοῖς)

[Cf. *On the Equilibrium of Planes*, I. 15]

Therefore $\triangle ACF$: (segment ABC) $= HK : KW$
$= 3 : 1.$

Therefore segment $ABC = 1/3 \triangle ACF$.

But $\triangle ACF = 4 \triangle \mathrm{ABC}$.

Therefore segment $ABC = 4/3 \triangle ABC$.

"Now the fact here stated is not actually demonstrated

by the argument used; but that argument has given a sort of indication that the conclusion is true. Seeing then that the theorem is not demonstrated, but at the same time suspecting that the conclusion is true, we shall have recourse to the geometrical demonstration which I myself discovered and have already published."

PROPOSITION 2.

We can investigate by the same method the propositions that

(1) *Any sphere is (in respect of solid content) four times the cone with base equal to a great circle of the sphere and height equal to its radius; and*

(2) *the cylinder with base equal to a great circle of the sphere and height equal to the diameter is* $1\frac{1}{2}$ *times the sphere.*

●

QUADRATURE OF THE PARABOLA

"ARCHIMEDES to Dositheus greeting.

"When I heard that Conon, who was my friend in his lifetime, was dead, but that you were acquainted with Conon and withal versed in geometry, while I grieved for the loss not only of a friend but of an admirable mathematician, I set myself the task of communicating to you, as I had intended to send to Conon, a certain geometrical theorem which had not been investigated before but has now been investigated by me, and which I first discovered by means of mechanics and then exhibited by means of geometry. Now some of the earlier geometers tried to prove it possible to find a rectilineal area equal to a given circle and a given segment of a circle; and after that they endeavoured to square the area bounded by the section of the whole cone and a straight line, assuming lemmas not easily conceded, so that it was recognised by most people that the problem was not solved. But I am not aware that any one of my predecessors has attempted to square the segment bounded by a straight line and a section of a right-angled cone [a parabola], of which problem I have now discovered the solution. For it is here shown that every segment bounded by a straight line and a section of a right-angled cone [a parabola] is four-thirds of the triangle which has the same base and equal height with the segment, and for the demonstration of this property the following lemma is assumed: that the excess by which the greater of (two) unequal areas exceeds the less can, by being added to itself, be made to exceed any given finite area. The earlier geometers have also used this lemma; for it is by the use of this same lemma that they have shown that circles are to one another in the duplicate ratio of their diameters, and that spheres are to one another in the triplicate ratio of their diameters, and further that every pyramid is one third part of the prism which has the same base with the pyramid and equal height; also, that every cone is one third part of the cylinder having the same base as the cone and equal height they proved by assuming a certain lemma similar to that aforesaid. And, in the result, each of the aforesaid theorems has been accepted no less than those proved without the lemma. As therefore my work now published has satisfied the same test as the propositions referred to, I have written out the proof and send it to you, first as investigated by means of mechanics, and afterwards too as demonstrated by geometry. Prefixed are, also, the elementary propositions in conics which are of service in the proof **(στοιχεῖα κωνικὰ χρεῖαν ἔχοντα ἐς τὰν ἀπόδειξιν)** Farewell."

Def. "In segments bounded by a straight line and any curve I call the straight line the *base,* and the *height* the greatest perpendicular drawn from the curve to the base of the segment, and the *vertex* the point from which the greatest perpendicular is drawn."

PROPOSITION 20.

If Qq be the base, and P the vertex, of a parabolic segment, then the triangle PQq is greater than half the segment PQq.

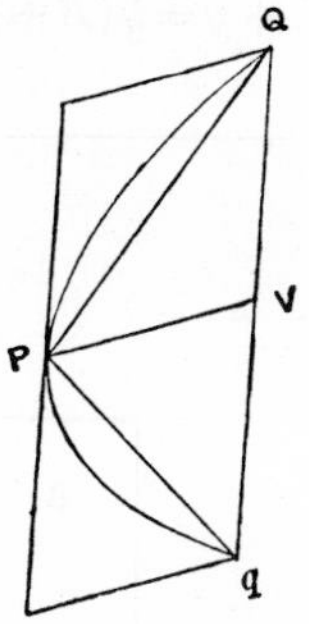

For the chord Qq is parallel to the tangent at P, and the triangle PQq is half the parallelogram formed by Qq, the tangent at P, and the diameters through Q, q.

Therefore the triangle PQq is greater than half the segment.

COR. It follows that *it is possible to inscribe in the segment a polygon such that the segments left over are together less than any assigned area.*

PROPOSITION 23.

Given a series of areas $A, B, C, D, \ldots Z$, of which A is the greatest, and each is equal to four times the next in order, then

$$A+B+C+\ldots+Z+\tfrac{1}{3}Z=\tfrac{4}{3}A.$$

Take areas $b, c, d, \ldots$ such that

$$b=\tfrac{1}{3}B,$$
$$c=\tfrac{1}{3}C,$$
$$d=\tfrac{1}{3}D, \text{ and so on.}$$

Then, since $b = \frac{1}{3}B,$
and $B = \frac{1}{4}A,$

$$B + b = \tfrac{1}{3}A.$$

Similarly $C + c = \frac{1}{3}B.$

. . . .

Therefore

$$B+C+D+\ldots+Z+b+c+d+\ldots+z=\tfrac{1}{3}(A+B+C+\ldots+Y).$$

But $b+c+d+\ldots+y=\frac{1}{3}(B+C+D+\ldots+Y).$

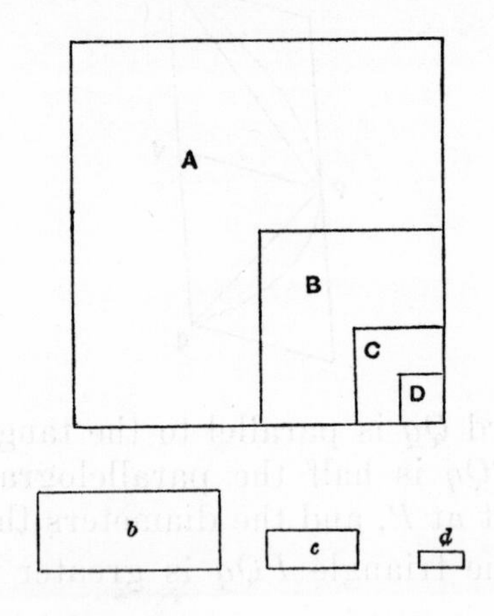

Therefore, by subtraction,

$$B+C+D+\ldots+Z+z=\tfrac{1}{3}A$$
$$A+B+C+\ldots+Z+\tfrac{1}{3}Z=\tfrac{4}{3}A.$$

[The algebraical equivalent of this result is of course

$$1+\tfrac{1}{4}+(\tfrac{1}{4})^2+\ldots+(\tfrac{1}{4})^{n-1}=\tfrac{4}{3}-\tfrac{1}{3}(\tfrac{1}{4})^{n-1}$$
$$=\frac{1-(\frac{1}{4})^n}{1-\frac{1}{4}}.]$$

Proposition 24.

Every segment bounded by a parabola and a chord Qq is equal to four-thirds of the triangle which has the same base as the segment and equal height.

Suppose $K = 4/3 \Delta PQq$

where P is the vertex of the segment; and we have then to prove that the area of the segment is equal to K.

For, if the segment be not equal to K, it must either be greater or less.

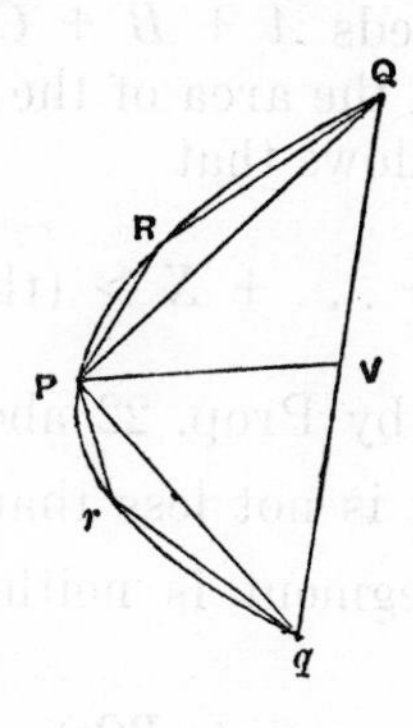

I. Suppose the area of the segment greater than K.

If then we inscribe in the segments cut off by PQ, Pq triangles which have the same base and equal height, i.e. triangles with the same vertices R, r as those of the segments, and if in the remaining segments we inscribe triangles in the same manner, and so on, we shall finally have segments remaining whose sum is less than the area by which the segment PQq exceeds K.

Therefore the polygon so formed must be greater than the area K; which is impossible, since [Prop. 23]

$$A + B + C + \ldots + Z < \tfrac{4}{3}A,$$

where
$$A = \Delta PQq.$$

Thus the area of the segment cannot be greater than K.

II. Suppose, if possible, that the area of the segment is less than K.

If then $\Delta PQq = A$, $B = 1/4 A$, $C = 1/4 B$, and so on, until we arrive at an area X such that X is less than the difference between K and the segment, we have

$$A+B+C+\ldots+X+\tfrac{1}{3}X=\tfrac{4}{3}A \qquad \text{[Prop. 23]}$$
$$=K.$$

Now, since K exceeds $A + B + C + \ldots + X$ by an area less than X, and the area of the segment by an area greater than X, it follows that

$$A + B + C + \ldots + X > \text{(the segment)};$$

which is impossible, by Prop. 22 above.

Hence the segment is not less than K.

Thus, since the segment is neither greater nor less than K,

$$\text{(area of segment } PQq)=K=\tfrac{4}{3}\triangle PQq.$$

ĀRYABHATA, THE ELDER

(b. 476 A.D.)

Aryabhata, the earliest Indian author on scientific astronomy whose work is extant, was the author of the *Āryabhatīya,* the first Indian astronomical text to contain a section devoted entirely to basic mathematics. The work, written in extremely concise, frequently poetical style, presents a series of rules apparently presupposing oral instructions to which the rules were a supplement. No detailed instruction is given. There may perhaps have been a more detailed work not yet rediscovered accompanying the rules.

Āryabhata states in his *Āryabhatīya* that he was born in 476 A.D. and that he was twenty-three years of age when he wrote this work in the city of Kusumapura ("City of Flowers"). By this statement, the scene of his major scientific activity was a city just above the Ganges near the present Patna which the ancient Buddhists called Pataliputra. These are the cities which, on various grounds, have been mentioned by historians as the place of his birth.

The text of the *Āryabhatīya* indicates that Āryabhata made astronomical observations, that he had a device for measuring time intervals, that he systematized previous astronomical achievements, discarding such as were in error, and that he possessed the technical mathematical knowledge needed for his astronomical calculations. The thirty three verses specifically on mathematics were brief rules for computational procedures including the extraction of square and cube roots, the solution of quadratic equations, the sum of the powers of the first *n* natural numbers and the sine or semi-chord.

Numerous later writers explained and enlarged the *Āryabhatīya,* although at times there was no lack of criticism of some particulars of his astronomical beliefs which ran counter to tradition. Brahmagupta, especially, made frequent adverse mention of Āryabhata. Indeed, in his *Brahmasphuta-sidd'hanta* (628 A.D.) much of the eleventh chapter is given to a bitter denunciation of Aryabhata's innovations. These criticisms themselves became the subject of long and protracted controversy, in the course of which the *Āryabhatīya* was again closely studied. Under the subsequent intensive scrutiny, the words of Āryabhata gained in respect and honor, and as the centuries passed they continued to influence and inspire succeeding generations of scholars.

THE ĀRYABHATĪYA of ĀRYABHATA

Translated with notes by Walter Eugene Clark*

CHAPTER I

DASAGĪTIKA OR THE TEN GĪTI STANZAS

A. Having paid reverence to Brahman, who is one (in causality, as the creator of the universe, but) many (in his manifestations), the true deity, the Supreme Spirit, Aryabhata sets forth three things: mathematics [*ganita*], the reckoning of time [*kālakriyā*], and the sphere [*gola*].

B. Beginning with *ka* the *varga* letters (are to be used) in the *varga* places, and the *avarga* letters (are to be used) in the *avarga* places. *Ya* is equal to the sum of *na* and *ma.* The nine vowels (are to be used) in two nines of places *varga* and *avarga. Navantyavarge va.*

The words *varga* and *avarga* seem to refer to the Indian method of extracting the square root . . .

The *varga* or "square" places are the first, third, fifth, etc., counting from the right. The *avarga* or "non-square" places are the second, fourth, sixth, etc., counting from the right. The words *varga* and *avarga* seem to be used in this sense in II, 4.

CHAPTER II

GANITAPADA OR MATHEMATICS

1. Having paid reverence to Brahman, the Earth, the Moon, Mercury, Venus, the Sun, Mars, Jupiter, Saturn, and the asterisms, Aryabhata sets forth here [in this work] the science which is honored at Kusumapura.[1]

---

* Ed. Note: Those paragraphs opening with letters A, B, and numbers 1 to 26 are translations of the Aryabhatiya; the material following those paragraphs is commentary by Walter Eugene Clark, the translator.

[1] Translated by Fleet, *JRAS,* 1911, p. 110.

The translation "here at Kusumapura the revered science" is possible. At any rate, Aryabhata states the school to which he belongs. Kusumapura may or may not have been the place of his birth.

2. The numbers *eka* (one), *dasa* (ten), *sata* (hundred), *sahasra* (thousand), *ayuta* (ten thousand), *niyuta* (hundred thousand), *prayuta* (million), *koti* (ten million), *arbuda* (hundred million), and *vrnda* (thousand million) are from place to place each ten times the preceding.[2]

The names for classes of numbers are given only to ten places, although I, B describes a notation which reaches at least to the eighteenth place. The highest number actually used by Aryabhata himself runs to ten places.

3. A square, the area of a square, and the product of two equal quantities are called *varga*. The product of three equal quantities, and a solid which has twelve edges are called *ghana*.

4. One should always divide the *avarga* by twice the (square) root of the (preceding) *varga*. After subtracting the square (of the quotient) from the *varga* the quotient will be the square root to the next place.

Counting from right to left, the odd places are called *varga* and the even places are called *avarga*. According to Paramesvara, the nearest square root to the number in the last odd place on the left is set down in a place apart, and after this are set down the successive quotients of the division performed. The number subtracted is the square of that figure in the root represented by the quotient of the preceding division. The divisor is the square of that part of the root which has already been found. If the last subtraction leaves no remainder the square root is exact. "Always" indicates that if the divisor is larger than the number to be divided a zero is to be placed in the line (or a blank space left there).

* * *

[2] See *JRAS,* 1911, p. 116.

The words of Aryabhata exactly fit the method employed in later Indian mathematics. . .

In the following example the sign ° indicates the *varga* places, and the sign — indicates the *avarga* places.

```
                      °—°—°
                      15129 (root=1
Square of the root    1
                      —
Twice the root     2)05(2=quotient (or next digit of root)
  (2×1)               4
                      —
                      11
Square of the
quotient              4
                      —
Twice the root     24)72(3=quotient
                          (or next digit of root)
  (2×12)              72
                      —
                      09
Square of the
quotient              9
                      —
                      0
                Square root is 1 2 3
```

5. One should divide the second *aghana* by three times the square of the (cube) root of the (preceding) *ghana*. The square (of the quotient) multiplied by three times the *purva* (that part of the cube root already found) is to be subtracted from the first *aghana,* and the cube (of the above division) is to be subtracted from the *ghana.*

Counting from right to left, the first, fourth, etc., places are named *ghana* (cubic); the second, fifth, etc., places are called the first *aghana* (non-cubic) places; and the third, sixth, etc., places are called the second *aghana* (non-cubic) places. The nearest cube root to the number in (or up to and including) the last *ghana* place on the left is the first figure of the cube root. After it are placed the quotients of the successive divisions. If the last subtraction leaves no remainder the cube root is exact.

In the following example the sign ° indicates the *ghana* places and the sign — indicates the *aghana* places.

	°—°—°
	1860867 (root=1
Cube of root	1
	—
Three times square of root (3×1^2)	3)08(2=quotient (or next digit of root)
	6
	—
	26
Square of quotient multiplied by three times the *purva* ($2^2 \times 3 \times 1$)	12
	——
	140
Cube of quotient	8
	——
Three times square of root (3×12^2)	432)1328(3=quotient (or next digit of root)
	1296
	——
	326
Square of quotient multiplied by three times the *purva* ($3^2 \times 3 \times 12$)	324
	——
	27
Cube of quotient	27
	—
	0

Cube root is 1 2 3

9. . . . The chord of the sixth part of the circumference is equal to the radius.

10. Add 4 to 100, multiply by 8, and add 62,000. The result is approximately the circumference of a circle of which the diameter is 20,000.

The circumference is 62,832. The diameter is 20,000.

By this rule the relation of circumference to diameter is 3.1416.

15. Multiply the length of the gnomon by the distance between the gnomon and the *bhuja* and divide by the difference between the length of the gnomon and the

length of the *bhuja*. The quotient will be the length of the shadow measured from the base of the gnomon.

Because of the use of the word *koti* in the following rule Rodet is inclined to think that the gnomon and the *bhuja* were not perpendicular but projected horizontally from a wall. *Bhuja* denotes any side of a triangle, but *koti* usually refers to an upright. It is possible, however, for *koti* to denote any perpendicular to the *bhuja* whether horizontal or upright.

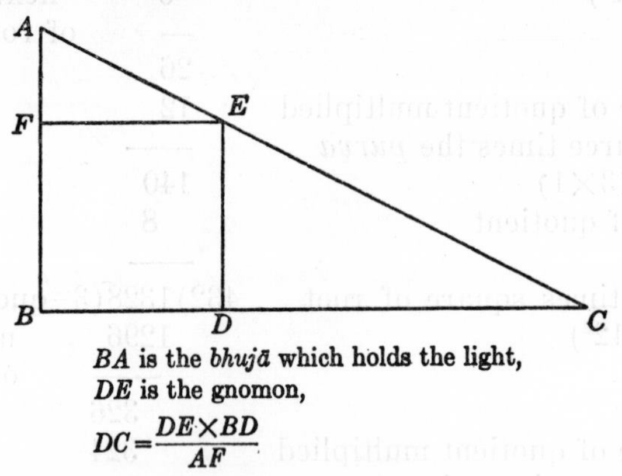

BA is the *bhujā* which holds the light,
DE is the gnomon,

$$DC=\frac{DE\times BD}{AF}$$

17a. The square of the *bhuja* plus the square of the *koti* is the square of the *karna*.

17b. In a circle the product of two *saras* is the square of the half-chord of the two arcs.

The *bhuja* and *koti* are the sides of a right-angle triangle. The *karna* is the hypotenuse.

The *saras* or "arrows" are the segments of a diameter which bisects any chord.

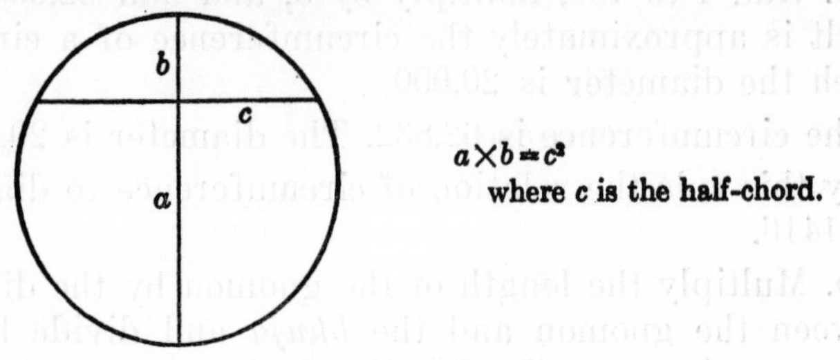

$a\times b=c^2$
where c is the half-chord.

19a. The desired number of terms minus one, halved,

plus the number of terms which precedes, multiplied by the common difference between the terms, plus the first term, is the middle term. This multiplied by the number of terms desired is the sum of the desired number of terms.

19b. Or the sum of the first and last terms is multiplied by half the number of terms.

This rule tells how to find the sum of any desired number of terms taken anywhere within an arithmetical progression. Let n be the number of terms extending from the $(p+1)$th to the $(p+n)$th terms in an arithmetical progression, let d be the common difference between the terms, let a be the first term of the progression, and l the last term.

The second part of the rule applies only to the sum of the whole progression beginning with the first term.

$$S = n\left[a + \left(\frac{n-1}{2} + p\right)d\right],$$

$$S = \frac{(a+l)n}{2}.$$

20. Multiply the sum of the progression by eight times the common difference, add the square of the difference between twice the first term and the common difference, take the square root of this, subtract twice the first term, divide by the common difference, add one, divide by two. The result will be the number of terms.

$$n = \frac{1}{2}\left[\frac{\sqrt{8dS + (d-2a)^2} - 2a}{d} + 1\right].$$

As Rodet says, the development of this formula from the one in the preceding rule seems to indicate knowledge of the solution of quadratic equations in the form $ax^2+bx+c=0$.

22. The sixth part of the product of three quantities consisting of the number of terms, the number of terms plus one, and twice the number of terms plus one is the

sum of the squares. The square of the sum of the (original) series is the sum of the cubes.

From the series 1 2 3 4, etc., form the series 1 4 9 16, etc., and 1 8 27 64, etc., consisting of the squares and cubes of the terms of the first series. The rule tells how to find the sums of the second and third series.

The rule for finding the sum of the first series was given above in stanza 19.

The sum of the squares is

$$\frac{n(n+1)(2n+1)}{6}.$$

23. One should subtract the sum of the squares of two factors from the square of their sum. Half the result is the product of the two factors.

$$ab=\frac{(a+b)^2-(a^2+b^2)}{2}.$$

24. Multiply the product (of two factors) by the square of two (4), add the square of the difference between the two factors, take the square root, add and subtract the difference between the two factors, and divide the result by two. The results will be the two factors.

$$\frac{\sqrt{4ab+(a-b)^2}\pm(a-b)}{2}\text{ will give } a \text{ and } b.$$

26. In the rule of three multiply the fruit by the desire and divide by the measure. The result will be the fruit of the desire.

The rule of three corresponds to proportion.

In the proportion a is to b as c is to x the measure is a, the fruit is b, the desire is c, and the fruit of the desire is x.

$$x=\frac{bc}{a}.$$

THE BABYLONIANS

(3rd Millennium B.C. to 0)

The startling finds of a highly developed ancient culture in the Mesopotamian Valley, made by French and British archaeologists in the decade of the 1840's, were followed in the next hundred years by scientific exploration of the ruins of the ancient cities of Babylonia. Archaeological excavation of the mounds marking the ancient sites revealed a complex civilization which flourished more than four thousand years ago in the fertile crescent of land watered by the Tigris and Euphrates Rivers. It was a civilization characterized by prospering agricultural settlements. Networks of canals whose purpose was to reclaim swamps and feed parched areas, were found. Here, according to Herodotus, wheat returned to the sower from two hundred- to three hundredfold. There were also numerous individuals who were occupied with laws, religion, science, art, architecture, trading, teaching, and engineering. Large palace sculptures, metal bas-reliefs, copper and bronze figures, painted pottery, cylinder seals, and other artifacts of great antiquity were recovered. Most significant of all the finds, however, were the thousands upon thousands of clay tablets unearthed at Nineveh, Assur, Nippur, and other sites, bearing the written records of the economic, juridical, educational and scientific phases of daily life in this remote period previously known to us, in the main, through Biblical allusions. The cuneiform writings incised on the tablets, painstakingly copied and deciphered by scholars of our own time, disclose an intricate system of trading in which weights and measures were standardized, and exchange was in kind or in money. Gold, silver and copper, used for ornamentation, also served as a medium of exchange. The shekel and fractional parts of the shekel were in common use. Skilled in the working of clay and metals, the Babylonians brought the carving of precious stones to a fine art. Great numbers of the tablets served as legal documents relating to business contracts, loans, property, inheritance, and marriage. Astronomical observations formed the basis of a calendar, the initial motivation being principally the timing of religious festivals. Later, under the intense interest attaching to all methods of divination, the vogue for astrological interpretations of astronomy grew to great proportions.

Underlying the commercial, monetary and astronomical systems employed by the Babylonians, were their achievements in mathematics, made known to us through the continuing study and decipherment of the cuneiform inscriptions on the ancient tablets by scholars who happily combine the requisite linguistic power with the technical scientific knowledge needed. Although the tablets containing mathematical subject matter are only a small portion of the huge collections of tablets recovered, they are cogent evidence of a high degree of skill and originality on the part of Babylonian mathematicians. Outstanding among the contributions of the Babylonians to the development of mathematics is their use of place values in their system of numeration. The remarkable accuracy of Babylonian astronomical computations was due in no small measure to the convenient form of their number system. The first record we possess of any study of problems in number theory is contained in a Babylonian mathematical tablet (Plimpton 322, Columbia University, N. Y.).

Most of the mathematical tablets have been classified either as "table texts" or as "problem texts." The latter appear in many cases to have been school texts illustrating rules for the solution of problems. The table texts were ever present aids both for instructional problems and for practical use. They included tables of reciprocals, squares and square roots, cubes and cube roots as well as multiplication tables. With these tables at their disposal for the numerical calculations involved, the Babylonians developed many ingenious rules and methods for the solution of a wide variety of mathematical problems.

THE EXACT SCIENCES IN ANTIQUITY

by O. Neugebauer

Chapter I

The texts of which I speak are clay tablets, generally about the size of a hand, inscribed with signs which were pressed into the surface of the once soft clay by means of a sharpened stylus. This script is called "cuneiform," i.e. wedge-shaped, because the individual impressions have a deeper "head" and a finer line at the end, thus resembling a wedge. Cuneiform tablets with mathematical contents are known to us mostly from the so-called "Old-Babylonian" period, about 1600 B.C. No astronomical texts of any scientific significance exist from this period, while the mathematical texts already show the highest level ever attained in Babylonia.

The second period from which we have a larger number of texts is the latest period of Babylonian history, when Mesopotamia had become a part of the empire of Alexander's successors, the "Seleucids." This period, from about 300 B.C. to the beginning of our era, has furnished us with a great number of astronomical texts of a most remarkable mathematical character, fully comparable to the astronomy of the Almagest. Mathematical texts from this period are scarce, but they suffice nevertheless to demonstrate that the knowledge of Old-Babylonian mathematics had not been lost during the intervening 1300 years for which texts are lacking.

Plate 4-b. VAT 12770 obv. Economic Text from Fara

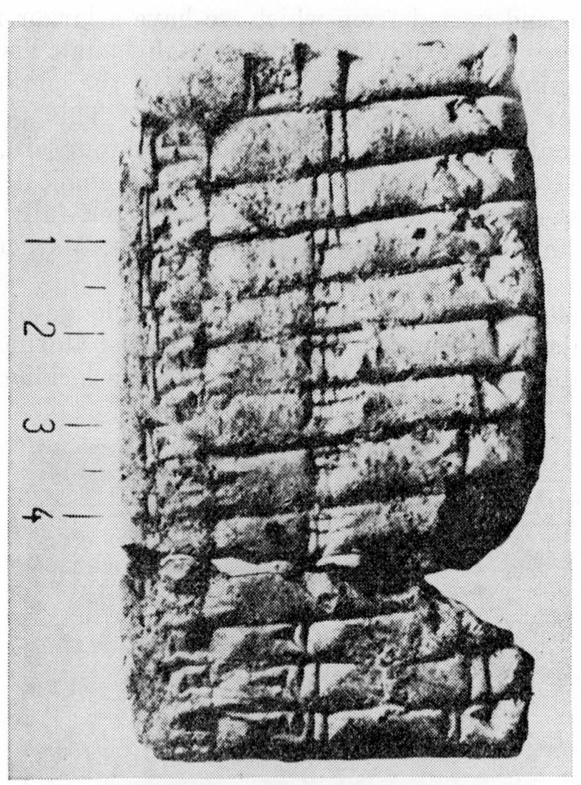

Plate 4-a. VAT 7858 obv.
Multiplication Table for 10

12. The development of the numerical notations in Mesopotamia took as many centuries as the development of writing from a crude picture script to a well defined system of complicated signs. We shall for the moment deal only with the final product as it appears in the mathematical texts of the Old-Babylonian period. And we shall again use the most direct approach by deciphering an actual text.

Pl. 4, a shows a tablet whose size is about 3-1/8 by 2 inches (and about ¾ of an inch thick). In the middle of the text is visible a column of signs which obviously represent numbers in ascending order. The tablet is not quite cleaned from incrustation of salt or dirt but it is clear that the signs look about as follows:

Counting of the vertical wedges leads directly to the readings 1, 2, 3, etc. up to 9. Then follows < which must be 10, and consequently we can also read the remaining signs as 11, 12, 13. Using this exceedingly plausible hypothesis, we should also be able to read the right-hand column of signs. The first five look as follows:

Obviously we must read these signs as 10, 20, 30, 40, 50 if the first sign represents 10 as we have established in our first list. But what follows is

* * *

which we transcribe consistently as

1 1,10 1,20 * * * 2 2,10

each * indicating a broken line. These signs continue the previous ones if we interpret the first "1" as 60 and then read 1,10 as $60 + 10 = 70$ and 1,20 as $60 + 20 = 80$. The broken lines should contain 90, 100, and 110. The next sign "2" should be 120, in excellent agreement with our interpretation of "1" as 60, while the last sign 2,10 must be $120 + 10 = 130$. Thus we have obtained all multiples of 10 from 10 to 130, line by line, corresponding to the numbers 1 to 13. In other words, our table is a multiplication table for 10, which we now can transcribe as follows:

1	10
2	20
3	30
4	40
5	50
6	1
7	1,10
8	1,20
9	1,30
10	1,40
11	1,50
12	2
13	2,10

The notation 1,10 = 70 1,20 = 80 2,10 = 130 etc. is "sexagesimal" in the sense that 60 units of one kind are written as 1 of the next higher order.

13. The example of our present system of numeration for degrees, hours, measures and ordinary numbers should suffice totally to discredit the popular idea that a number system was "invented" at a certain moment. Yet innumerable "reasons" have been advanced why the Babylonians used the basis 60 for their number system. I shall not make any attempt to discuss here the history of the sexagesimal system in any detail, but a few points must be mentioned because they are of importance for the historical approach to the development of number systems as a whole.

First of all, there exists a common misconception as to the generality of the use of the sexagesimal system. The very same tablet which contains hundreds of sexagesimal numbers, column beside column, to compute the dates of the new moons for a given year, might end with a "colophon" containing the name of the owner of the tablet, the name of the scribe, and the date of writing of the text, the year being expressed in the form 2 *me* 25 "2 hundred 25" where the main text would express the very same date sexagesimally as 3,45. In other words, it is only in strictly mathematical or astronomical contexts that the sexagesimal system is consistently applied. In all other matters (dates, measures of weight, areas, etc.), use was made of mixed systems which have their exact parallel in the chaos of 60-division, 24-division, 12-division, 10-division, 2-division which characterizes the units of our own civilization. The question of the origin of the sexagesimal system is therefore inextricably related to the much more complex problem of the history of many concurrent numerical notations and their innumerable local and chronological variations.

14. The Babylonian place value notation shows in its earlier development two disadvantages which are due to the lack of a symbol for zero. The first difficulty consists in the possibility of misreading a number 1 20 as 1,20 = 80 when actually 1,0,20 = 3620 was meant. Occasionally this ambiguity is overcome by separating the two numbers very clearly if a whole sexagesimal place is missing. But this method is by no means strictly applied and we have many cases where numbers are spaced widely apart without any significance. In the latest period, however, when astronomical texts were computed, a special symbol for "zero" was used. This symbol also occurs earlier as a separation mark between sentences, and I therefore transcribe it by a "period." Thus we find in Seleucid astronomical texts many instances of numbers like 1,.,20 or even 1,.,.,20 which apply exactly the same principle as our 201 or 2001.

But even in the final phase of Babylonian writing we do not find any examples of zero signs at the end of numbers. Though there are many instances of cases like .,20 there is no safe example of a writing like 20,. known to me. In other words, in all periods the context alone decides the absolute value of a sexagesimally written number. In Old-Babylonian mathematical texts we find several cases where a final result was written by means of individual symbols for the fractions, e.g., 1,30 might be called "1 and ½" which shows that we should transcribe 1;30 = 1½ and not 1,30 = 90.

The ambiguity with respect to fractions and integers

is of no importance for the practice of computation. Exactly as we multiply two numbers regardless of the position of the decimal point, one can also operate with the Babylonian numbers and determine the absolute value at the end if necessary. For the numerical process itself it is indeed a great advantage that one does not need to worry about special values for fractions and integers. It is precisely this feature which gave the Babylonian system its tremendous advantage over all other number systems in antiquity.

16. The mathematical texts can be classified into two major groups: "table texts" and "problem texts". A typical representative of the first class is the multiplication table discussed above (p. 50). The second class comprises a great variety of texts which are all more or less directly concerned with the formulation or solution of algebraic or geometrical problems.

17. The table texts allow us to reconstruct a small, however insignificant, bit of historical information. The archives from the city of Nippur, now dispersed over at least three museums, Philadelphia, Jena, and Istanbul, have given us a large percentage of table texts, many of which are clearly "school texts", i.e., exercises written by apprentice scribes. This is evident, e.g., from the repetition in a different hand of the same multiplication table on obverse and reverse of the same tablet. Often we also find vocabularies written on one side of a tablet which shows mathematical tables on the other side. These vocabularies are the backbone of the scribal instruction, necessary for the mastery of the intricacies of cuneiform writing in Akkadian as well as in Sumerian. Finally, many of our mathematical tables are combined with tables of weights and measures which were needed in daily economic life. There can be little doubt that the tables for multiplication and division were developed simultaneously with the economic texts. Thus we find explicitly confirmed what could have been concluded indirectly from our general knowledge of early Mesopotamian civilization.

Ignoring variations in small details, tables of reciprocals are lists of numbers as follows

2	30	16	3,45	45	1,20		
3	20	18	3,20	48	1,15		
4	15	20	3	50	1,12		
5	12	24	2,30	54	1,6,40		
6	10	25	2,24	1	1		
8	7,30	27	2,13,20	1,4	56,15		
9	6,40	30	2	1,12	50		
10	6	32	1,52,30	1,15	48		
12	5	36	1,40	1,20	45		
15	4	40	1,30	1,21	44,26,40		

...Thus our stock of multiplication tables is not a collection of tables for all products $a \cdot b$, for a and b from 1 to 59, but tables for the products $a \cdot \overline{b}$ where $\overline{b}$ is a number from the right-hand side of our last list. The character of these numbers $\overline{b}$ is conspicuous enough; they are the reciprocals of the numbers b of the left column, written as sexagesimal fractions:

$$1/2 = 0;30$$
$$1/3 = 0;20$$
$$1/4 = 0;15$$
etc.
$$1/1,21 = 0;0,44,26,40.$$

We can express the same fact more simply and historically more correctly in the following form. The above "table of reciprocals" is a list of numbers, b and $\overline{b}$, such that the products $b \cdot \overline{b}$ are 1 or any other power of 60. It is indeed irrelevant whether we write

$$2 \cdot 30 = 1,0$$

or

$$2 \cdot 0;30 = 1$$

or

$$0;2 \cdot 30 = 1$$

or

$$0;2 \cdot 0;30 = 0;1 \quad \text{etc.}$$

Experience with the mathematical problem texts demonstrates in innumerable examples that the Babylonian mathematicians made full use of this flexibility of their system.

Thus we have seen that the tables of multiplication combined with the tables of reciprocals form a complete system, designed to compute all products $a \cdot \overline{b}$ or, as we now can write, all sexagesimal divisions a/b within the range of the above-given table of reciprocals. This table is not only limited but it shows gaps. There is no reciprocal for 7, for 11, for 13 or 14, etc. The reason is obvious. If we divide 7 into 1 we obtain the recurrent sexagesimal fraction 8,34,17,8,34,17 . . . ; similarly for 1/11 the group 5,27,16,21,49 appears in infinite repetition. We have tables which laconically remark "7 does not divide", "11 does not divide", etc. This holds true for all numbers which contain prime numbers not contained in 60, i. e. prime numbers different from 2, 3, and 5. We shall call these numbers "irregular" numbers in contrast to the remaining "regular" numbers whose reciprocals can be expressed by a sexagesimal fraction of a finite number of places. . . .

The limitations of the "standard" table of reciprocals which we reproduced above (p. 53) did not mean that one could not transgress them at will. We have texts from the same period teaching how to proceed in cases not contained in the standard table. We also have tables of reciprocals for a complete sequence of consecutive numbers, regular and irregular alike. The reciprocals of the irregular numbers appear abbreviated to three or four places only. But the real expansion came in the Seleucid period with tables of reciprocals of regular numbers up to 7 places for b and resulting reciprocals up to 17 places for $\overline{b}$. A table of this extent, containing the regular numbers up to about $17 \cdot 10^{12}$, can be readily used also for determining approximately the reciprocals of irregular numbers by interpolation. Indeed, in working with astronomical texts I have often used this table exactly for this purpose and I do not doubt that I was only repeating a process familiar to the Seleucid astronomers.

PLATE 7

a. Plimpton 322.
Pythagorean Numbers

MATHEMATICAL CUNEIFORM TEXTS

Edited by O. Neugebauer and A. Sachs

CHAPTER III. PROBLEM-TEXTS

§1. Introduction

The Old-Babylonian texts vary greatly as to type and content. Some tablets contain only one example, which gives all the details of the solution of the problem stated at the beginning of the text. We even have tablets which contain only a part of the working out of the solution of a problem. At the other extreme are tablets which state hundreds of problems in a very condensed form but give no answers. Between these two extremes lie all sorts of intermediate types: texts with two or more examples which are worked out in detail and which are well arranged according to the degree of mathematical complication, texts with many examples of quite diverse character arranged very carelessly, and texts which represent a smaller collection of coordinated problems.

The text (§2) tabulates the answers to a problem containing Pythagorean numbers (or Pythagorean triangles). It is the oldest preserved document in ancient number theory.

§2. Pythagorean Numbers

A. Plimpton 322

Obverse	I	II	III	IV
1	[*ta-k*]*i-il-ti si-li-ip-tim*	ib-si$_8$ sag	ib-si$_8$ *si-li-ip-tim*	mu-bi-im
2	[*sa in-*]*na-as-sa-hu-u-*[*m*]*a sag i-*	...-*u*		
3	[1,59],15	1,59	2,49	ki-1
4	[1,56,56],58,14,50,6[105],15	56,7	3,12,1[108]	ki-2
5	[1,55,7],41,15,33,45	1,16,41	1,50,49	ki-3
6	[1],5[3,1]0,29,32,52,16	3,31,49	5,9,1	ki-4
7	[1],48,54,1,40	1,5	1,37	ki[-5]
8	[1],47,6,41,40	5,19	8,1	[ki-6]
9	[1],43,11,56,28,26,40	38,11	59,1	ki-7
10	[1],41,33,59,3,45	13,19	20,49	ki-8
11	[1],38,33,36,36	9,1[106]	12,49	ki-9
12	[1],35,10,2,28,27,24,26,40	1,22,41	2,16,1	ki-10
13	[1],33,45	45	1,15	ki-11
14	[1],29,21,54,2,15	27,59	48,49	ki-12
15	[1],27,3,45	7,12,1[107]	4,49	ki-13
16	[1],25,48,51,35,6,40	29,31	53,49	ki-14
17	[1],23,13,46,4[0]	56	53[109]	ki[-15]

[105] 50,6 written like 56.

[106] 9,1 error for 8,1.

[107] 7,12,1 (the square of 2,41) error for 2,41.

[108] 3,12,1 error for 1,20,25.

[109] 53 error for 1,46 (i.e., 2 • 53).

Commentary

a. Description of the Tablet

In its present state, the tablet represents the right-hand part of a larger text. The presence of modern glue, until the recent baking of the tablet, on the left (broken) edge shows that the missing part must have been lost after the excavation of the tablet. The size of the preserved part, 4-7/8 by 3-3/8 in. (12.7 by 8.8 cm), would make it unlikely that much more than half (or even less) of the existing part is missing. The reverse is uninscribed.

The script is clearly Old-Babylonian, i.e., it falls in the period between 1900 and 1600 B.C. The sign for 9 consists of three superimposed rows of three vertical wedges each. Zeros are not indicated by a special sign, but a blank space occurs in lines 3 and 15 where zero is called for; on the other hand, lines 7, 8, 10, etc., show that a blank space does not necessarily indicate zero.

b. Content

The text deals with "Pythagorean triangles": right triangles whose sides are integers. Let l denote the longer, b the shorter leg of a right triangle, d its hypotenuse; then l, b and d are integers which fulfill the relation

$$l^2 + b^2 = d^2. \tag{1}$$

The values of d and b for 15 such Pythagorean triangles are given in the second and third preserved columns of our text. One might assume that the missing part contained the corresponding values of l. The first preserved column gives the ratios of d^2 to l^2. Although the values of d and b vary in a very irregular manner, the ratios $\frac{d^2}{l^2}$ decrease almost linearly. Because the difference from line to line is very small (average 0;2,34), this is virtually equivalent to saying that $\frac{d}{l}$ decreases almost linearly (average difference 0;0,59,17, . . . i.e., almost 0;1), and we shall see that this is indeed the proper formulation of the problem. Formulating the problem with respect to the triangles we can say that we start out with almost half a square (because the value of $b:l$ which corresponds to the first line [line 3] is 0;59,30) and gradually diminish the angle between l and d step by step, the lowest value being almost exactly 31°. It must, however, be kept in mind that the actual size of these triangles varies considerably owing to the fact that all sides are integral solutions of (1) and not approximations.

The numbers 1, 2, . . ., 15 in the last column have no exact relationship to the preceding numbers but merely indicate the number of the steps.

d. Method of Solution

We turn now to the question of great historical interest: How were the mathematicians of the Old-Babylonian period able not only to solve the Pythagorean equation (1) in integers but to adapt the solutions to the further condition that the proportion $\frac{d}{l}$ decrease from step to step by a number deviating very little from one-sixtieth?

In order to answer this question, we must first compare the solutions for l, b, and d given in the tablet. These are listed in the following table with the correction of the four errors in lines 4, 11, 15, and 17 mentioned in the foot-notes to the transcription:

Line	l	b	d
3	2, 0	1,59	2,49
4	57,36	56, 7	1,20,25
5	1,20, 0	1,16,41	1,50,49
6	3,45, 0	3,31,49	5, 9, 1
7	1,12	1, 5	1,37
8	6, 0	5.19	8, 1

Line	l	b	d
9	45, 0	38,11	59, 1
10	16, 0	13,19	20,49
11	10, 0	8, 1	12,49
12	1,48, 0	1,22,41	2,16, 1
13	1, 0	45	1,15
14	40, 0	27,59	48,49
15	4, 0	2,41	4,49
16	45, 0	29,31	53,49
17	1,30	56	1,46

Before proceeding, it is necessary to note in the first place that line 13 gives the 15-fold values of the triangle with the sides $l = 4$, $b = 3$, $d = 5$; and secondly, that the last line contains the common factor 2. All the other solutions are relatively prime.

The most important feature in this table is the obvious difference in character of the numbers l on the one hand and the b's and d's on the other: the b's and d's are "complicated" numbers, but the l's are very "simple." This offhand impression can be translated into precise terms by using the well known theorem[114] that all relatively prime Pythagorean numbers are contained exactly once in the set of numbers

$$(2) \qquad l = 2pq \qquad b = p^2 - q^2 \qquad d = p^2 + q^2$$

where p and q are relatively prime integers, both not being simultaneously odd and $p > q$. If one calculates the numbers p and q which bring our numbers l, b, and d to the form (2), one will find that the p's as well as the q's are "regular numbers." In other words, the p's and q's can be characterized by three numbers α, β, and γ, the exponents of 2, 3, and 5, respectively. If we write

$$2^{\alpha} 3^{\beta} 5^{\gamma} = (\alpha, \beta, \gamma),$$

[114] Kronecker, Zahlentheorie p. 31.

we then obtain the following list of numbers p and q which satisfy (2):[116]

Line	p	q
3	12 = (2,1,0)	5 = (0,0,1)
4	1, 4 = (6,0,0)	27 = (0,3,0)
5	1,15 = (0,1,2)	32 = (5,0,0)
6	2, 5 = (0,0,3)	54 = (1,3,0)
7	9 = (0,2,0)	4 = (2,0,0)
8	20 = (2,0,1)	9 = (0,2,0)
9	54 = (1,3,0)	25 = (0,0,2)
10	32 = (5,0,0)	15 = (0,1,1)
11	25 = (0,0,2)	12 = (2,1,0)
12	1,21 = (0,4,0)	40 = (3,0,1)
13	2 = (1,0,0)	1 = (0,0,0)
14	48 = (4,1,0)	25 = (0,0,2)
15	15 = (0,1,1)	8 = (3,0,0)
16	50 = (1,0,2)	27 = (0,3,0)
17	9 = (0,2,0)	5 = (0,0,1)

The sense in which the numbers $l = 2pq$ are "simple" is now made clear by this list: they are numbers of the form (α, β, γ), i.e., so-called "regular numbers" or numbers whose reciprocals are *finite* sexagesimal fractions.[117]

This latter quality of the p's and q's also yields the answer to the question how the numbers of our list were found which not only solve equation (1) but also furnish within narrow limits given proportions $\frac{d}{l}$. Using (2), we find for this proportion

$$(3) \qquad \frac{d}{l} = \tfrac{1}{2}(p \cdot \bar{q} + q \cdot \bar{p})$$

where $\bar{p}$ and $\bar{q}$ represent the reciprocals of p and q, respectively. In other words, our problem *requires* that p

[116] We include here the values from lines 13 and 17 although a common factor 15 of l, b, and d occurs in line 13, and p and q are both odd in line 17.

[117] Cf., e.g., Neugebauer, Vorlesungen pp. 6 and 12ff.

and q be regular numbers in order to obtain expressions all the numbers p and q of our list are contained in the (3) with finite sexagesimal fractions.

We can say more. With the single exception of $2{,}5 = 5^3$, group of regular numbers which constitute the "reciprocal tables." . . .

Our final result, then, is that our tablet was calculated by selecting numbers $\overline{pq}$ and $\overline{qp}$ from combined multiplication tables such that (3) has a value as near as possible to the required values of $\frac{d}{l}$; Pythagorean numbers were then formed with these values of p and q according to (2).

e. Historical Consequences

We now see that Babylonian number theory was acquainted with rules like (2) to produce Pythagorean numbers, i.e., a theorem like Euclid X 29 lemma 1.

There can be little doubt that the Pythagorean numbers did not remain the only problem treated by this part of Babylonian mathematics. We have an explicit hint in this direction from the extant material itself: tables giving the powers c^n for exponents $n = 1, 2, \ldots,$ 10 for the bases $c = 9, 16, 1{,}40$ and 3,45.[124] All these are regular numbers, and it would be only natural to extend both problems and methods as described above to combinations of other numbers and different exponents. The study of sequences Σn, Σn^2 etc.[125] points in the same direction. Details can be disclosed only by the discovery of new texts, but their general direction seems evident.

In summary, our text gives the final link which connects the different parts of Old-Babylonian mathematics by the investigation of the fundamental laws of the numbers themselves.

---

[124] MKT I pp. 77ff.

[125] MKT I pp. 102f., 497f., and MKT III pp. 13f.

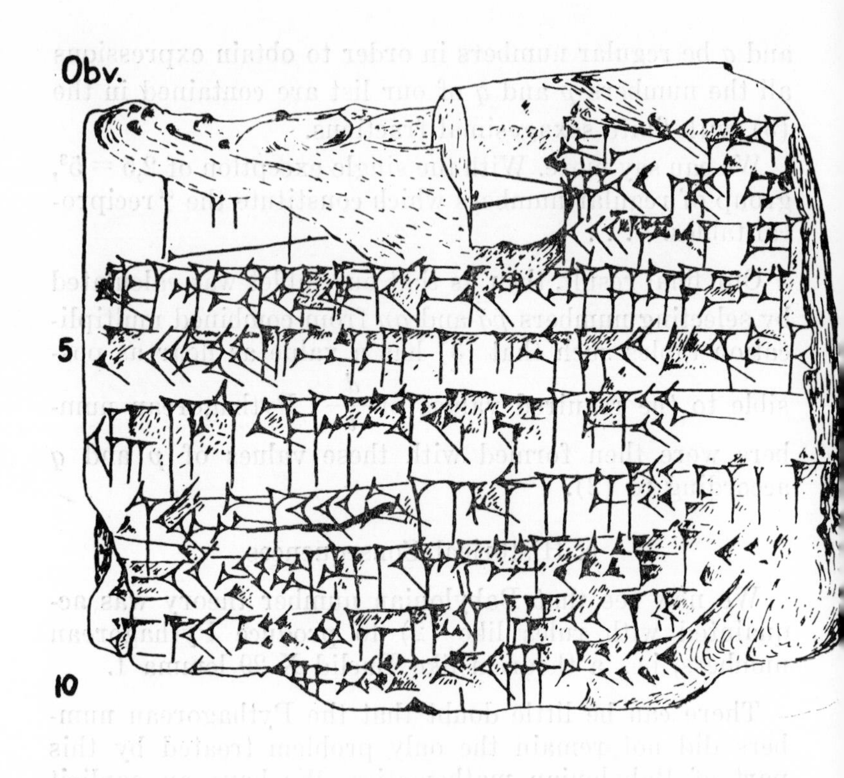

Edge of Rev.

Ca. MLC 1950

Ca. MLC 1950

Transcription

Obverse

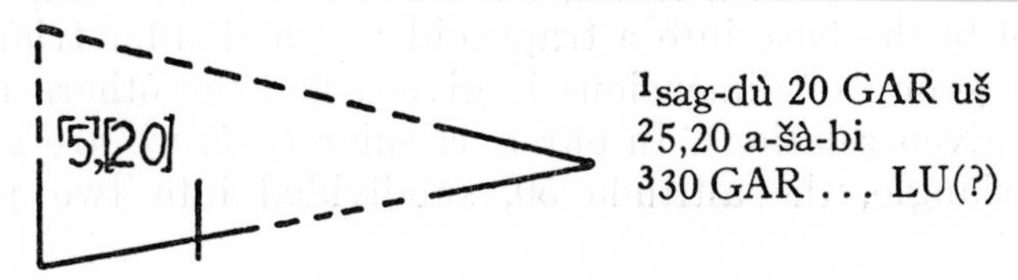

[1]sag-dù 20 GAR uš
[2]5,20 a-šà-bi
[3]30 GAR . . . LU(?)

[4]sag-an-ta *ù* sag-ki-ta *mi-nu-um* za-e kì-ta[-zu-dè]
[5]igi 20 du$_8$ 3 *ta-mar* 3 *a-na* 5,20 *i-ši-ma* 1[6]
[6]16 *a-na* sag-an-ta ù . . .-. . .-LU-*bu*
[7]. . .-. . .-*ma* 30 uš *a-na* 2 *e-ṣí*(?)-*ip*[135a] 1
[8]*ù* 20 *mu-ta-ri-tam* an-ta UL-gar 1,20
[9]igi 1,20 du$_8$ 45 *a-na* 5,20 a-šà [*i-ši-ma* 4]
[10][4 *a-na*] 16 daḫ *i-na* 16 zi 2[0 sag-an-ta]
[11][12 sag-ki-ta]

Reverse destroyed except for traces at end

Translation

Obverse
[1]A triangle. 20 GAR is the length
[2]5,20 its area,
[3]30 GAR the . . .
[4]What are the upper width and the lower width? [When you] perform (the operations),
[5]take the reciprocal of 20, (and) you will see 0;3. Multiply 0;3 by 5,20, and (the result is) 1[6].
[6]16 to(?) the upper width and . . .
[7–8]. . . 30, the length, multiply by 2, add (the resulting) 1,0 and 20, the upper perpendicular, (and the result is) 1,20.
[9]Take the reciprocal of 1,20, [multiply] (the resulting) 0;0,45 by 5,20, the area, [and (the result is) 4].
[10]Add [4 to] 16, subtract from 16. [The upper width is] 2[0];
[11][the lower width is 12.]
Reverse destroyed except for traces at the end.

[135a] This reading, if correct, presupposes that the scribe inverted the order of the two components of the sign ZI.

Commentary

The problem presented here belongs to a class which is well attested: a triangle is subdivided by a line parallel to the base into a trapezoid and a smaller triangle. One group of dimensions is given; find the others from the given relations. In our particular case, we are given a triangle, the altitude 50, subdivided into two parts

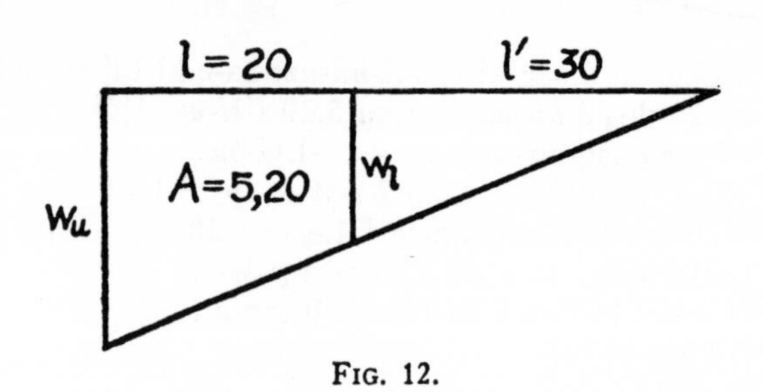

FIG. 12.

$l = 20$ and $l' = 30$.[135c] In addition, the area $A = 5{,}20$ of the trapezoid is given. Find the lengths w_u and w_l of the parallel sides of this trapezoid.[135d]

The method of solving the problem in question consists in finding both $\frac{1}{2}(w_u + w_l)$ and $\frac{1}{2}(w_u - w_l)$ such that the sum and difference of these expressions give the answer. The first expression is easily found. From the formula

$$(1) \qquad A = \tfrac{1}{2}(w_u + w_l)l$$

for the area of the trapezoid, it follows that we have

$$(2) \qquad \frac{A}{l} = \frac{5{,}20}{20} = 5{,}20 \cdot 0;3 = 16 = \tfrac{1}{2}(w_u + w_l),$$

as given in the text.

The next step requires explanation. We introduce the

[135c] For the sake of convenience, a right triangle is assumed in our commentary. It is equally possible to assume an isosceles triangle, each side 50. One would then also have to assume the approximate formula for the area of a trapezoid.

[135d] The left side is, as usual, called the "upper width" because we must turn the figure 90° in clockwise direction.

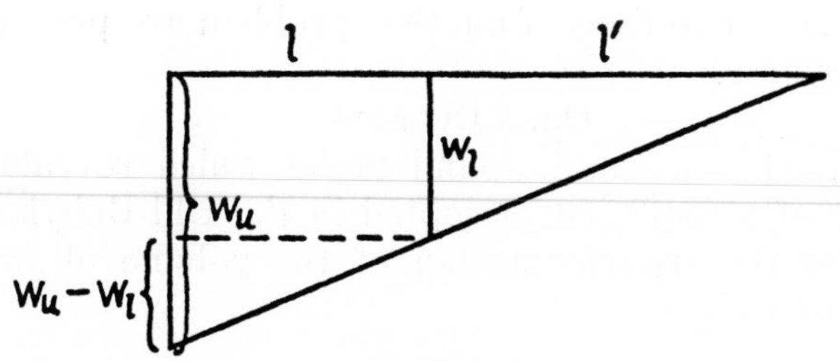

FIG. 13.

dotted line as given in fig. 13 and then find, from similar triangles,

$$\frac{w_u}{l+l'} = \frac{w_l}{l'} = \frac{w_u - w_l}{l}$$

or

$$w_u = \frac{l+l'}{l}(w_u - w_l) \qquad w_l = \frac{l'}{l}(w_u - w_l).$$

By adding, we obtain

$$w_u + w_l = \frac{2l'+l}{l}(w_u - w_l)$$

and consequently

$$\tfrac{1}{2}(w_u - w_l) = \frac{(w_u + w_l)l}{2(2l'+l)}\cdot$$

Using (1), we can therefore write

$$\tfrac{1}{2}(w_u - w_l) = \frac{A}{2l'+l} \tag{3}$$

and this is precisely the relation used by the scribe. He computes:

$$2l' = 2 \cdot 30 = 1{,}0 \qquad\qquad 2l' + l = 1{,}0 + 20 = 1{,}20$$

$$\frac{1}{2l'+l} = 0;0{,}45$$

and therefore

$$\frac{A}{2l'+l} = 0;0{,}45 \cdot 5{,}20 = 4 = \tfrac{1}{2}(w_u - w_l). \tag{4}$$

The relations (2) and (4) now provide the final answer

$$\tfrac{1}{2}(w_u + w_l) + \tfrac{1}{2}(w_u - w_l) = 16 + 4 = 20 = w_u$$

and

$$\tfrac{1}{2}(w_u + w_l) - \tfrac{1}{2}(w_u - w_l) = 16 - 4 = 12 = w_l.$$

Only parts of two lines of another problem are preserved on the reverse.

Oa. YBC 7284

YBC 7284 is a small, round tablet which reveals the existence of a coefficient accepted in the Old-Babylonian period for the transformation of the volume of bricks to units of weight.

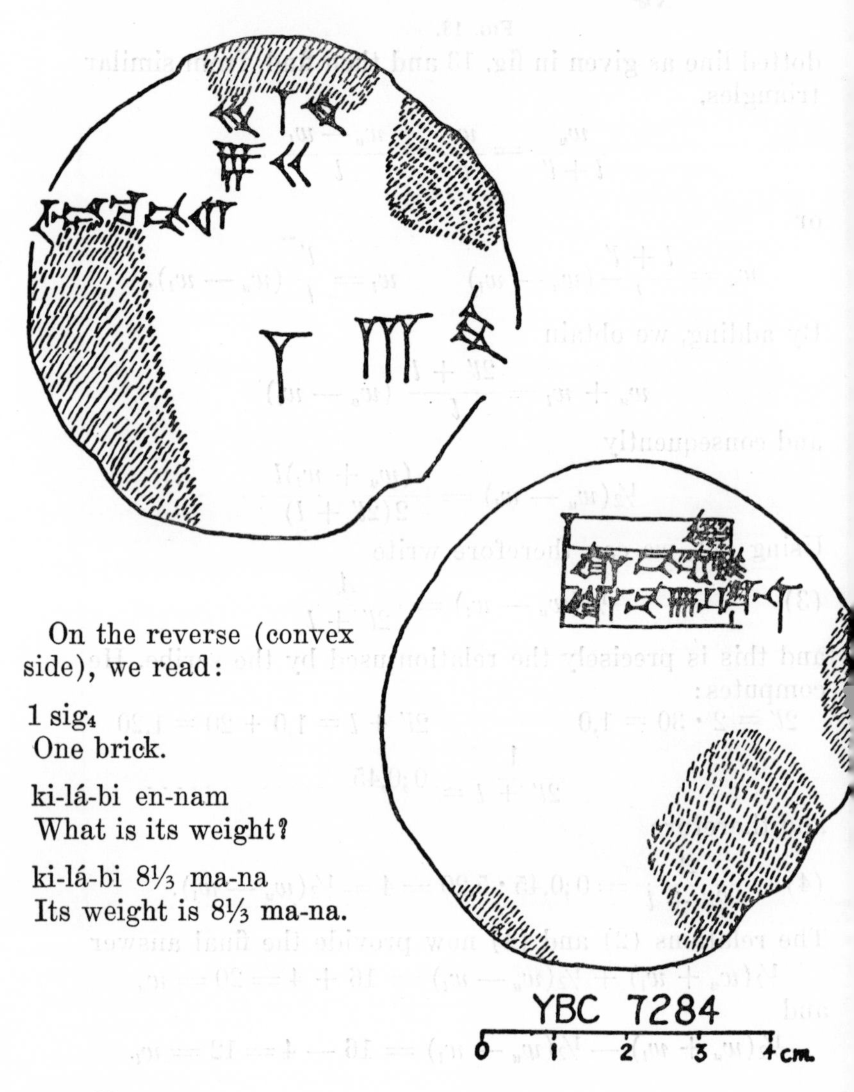

On the reverse (convex side), we read:

1 sig₄
One brick.

ki-lá-bi en-nam
What is its weight?

ki-lá-bi 8⅓ ma-na
Its weight is 8⅓ ma-na.

YBC 4652

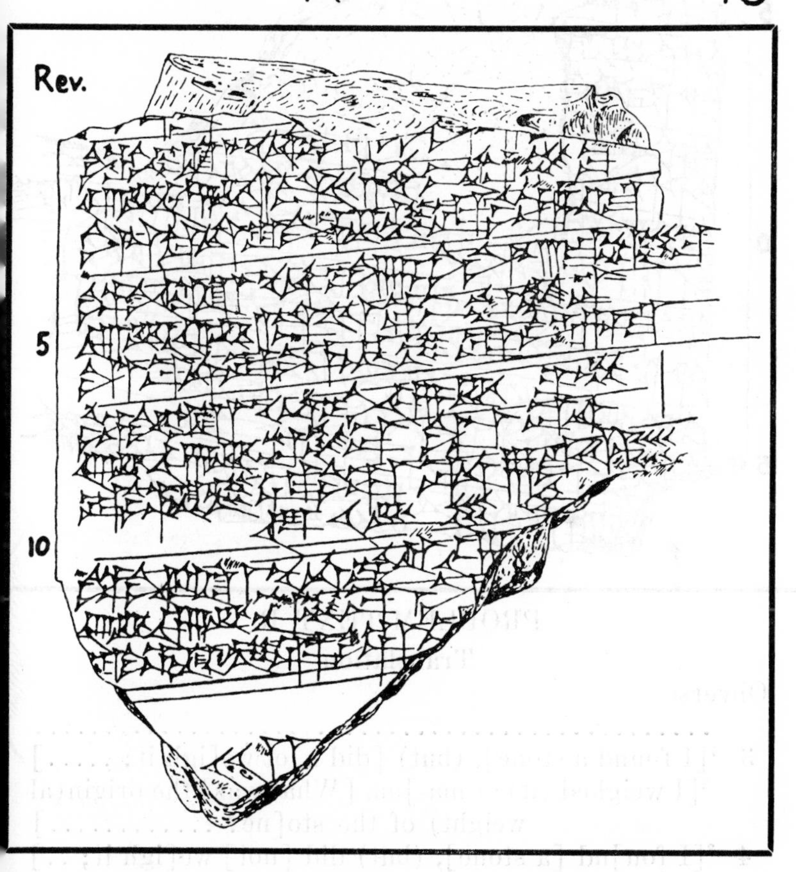

YBC 4652

PROBLEM-TEXT R

Translation

Obverse

. . . .

3 [1][I found a stone], (but) [did n]ot we[igh it; . . . . .]
[2][I weighed (it): 1 ma-]na. [What was] the origin(al weight) of the sto[ne? . . . .]

4 [3][I fou]nd [a stone], (but) did [not] we[igh it; . .]
[4]one-eleventh and [. . . . ., I weighed (it): 1 ma-na].
[5][What] was the origin(al weight) of the stone? [. . . . .]

5 [6]I found a stone, [(but) did not] we[igh it; ......],
[7]I weighed (it): 1 ma-na. [What was the] origin(al weight) of the stone? [............]

6 [8]I found a stone, [(but) did not] we[igh it; (after) ....],
[9]I weighed (it): 1 ma-na. What [was the origin(al weight) of the stone]? The origin(al weight) of the sto[ne was ....]

7 [10]I found a stone, [(but) did not] weig[h it]; (after) I a[dd]ed one-seventh (and) a[dd]ed one-eleventh,
[11]I weighed (it): 1 ma-na. What was the origin(al) weight of the stone? The origin(al weight) of the stone was 2/3 ma-na, 8 gin (and) 22½se.

8 [12]I found a stone, (but) did not weigh it; (after) I subtracted one-seventh (and) subtracted one-thirteenth,
[13]I weighed (it): 1 ma-na. What was the origin(al weight) of the stone? The origin(al weight) of the stone was 1 ma-na (and) 15-5/6 gin.

9 [14]I found a stone, (but) did not weigh it; (after) I subtracted one-seventh, added one-eleventh, (and) [15]subtracted one-thir[teenth], I weighed (it): 1 ma-na. What was the origin(al weight) of the stone? [16][The origin(al weight)] of the stone was 1 ma-na, 9½ gin, (and) 2½se.

10 [17][I fou]nd [a stone], (but) did not weigh (it); (after) I subtracted one-seventh, added one-eleventh,
[18][......] added [......], I weighed (it): 1 ma-na. What was the origin(al weight) of the stone?

Reverse

....

19 [1]I found a stone, (but) did not weigh it; (after) I weighed (out) 6 times (its weight), [added] 2 gin, (and)
[2]added one-third of one-seventh multiplied by 24,

[3]I weighed (it): 1 ma-na. What was the origin(al weight) of the stone? The origin(al weight) of the stone was $4\frac{1}{3}$ gin.

20 [4]I found a stone, (but) did not weigh it; (after) I weighed (out) 8 times (its weight), added 3 gin, [5]one-third of one-thirteenth I multiplied by 21, added (it), and then [6]I weighed (it): 1 ma-na. What was the origin(al weight) of the stone? The origin(al weight) of the stone was $4\frac{1}{2}$ gin.

21 [7]I found a stone, (but) did not weigh it; (after) I subtracted one-sixth (and) [8]added one-third of one-eighth, I weighed (it): 1 ma-na. [9]What was the origin(al weight) of the stone? The origin(al weight) of the stone was 1 ma-na, 9 gin, $21\frac{1}{2}$ se, [10]and one-tenth of a se.

22 [11]I found a stone, (but) did not weigh it; (after) I [......] 2/3 of one-sixth [......], [12]added one-third of one-eighth, I weighed (it): [1 ma-na]. [13]What was the origin(al weight) of the stone? The origin(al weight) of the stone was 1 m[a-na ...].

[14]22 [sections].

Commentary

a. Mathematical Commentary

According to the colophon, the tablet contained 22 examples when complete, but only 11 are even partly preserved; of these, 6 can be fully restored. All the problems of the tablet are obviously of the same type, resulting in a linear equation for one unknown quantity, the "original" weight of a stone.

The preserved problems are the following:

No. 7

$$\left(x+\frac{x}{7}\right)+\frac{1}{11}\left(x+\frac{x}{7}\right)=1{,}0$$

Solution: $x = \frac{2}{3}$ ma-na + 8 gin + 22½ se

$= 48;7,30$ gin.

Indeed, $\frac{x}{7} = 6;52,30 \quad x + \frac{x}{7} = 55 \quad \frac{1}{11}\left(x+\frac{x}{7}\right) = 5.$

No. 8

$$\left(x-\frac{x}{7}\right)-\frac{1}{13}\left(x-\frac{x}{7}\right)=1{,}0$$

Solution: $x = 1$ ma-na + $15\frac{5}{6}$ gin = 1,15;50 gin.

Indeed, $\frac{x}{7} = 10;50 \quad x - \frac{x}{7} = 1{,}5 \quad \frac{1}{13}\left(x-\frac{x}{7}\right) = 5.$

No. 9

$$\left(x-\frac{x}{7}\right)+\frac{1}{11}\left(x-\frac{x}{7}\right)-\frac{1}{13}\left[\left(x-\frac{x}{7}\right)+\frac{1}{11}\left(x-\frac{x}{7}\right)\right]=1{,}0$$

Solution: $x = 1$ ma-na + $9\frac{1}{2}$ gin + $2\frac{1}{2}$ se

= 1,9;30,50 gin.

Indeed, $\frac{x}{7} = 9;55;50 \qquad x - \frac{x}{7} = 59;35$

$\frac{1}{11}\left(x-\frac{x}{7}\right) = 5;25$

$\frac{1}{13}\left[\left(x-\frac{x}{7}\right) + \frac{1}{11}\left(x-\frac{x}{7}\right)\right] = 5.$

No. 19

$$(6x + 2) + \frac{1}{3} \cdot \frac{1}{7} \cdot 24(6x + 2) = 1{,}0$$

Solution: $x = 4\frac{1}{3}$ gin.

Indeed, $6x + 2 = 28 \qquad \frac{24}{21}\ (6x + 2) = 32.$

No. 20

$$(8x + 3) + \frac{1}{3} \cdot \frac{1}{13} \cdot 21(8x + 3) = 1{,}0$$

Solution: $x = 4\frac{1}{2}$ gin.

Indeed, $8x + 3 = 39 \qquad \frac{21}{39}\ (8x + 3) = 21.$

No. 21

$$\left(x - \frac{x}{6}\right) + \frac{1}{3} \cdot \frac{1}{8}\left(x - \frac{x}{6}\right) = 1{,}0$$

Solution: $x = 1$ ma-na $+ 9$ gin $+ 21\frac{1}{2}$ se $+ \frac{1}{10}$ se

$+ 1{,}9;7{,}12$ gin.

Indeed, $\frac{x}{6} = 11;31{,}12 \qquad x - \frac{x}{6} = 57;36$

$$\frac{1}{24}\left(x - \frac{x}{6}\right) = 2;24.$$

The remaining problems are completely broken away or too badly preserved to be restored with certainty.

The main difficulty encountered in interpreting the text of the problem consists in placing the parentheses correctly. The terminology alone is in itself inadequate; only experience with analogous problems,[268] when combined with the given solution, indicates the correct interpretation. The ancient scribes of course had the oral interpretation of their teachers at their disposal.

[268] Cf. e.g., MKT I p. 483.

YBC 4612

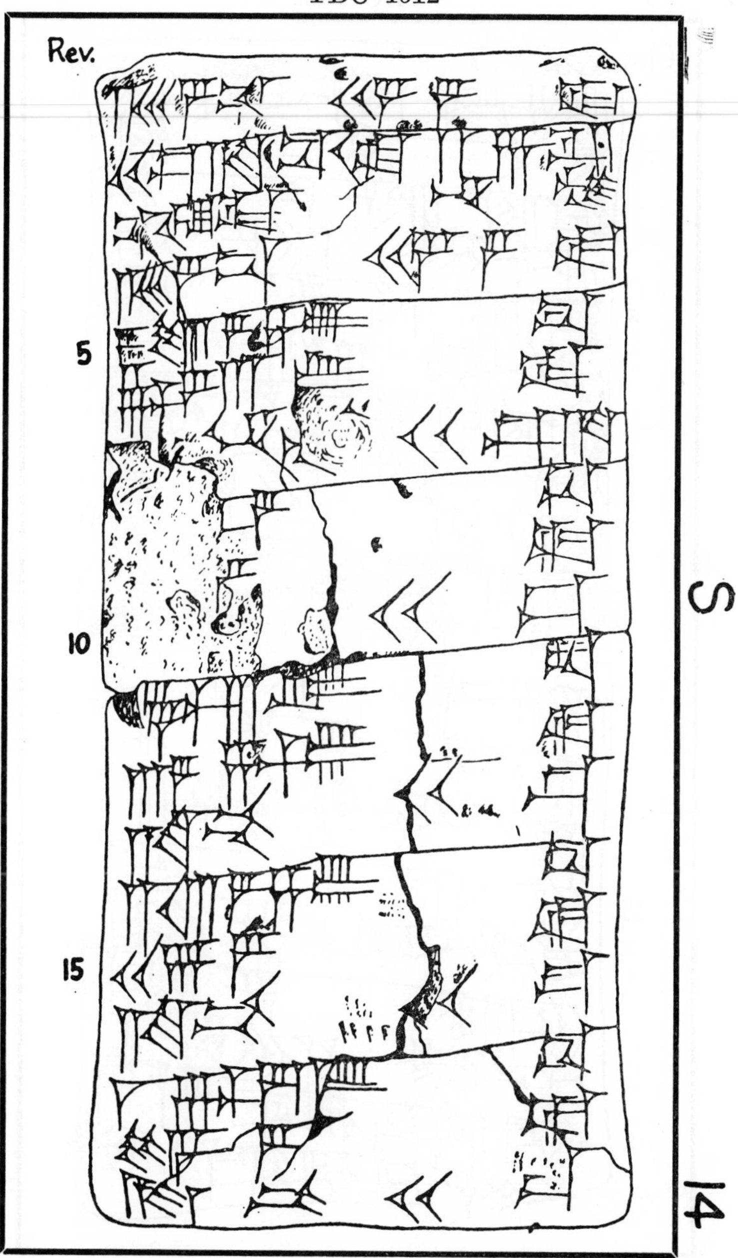

YBC 4612

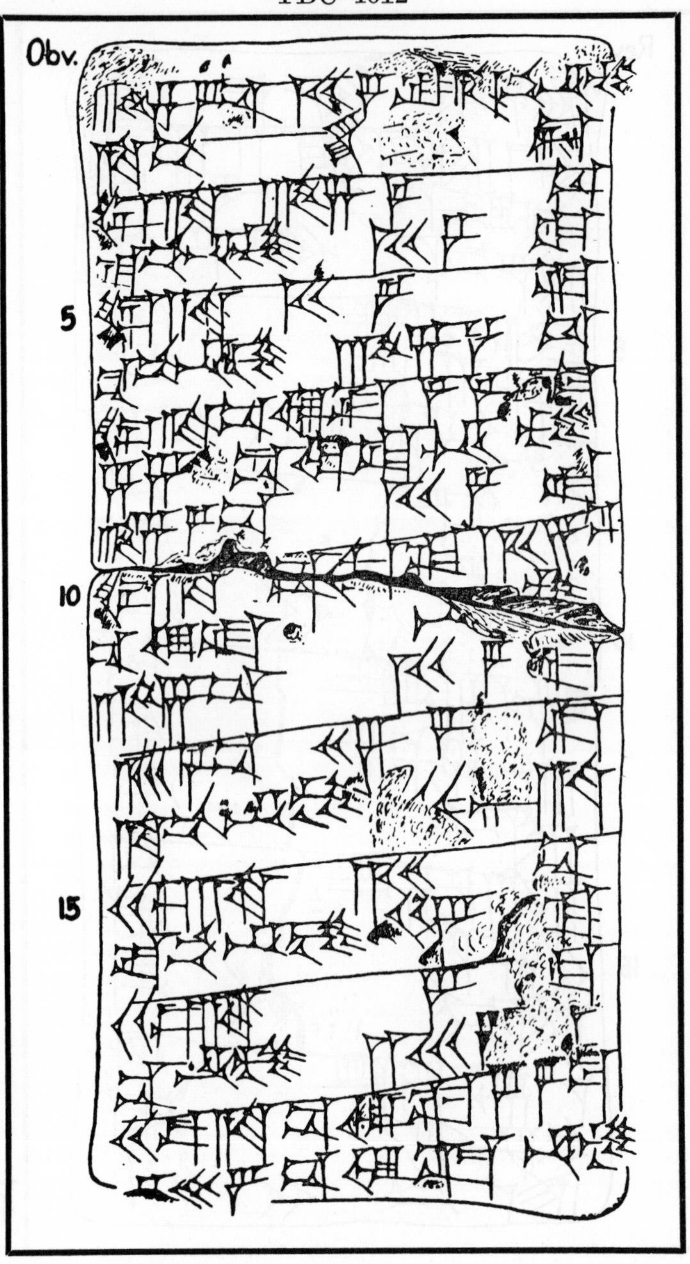

PROBLEM-TEXT S

Translation

Obverse

1 [1]3,45 GAR is the length, 1,20 GAR the width.
What is its area?
[2]Its area is 1 bur'u.

2 [3]1 bur'u is the area, 3,45 GAR the length.
[4]What is its width? 1,20 GAR is the width.

3 [5]1 bur'u is the area, 1,20 GAR the width.
[6]What is its length? 3,45 GAR is the length.

4 [7]1 bur'u is the area; I added the length and the width, and (the result is)
[8]5,5. What are the length and the width?
[9]3,45 GAR is the length; 1,20 GAR is the width.

5 [10]1 bur'u is the area; the length exceeded the width by 2,25.
[11]What are the length and the width?
[12]3,45 (GAR) is the length; 1,20 GAR is the width.

6 [13]2,30 GAR is the length, 24 GAR the width.
[14]What is its area? 2 bur is the area.

7 [15]2 bur is the area, 2,30 (GAR) the length.
[16]What is its width? 24 (GAR) is the width.

8 [17]2 bur is the area, 24 (GAR) the width.
[18]What is the length? 2,30 GAR is the length.

9 [19]2 bur is the area; I added the length and the width, and (the result is)
[20]2,54 (GAR). What are the length and the width?

Reverse

[1]2,30 GAR is the length; 24 GAR is the width.

10 [2]2 bur is the area; the length exceeded the width by 2,6 (GAR).
[3]What are the length and the width?
[4]2,30 GAR is the length; 24 GAR is the width.

11 [5]8,53 GAR (and) 4 kus is the length,
[6]6½ GAR (and) 3 kus the width.
[7]What is its [area]? 2 bur is the area.

12 [8][1,52]½ GAR is the length,
[9][32] GAR the width. (What is its area?)
[10]Its [area] is 2 bur.

13 [11]17½ <GAR> (and) 3⅓ kus is the length,
[12]3 GAR (and) 4½ kus the width. (What is its area?)
[13]Its area is 2 bur.

14 [14]2,13 GAR (and) 4 kus is the length.
[15]27 GAR the width. (What is its area?)
[16]Its area is 2 bur.

15 [17]1,6½ GAR (and) 2 kus is the length,
[18]54 GAR the width. (What is its area?)
[19]Its area is 2 bur.

Commentary

The mathematical aspect of this group of 15 problems is extremely simple. The only relation used is the fact that the area of a rectangle of sides x and y $(x > y)$ is xy. The numerical values of the magnitudes used are

Nos. 1 to 5 $x = 3{,}45$ GAR $y = 1{,}20$ GAR
$xy = 5{,}0{,}0 \text{ GAR}^2 = 1$ bur'u

Nos. 6 to 10 $x = 2{,}30$ GAR $y = 24$ GAR
$xy = 1{,}0{,}0 \text{ GAR}^2 = 2$ bur

and the problems are:

Nos.	given	find
1 and 6	x, y	xy
2 and 7	xy, x	y
3 and 8	xy, y	x
4 and 9	$xy, x + y$	x, y
5 and 10	$xy, x - y$	x, y

The solution of the last two pairs requires quadratic equations of the standard type.

The last group (Nos. 11 to 15) is even simpler: find xy if x and y are given. The emphasis of these problems obviously lies in the metrological aspect. If we express the area in GAR^2, we find the value $1{,}0 \text{ GAR}^2$ for the area in No. 13, but $1{,}0{,}0 \text{ GAR}^2$ in the remaining four examples. The text, however, gives all five areas as $1{,}0{,}0$ GAR^2.

Because the area is supposed to be $1{,}0{,}0 \text{ GAR}^2$ (i.e.,

2 bur) in all five cases, x and y (expressed in GAR) are reciprocal numbers. The values are:

No.	x	y
11	8,53;20 GAR	6;45 GAR
12	[1,52;]30 GAR	[32] GAR
13	17;46,40 GAR	3;22,30 GAR
14	2,13;20 GAR	27 GAR
15	1,6;40 GAR	54 GAR

The restoration in No. 12 is uniquely determined by the fact that there is no other pair of numbers x and y such that $x \cdot y = 1,0,0$ and $x = a + 0;30\ y = b$, where a and b are integers and where $x > y$.

As indicated above, the solution given in No. 13 is wrong because the product xy is only 1,0, not 1,0,0. This shows that the scribe's starting-point was a table of reciprocals but that he committed an error in determining the sexagesimal place. The correct value would have been 17,46;40 GAR = 17,46½ GAR 2 kus.

PROBLEM-TEXT T

Translation

42 [18]Area, 1 ese.
[19]One-fourteenth of the len[gth and the wid]th,
[20–21]and 2 times [that by which the length] exceeded the width; [I added 2,29];
[22]one-seventh of one-eleventh (thereof)
[23]I added to the length: 32.
43 [24]I multiplied by 2, I added: 34.
44 [25]I subtracted: 28.
45 [26]I multiplied by 2, I subtracted: [26].
46 [27][I multiplied] by [1]5: [the length].
47 [28]I multiplied by 20: it exceeded by 10.
48 [29]I multiplied by 10: it was less by 10.
49 [30]I added to the width: 22.
119 [13]Area, 1 ese.
[14]One-half of [the length ....]
[15][............ one-]sixth
[16]one[- ......] ... 8 ... I subtracted
[17]one[- ....] I added to the [len]gth: 32.
120 [18][I multiplied by 2, I added: 3]4.

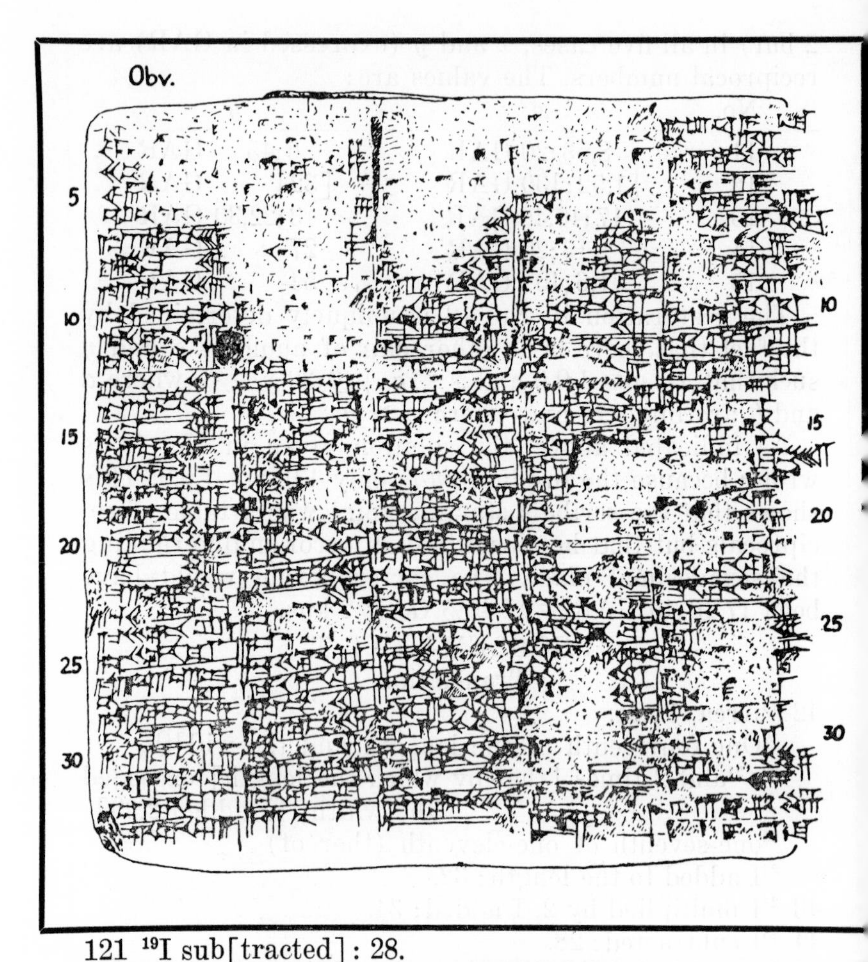

121 [19]I sub[tracted] : 28.
122 [20][I multiplied by 2, I sub]tracted: 26.
123 [21][I multipl]ied [by 15] : the length.
124 [22]I multiplied by 20: it exceeded by 10.
125 [23]I multiplied by 10: it was [less] by 10.
126 [24]I added to the width: 22.
127 [25][I multiplied] by 2, [I added] : 24.
139 [3]Area, 1 ese.
[4]I subtracted one-third from one-half the length,
[5]I added 25, one-seventh (thereof) and . . . .;
[6]I added one-eleventh thereof to the length: 32.
140 [7]I multiplied by 2, I added: 34.

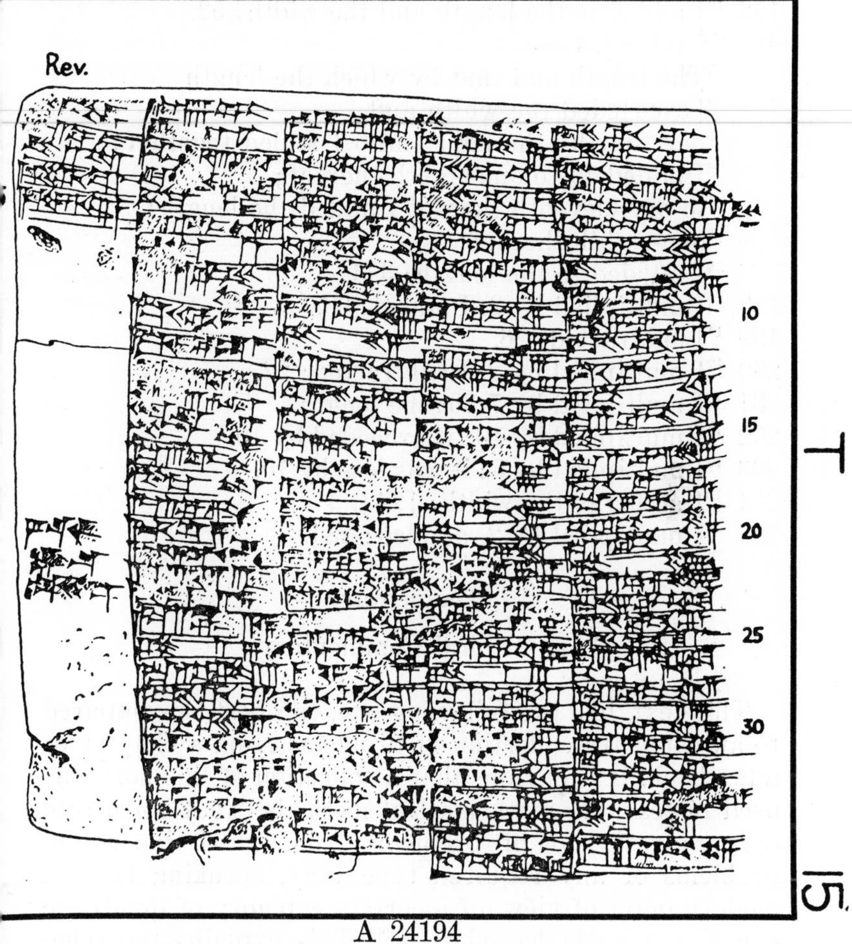

A 24194

141 [8]I subtracted: 28.
143 [10]I multiplied by 15: the length.
144 [11]I multiplied by 20: it exceeded by 10.
145 [12]I multiplied by 10: it was less by 10.
146 [13]I added to the width: 22.
147 [14]I multiplied by 2, I added: 24.
148 [15]I subtracted: 18.
149 [16]I multiplied by 2, I subtracted: 16.
150 [17]I multiplied by 10: the width.
151 [18]I multiplied by 15: it exceeded by 10.

152 [19]I added to the length and the width: 52.
197 [[2]Ar[ea], 1 ese.
[3]The length and that by which the length
[4][exce]eded the width and
[5]one-fourth (thereof) and 6 I added together;
[6]I added 15 to one-eighth thereof;
[7]to one-eleventh thereof I added the length;
[8]one-eighth thereof
[9]I ad[ded to the length: 3]4.
198 [10]I multiplied by 2, I added: 38.
199 [11]I subtracted: 26.
200 [12]I multiplied by 2, I subtracted: 22.
201 [13]I multiplied by 7;30: the length.
202 [14]I multiplied by 10: it exceeded by 10.
203 [15]I multiplied by 5: it was less by 10.
204 [16]I added to the width: [24].
205 [17]I multiplied by 2, a[dded: 28].

Commentary

a. General Commentary

This text, like the following one, can best be compared to an extensive collection of problems from a chapter of a textbook. It is obvious that a collection of this sort was used in teaching mathematical methods. They constitute a large reservoir of problems from which individual problems of any required type (say, speaking from a modern point of view, of a certain category of quadratic equations) could be selected.[283] This explains the schematic arrangement of the examples and made possible the employment of a terse style which, if isolated, would be extremely ambiguous.

The tablets are written with very small characters; this permitted the scribe to include 200 or more examples on a single tablet measuring about 3 by 4 inches. The difficulty in reading such small writing is considerably increased by the state of preservation, which is far

[283] For a classification of Babylonian quadratic equations, see Gandz [1].

from good. As a matter of fact, it is frequently only the systematic structure of the contents which makes it possible to interpret faint traces of signs.

We now turn to the explanation of the contents and the arrangement of the examples in our text, all of which deal with quadratic equations for two unknown quantities: "length" (us, henceforth called x) and "width" (sag, denoted by y). It is necessary to distinguish between two types of examples: "main examples" and "variants." A characteristic case of a main example is the following: the first condition for the unknown quantities is that the "area" (a-sa) is 1 ese = 10,0 GAR, i.e.,

(1) $$xy = 10{,}0.$$

Then a function $f(x,y)$ is defined by the expression

(2a) $$f(x,y) = 1/11\ \{1/13[(x + 4y) + 2(x - y)] + 45\}$$

and it is furthermore stated that

(2b) $$x + f(x,y) = 35.$$

It is evident that (1) and (2) lead to a quadratic equation for x and y.

The "variants" assume that (1) and (2a) are kept unchanged while (2b) is replaced by one of the following equations:

(2c)
$$\begin{aligned}
x + 2f(x,y) &= 40 \\
x - f(x,y) &= 25 \\
x - 2f(x,y) &= 20 \\
x &= 6f(x,y) \\
x &= 8f(x,y) - 10 \\
y + f(x,y) &= 25 \\
y + 2f(x,y) &= 30 \\
y - f(x,y) &= 15 \\
&\text{etc.} \\
(x + y) + f(x,y) &= 55 \\
(x + y) + 2f(x,y) &= 1{,}0 \\
&\text{etc.} \\
(x - y) + f(x,y) &= 15 \\
&\text{etc.}
\end{aligned}$$

This list of variants shows the principle of arrangement: after a certain $f(x,y)$ is defined, it is added or subtracted with a factor 1 or 2 to or from $x, y, x+y, x-y$ etc.

A further observation can easily be made. If we compute x and y from (1), (2a) and (2b), or any of the equations (2c), we will always obtain

$$(3) \qquad x=30 \qquad y=20.$$

This statement can be immediately confirmed from our equations: it is evident that (1) is satisfied by (3); it follows from (2a) that $f(x,y)$ has the value 5 if we use (3); finally, it is again trivial that $x=30$ $y=20$ and $f(x,y)=5$ satisfy all equations (2*b*) or (2*c*).

The conditions (1) and (2) mentioned above are of course only typical examples of a main problem and some of its variants. The fact remains, however, that the same set of values for x and y which is given by (3) satisfies all the problems of the two tablets discussed here as well as many tablets published previously. This clearly illustrates the procedure followed in composing these collections of problems. In order to guarantee real and positive solutions of the quadratic equations, one started from simple solutions like (3) and constructed the equations accordingly. All variants follow the same principle and their purpose lies exclusively in the teaching of methods to reduce problems of types (1) and (2) to the "normal" form of quadratic equations which gives the product of the unknown quantities and their sum or difference. The factor ± 2 in the variants is of course chosen only to indicate any coefficient other than 1 in the previous variants, since a coefficient 1 can be overlooked in the numerical computation. The whole system of a main example with all its variants serves the purpose of giving the general rule of solution; this corresponds in a certain sense to an algebraic formula in which the letters can be replaced by special numbers in each individual case.

b. Mathematical Commentary

A 24194 contains 7 main examples and 240 variants. In 5 of the main examples (Nos. 1, 42, 81, 119, 139), the function $f(x,y)$ has the value 2 if we give x and y the values 30 and 20, respectively. The value 3 occurs in No. 54, the value 4 in No. 197. Unfortunately, the state of preservation of the text is such that only three of the main examples can be read or restored with some degree of probability. These are:

No. 42. $xy = 10{,}0 \qquad x + f(x,y) = 32,$

where $f(x,y)$ is an abbreviation for

$1/7 \cdot 1/11 \{1/14(x + y) + 2(x - y) + 2{,}29\} = f(x,y).$

The number 2,29 is, to be sure, restored; but this is necessary if the other readings are correct.

No. 139. The only restoration of this example which seems to conform to the preserved portion of the text is the following:

$$xy = 10{,}0 \qquad x + f(x,y) = 32,$$

where

$$f(x,y) = \frac{1}{11}\left\{\frac{1}{7}\left(\frac{x}{2} - \frac{1}{3}\frac{x}{2} + 25\right) + 17\right\}.$$

The number 17 which is added at the end is necessary to yield the correct result, but we do not see how this element of the formula was expressed in the text because we are unable to read the traces at the end of line 5.

No. 197. This is the only main example which is almost completely preserved in the text. We have

$$xy = 10{,}0 \qquad x + f(x,y) = 34,$$

where

$$f(x,y) = 1/8\ \{1/11[1/8[x + (x - y) + 1/4(x + (x - y)) + 6] + 15] + x\}$$

with the value $f(30,20) = 4$.

PROBLEM-TEXT L

Translation

Obverse

1 [1]A little canal. 5 US is the length, 3 kus the width, 3 kus its depth, [10 gin] (volume) the assignment, [2]6 se (silver) the wages of a hired man. What are the area, the volume, the (number of) workers, the (total expenses in) silver?

[3]1,15 SAR is the area; <2> iku (and) 25 SAR is the volume; 2 ges'u (and) 2,30 is the (number of) workers; [and 2/3] ma-na (and) 5 gin is the (total expenses in) silver.

2 [4]A little canal. 5 US is the length, 3 kus the width, 3 kus [its depth; (for the first) 1 kus] depth,[203] ⅓ ma-na (volume) is the *silutum;*
[5](for the next) 2 kus depth[203] a volume of 10 gin is the dusu. [How much length did] one man take? 3 kus (and) 6 su-si.

3 [6]A little canal. 5 US is the length, 3 kus the width, 3 kus [its depth; (for the first) 1 kus] depth,[203] ⅓ ma-na[196] volume is the *silutum*;
[7](for the next) 2 kus depth,[203] a volume of 10 gin is the dusu. How much length did 30 workers take? They took 8 GAR length.

4 [8]A little canal. 5 US is the length, 3 kus the width, 3 kus its depth; (for the first) 1 kus depth,[203] ⅓ ma-na[196] volume is the *silutum*;
[9](for the next) 2 kus depth,[203] a volume of 10 gin is the dusu. (In) how many days did 30 workers finish? They finished (after) 1 month (and) 7½ (days).[205]

5 [10]A little canal. 3 kus is the width, 3 kus its depth; (for the first) 1 kus depth,[203] <⅓ma-na[196]> volume is the *silutum*; (for the next) 2 kus depth,[203] <a volume of 10 gin> is the dusu;
[11]30 workers finished (after) 1 month (and) 7½ (days).[205] What is the length? 5 US is its length.

7 [15]A little canal. 5 US is the length, 3 kus the width, 3 kus its depth; (for the first) 1 kus depth,[203] ⅓ ma-na[196] (volume) is the *silutum*;
[16–18](for the next) 2 kus depth.[203] (a volume of) 10 gin is the dusu. What fraction of a day did one man dig the *silutum*? What fraction of a day did he dig

196 For: SAR.

203 The text abbreviates the word in question by writing the first syllable only.

205 The text uses the ordinal for the length of time; to avoid awkwardness, this has been ignored in the translation.

the dusu? And what is the volume? One-fifth of a day he extracted the *silutum,* (amounting to) 4 gin volume; 2/3 of a day and one-fifth of 2/3 of a day he dug the dusu, (amounting to) 8 gin volume.

8 [19]An old, little canal. 5 US is the length, 1 kus the width, 1 kus its depth;
[20]its increase cut off ½ kus of its *tarahhum.* What is its volume? ⅓ SAR (and) 5 gin.[199]

9 [21]An old, little canal. 5 US is the length, 1 kus the width, 1 kus its depth; its increase
[22]cut off ½ kus of its *tarahhum*[203]; ⅓ gin[196] (volume) is the assignment. How much length [did] one man [take? 4 GAR] length.

10 [23]An old, little canal. 5 US is the length, 1 kus the width, 1 kus its depth; [its increase]
[24]cut off ½ kus of its *tarahhum*[203]; ⅓ gin[196] (volume) is the assignment. [How much] length [did] 10 workers [take]?
[25]They took 40 GAR length.

11 [26]An [old], little [canal]. 5 US is the length, 1 kus the width, 1 kus [its depth];
[27]its increase cut off ½ kus of its *tarahhum*[203]; [⅓ gin (volume) is the assignment].
[28](In) how many days did 10 workers finish? [They finished] (after) 7½ days.[205]

Reverse

12 [1]An old, little canal. I kus is the width, 1 kus its depth; its increase <cut off> ½ kus of its *tarahhum*[203]; <⅓ gin is the assignment>.
[2]10 workers finished (in) 7½ days. What is its length? 5 US is [its length].

13 [3]An old, little canal. 5 US is its length, 2 kus the width, 1 kus its depth;
[4]its increase cut off ½ kus of its *tarahhum*[203] (and)
[5]added 1 kus to its depth. What is its volume? 1 iku is the volume.

14 [6]An old, little canal. 5 US is its <length>, 2 kus the width, 1 kus its depth;

---

199 Mistake for 25 SAR.

[7]its increase cut off ½ kus of its *tarahhum*[203] (and) [add]ed 1 kus to its depth;
[8]⅓ gin[196] volume is the assignment. How much length did one man take?
[9]He took 1 GAR length.

15 [10]An old, little canal. 5 US is its length, 3 kus the width, 1 kus its depth;
[11–12]its increase cut off ½ kus of its *tarahhum*[203] (and) added 1½ kus to its depth. What is its volume?

16 [13]An old, little canal. 5 US is its <length>, 2 kus the width, 1 kus its depth;
[14]its increase cut off ½ kus of its *tarahhum*[203] (and) added 1½ kus to its depth;
[15](for the first) 1 kus of its depth, ⅓ gin[196] volume is the assignment; (for the next) 1½ kus of its depth, 10 gin volume is the ....[206]
[16]How much length did one man take? He took 4-2/3 kus (and) 4 su-si length.

17 [17–18]A little canal. 1 kus is the width, 1 kus its depth. What .... waters of the watercourses ....

18 [19–20]A little canal. 2 kus is the width, 1½ kus its depth. What .... waters of the watercourses ....

a. Mathematical Commentary

All the examples of this text deal with a little canal (pa$_5$-sig) of rectangular cross-section. The first seven assume a width of 3 kus and a depth of 3 kus or more. Nos. 8-16 have to do with an old canal (pa$_5$-sig-libirra) of similar dimensions which must be enlarged because of deposited silt or because a flow of water greater than that permitted by the original canal is required. The work involved therefore consists in cleaning out and/or expanding the existing canal. The last two examples apparently deal with the water supplied by the canal.

No. 1

The dimensions given for the length (us), width (dagal), and depth (bur) are

[206] Unidentified sign, perhaps intended for dusu; one would expect the word for "assignment."

$l = 5{,}0$ GAR $\qquad b = 3$ kus $= 0;15$ GAR $\qquad h = 3$ kus.
The work λ assigned to one man per day amounts to

$$\lambda = 0;10 \text{ SAR}$$

volume. The wages are

$$w = 6 \text{ se} = 0;2 \text{ gin silver}$$

per man per day.

The text requires the answers for: the area (gagar) $g = lb$ covered by the canal; its volume (sahar) V; the number m of workers (erim-ha) necessary to complete the whole work in one day, i.e., the total number of man-days; and, finally, the total expenses E for the work expressed in silver.

The answers given satisfy the following relations:

$$g = lb = 1{,}15 \text{ SAR}$$
$$V = lbh = 3{,}45 \text{ SAR} = [2]^{207} \text{ iku } 25 \text{ SAR}$$
$$m = \frac{V}{\lambda} = 22{,}30 = 2 \text{ ges'u } 2{,}30$$
$$E = mw = 45 \text{ gin} = [2/3]^{208} \text{ ma-na } 5 \text{ gin.}$$

The ges'u in the third line literally means ten-sixties, i.e., 600.

Nos. 2-5.

The dimensions given for the canal in this group of four examples are the same as in No. 1, namely,
$l = 5{,}0$ GAR $\qquad b = 3$ kus $= 0;15$ GAR $\qquad h = 3$ kus.
The volume assigned to one man each day, however, is no longer 0;10 SAR but is raised to

$$\lambda = 0;12 \text{ SAR.}$$

This statement is not made explicitly, but the discussion of No. 7 will show that it is implicitly contained in the wording

1 kus *su* ⅓ ma-na (sahar) *si-lu-tum*
2 kus *su* sahar 10 gin dusu.

Anticipating this conclusion, we obtain the following results:

No. 2. The length l_λ which corresponds to one man's work per day is therefore given by

207 Omitted by the scribe.
208 Restored.

$$l_\lambda = \frac{\lambda}{bh} = \frac{0;12}{0;15 \cdot 3} = \frac{4}{15} = 0;16 \text{ GAR} = 3 \text{ kus } 6 \text{ su-si.}$$

No. 3. The length of the canal worked by 30 men during one day is therefore

$$30 \cdot l_\lambda = 0;16 \cdot 30 = 8 \text{ GAR.}$$

No. 4. The time required for 30 men to complete the total work on $l = 5,0$ GAR length is therefore

$$t = \frac{5,0}{8} = 37\frac{1}{2} \text{ days.}$$

This number is expressed as "1 month (and) 7½ (days)". The assumption of 30 days as the length of one month for purposes of computation is well attested by other texts.[209]

No. 5. This problem is the inverse of No. 4: 30 men finish a total length of $l = 5,0$ GAR in 37½ days.

Nos. 8-12.

Here begins a new type of problem characterized by the term pa$_5$-sig-libir-ra, "an old, little canal". The work no longer consists of digging out the entire profile of the canal but simply cleaning out the silted parts or perhaps even enlarging the existing profile beyond that of the

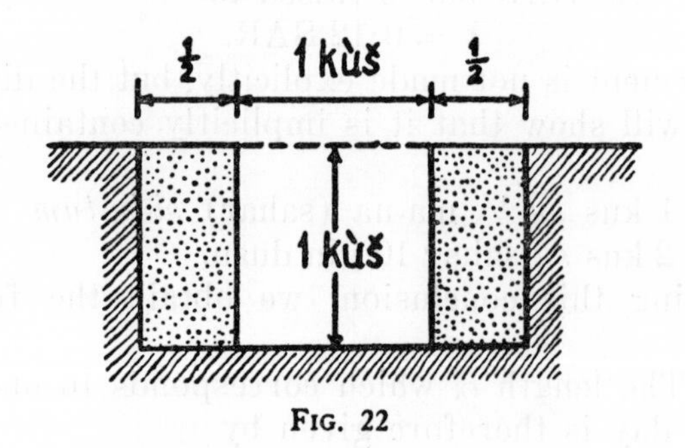

FIG. 22

[209] Cf., e.g., MKT III p. 63.

canal when it was first dug. All five examples of this group assume dimensions for the existing profile as indicated in fig. 22, where the dotted area represents the part which is to be removed (called *tarahhu*):

No. 8 gives the dimensions of the free profile of the canal

$l = 5{,}0$ GAR $\quad b = 1$ kus $= 0;5$ GAR $\quad h = 1$ kus

and asks for the volume V^* to be dug if the width should be increased by

$$c = \tfrac{1}{2} \text{ kus} = 0;2{,}30 \text{ GAR}$$

on each side. The answer should be

$$V^* = l \cdot 2c \cdot h = 5{,}0 \cdot 0;5 \cdot 1 = 25 \text{ SAR},$$

but by misinterpreting the order of magnitude, the scribe gives ⅓ SAR 5 gin, i.e., 0;25 SAR.

No. 9 introduces the assignment of work per man per day.

$$\lambda = 0;20 \text{ SAR},$$

written, however, ⅓ gin here and in the following examples where this value occurs. The values given for l, b, h and c are the same as above. The problem consists in finding the length dug by one man given by

$$\frac{\lambda}{2ch} = \frac{0;20}{0;5} = 4 \text{ GAR}.$$

Nos. 10 and 11 make the same assumptions but ask for the length l_{10} for 10 men (hence 40 GAR is the result) and the time needed to complete the whole work by 10 men, which is

$$\frac{l}{l_{10}} = \frac{5{,}0}{40} = 7\tfrac{1}{2} \text{ days}.$$

No. 12 is the inverse problem to No. 11, computing l from the number of men and the time.

Nos. 13-16.

This new group not only assumes an increase of the "old canal" in width but in depth as well (cf. fig. 23).

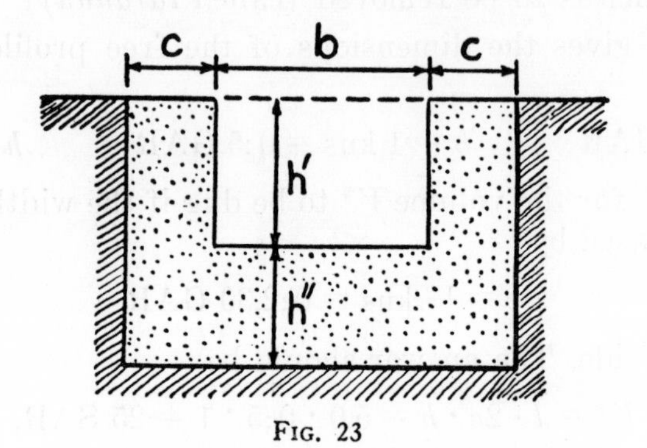

FIG. 23

THE BAKHSHALI MANUSCRIPT

(Composed 4th Century A.D. or earlier)

In the spring of 1881, in a village called Bakhshali, on the northwest border of India, a farmer, digging in a ruined enclosure, came upon an old manuscript written on some seventy leaves of birch bark, lying between stones. The contents of the manuscript proved to be mathematical, ranging over topics in arithmetic, algebra and mensurational geometry. Written in an old form of Sanskrit, it presented rules, illustrative examples, solutions, and verifications of the results obtained. In its partly preserved and partly mutilated form, it appeared to be an interior portion of a much larger work. Lacking the beginning and the end of the work, we know neither the name of the work nor its author. Indian authorities believe that it is a running commentary on an earlier work and not a treatise on mathematics in the true sense. Dr. A. F. Rudolf Hoernle was the first to study, edit and translate the manuscript.

Most of the illustrative problems are of the type requiring the solution of linear equations or of an indeterminate equation of the second degree. The solutions, performed principally by the method of false position, display the writer's knowledge of average value, series, and a considerable skill in operations with fractions. Consistent use is made throughout the work of the decimal system of numeration with place values, an especially noteworthy feature being the heavy dot which serves the purpose of a zero in the representation of numbers. The heavy dot, indicating an empty place, is also used as a "place-holder" for the unknown quantity in algebraic problems. Calculations involve positive and negative numbers, the sign (+) is used to denote a negative number or subtraction, and multiplication is frequently indicated by juxtaposition. While the manuscript itself may have been written as late as the ninth century, its contents were composed no later than the fourth century A.D. The mathematics of the Bakhshali manuscript thus antedates all known Hindu mathematical treatises.

THE BAKHSHALI MANUSCRIPT

By Dr. A. F. Rudolf Hoernle

The manuscript is written in Sarada characters of a rather ancient type, and on leaves of birch-bark which from age have become dry like tinder and extremely fragile. Unfortunately, probably through the careless handling of the finder, it is now in an excessively mutilated condition, both with regard to the size and the number of the leaves. Their present size is about 6 by 3¼ inches; their original size, however, must have been about 7 by 8¼ inches. This might have been presumed from the well-known fact that the old birch-bark manuscripts were always written on leaves of a squarish size. But I was enabled to determine the point by a curious fact. The mutilated leaf which contains a portion of the twenty-seventh *sutra* shows at top and bottom the remainders of two large square figures, such as are used in writing arithmetical notations. These, when completed, prove that the leaf in its original state must have measured approximately 7 by 8¼ inches. The number of the existing leaves is seventy. This can only be a small portion of the whole manuscript. For neither beginning nor end is preserved; nor are some leaves forthcoming which are specifically referred to in the existing fragments. From all appearances, it must have been a large work, perhaps divided into chapters or sections. The existing leaves include only the middle portion of the work or of a division of it. The earliest *sutra* that I have found is the ninth; the latest is the fifty-seventh. The lateral margins which usually exhibit the numbering of the leaves are broken off. It is thus impossible even to guess what the original number of the leaves may have been.

The leaves of the manuscript, when received by me, were found to be in great confusion. Considering that of each leaf the top and bottom (nearly two-thirds of the whole leaf) are lost, thus destroying their connection with one another, it may be imagined that it was no easy task to read the fragments and arrange them in order. After much trouble I have read and transcribed the whole, and have even succeeded in arranging in consecutive order a not inconsiderable portion of the leaves containing eighteen *sutras*. The latter portion I have also translated into English.

The subject-matter is divided in *sutras*. In each *sutra* the matter is arranged as follows: First comes the rule, and then the example introduced by the word *udaharana*.[4] Next, the example is repeated in the form of a notation in figures, which is called *sthapana*. This is followed by the solution which is called *karana*. Finally comes the proof, called *pratyaya*.

The system of notation used in the Bakhshali arithmetic is much the same as that employed in the arithmetical works of Brahmagupta and Bhaskara.[5] There is, however, a very important exception. The sign for the negative quantity is a cross (+). It looks exactly like our modern sign for the positive quantity, but it is placed after the number which it qualifies. Thus $\begin{matrix} 12 & 7+ \\ 1 & 1 \end{matrix}$ means 12 — 7 (*i.e.* 5). This is a sign which I have not met with in any other Indian arithmetic; nor, so far as I have been able to ascertain, is it now known in India at all. The sign now used is a dot placed over the number to which it refers. Here, therefore, there appears to be a mark of great antiquity.

The following statement, from the first example of the twenty-fifth *sutra*, affords a good example of the system of notation employed in the Bakhshali arithmetic:—

---

[4] This word is almost uniformly abbreviated *uda*. Owing to the graphic symbols for *u* and *ta* being indistinguishable, I at first took the word to be complete and read it *tada*. But quite lately I found on a fragment, which had hitherto escaped my notice, the word written in full *udaharana*.

[5] See Colebrooke's *Dissertation on the Algebra of the Hindus*, in his *Essays*, Vol. II, pp. 387 ff.

$$\begin{array}{|ccccc|l} \bullet & 1 & 1 & 1 & & \\ 1 & 1 & 1 & 1 & \textit{bha}\ 32 & \textit{phalam}\ 108 \\ & 3+ & 3+ & 3+ & & \end{array}$$

Here the initial dot is used very much in the same way as we use the letter x to denote the unknown quantity the value of which is sought. The number 1 under the dot is the sign of the whole (in this case, unknown) number. A fraction is denoted by placing one number under the other without any line of separation; thus $\begin{matrix}1\\3\end{matrix}$ is ⅓, *i. e.* one-third. A mixed number is shown by placing the three numbers under one another; thus $\begin{matrix}1\\1\\3\end{matrix}$ is 1 + ⅓ or 1⅓, *i. e.,* one and one-third. Hence $\begin{matrix}1\\1\\3+\end{matrix}$ means 1 — ⅓ (*i. e.* ⅔). Multiplication is usually indicated by placing the numbers side by side; thus

$$\begin{array}{|cc|l} 5 & 32 & \\ 8 & 1 & \textit{phalam}\ 20, \end{array}$$

means $5/8 \times 32 = 20$. Similarly $\begin{matrix}1 & 1 & 1\\1 & 1 & 1\\3+ & 3+ & 3+\end{matrix}$ means $2/3 \times 2/3 \times 2/3$ or $(2/3)^3$, *i. e.* 8/27. *Bha* is an abbreviation of *bhaga,* 'part,' and means that the number preceding it is to be treated as a denominator. Hence $\begin{matrix}1 & 1 & 1\\1 & 1 & 1\\3+ & 3+ & 3+\end{matrix}$ *bha* means 1 : 8/27 or 27/8. The whole statement, therefore means $27/8 \times 32 = 108$, and may

$$\begin{array}{|ccccc|l} \bullet & 1 & 1 & 1 & & \\ 1 & 1 & 1 & 1 & \textit{bha}\ 32 & \textit{phalam}\ 108 \\ & 3+ & 3+ & 3+ & & \end{array}$$

be thus explained,—"a certain number is found by dividing with 8/27 and multiplying with 32; that number is 108.''

The dot is also used for another purpose, namely as one of the ten fundamental figures of the decimal system of notation, or the zero (0 1 2 3 4 5 6 7 8 9). It is still so used in India for both purposes, to indicate the unknown quantity as well as the naught. With us the dot, or rather its substitute the circle (0), has only retained the latter of its two intents, being simply the zero figure, or the 'mark of position' in the decimal system. The Indian usage, however, seems to show how the zero arose, and that it arose in India. The Indian dot, unlike our modern zero, is not properly a numerical figure at all. It is simply a sign to indicate an empty place or a hiatus. This is clearly shown by its name *sunya* 'empty.' The empty place in an arithmetical statement might or might not be capable of being filled up, according to circumstances. Occurring in a row of figures arranged decimally or according to the 'value of position,' the empty place could not be filled up, and the dot therefore signified 'naught,' or stood in the place of the zero. Thus the two figures 3 and 7, placed in juxtaposition (37) mean 'thirty-seven,' but with an 'empty space' interposed between them (3 7), they mean 'three hundred and seven.' To prevent misunderstanding the presence of the 'empty space' was indicated by a dot (3 • 7); or by what is now the zero (307). On the other hand, occurring in the statement of a problem, the 'empty place' could be filled up, and here the dot which marked its presence, signified a 'something' which was to be discovered and to be put in the empty place. In the course of time, and out of India, the latter signification of the dot was discarded; and the dot thus became simply the sign for 'naught' or the zero, and assumed the value of a proper figure of the decimal system of notation, being the 'mark of position.' In its double signification, which still survives in India, we can still discern an indication of that country as its birthplace.

Generally speaking, the terms of an operation are set down side by side; and the particular operation intended is indicated by the initial syllable of a word of that import, subjoined to the terms which compose it. The operation of multiplication alone is not indicated by any special sign. Addition is indicated by *yu* (for *yuta*), subtraction by + (*ka* for *kanita*?) and division by *bha* (for *bhaga*). The whole operation is commonly enclosed between lines (or sometimes double lines), and the result is set down outside, introduced by *pha* (for *phala*). Occasionally the indicatory word is written in full. Vertical lines are usually interposed between the terms of a proportion or a progression. Thus:—

$$\left|\begin{matrix}5 & 7\\ 1 & 1\end{matrix}\ \textit{yu}\right|\ \textit{pha}\ 12 \qquad \text{means } 5 + 7 = 12$$

$$\left|\begin{matrix}12 & 7\\ 1 & 1\end{matrix} +\right|\ \textit{pha}\ \ 5 \qquad ,,\ 12 - 7 = 5$$

$$\left|\begin{matrix}5 & 32\\ 8 & 1\end{matrix}\right|\ \textit{pha}\ \ 20 \qquad ,,\ \tfrac{5}{8} \times 32 = 20$$

$$\left|\begin{matrix}\overset{\bullet}{1} & 1 & 1 & 1\\ & 1 & 1 & 1\\ & 3+ & 3+ & 3+\end{matrix}\ \textit{bhá}\ 32\right|\ \textit{pha}\ 108 \ ,,\ (1:\tfrac{8}{27}) \times 32 = 108$$

$$\left|\begin{matrix}10\\ 1\end{matrix}\middle|\begin{matrix}30\\ 1\end{matrix}\middle|\begin{matrix}4\\ 1\end{matrix}\right|\ \textit{pha}\ \begin{matrix}12\\ 1\end{matrix} \qquad ,,\ 10 : 30 = 4 : 12$$

Regarding the age of the manuscript, I am unable to offer a very definite opinion. The composition of a Hindu work on arithmetic, such as that contained in the Bakhshali MS., seems necessarily to presuppose a country and a period in which Hindu civilisation and Brahmanical learning flourished. Now the country in which Bakhshali lies and which formed part of the Hindu kingdom of Kabul, was early lost to Hindu civilisation through the conquests of the Muhammadan rulers of Ghazni, and especially through the celebrated expeditions of Mahmud, towards the end of the 10th and the beginning of the 11th centuries A. D. In those troublous times it was a common practice for the learned Hindus to bury their manuscript treasures. Possibly the Bakhshali MS. may be one of these. In any case it cannot well be placed much later than the 10th century A. D. It is quite possible that it may be somewhat older. The

Sarada characters used in it, exhibit in several respects a rather archaic type, and afford some ground for thinking that the manuscript may perhaps go back to the 8th or 9th century. But in the present state of our epigraphical knowledge, arguments of this kind are always somewhat hazardous. The usual form in which the numeral figures occur in the manuscript are the following:—

or or or

1 2 3 4

5 6 7 8 9 0

Quite distinct from the question of the age of the manuscript, is that of the age of the work contained in it. There is every reason to believe that the Bakhshali arithmetic is of a very considerably earlier date than the manuscript in which it has come down to us. I am disposed to believe that the composition of the former must be referred to the earliest centuries of our era, and that it may date from the 3rd or 4th century A. D. The arguments making for this conclusion are briefly the following:—

In the first place, it appears that the earliest mathematical works of the Hindus were written in the *sloka* measure;[7] but from about the end of the 5th century A. D. it became the fashion to use the *arya* measure. Aryabhata *c.* 500 A. D., Varahamihira c. 550, Brahmagupta *c.* 630, all wrote in the latter measure. Not only were new works written in it, but also *sloka*-works were revised and recast in it. Now the Bakhshali arithmetic is written in the *sloka* measure; and this circumstance carries its composition back to a time anterior to that change of literary fashion in the 5th century A. D.

In the second place the Bakshali arithmetic is written

---

[7] See Professor Kern's Introduction to the *Brihat Samhita* of Varahamihira.

in that peculiar language which used to be called the Gatha dialect, but which is rather the literary form of the ancient North-Western Prakrit (or Pali). It exhibits a strange mixture of what we should now call Sanskrit and Prakrit forms. As shown by the inscriptions (*e.g.* of the Indo-Scythian kings in Mathura) of that period, it appears to have been in general use, in North-Western India, for literary purposes till about the end of the 3rd century A. D., when the proper Sanskrit, hitherto the language of the Brahmanic schools, gradually came into general use also for secular compositions. The older literary language may have lingered on some time longer among the Buddhists and Jains, but this would only have been so in the case of religious, not of secular, compositions. Its use, therefore, in the Bakhshali arithmetic points to a date not later than the 3rd or 4th century A. D. for the composition of that work.

In the third place, in several examples, the two words *dinara* and *dramma* occur as denominations of money. These words are the Indian forms of the Latin *denarius* and the Greek *drakhme*. The former, as current in India, was a gold coin, the latter a silver coin. Golden *denarii* were first coined at Rome in B. C. 207. The Indian gold pieces, corresponding in weight to the Roman gold *denarius,* were those coined by the Indo-Scythian kings, whose line, beginning with Kadphises, about the middle of the 1st century B. C., probably extended to about the end of the 3rd century A.D. Roman gold *denarii* themselves, as shown by the numerous finds, were by no means uncommon in India, in the earliest centuries of our era. The gold *dinaras* most numerously found are those of the Indo-Scythian kings Kanishka and Huvishka, and of the Roman emperors Trajan, Hadrian and Antoninus Pius, all of whom reigned in the 2nd century A.D. The way in which the two terms are used in the Bakhshali arithmetic seems to indicate that the gold *dinara* and the silver *dramma* formed the ordinary currency of the day. This circumstance again points to some time within the three first centuries of the Christian era as the date of its composition.

A fourth point, also indicative of antiquity, which I have already adverted to, is the peculiar use of the cross (+) as the sign of the negative quantity.

There is also a diffusedness in the mode of composition of the Bakhshali work which reminds one of the similar characteristic observed in Buddhist and Jain literature. All these circumstances put together seem to render it probable that in the Bakhshali MS. there has been preserved to us a fragment of an early Buddhist or Jain work on arithmetic (perhaps a portion of a larger work on astronomy), which may have been one of the sources from which the later Indian astronomers took their arithmetical information. These earlier sources, as we know, were written in the *sloka* measure, and when they belonged to the Buddhist or Jain literature, must have been composed in the ancient North-Western Prakrit. Both these points are characteristics of the Bakhshali work. I may add that one of the reasons why the earlier works were, as we are told by tradition, revised and re-written in the *arya* measure by later writers such as Brahmagupta, may have been that in their time the literary form ('Gatha dialect') of the North-Western Prakrit had come to be looked upon as a barbarous and ungrammatical jargon as compared with their own classical Sanskrit. In any case the Buddhist or Jain character of the Bakhshali arithmetic would be a further mark of its high antiquity.

TRANSLATION

18th Sutra.

Twice the difference of the two initial terms, divided by the difference of the (two) increments, and further augmented by one, shall be the time that determines the progression.

First Example.

A person has an initial (speed) of two and an increment of three, another has an increment of two and an initial (speed) of three. Let it now be determined in what time the two persons will meet in their journey.

The statement is as follows:

No. 1, init. term 2, increment 3, period x

No. 2, init. term 3, increment 2, period x

Solution:—"the difference of the two initial terms" (2 and 3 is 1; the difference of the two increments 3 and 2 is 1; twice the difference of the initial terms 1 is 2, and this, divided by the difference of the increments 1, is 2/1, and augmented by 1, is 3/1; this is the period. In this time [3] they meet in their journey which is 15).

27th Sutra.

Now I shall discuss the wastage (in the working) of gold, the rule about which is as follows:—

Having multiplied severally the parts of gold with the wastage, let the total wastage be divided by the sum of the parts of gold. The result is the wastage of each part (of the whole mass) of gold.

First Example.

Suvarnas numbering respectively one, two, three, four, are subject to a wastage of mashakas numbering respectively one, two, three, four. Irrespective of such wastage they suffer an equal distribution of wastage. (What is the latter?)

The statement is as follows:—

Wastage —	1, —	2, —	3, —	4 mashaka.
Gold	1,	2,	3,	4 suvarna.

Solution:—"Having multiplied severally the parts of gold with the wastage," etc.; by multiplying with the wastage, the products 1, 4, 9, 16 are obtained; "let the total wastage," its sum is 30; the sum of the parts of gold is 10; dividing with it, we obtain 3. (This is the wastage of each part, or the average wastage, of the whole mass of gold.)

(Proof by the rule of three is the following):—as the

sum of gold 10 is to the total wastage of 30 mashakas, so the sum of gold 4 is to the wastage of 12 mashakas, etc.

Second Example.

There are suvarnas numbering one, two, three, four. There are thrown out the following mashakas; one-half, one-third, one-fourth, one-fifth. What is the (average) wastage (in the whole mass of gold)?

Statement:—

quantities of gold,	1,	2,	3,	4	suvarna.
wastage	1/2,	1/3,	1/4,	1/5	mashaka.

Solution:—"Having multiplied severally the parts of gold with the wastage," the products may thus be stated,—1/2, 2/3, 3/4, 4/5. "Let the total wastage be divided;" the division being directed to be made the total wastage is 163/60; dividing "by the sum of the parts of gold;" here the sum of the parts of gold is 10: being divided by this, the result is 163/600. This is the wastage of each part of the whole mass of gold.

Proof may be made by the rule of three:—as the sum of the parts of gold 10 is to the total wastage of 163/60 mashaka, so the sum of gold 4 is to the wastage of 163/150 mashaka, etc.

50th Sutra.

(The *sutra* is lost, but can be partially restored from the solution, and may be thus translated:—"The sum of the additive and subtractive numbers is divided by an assumed number; the quotient, lessened by the same number and halved, is squared and added to the subtractive number.")

Example.

Which number added to five is a square, that (same) number lessened by seven is a square. Which number is that? This is the question.

53rd Sutra.

(Having found) the two fractions (indicative) of the daily earnings, divide by their difference what is given towards (producing) equal possessions. The quotient, being doubled, is the time (in which their possessions become equal).

First Example.

Let one hired Pandit earn five in three days; another learned man earns six in five days. The first gives seven to the second from his earnings. Say, in what time, after having given it, their possessions become equal?

Statement:—No. I, 5/3 = earnings of 1 day; No. II, 6/5 = earnings of 1 day; gift 7.

Solution: "The difference of the daily earnings; the two fractions; their difference;" (here the daily earnings are 5/3 and 6/5; their difference is 7/15; the gift is 7; divided by the difference of the daily earnings 7/15, the result is 15; being doubled, it is 30; this is the time), in which their possessions become equal.

Proof may be made by the rule of three:—3 : 5 = 30 : 50, and 5 : 6 = 30 : 36; "the first gives seven to the second" 7, remainder 43; hence 43 and 43 are their equal possessions.

Second Example.

Two Rajputs are the servants of a king. The wages of one (of them) per day are two and one-sixth, of the other one and one-half. The first gives to the second ten *dinaras*. Calculate and tell me quickly, in what time there will be equality (in their possessions)?

Statement:—daily wages 13/6 and 3/2; gift 10.

Solution:—"and difference of the daily earnings;" here (the daily earnings are 13/6 and 3/2; their difference is 2/3; the gift is 10; divided by the difference of the daily earnings 2/3, the result is 15; being doubled, it is 30. This is the time, in which their possessions become equal).

Proof by the rule of three:—1 : 13/6 = 30 : 65; and 1 : 3/2 = 30 : 45. The first gives 10 to the second; hence 55 and 55 are their equal possessions.

Sutra.

(Only the first portion of this *sutra* is preserved; *viz.* "put into the empty place the number 1 representing the desired quantity, and then make up the series of items." The purport of this rule will be understood from the following examples).

First Example.

(Its purport is:—B gives 2 times as much as A, C gives 3 times as much as B, D gives 4 times as much as C. Their total gift is 132. What is the gift of A?)

Statement:—A gives x, B 2, C 3, D 4. Total 132.

Solution:—"Put 1 in the place of x; then form the series of items" 1, 2, 3×2, 4×6, multiplying these several rates, 1, 2, 6, 24, their total is 33; with it divide the given total thus 132/33; the resulting item is 4, and this is the gift of A. Hence the series of gifts is as follows:—4, 8, 24, 96, and the total gift is 132. This is calculated from the series of items, and hence the total of the items is one hundred and thirty-two.

(Here follows what appears to be intended as a modification of the same *sutra* since it is not specialised as a separate *sutra.* What remains of it, runs thus:—"the number 1 is put into the empty place, and then (the items) are successively multiplied." The purport of the rule will be again understood from the example.)

Second Example.

(Its purport is:—B possesses 2 times as much as A; C has 3 times as much as A and B together; D has 4 times as much as A, B and C together. Their total possessions are 300. What is the possession of A?)

Statement:—A has x, B 2, C 3×3, D 4×12. Total 300.

Solution:—"the desired quantity is put in the empty place;" the desired quantity is 1; this is placed as the first number; then the successive multiplications are made, 1, 2, 9, 48. Their addition gives the sum of the rates 60; with this the given total is divided, thus 300/60; the result is 5, and this is the possession of A. With this by multiplication the several rates are obtained, thus 5, 10, 45, 240. Thence the total of the items is calculated to be 300.

Fourth Example.

(Its purport is:—A possesses something and 1½ in addition; B has 2 times as much as A and 2½ in addition; C has 3 times as much as B and 3½ in addition; D has 4 times as much as C and 4½ in addition. Their total possessions are one hundred and forty-four and one half. What is the possession of A?).

Statement:—A has $x + 1½$, B $2 + 2½$, C 3 $+ 3½$, D $4 + 4½$. Total 144½.

Solution:—"Having put one in the empty place," thus $1 + 1½$: "the several additions and multiplications are then made:" in making the additions and multiplications, let the proper order of calculation be observed, (hence by addition) 5/2; next comes multiplication; (here) multiply numerator with numerator and denominator with denominator, 10/2 (*i.e.* $2/1 \times 5/2$); two and one half are now added, thus 15/2: now comes the multiplication with the third number, or three (is multiplied) with seven and one half (*i.e.* $15/2 = 7½$), thus 45/2; three and one half are now added, thus 52/2; now multiply the number four with twenty-six (*i.e.* $52/2 = 26$); the result is 208/2; four and one half are now added, thus 217/2. The total of these rates is 289/2 which is the given total of the possessions. All the rest remains the same; (*i.e.* dividing the given total 289/2 by the sum of the rates 289/2 we obtain 1 as the value of x, hence the possessions of A, B, C, D and respectively 5/2,

15/2, 52/2 and 217/2, the same as the rates mentioned above).

Seventh Example.

(Its purport is:—A has 1½ *plus* a certain amount; B has 2½ less than 2 times A; C has 3½ less than 3 times A; D has 4½ less than 4 times A. Their total possessions are 29/2. What is the possession of A?)

(The statement is wanting).

Solution:—"Having put the number one in the empty place," the addition is made 5/2; twice the rate of A less five halves is 5/2; three times the rate of A, less seven halves, is 8/2; four times the rate of A, less nine halves, is 11/2. The series of these rates is as follows: 5/2, 5/2, 8/2, 11/2. The given total is 29/2. The sum of the rates is 29/2. Dividing the one by the other, 29·2/2·29, we obtain 1. Multiplying by this, the same amount is obtained (as the gift of A; *viz.* 5/2). The same is the case with the negative quantities, (*i.e.* B $1 \times [(2 \times 5/2) - 5/2] = 5/2$; similarly C 8/2, D 11/2).

ISAAC BARROW
(1630—1677)

Isaac Barrow, descended from an ancient Suffolk family, was born in London in October 1630. One of England's most brilliant and versatile scholars, he would have achieved lasting fame for his contribution to any single one of the fields of his interest, the classics, mathematics, science, or theology. Reports of his behaviour at his first school, Charterhouse, in London, however, gave surprisingly little promise of the greatness to which he was destined. Here, it was said, he was given to fighting and even to promoting fighting among his fellow pupils. A transfer to Felstead, in Essex, provided a salutary change of environment and Barrow immediately proved to be an excellent student in all areas of work. He entered Trinity College, Cambridge, in 1644; he received the degree of B. A. in 1648, and was elected fellow of his College the following year.

In 1655, although he was eminently qualified for a professorship in Greek, his application for the position was denied because of a suspicion of sympathy with Arminianism. Deeply disappointed, he sold all his books and left England. The next four years were spent in travel, at times highly adventurous, over eastern Europe. His tour of the continent was made feasible and successful to a large extent by the kind reception and assistance given him by the English ambassadors and others of his countrymen in the regions he visited. A small, lean man of unusual strength and courage, Barrow was widely admired and respected for his learning and lively companionship.

Barrow returned to England in 1659. He was ordained by Bishop Brownrig the next year, and soon thereafter, in June 1660 (the year that Newton entered Trinity College), he was chosen for the Greek professorship at Cambridge. In 1662 he was elected professor of geometry in Gresham College. He also served as a substitute for Dr. Pope, a professor of astronomy. In 1663, he became the first Lucasian professor of mathematics at Cambridge. In 1669, desiring to devote himself completely to the study of theology, Barrow resigned the Lucasian chair to his great pupil and friend Isaac Newton. Newton had already seen to the preparation of Barrow's *Lectiones Opticae* for publication (1669). In 1670, Newton also supervised the publication of Barrow's *Lectiones Geometricae.* During this year, too, Barrow became chaplain to Charles II. The king openly admired the outspoken Barrow as a scholar and a divine whose brilliant conversation enlivened and elevated the English court. Barrow was appointed Master of Trinity in 1672, and in 1675, he was chosen vice-chancellor of the university. He died suddenly of a fever on May 4, 1677 and was interred in Westminster Abbey.

Barrow was in the first group of scientists to be elected to membership in the Royal Society. A prolific writer on theology, mathematics and poetry, his Latin and English translations of Euclid, Archimedes, Apollonius and Theodosius were widely read both in England and on the continent. Most of his contributions to mathematics appeared in the three published collections of his lectures, *Lectiones Mathematicae* (1683, posthumously), *Lectiones Opticae,* and *Lectiones Geometricae.* The last mentioned work contains the foundations of the calculus in geometrical form. It presents differentiation and integration as inverse processes, integration as a summation, and nomenclature and methods which were direct forerunners of the algorithmic procedures of the calculus. Lecture X, in particular, which contains Barrow's presentation of the differential triangle, clearly indicates the mutual influence of Barrow and Newton upon each other. Barrow's influence upon Leibniz, too, may be inferred from the fact that Leibniz is known to have purchased a copy of Barrow's *Lectiones Geometricae* in 1673. The *Lectiones Geometricae,* the greatest of Barrow's mathematical works, was translated into English from the Latin in 1916 by James Mark Child under the title, *The Geometrical Lectures of Isaac Barrow.*

THE GEOMETRICAL LECTURES OF ISAAC BARROW

Translated, with notes and proofs, by JAMES MARK CHILD

LECTURE X

Rigorous determination of ds/dx. Differentiation as the inverse of integration. Explanation of the "Differential Triangle" method; with examples. Differentiation of a trigonometrical function.

1. Let AEG be any curve whatever, and AFI another curve so related to it that, if any straight line EF is drawn parallel to a straight line given in position (which cuts AEG in E and AFI in F), EF is always equal to

the arc AE of the curve AEG, measured from A; also let the straight line ET touch the curve AEG at E, and let ET be equal to the arc AE; join TF; then TF touches the curve AFI.

2. Moreover, if the straight line EF always bears any the same ratio to the arc AE, in just the same way FT can be shown to touch the curve AFI.*

3. Let AGE be any curve, D a fixed point, and AIF be another curve such that, if any straight line DEF is drawn through D, the intercept EF is always equal to the arc AE; and let the straight line ET touch the curve AGE; make TE equal to the arc AE**; let TKF be a curve such that, if any straight line DHK is drawn through D, cutting the curve TKF in K and the straight line TE in H, $HK = HT$; then let FS be drawn† to touch TKF at F; FS will touch the curve AIF also.

4. Moreover, if the straight line EF is given to bear any the same ratio to the arc AE, the tangent to it can easily be found from the above and Lect. VIII, § 8.

5. Let a straight line AP and two curves AEG, AFI be so related that, if any straight line DEF is drawn (par-

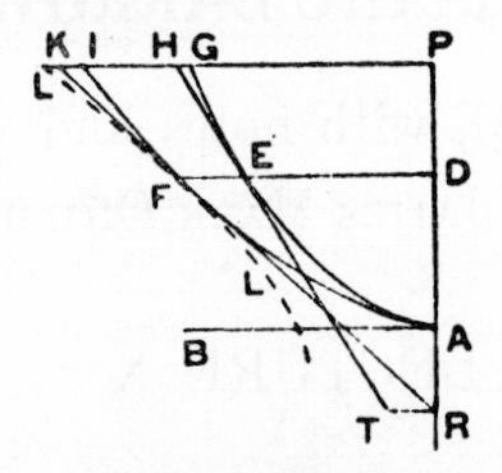

Fig. 106.

allel to AB, a straight line given in position), cutting AP, AEG, AFI, in the points D, E, F respectively DF is always equal to the arc AE; also let ET touch the

* Since the arc is a function of the ordinate, this is a special case of the differentiation of a sum, Lect. IX, § 12; it is equivalent to $d(as+y)/dx = a \cdot ds/dx + dy/dx$; see note to § 5.

** TE, AE are drawn in the same sense.

† By Lect. VIII, § 19.

curve AEG at E; take TE equal to the arc AE, and draw TR parallel to AB to cut AP in R; then, if RF is joined, RF touches the curve AFI.

For, assume that LFL is a curve such that, if any straight line PL is drawn parallel to AB, cutting AEG in G, TE in H, and LFL in L, the straight line PL is always equal to TH and HG taken together. Then $PL >$ arc $AEG > PI$; and therefore the curve LFL touches the curve AFI. Again, by Lect VI, § 26, $PK = TH$ (or $KL = GH$); hence the curve LFL touches the line RFK (by Lect. VII, § 3); therefore the line RFK touches the curve AFI.*

6. Also, if DF always bears any the same ratio to the arc AE, RF will still touch the curve AFI; as is easily shown from the above and Lect. VIII, § 6.

7. Let a point D and two curves AGE, DFI be so related that, if any straight line DFE is drawn through D, the straight line DF is always equal to the arc AE; also let the straight line ET touch the curve AGE at E; make ET equal to the arc AE; and assume that DKK is a curve such that, if any straight line DH is drawn through D, cutting DKK in K and TE in H, the straight line DK is always equal to TH. Then, if FS is drawn (by Lect. VIII, § 16) to touch the curve DKK at F, FS touches the curve DIF also.

8. Moreover, if DF always bears any the same ratio to the arc AE, the straight line touching the curve DIF can likewise be drawn; and in every case the tangent is parallel to FS.

9. By this method can be drawn not only the tangent to the Circular Spiral, but also the tangents to innumerable other curves produced in a similar manner.

10. Let AEH be a given curve, AD any given straight

* The proof of this theorem is given in full, since not only is it a fine example of Barrow's method, but also it is a *rigorous* demonstration of the principle of fluxions, that the motion along the path is the resultant of the two rectilinear motions producing it. Otherwise, for rectangular axes, $(ds/dx)^2 = 1+(dy/dx)^2$; for $ds/dx = DF/DR = ET/DR = Cosec\ DET$ and $dy/dx = Cot\ DET$.

line in which there is a fixed point D, and DH a straight line given in position; also let AGB be a curve such that, if any point G is taken in it, and through G and D a straight line is drawn to cut the curve AEH in E, and GF is drawn parallel to DH to cut AD in F, the arc AE bears to AF a given ratio, X to Y say; also let ET touch the curve AEH; along ET take EV equal to the arc AE; let OGO be a curve such that, if any straight line DOL is drawn, cutting the curve OGO in O and ET in L, and if OQ is drawn parallel to GF, meeting AD in Q, $LV : AQ = X : Y$. Then the curve OGO is a hyperbola (as has been shown).* Then, if GS touches this curve, GS will touch the curve AGB also.

If the curve AEH is a quadrant of a circle, whose centre is D, the curve AGB will be the ordinary Quadratrix. Hence the tangent to this curve (together with tangents to all curves produced in a similar way) can be drawn by this method.

I meant to insert here several instances of this kind; but really I think these are sufficient to indicate the method, by which, without the labour of calculation, one can find tangents to curves and at the same time prove the constructions. Nevertheless, I add one or two theorems, which it will be seen are of great generality, and not lightly to be passed over.

11. Let ZGE be any curve of which the axis is AD; and let ordinates applied to this axis, AZ, PG, DE, continually increase from the initial ordinate AZ; also let AIF be a line such that, if any straight line EDF is drawn perpendicular to AD, cutting the curves in the points E, F, and AD in D, the rectangle contained by DF and a given length R is equal to the intercepted space $ADEZ$; also let $DE : DF = R : DT$, and join FT. Then TF will touch the curve AIF.

For, if any point I is taken in the line AIF (first on the side of F towards A), and if through it IG is drawn

* Only proved for a special case in Lect. VI, § 17; but the method can be generalized without difficulty.

parallel to AZ, and KL is parallel to AD, cutting the

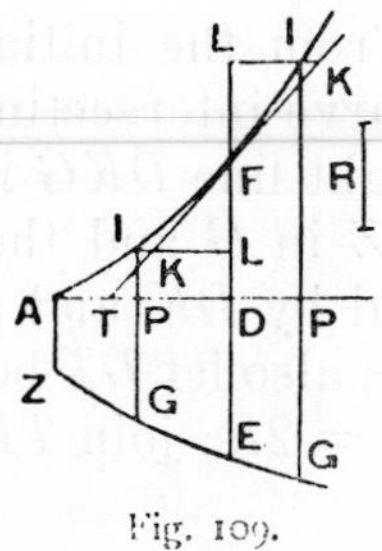

Fig. 109.

given lines as shown in the figure; then $LF : LK = DF : DT = DE : R$, or $R \cdot LF = LK \cdot DE$.

But, from the stated nature of the lines DF, PK, we have $R \cdot LF =$ area $PDEG$; therefore $LK \cdot DE =$ area $PDEG < DP \cdot DE$; hence $LK < DP < LI$.

Again, if the point I is taken on the other side of F, and the same construction is made as before, plainly it can be easily shown that $LK > DP < LI$.

From which it is quite clear that the whole of the line $TKFK$ lies within or below the curve $AIFI$.

Other things remaining the same, if the ordinates, AZ, PG, DE, continually decrease, the same conclusion is attained by similar argument; only one distinction occurs, namely, in this case, contrary to the other, the curve $AIFI$ is concave to the axis AD.

Cor. It should be noted that $DE \cdot DT = R \cdot DF =$ area $ADEZ$.*

12. From the preceding we can deduce the following theorem.

Let ZGE, AKF be any two lines so related that, if any straight line EDF is applied to a common axis AD, the square on DF is always equal to twice the space $ADEZ$; also take DQ, along AD produced, equal to DE, and join FQ; then FQ is perpendicular to the curve AKF.

I will also add the following kindred theorems.

---

* See note at end of this lecture.

13. Let $AGEZ$ be any curve, and D a certain fixed point such that the radii, DA, DG, DE, drawn from D, decrease continually from the initial radius DA; then let DKE be another curve intersecting the first in E and such that, if any straight line DKG is drawn through D, cutting the curve AEZ in G and the curve DKE in K, the rectangle contained by DK and a given length R is equal to the area ADG; also let DT be drawn perpendicular to DE, so that $DT = 2R$; join TE. Then TE touches the curve DKE.

Moreover, if any point, K say, is taken in the curve DKE, and through it DKG is drawn, and $DG : DK = R : P$; then if DT is taken equal to $2P$ and TG is joined, and also KS is drawn parallel to GT; KS will touch the curve DKE.

Observe that Sq. on DG : Sq. on $DK = 2R : DS$.

Now, the above theorem is true, and can be proved in a similar way, even if the radii drawn from D, DA, DG, DE, are equal (in which case the curve $AGEZ$ is a circle and the curve DKE is the Spiral of Archimedes), or if they continually increase from A.

14. From this we may easily deduce the following theorem.

Let AGE, DKE be two curves so related that, if straight lines DA, DG are drawn from some fixed point D in the curve DKE (of which the latter cuts the curve DKE in K), the square on DK is equal to four times the area ADG; draw DH perpendicular to DG, and make $DK : DG = DG : DH$; join HK; then HK is perpendicular to the curve DKE.

We have now finished in some fashion the first part, as we declared, of our subject. Supplementary to this we add, in the form of appendices, a method for finding tangents by calculation frequently used by us (*a nobis usitatum*). Although I hardly know, after so many well-known and well-worn methods of the kind above, whether there is any advantage in doing so. Yet I do so on the *advice of a friend*; and all the more willingly, because it seems to be more profitable and general than those which I have discussed.*

Let AP, PM be two straight lines given in position, of which PM cuts a given curve in M, and let MT be supposed to touch the curve at M, and to cut the straight line at T.

In order to find the quantity of the straight line PT,* I set off an indefinitely small arc, MN, of the curve; then I draw NQ, NR parallel to MP, AP; I call $MP = m$, $PT = t$, $MR = a$, $NR = e$, and other straight lines, deter-

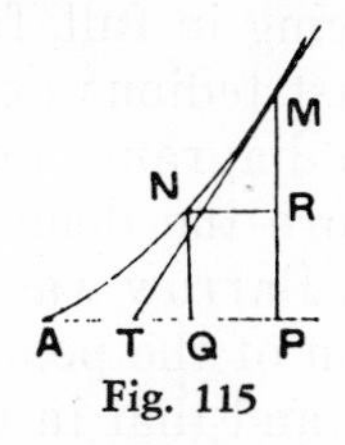

Fig. 115

mined by the special nature of the curve, useful for the matter in hand, I also designate by name; also I compare MR, NR (and through them, MP, PT) with one another by means of an equation obtained by calculation; meantime observing the following rules.

Rule 1. In the calculation, I omit all terms containing a power of a or e, or products of these (for these terms have no value).

Rule 2. After the equation has been formed, I reject all terms consisting of letters denoting known or determined quantities, or terms which do not contain a or e (for these terms, brought over to one side of the equation, will always be equal to zero).

Rule 3. I substitute m (or MP) for a, and t (or PT) for e. Hence at length the quantity of PT is found.

Moreover, if any indefinitely small arc of the curve enters the calculation, an indefinitely small part of the tangent, or of any straight line equivalent to it (on account of the indefinitely small size of the arc) is substi-

* See note at the end of this lecture.

tuted for the arc. But these points will be made clearer by the following examples.

Note

Barrow gives five examples of this, the "differential triangle" method. As might be expected, two of these are well-known curves, namely the Folium of Descartes, called by Barrow *La Galande*, and the *Quadratrix*; a third is the general case of the quasi-circular curves $x^n + y^n = a^n$; the fourth and fifth are the allied curves $r = a . tan\ \theta$ and $y = a . tan\ x$.

The fifth example, the case of the curve $y = a . tan\ \theta$, I have selected for giving in full, for several reasons. It is the clearest and least tedious example of the method, it is illustrated by two diagrams, one being derived from the other, and therefore the demonstration is less confused, it suggests that Barrow was aware of the analogy of the differential form of the polar subtangent with the Cartesian subtangent, and that in this is to be found the reason why Barrow gives, as a rule, the polar forms of all his Cartesian theorems; and lastly, and more particularly, for its own intrinsic merits, as stated below. Barrow's enunciation and proof are as follows:—

Example 5. Let *DEB* be a quadrant of a circle, to which *BX* is a tangent; then let the line *AMO* be such that, if in the straight line *AV* any part *AP* is taken equal to the arc *BE*, and *PM* is erected perpendicular to *AV*, then *PM* is equal to *BG* the tangent of the arc *BE*.

Take the arc *BF* equal to *AQ* and draw *CFH*; drop *EK*, *FL* perpendicular to *CB*. Let $CB = r$, $CK = f$, $KE = g$.

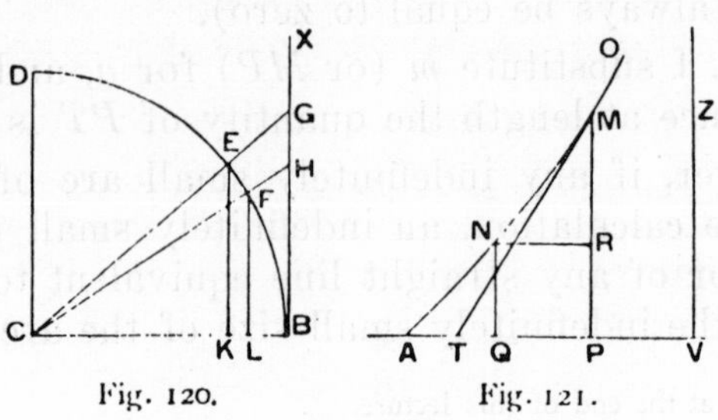

Fig. 120. Fig. 121.

Then, since $CE : EK = \text{arc } EF : LK = QP : LK$; therefore $r : g = e : LK$, or $LK = ge/r$, and $CL = f + ge/r$; hence also $LF = \sqrt{(r^2 - f^2 - 2fge/r)} = \sqrt{(g^2 - 2fge/r)}$.

But $CL : LF = CB : BH$, or $f + ge/r : \sqrt{(g^2 - 2fge/r)} = r : m - a$; and squaring, we have

$$f^2 + 2fge/r : g^2 - 2fge/r = r^2 : m^2 - 2ma.$$

Hence, omitting the proper terms, we obtain the equation

$$rfma = gr^2e + gm^2e;$$

and, on substituting m, t for a, e, we get

$$rfm^2 = gr^2t + gm^2t, \text{ or } rfm^2/(gr^2 + gm^2) = t.$$

Hence since $m = rg/f$, we obtain

$$t = m \,.\, r^2/(r^2 + m^2) = BG \,.\, CB^2/CG^2 = BG \,.\, CK^2/CE^2.$$

In other words, this theorem states that, if $y = \tan x$, where x is the circular measure of an "angle" or an "arc," then $dy/dx = m/t = CE^2/CK^2 = \sec^2 x$.

Moreover, although Barrow does not mention the fact, he must have known (for it is so self-evident) that the same two diagrams can be used for any of the trigonometrical ratios. Therefore *Barrow must be credited with the differentiation of the circular functions.* (See Note to §15 of App. 2 of Lect. XII.)

As regards this lecture, it only remains to remark on the fact that the theorem of §11 is a rigorous proof that differentiation and integration are inverse operations, where integration is defined as a summation. Barrow, as is well known, was the first to recognise this.

BHASCARA ACHARYA

(1114—c. 1185)

Bháscara Áchárya (Bháscara, the Learned), celebrated Indian astronomer and mathematician, head of the astronomical observatory at Ujjain, where Brahmagupta had served in a similar capacity some five hundred years earlier, was born in 1114. He came of an old, learned family, of some nobility and title, possessing an established tradition of scholarship. Bháscara, greatly honored as one who was deeply conversant with the Vedas, grew to be its outstanding representative. He was widely acclaimed during his own lifetime and later for his extraordinary skill in mechanical arts, as well as in the sciences, such as astronomy and mathematics. Bháscara's grandson, Changadeva, a court astronomer and chief astrologer for King Singhana, was the recipient of a grant of land and the financial means with which he founded a college where the works composed by Bháscara and by Bháscara's ancestors and descendants were taught. An inscription discovered in a ruined temple in the Bombay Presidency extols the virtues and achievements of Bháscara and records the grant as having been made in 1206, on the occasion of a lunar eclipse.

By his own statement, Bháscara completed his great astronomical work the *Sidd'hanta-siromani* in the year 1150 when he was thirty-six years of age. The survival of the original text of Bháscara's *Sidd'hanta* is due to the respect amounting almost to veneration with which the work was regarded by succeeding writers and the method employed by them in conveying Bháscara's teaching. In the numerous commentaries on the *Sidd'hanta-siromani* each passage was stated exactly as it appeared in the original work. This was followed by the commentator's explanation of the passage and such examples as he considered useful as illustrations. H. T. Colebrooke, whose translation (1817) of the mathematical chapters of Bháscara's *Sidd-'hanta* remains unsurpassed, found many commentaries written in Sanskrit and one written in Persian. These commentaries, widely separated in time and distance, were in remarkable agreement in their recitals of the original text. The consistency which thus appeared in works published at different times and in different languages constitutes clear and convincing evidence of the authenticity of the text now in our possession.

Four chapters of the original work have survived. Two are mathematical. Chapter 1, *Lilavati,* deals with arithmetic and geometrical-numerical problems; Chapter 2, *Vija-Ganita,* deals with algebraic problems. Although Bháscara freely acknowledged his dependence on previous writers whose work he compiled, his correction and improvement of their methods was substantial. Moreover, in his own contributions, Bháscara advanced far beyond any who preceded him. Bháscara presented a complete and systematic explanation of the Indian method of solving determinate and indeterminate problems, of the notation employed, of the rules for positive and negative numbers, and the use of color to represent quantities, both known and unknown. The work also included problems in permutations and combinations, and a chapter on operations with zero in which it is clear that Bháscara knew that there could be no exact division by zero, an infinite quotient resulting from division of any quantity by a number which is made to approach zero as a limit. Bháscara's problems, more varied than those of his predecessors, included the topics of purchase and sale, interest, gems, gold, and permutation of the syllables in a stanza, military marches, excavations, and the measures of grain. However, his indeterminate problems in number theory provided the greatest and most lasting interest. The famous challenge sent by Fermat to Wallis and Brouncker (1657) concerned such a problem. It may be stated as requiring the solution of the equation $cx^2 + 1 = y^2$. As late as 1946, the *Bulletin of the Calcutta Mathematical Society* (v. 38, pp. 21—24), carried an article discussing a problem proposed by Bháscara (Par. 182, *Vija-Ganita*). Numerical solutions of the problems were given in the *Bulletin* in addition to those found by Bháscara and, in line with modern interests, the general formulas for the solution were also presented. The history of the theory of numbers contains ample testimony of continuing interest in Bháscara's problems.

●

LILAVATI[1]

CHAPTER III, SECTION VI.

RULE OF PROPORTION.

74. Rule of three inverse.[2]

If the fruit diminish as the requisition increases, or augment as that decreases, they, who are skilled in ac-

[1] Selections from chapters entitled, *Lilavati* and *Vija-Ganita,* of the *Sidd'hanta-siromani* are taken from the translation from the Sanscrit: *Algebra, with Arithmetic and Mensuration* by Henry Thomas Colebrooke.

[2] *Vyasta-trairasica* or *Viloma-trairasica,* rule of three terms inverse.

counts, consider the rule of three terms to be inverted.[2]

When there is diminution of fruit, if there be increase of requisition, and increase of fruit if there be diminution of requisition, then the inverse rule of three is [employed]. For instance,

75. When the value of living beings[3] is regulated by their age; and in the case of gold, where the weight and touch are compared; or when heaps[5] are subdivided; let the inverted rule of three terms be [used].

76. Example. If a female slave sixteen years of age, bring thirty-two [*nishcas*], what will one aged twenty cost? If an ox, which has been worked a second year, sell for four *nishcas* what will one, which has been worked six years, cost?

1st Qu. Statement: 16 32 20. Answer: 25-3/5 *nishcas.*

2d Qu. Statement: 2 4 6. Answer: 1-1/3 *nishca.*

77. Example. If a *gadyánaca* of gold of the touch of ten may be had for one *nishca* [of silver], what weight of gold of fifteen touch may be bought for the same price?

Statement: 10 1 15. Answer 2/3.

78. Example. A heap of grain having been meted with a measure containing seven *ad'hacas,* if a hundred such measures were found, what would be the result with one containing five *ad'hacas?*

Statement: 7 100 5. Answer 140.

80. Example. If the interest of a hundred for a month be five, say what is the interest of sixteen for a year? Find likewise the time from the principal and interest;

---

[2] The method of performing the inverse rule has been already taught (§ 70). "In the inverse method, the operation is reversed." That is, the fruit to be multiplied by the argument and divided by the demand. SUR.

When fruit increases or decreases, as the demand is augmented or diminished, the direct rule (*crama-trairasica*) is used. Else the inverse. GAN.

[3] Slaves and cattle. The price of the older is less; of the younger, greater. GANG. and SUR.

[5] When heaps of grain, which had been meted with a small measure, are again meted with a larger one, the number decreases; and when those, which had been meted with a large measure, are again meted with a smaller one, there is increase of number. GANG and SUR.

and knowing the time and produce, tell the principal sum.

<table><tr><td rowspan="3">Statement:</td><td>1</td><td>12</td><td rowspan="3">Answer: the interest is 9-3/5.</td></tr><tr><td>100</td><td>16</td></tr><tr><td>5</td><td></td></tr></table>

<table><tr><td rowspan="3">To find the time; Statement:</td><td>1</td><td></td></tr><tr><td>100</td><td>16</td></tr><tr><td>5</td><td>48/5</td></tr></table>

Answer: months 12.

<table><tr><td rowspan="3">To find the principal; Statement:</td><td>1</td><td>12</td></tr><tr><td>100</td><td></td></tr><tr><td>5</td><td>48/5</td></tr></table>

Answer: principal 16.

81. Example. If the interest of a hundred for a month and one-third, be five and one fifth, say what is the interest of sixty-two and a half for three months and one fifth?

Statement: $\begin{matrix} \frac{4}{3} & \frac{16}{5} \\ \frac{100}{1} & \frac{125}{2} \\ \frac{26}{5} & \end{matrix}$ Answer: interest 7-4/5.

82. Example of the rule of seven: If eight, best, variegated, silk scarfs, measuring three cubits in breadth and eight in length, cost a hundred [*nishcas*]; say quickly, merchant, if thou understand trade, what a like scarf, three and a half cubits long and half a cubit wide, will cost.

<table><tr><td rowspan="4">Statement:</td><td>3</td><td>1/2</td><td rowspan="4">Answer: Nishca 0, drammas 14, panas 9, cacini 1, cowryshells 6-2/3.</td></tr><tr><td>8</td><td>7/2</td></tr><tr><td>8</td><td>1</td></tr><tr><td>100</td><td></td></tr></table>

83. Example of the rule of nine: If thirty benches, twelve fingers thick, square of four wide, and fourteen cubits long, cost a hundred [*nishcas*]; tell me, my friend, what price will fourteen benches fetch, which are four less in every dimension?

Statement: 12 8 Answer: *Nishcas* 16-2/3.
16 12
14 10
30 14
100

CHAPTER IV, SECTION VI.

PERMUTATION AND COMBINATION.

114. Example: In a pleasant, spacious and elegant edifice, with eight doors,[2] constructed by a skilful architect, as a palace for the lord of the land, tell me the permutations of apertures taken one, two, three, &c.[3] Say, mathematician, how many are the combinations in one composition, with ingredients of six different tastes, sweet, pungent, astringent, sour, salt and bitter,[4] taking them by ones, twos, or threes, &c.

Statement [1st Example]: 8 7 6 5 4 3 2 1
1 2 3 4 5 6 7 8.

Answer: the number of ways in which the doors may be opened by ones, twos, or threes, &c. is 8, 28, 56, 70, 56, 28, 8, 1. And the changes on the apertures of the octagon* palace amount to 255.
(1 2 3 4 5 6 7 8)

Statement 2d example: 6 5 4 3 2 1
1 2 3 4 5 6.

Answer: the number of various preparations with ingredients of divers tastes is 6, 15, 20, 15, 6, 1.†
(1 2 3 4 5 6)

---

[2] *Muc'ha,* aperture for the admission of air: a door or window; (same with *gavacsha;*—GAN.) a portico or terrace, (*bhumi-visesha;*—GANG. and SUR.)

[3] The variations of one window or portico open (or terrace unroofed) and the rest closed; two open, and the rest shut; and so forth.

[4] *Amera-cosha* 1.3.18.

* An octagon building, with eight doors (or windows; porticos or terraces;) facing the eight cardinal points of the horizon, is meant. See GAN.

† Total number of possible combinations, 63. GANG.

CHAPTER V.

PROGRESSIONS.

SECTION I.

ARITHMETICAL PROGRESSION.

115. Rule: Half the period, multiplied by the period added to unity, is the sum of the arithmeticals one, &c. and is named their addition. This, being multiplied by the period added to two, and being divided by three, is the aggregate of the additions.

123. Rule:[1] half a stanza. The sum divided by the period, and the first term subtracted from the quotient, the remainder, divided by half of one less than the number of terms, will be the common difference.

124. Example: On an expedition to seize his enemy's elephants, a king marched two *yojánas* the first day. Say, intelligent calculator, with what increasing rate of daily march did he proceed, since he reached his foe's city, a distance of eighty *yojánas,* in a week?

Statement: First term 2; Com. diff.? Period 7; Sum 80.
Answer: Com. diff. 22/7.

125. Rule:[4] From the sum of the progression multiplied by twice the common increase, and added to the square of the difference between the first term and half that increase, the square root being extracted, this root less the first term and added to the [above-mentioned] portion of the increase, being divided by the increase, is pronounced to be the period.

126. Example: A person gave three *drammas* on the first day, and continued to distribute alms increasing by two [a day]; and he thus bestowed on the priests three hundred and sixty *drammas*: say quickly in how many days?

---

[1] The first term, period and sum being known, to find the common difference which is unknown. Gan.

[4] The first term, common difference and sum being known, to find the period which is unknown. Gan.

Statement: First term 3; Com. diff. 2; Period? Sum. 360.

Answer: Period 18.

SECTION II.

GEOMETRICAL PROGRESSION.

127. Rule: a couplet and a half. The period being an uneven number, subtract one, and note "multiplicator;" being an even one, halve it, and note "square:" until the period be exhausted. Then the produce arising from multiplication and squaring [of the common multiplier] in the inverse order from the last, being lessened by one, the remainder divided by the common multiplier less one, and multiplied by the initial quantity, will be the sum of a progression increasing by a common multiplier.

128. Example: A person gave a mendicant a couple of cowry shells first; and promised a two-fold increase of the alms daily. How many *nishcas* does he give in a month?

Statement: First term, 2; Two-fold increase, 2; Period, 30.

Answer, 2147483646 cowries; or 104857 *nishcas,* 9 *drammas,* 9 *panas,* 2 *cacinis,* and 6 shells.

CHAPTER VI.

PLANE FIGURE.

158. Example. Where the difference of the side and upright is seven and hypotenuse is thirteen, say quickly, eminent mathematician, what are the side and upright?[1]

Statement. Difference of side and upright 7. Hypotenuse 13. Proceeding as directed, the side and upright come out 5 and 12. See

12 13
5

[1] This example of a case where the difference of the sides is given, is omitted by SURYADASA, but noticed by GANESA. Copies of the text vary; some containing, and others omitting, the instance.

159. Rule.[2] The product of two erect bambus being divided by their sum, the quotient is the perpendicular from the junction [intersection] of threads passing reciprocally from the root [of one] to the tip [of the other.] The two bambus, multiplied by an assumed base, and divided by their sum, are the portions of the base on the respective sides of the perpendicular.

160. Example. Tell the perpendicular drawn from the intersection of strings stretched mutually from the roots to the summits of two bambus fifteen and ten cubits high standing upon ground of unknown extent.

Statement Bambus 15, 10. The perpendicular is found 6.

Next to find the segments of the base: let the ground be assumed 5; the segments come out 3 and 2. Or putting 10, they are 6 and 4. Or taking 15, they are 9 and 6. See the figures

15 10 15 10 15 10
6 6 6
3 2 6 4 9 6

In every instance the perpendicular is the same: viz. 6.

The proof is in every case by the rule of three: if with a side equal to the base, the bambu be the upright, then with the segment of the base what will be the upright?[1]

161. Aphorism.[2] That figure, though rectilinear, of which sides are proposed by some presumptuous person,

[2] Having taught fully the method of finding the sides in a right-angled triangle, the author next propounds a special problem.—GAN. To find the perpendicular, the base being unknown.—SUR.

[1] On each side of the perpendicular, are segments of the base relative to the greater and smaller bambus, and larger or less analogously to them. Hence this proportion. "If with the sum of the bambus, this sum of the segments equal to the entire base be obtained, then, with the smaller bambu, what is had?" The answer gives the segment, which is relative to the least bambu. Again: "if with a side equal to the whole base, the higher bambu be the upright, then with a side equal to the segment found as above, what is had?" The answer gives the perpendicular let fall from the intersection of the threads. Here a multiplicator and a divisor equal to the entire base are both cancelled as equal and contrary: and there remain the product of the two bambus for numerator and their sum for denominator. Hence the rule. GAN.

[2] The aphorism explains the nature of impossible figures proposed by dunces. —SUR. It serves as a definition of plane figure (*cshetra*).—GAN. In a triangle or other plane rectilinear figure, one side is always less than the sum of the rest. If equal, the perpendicular is nought, and there is no complete figure. If greater, the sides do not meet.—SUR. Containing no area, it is no figure.—*Caum.* RANG.

wherein one side[3] exceeds or equals the sum of the other sides, may be known to be no figure.

162. Example: Where sides are proposed two, three, six and twelve in a quadrilateral, or three, six and nine in a triangle, by some presumptuous dunce, know it to be no figure.

CHAPTER XII.

PULVERIZER.[1]

248—252. RULE. In the first place, as preparatory to

---

[3] The principal or greatest side.—GAN. *Caum.* RANG.

[1] *Cuttaca-vyavahara* or *cuttacad'hyaya* determination of a grinding or pulverizing multiplier, or quantity such, that a given number being multiplied by it, and the product added to a given quantity, the sum (or, if the additive be negative, the difference) may be divisible by a given divisor without remainder.

See *Vija-Ganita,* chapter 2, from which this is borrowed, the contents being copied, (with some variation of the order,) nearly word for word. For this, as well as the following chapter 13, on Combination, belongs to algebra rather than arithmetic; according to the remark of the commentator GANESA BHATTA: and they are here introduced, as he observes, and treated without employing algebraic forms, to gratify such as are unacquainted with analysis.

The commentator begins by asking 'why this subject has been admitted into a treatise of arithmetic, while a passage of ARYA-BHATTA expressly distinguishes it from both arithmetic and algebra: "the multifarious doctrine of the planets, arithmetic, the pulverizer, (*cuttaca*) and analysis (*vija*), and the rest of the science treating of seen objects;" and BRAHMEGUPTA, at the beginning of his chapter on Arithmetic, excludes it from this head; when describing the complete mathematician (see Arithm. of BRAHM. § 1)? The commentator proceeds to answer,—'Mathematics consist of two branches treating of known and of unknown quantity; as expressly declared: "The science of computation (*ganita*) is pronounced two-fold, denominated *vyacta* and *avyacta* (distinct and indistinct)." The investigation of the pulverizer, like the problem of the affected square, (*varga-pracriti.* See *Vija-ganita,* ch. 3), is comprehended in algebra, being subservient to its solutions; as hinted by the author. (See *Vija.* § 99). The separate mention of the head of investigation of the pulverizer, in passages of ÁRYA-BHATTA and other ancient authors, as well as in those of BHASCARA and the rest ("By arithmetic, by algebra, by investigation of the pulverizer, and by resolution of the affected square, answers are found") is designed as an intimation of the difficulty and importance of the matter; not to indicate it as the subject of a separate treatise: and this, no less than the head of combination treated in the next chapter (chapter 13), with other topics (all exclusive of arithmetic, which comprises logistics and the rest of the enumerated heads terminating with measurement by shadow,) falls within algebra, as the precepts of the rules concur with exercise of sagacity to effect the solution. (See *Vija,* § 224). It is then true, concludes this commentator, that mathematics consist but of two branches. Nevertheless the subjects of this and of the following chapter are here introduced, to be treated without reference to algebraic solutions, as the *Bhadra-ganita* and other problems have found place in the arith-

the investigation of a pulverizer,[1] the dividend, divisor and additive quantity[2] are, if practicable, to be reduced by some number.[3] If the number, by which the dividend and divisor are both measured, do not also measure the additive quantity, the question is an ill put [or impossible] one.

249—251. The last remainder, when the dividend and divisor are mutually divided, is their common measure.[3] Being divided by that common measure, they are termed reduced quantities.[4] Divide mutually the reduced dividend and divisor, until unity be the remainder in the dividend. Place the quotients one under the other; and the additive quantity beneath them, and cipher at the bottom.[1] By the penult multiply the number next above it and add the lowest term. Then reject the last and repeat the operation until a pair of numbers be left. The

---

metical treatises of NARAYANA and other writers, to be there wrought without algebra; and for the same purpose of gratifying such as are not conversant with this branch. GAN.

In BRAHMEGUPTA'S work the whole of algebra is comprised under this title of *Cuttacad'hyaya,* chapter on the pulverizer. See BRAHM. ch. 18, and CHATURVEDA on BRAHMEGUPTA, ch. 12, § 66.

[1] *Cuttaca* or *Cutta,* from *cutt,* to grind or pulverize; (to multiply: all verbs importing tendency to destruction also signifying multiplication.—GAN.)

The term is here employed in a sense independent of its etymology to signify a multiplier such, that a given dividend being multiplied by it, and a given quantity added to (or subtracted from) the product, the sum (or difference) may be measured by a given divisor. SUR. on *Vij.-gan.* and *Lil.* RANG. on *Vas.* GAN. on *Lil.*

The derivative import is, however, retained in the present version to distinguish this from multiplier in general; *cuttaca* being restricted to the particular multiplier of the problem in question.

[2] *Cshepa,* or *cshepaca,* or *yuti,* additive. From *cship* to cast or throw in, and from *yu* to mix. A quantity superinduced, being either affirmative or negative, and consequently in some examples an additive, in others a subtractive, term.

Visudd'hi, subtractive quantity, contradistinguished from *cshepa* additive, when this is restricted to an affirmative one. See § 263.

[3] *Apavartana,* abridgment; abbreviation.—GAN. Depression or reduction to least terms; division without remainder: also the number which serves to divide without residue; the common measure, or common divisor of equal division. SUR.

[4] *Drid'ha,* firm: reduced by the common divisor to the least term. The word is applicable to the reduced additive, as well as to the dividend and divisor. BRAHMEGUPTA uses *nich'heda* and *nirapavarta* in this sense.—*Brahm.* 18, § 9.

[1] *Tashta,* abraded; from *tacsh,* to pare or abrade: divided, but the residue taken, disregarding the quotient: reduced to a residue.—SUR. As it were a residue after repeated subtractions. GANG.

Tacshana, the abrader; the divisor employed in such operation.

uppermost of these being abraded[2] by the reduced dividend, the remainder is the quotient. The other [or lowermost] being in like manner abraded by the reduced divisor, the remainder is the multiplier.

252. Thus precisely is the operation when the quotients are an even number.[3] But, if they be odd, the numbers as found must be subtracted from their respective abraders, the residues will be the true quotient and multiplier.

253. Example. Say quickly, mathematician, what is that multiplier, by which two hundred and twenty-one being multiplied, and sixty-five added to the product, the sum divided by a hundred and ninety-five becomes exhausted?

Statement: Dividend 221 Additive 65.
Divisor 195

Here the dividend and divisor being mutually divided, the last of the remainders (or divisors) is 13. By this common measure, the dividend, divisor and additive, being reduced to their least terms, are Divd. 17 Addve. 5.
Divr. 15

The reduced dividend and divisor being divided reciprocally, and the quotients put one under the other, the additive under them, and cipher at the bottom, the series which results is 1 7 5 0 Then multiplying by the penult the number above it and proceeding as directed, the two quantities are obtained 40 35 These being abraded by the reduced dividend and divisor 17 and 15, the quotient and multiplier are obtained 6 and 5. Or, by the subsequent rule (§ 262), adding them to their abraders multiplied by an assumed number, the quotient and multiplier [putting 1] are 23 and 20; or, putting 2, they are 40 and 35: and so forth.[1]

254. Rule: The multiplier is also found by the method

---

[2] *P'hala-valli,* the series of quotients; to be reduced by the operation forthwith directed to only two terms.

[3] Even, as 2, 4, 6, &c.—*Manor.*

[1] Putting 3, they are 57 and 50. SUR. and GANG.

of the pulverizer, the additive quantity and dividend, being either reduced by a common measure [or used unreduced.][2] But if the additive and divisor be so reduced, the multiplier found, being multiplied by the common measure, is the true one.

255. Example. If thou be expert in the investigation of such questions, tell me the precise multiplier by which a hundred being multiplied, with ninety added to the product, or subtracted from it, the sum, or the difference, may be divisible by sixty-three without a remainder.

265. Rule for a conjunct pulverizer. If the divisor be the same and the multipliers various; then, making the sum of those multipliers the dividend, and the sum of the remainders a single remainder, and applying the foregoing method of investigation, the precise multiplier so found is denominated a conjunct one.

266. Example. What quantity is it, which multiplied by five, and divided by sixty-three, gives a residue of seven; and the same multiplied by ten and divided by sixty-three, a remainder of fourteen? declare the number.

Here the sum of the multipliers is made the dividend; and the sum of the residues, a subtractive quantity; and the statement is $\begin{matrix}\text{Dividend } 15\\ \text{Divisor } 63\end{matrix}$ Subtractive 21. Or reduced to least terms $\begin{matrix}\text{Dividend } 5\\ \text{Divisor } 21\end{matrix}$ Subtractive 7.

Proceeding as before, the multiplier is found 14.

CHAPTER XIII.

COMBINATION.[1]

267. Rule. The product of multiplication of the arithmetical series beginning and increasing by unity and continued to the number of places, will be the variations

---

[2] GAN.

[1] *Anca-pasa-vyavahara* or *Anca-pasa'd'hyaya,* concatenation of digits: a mutual mixing of the numbers, as it were a rope or halter of numerals: their variations being likened to a coil. See GAN. and SUR.

of number with specific figures: that, divided by the number of digits and multiplied by the sum of the figures, being repeated in the places of figures and added together, will be the sum of the permutations.

268. Example. How many variations of number can there be with two and eight? or with three, nine and eight? or with the continued series from two to nine? and tell promptly the several sums of their numbers.

Statement 1st Example: 2. 8.

Here the number of places is 2. The product of the series from 1 to the number of places and increasing by unity, (1, 2). Thus the permutations of number are found 2.

That product 2, multiplied by the sum of the figures, 10 [2 and 8] is 20; and divided by the number of digits 2, is 10. This, repeated in the places of figures [10
10]
and added together, is 110; the sum of the numbers.

Statement 2d Example: 3. 9. 8.

The arithmetical series is 1. 2. 3; of which the product is 6; and so many are the variations of number. That, multiplied by the sum 20, is 120; which, divided by the number of digits 3, gives 40; and this, repeated in the places of figures [40
40
40]
and summed, makes 4440 the sum of the numbers.

Statement 3d Example: 2.3.4.5.6.7.8.9.

The arithmetical series beginning and increasing by unity is 1.2.3.4.5.6.7.8. The product gives the permutation of numbers 40320. This, multiplied by the sum of the figures 44, is 1774080; and divided by the number of terms 8, is 221760; and the quotient being repeated in the eight places of figures and summed, the total is the sum of the numbers 2463999935360.

269. Example. How many are the variations of form of the god Sambhu by the exchange of his ten attributes held reciprocally in his several hands: namely the rope,

the elephant's hook, the serpent, the tabor, the skull, the trident, the bedstead, the dagger, the arrow, and the bow:[1] as those of HARI by the exchange of the mace, the discus, the lotus and the conch?

Statement: Number of places 10.

In the same mode, as above shown, the variations of form are found 3628800.

So the variations of form of HARI are 24.

270. Rule. The permutations found as before, being divided by the combinations separately computed for as many places as are filled by like digits, will be the variations of number; from which the sum of the numbers will be found as before.

271. Example. How many are the numbers with two, two, one and one? and tell me quickly, mathematician their sum: also with four, eight, five, five and five; if thou be conversant with the rule of permutation of numbers.

Statement 1st Example: 2.2.1.1.

Here the permutations found as before (§267) are 24: First, two places are filled by like digits (2.2); and the combinations for that number of places are 2. Next two other places are filled by like digits (1.1.); and the combinations for these places are also 2. Total 4. The permutations as before 24, divided by (4) the twofold combinations for two pairs of like digits, give 6 for the variations of number: viz. 2211, 2121, 2112, 1212, 1221, 1122. The sum of the numbers is found as before 9999.

---

[1] SAMBU or SIVA is represented with ten arms, and holding in his ten hands the ten weapons or symbols here specified; and, by changing the several attributes from one hand to another, a variation may be effected in the representation of the idol: in the same manner as the image of HARI or VISHNU is varied by the exchange of his four symbols in his four hands. The twenty-four different representations of VISHNU, arising from this diversity in the manner of placing the weapons or attributes in his four hands, are distinguished by as many discriminative titles of the god allotted to those figures in the theogonies or *Puranas.* It does not appear that distinct titles have been in like manner assigned to any part of the more than three millions of varied representations of SIVA.

The ten attributes of *Siva* are, 1st, *pasa,* a rope or chain for binding an elephant; 2d, *ancusa,* a hook for guiding an elephant; 3d, a serpent; 4th, *damaru,* a tabor; 5th, a human skull; 6th, a trident; 7th, *c'hatwanga,* a bedstead, or a club in form of the foot of one; 8th, a dagger; 9th, an arrow; 10th, a bow.

Statement 2d Example: 4.8.5.5.5.

Here the permutations found as before are 120; which, divided by the combinations for three places 6, give the variations 20: viz. 48555, 84555, 54,855, 58455, 55485, 55845, 55548, 55584, 45855, 45585, 45558, 85455, 85545, 85554, 54585, 58545, 55458, 55854, 54558, 58554.

The sum of the numbers comes out 1199988.

274. Rule:[2] a stanza and a half. If the sum of the digits be determinate, the arithmetical series of numbers from one less than the sum of the digits, decreasing by unity, and continued to one less than the places, being divided by one and so forth, and the quotients being multiplied together, the product will be equal to the variations of the number.

This rule must be understood to hold good, provided the sum of the digits be less than the number of places added to nine.

A compendium only has been here delivered for fear of prolixity: since the ocean of calculation has no bounds.

275. Example. How many various numbers are there, with digits standing in five places, the sum of which is thirteen? If thou know, declare them.

Here the sum of the digits less one is 12. The decreasing series from this to one less than the number of digits, divided by unity, &c. being exhibited, the statement is $\frac{12}{1}\ \frac{11}{2}\ \frac{10}{3}\ \frac{9}{4}$. The product of their multiplication $\left[\frac{11880}{24}\right]$ is equal to the variations of the number, 495.[3]

277. Joy and happiness is indeed ever increasing in this world for those who have *Lilavati* clasped to their throats, decorated as the members are with neat reduc-

[2] To find the combinations with indeterminate digits for a definite sum and a specific number of places. GAN.

[3] 91111, 52222, 13333; each five ways. 55111, 22333; each ten ways. 82111, 73111, 64111, 43222, 61222; each twenty ways. 72211, 53311, 44221, 44311; each thirty ways. 63211, 54211, 53221, 43321; each sixty ways. Total four hundred and ninety-five.

tion of fractions, multiplication and involution, pure and perfect as are the solutions, and tasteful as is the speech which is exemplified.

●

VIJA-GANITA

CHAPTER I.

SECTION II.

LOGISTICS OF NEGATIVE AND AFFIRMATIVE QUANTITIES.

ADDITION.

3. Rule for addition of affirmative and negative quantities: half a stanza. In the addition of two negative or two affirmative[1] quantities, the sum must be taken: but the difference of an affirmative and a negative quantity is their addition.

4. Example. Tell quickly the result of the numbers three and four, negative or affirmative, taken together: that is, affirmative and negative, or both negative or both affirmative, as separate instances: if thou know the addition of affirmative and negative quantities.

The characters, denoting the quantities known and unknown,[3] should be first written to indicate them generally; and those, which become negative, should be then marked with a dot over them.

---

[1] *Rina* or *cshaya,* minus; literally debt or loss: negative quantity.
D'hana or *swa,* plus; literally wealth or property: affirmative or positive quantity.

[3] *Rasi,* quantity, is either *vyacta,* absolute, specifically known, (which is termed *rupa,* form, species;) or it is *avyacta,* indistinct, unapparent, unknown (*ajnyata*). It may either be a multiple of the arithmetical unit, or a part of it, or the unit itself.

Statement: 3.4. Adding them, the sum is found 7.

Statement: $\dot{3}.\dot{4}$. Adding them, the sum is $\dot{7}$.

Statement: $3.\dot{4}$. Taking the difference, the result of addition comes out $\dot{1}$.

Statement: $\dot{3}.4$. Taking the difference, the result of addition is 1.

So in other instances, and in fractions likewise.

SUBTRACTION.

5. Rule for subtraction of positive and negative quantities: half a stanza. The quantity to be subtracted being affirmative, becomes negative; or, being negative, becomes affirmative: and the addition of the quantities is then made as above directed.

6. Example: half a stanza. Subtracting two from three, affirmative from affirmative, and negative from negative, or the contrary, tell me quickly the result.

Statement: 3.2. The subtrahend, being affirmative, becomes negative; and the result is 1.

Statement: $\dot{3}.\dot{2}$. The negative subtrahend becomes affirmative; and the result is $\dot{1}$.

Statement: $3.\dot{2}$. The negative subtrahend becomes affirmative; and the result is 5.

Statement: $\dot{3}.2$. The affirmative subtrahend becomes negative; and the result is $\dot{5}$.

MULTIPLICATION.

7. Rule for multiplication [and division] of positive and negative quantities: half a stanza. The product of

two quantities both affirmative, is positive.* When a positive quantity and a negative one are multiplied together, the product is negative.† The same is the case in division.

SECTION III.

CIPHER.

12. Rule for addition and subtraction of cipher: part of a stanza. In the addition of cipher, or subtraction of it, the quantity,[1] positive or negative, remains the same. But, subtracted from cipher, it is reversed.[2]

13. Example: half a stanza. Say what is the number three, positive, or [the same number] negative, or cipher, added to cipher, or subtracted from it?[3]

Statement: 3.$\dot{3}$.0. These, having cipher added to, or subtracted from, them, remain unchanged: 3.$\dot{3}$.0.

Statement: 3.$\dot{3}$.0. Subtracted from cipher, they become $\dot{3}$.3.0.[5]

---

* The sign only of the product is taught. All the operations upon the numbers are the same which were shown in simple arithmetic (*Lila.* § 14—16). CRISHN.

† Multiplication, as explained by the commentators, is a sort of addition resting on repetition of the multiplicand as many times as is the number of the multiplicator. Now a multiplicator is of two sorts, positive or negative. If it be positive, the repetition of the multiplicand, which is affirmative or negative, will give correspondently an affirmative or negative product. The multiplication then of positive quantities is positive; and that of a negative multiplicand by a positive multiplier is negative: as is plain. The question for disquisition concerns a negative multiplier. It has been before observed that negation is contrariety. A negative multiplier, therefore, is a contrary one: that is, it makes a contrary repetition of the multiplicand. Such being the case, if the multiplicand be positive, (the multiplier being negative), the product will be negative; if the multiplicand be negative, the product will be affirmative. In the latter case the multiplication of two negative quantities gives an affirmative product. In the middle instances, either of the two (multiplicator or multiplicand) being positive, and the other negative, the product is negative: as is taught in the text.

[1] Whether absolute, expressed by digits, or unknown, denoted by letter, colour, &c. or an irrational and surd root. CRISHN.

[2] In both cases of addition, and in the first of subtraction, the absolute number, unknown quantity, or surd, retains its sign, whether positive or negative. In the other case of subtraction, the sign is reversed. CRISHN.

[3] Or having cipher added to, or subtracted from, it. CRISHN.

[5] Cipher is neither positive nor negative; and it is therefore exhibited with no distinction of sign. No difference arises from the reversing of it; and none is here shown. CRISHN.

14. Rule: (completing the stanza, § 12.) In the multiplication and the rest of the operations[1] of cipher, the product is cipher; and so it is in multiplication by cipher: but a quantity, divided by cipher, becomes a fraction the denominator of which is cipher.[2]

15. Example: half a stanza. Tell me the product of cipher multiplied by two;[3] and the quotient of it divided by three, and of three divided by cipher; and the square of nought; and its root.

Statement: Multiplicator 2. Multiplicand 0. Product 0.

[Statement: Multiplicator 0. Multiplicand 2. Product 0[4].]

Statement: Dividend 0. Divisor 3. Quotient 0.

Statement: Dividend 3. Divisor 0. Quotient the fraction 3/0.

This fraction, of which the denominator is cipher, is termed an infinite quantity.[5]

---

[1] Multiplication, division, square and square-root. SUR. and CRISHN.

Multiplication and division are each two-fold: viz. multiplication of nought by a quantity; or the multiplication of this by nought: so division of cipher by a quantity; and the division of this by cipher. But square and square-root are each single. CRISHN.

[2] The more the multiplicand is diminished, the smaller is the product; and, if it be reduced in the utmost degree, the product is so likewise: now the utmost diminution of a quantity is the same with the reduction of it to nothing: therefore, if the multiplicand be nought, the product is cipher. In like manner, as the multiplier decreases, so does the product; and, if the multiplier be nought, the product is so too. In fact multiplication is repetition: and, if there be nothing to be repeated, what should the multiplicator repeat, however great it be?

So, if the dividend be diminished, the quotient is reduced: and, if the dividend be reduced to nought, the quotient becomes cipher.

As much as the divisor is diminished, so much is the quotient raised. If the divisor be reduced to the utmost, the quotient is to the utmost increased. But, if it can be specified, that the amount of the quotient is so much, it has not been raised to the utmost: for a quantity greater than that can be assigned. The quotient therefore is indefinitely great, and is rightly termed infinite. CRISHN.

[3] Or else multiplying two. CRISHN.

[4] CRISHN.

[5] *Ananta-rasi,* infinite quantity. *C'ha-hara,* fraction having cipher for its denominator.

This fraction, indicating an infinite quantity, is unaltered by addition or subtraction of a finite quantity. For, in reducing the quantities to a common denominator, both the numerator and denominator of the finite quantity, being multiplied by cipher, become nought: and a quantity is unaltered by the addition or subtraction of nought. The numerator of the infinite fraction may indeed be varied by the addition or subtraction of a finite quantity, and so it may by that of another infinite fraction: but whether the finite numerator of a fraction, whose denominator is cipher, be more or less, the quotient of its division by cipher is alike infinite. CRISHN.

16. In this quantity consisting of that which has cipher for its divisor, there is no alteration, though many be inserted or extracted; as no change takes place in the infinite and immutable GOD, at the period of the destruction or creation of worlds, though numerous orders of beings are absorbed or put forth.

Statement: 0. Its square 0. Its root 0.

SECTION IV.

ARITHMETICAL OPERATIONS ON UNKNOWN QUANTITIES.

17. "So much as" and the colours "black, blue, yellow and red,"[1] and others besides these, have been selected by venerable teachers for names of values[2] of unknown quantities, for the purpose of reckoning therewith.[3]

18. Rule for addition and subtraction: Among quantities so designated, the sum or difference of two or more which are alike must be taken: but such as are unlike,[4] are to be separately set forth.

19. Example. Say quickly, friend, what will affirmative one unknown with one absolute, and affirmative pair unknown less eight absolute, make, if addition of the two sets take place? and what will they make, if the sum be taken inverting the affirmative and negative signs?[5]

Statement: *ya* 1 *ru* 1 Answer: the sum is *ya* 3 *ru* $\dot{7}$.

ya 2 *ru* $\dot{8}$

---

[1] *Yavat-tavat,* correlatives, quantum, tantum; quot, tot: as many, or as much, of the unknown, as this coefficient number. *Yavat* is relative of the unknown; and *tavat* of its coefficient.

The initial syllables of the *Sanscrit* terms enumerated in the text are employed as marks of unknown quantities; viz. *ya, ca, ni, pi, lo,* (also *ha, swe, chi,* &c. for green, white, variegated and so forth). Absolute number is denoted by *ru,* initial of *rupa* form, species. The letters of the alphabet are also used (ch. 6), as likewise the initial syllables of the terms for the particular things (§ 111).

[2] *Mana, miti, unmana* or *unmiti,* measure or value. See note on § 130.

[3] For the purpose of reckoning with unknown quantities. SUR. and CRISHN.

[4] Heterogeneous: as *rupa,* known or absolute number: *yavat-tavat* (so much as) the first unknown quantity, its square, its cube, its biquadrate, and the product of it and another factor; *calaca* (black) the second unknown quantity, its power, and the product of it with factors: *nilaca* (blue) the third unknown, its powers, and so forth. See CRISHN.

[5] Inverting the signs of the first set, of the second, or of both. CRISHN.

CHAPTER IV.

SIMPLE EQUATION.

121. Example: If thou be expert in this computation, declare quickly two numbers, of which the sum and the difference shall severally be squares; and the product of their multiplication, a cube.

Here the two numbers are put *ya v* 4 *ya v* 5; so assumed, that being added or subtracted, the sum or difference may be a square. The product of their multiplication is *ya v v* 20. It is a cube. By making it equal to the cube of ten times the assumed *yavat-tavat,* and depressing the two sides of the equation by the common divisor, cube of *yavat-tavat,* and proceeding as before, the two numbers are found 10000 and 12500.

122. Example: If thou know two numbers, of which the sum of the cubes is a square, and the sum of their squares is a cube, I acknowledge thee an eminent algebraist.

In this instance the two numbers are put *ya v* 1, *ya v* 2. The sum of their cubes is *ya v gh* 9. This of itself is a square as required. Its root is *ya gh* 3.

Is not that quantity the cube of a square, not the square of a cube? No doubt the root of the square of a cube is cube. But how is the root of the cube of a square, a cube? The answer is, the cube of the square is precisely the same with the square of the cube. Hence if squares be raised twice, or four, or six, or eight times, their roots will be so once, twice, thrice, or four times, respectively. It must be so understood in all cases.

Now the sum of the squares of those quantities is *ya v v* 5. It must be a cube. Making it equal to the cube of five times *yavat-tavat,* and depressing the two sides of the equation by the common divisor, cube of *yavat-tavat,* and proceeding as before, the two numbers are found 625 and 1250.

124. Example: If a bambu, measuring thirty-two cubits, and standing upon level ground, be broken in

one place by the force of the wind; and the tip of it meet the ground at sixteen cubits; say, mathematician, at how many cubits from the root is it broken?

CHAPTER VI.

EQUATIONS INVOLVING MORE THAN ONE UNKNOWN QUANTITY.

This is analysis by equation comprising several colours.

In this, the unknown quantities are numerous, two, three or more. For which *yavat-tavat* and the several colours are to be put to represent the values. They have been settled by the ancient teachers of the science:[4] viz. "so much as" (*yavat-tavat*), black (*calaca*), blue (*nilaca*), yellow (*pitaca*), red (*lohitaca*), green (*haritaca*), white (*swetaca*), variegated (*chitraca*), tawny (*capilaca*), tan-coloured (*pingala*), grey (*d'humraca*), pink (*patalaca*), white (*savalaca*), black (*syamalaca*), another black (*mechaca*), and so forth. Or letters[1] are to be employed; that is the literal characters *c*, &c. as names of the unknown, to prevent the confounding of them.

Here also, the calculator, performing as before directed every operation implied by the conditions of the example, brings out two equal sides, or more sides, of equation. Then comes the application of the rule: 'From one of the two sides of the equation, subtract the first (letter of) colour of the other. Then subtract from that other side the rest of the (letters or) colours, as well as

[4] *Purvacharyaih,* by former teachers. What particular authors are intended is unexplained. BRAHMEGUPTA employs names of colours to designate the unknown, without any remark; whence it appears that the use was already familiar.

[1] *Varna,* colour or letter: for the word bears both imports. Former writers used it in the one sense, and directed all the unknown quantities after the first to be represented by colours. But the author takes it also in the second acceptation; and directs letters to be employed, instancing the consonants in their alphabetical order. He appears to intend initial syllables. His predecessors, however, likewise made use of initial syllables for algebraic symbols; for instance the marks of square, cube and other powers; and the sign of a surd root: as well as the initials of colours as tokens of unknown quantities.

the known quantities. Hence the one side being divided by the residue of the first (letter or) colour, a value of the (letter or) colour which furnishes the divisor is obtained. If there be many such sides, by so treating those that constitute equations, by pairs, other values are found.

CHAPTER VII.

VARIETIES OF QUADRATICS.

178. Example from ancient authors: The square of the sum of two numbers, added to the cube of their sum, is equal to twice the sum of their cubes. Tell the numbers, mathematician!

The quantities are to be so put by the intelligent algebraist, as that the solution may not run into length. They are accordingly put *ya* 1 *ca* $\dot{1}$ and *ya* 1 *ca* 1. Their sum is *ya* 2. Its square *ya v* 4. Its cube *ya gh* 8. The square of the sum added to the cube is *ya gh* 8 *ya v* 4. The cubes of the two quantities respectively are *ya gh* 1 *ya v. ca bh* $\dot{3}$ *ca v. ya bh* 3 *ca gh* $\dot{1}$ cube of the first; and *ya gh* 1 *ya v. ca bh* 3 *ca v. ya bh* 3 *ca gh* 1 cube of the second; and the sum of these is *ya gh* 2 *ca v. ya bh* 6; and doubled, *ya gh* 4 *ca v. ya bh* 12. Statement for equal subtraction:

ya gh 8 *ya v* 4 *ca v. ya bh* 0 After equal subtraction
ya gh 4 *ya v* 0 *ca v. ya bh* 12

made, depressing both sides by the common divisor *ya*, and superadding unity, the root of the first side of equation is *ya* 2 *ru* 1. Roots of the other side (*ca v* 12 *ru* 1) are investigated by the rule of the affected square, and are L2 G7 or *L*28 *G*97. "Least" root is a value of *ca*. Making an equation of a "greatest" root with *ya* 2 *ru* 1, the value of *ya* is obtained: viz. 3 or 48. Substitution being made with the respective values, the two quantities come out 1 and 5, or 20 and 76, and so forth.

182. Example: Most learned algebraist! tell various

pairs of integer numbers, the difference of which is a square, and the sum of their squares a cube.

Put the two numbers *ya* 1 and *ca* 1. Their difference is *ya* $\dot{1}$ *ca* 1. Making it equal to the square of *ni,* the value of *ya* is had, *ca* 1 *ni v* $\dot{1}$. Substituting with this for *ya,* the two quantities become *ca* 1 *ni v* $\dot{1}$ and *ca* 1. The sum of their squares is *ca v* 2 *ni v. ca bh* $\dot{2}$ *ni v v.* 1. It is a cube. Make it then equal to the cube of the square of *ni*; and, subtraction taking place, there results, in the first side of equation, *ni v gh* 1 *ni v v* $\dot{1}$; and, in the second, *ca v* 2 *ni v. ca bh* 2. Multiplying both sides by two and superadding the biquadrate of *ni,* the square-root of the second side of the equation is *ca* 2 *ni v* $\dot{1}$. Depressing the first side by the biquadrate of *ni* as common divisor, to *ni v* 2 *ru* $\dot{1}$, the roots investigated by the rule of affected square, are L 5 G 7; or *L* 29 *G* 41. Then multiplying "greatest" by square of "least," conformably to the rule (§180), it comes out *G* 175, or 34481. "Least" root is the value of *ni.* Substituting with that, the former root becomes *ca* 2 *ru* $\dot{25}$; or *ca* 2 *ru* $\dot{841}$. Making an equation of this with "greatest" root, the value of *ca* is obtained 100 or 17661. Substituting these values respectively, the pair of numbers is brought out 75 and 100; or 16820 and 17661; and so forth.

184. Example: Say in what period (or number of terms) is the sum of a progression continued to a certain period tripled; its first term being three and the common difference two?

CHAPTER IX.

CONCLUSION.

A particle of tuition conveys science to a comprehensive mind; and having reached it, expands of its own impulse. As oil poured upon water, as a secret entrusted to the vile, as alms bestowed upon the worthy, however little, so does science infused into a wise mind spread by intrinsic force.

It is apparent to men of clear understanding, that the rule of three terms constitutes arithmetic; and sagacity, algebra. Accordingly I have said in the chapter on Spherics:

224. 'The rule of three terms is arithmetic; spotless understanding is algebra.[2] What is there unknown to the intelligent? Therefore, for the dull alone, it[3] is set forth.'

225. To augment wisdom and strengthen confidence, read, do read, mathematician, this abridgment elegant in stile, easily understood by youth, comprising the whole essence of computation, and containing the demonstration of its principles, replete with excellence and void of defect.

---

[2] *Vija.*

[3] The solution of certain problems set forth in the section. The preceding stanza, a part of which is cited by the scholiast of the *Lilavati,* (Ch. 12), premises, "I deliver for the instruction of youth a few answers of problems found by arithmetic, algebra, the pulverizer, the affected square, the sphere, and [astronomical] instruments." *Gol.* Sect. II. §2.

IMMANUEL BEN JACOB BONFILS

(c. 1350)

The physician, mathematician and astronomer, Rabbi Immanuel Bonfils, taught and wrote in Orange, France, and also in Tarascon, during the fourteenth century. Manuscripts of fifteen of his works have survived to our time. Nine of them are in the National Library of Paris. The astronomical observations which were made and published by Bonfils primarily as an aid in the determination of the Hebrew calendar, enjoyed great popularity in his day. Many manuscript copies of this work including extensions to the end of the fifteenth century are extant. Immanuel's highly regarded astronomical tables, *Kanfe Nesharim* (Wings of Eagles), earned him the nickname "Ba'al kenafayim" (Master of the Wings). The tables were translated into Latin in 1406 and commented upon in Greek.

Immanuel Bonfils also taught mathematics and a mathematical manuscript written by him in the Hebrew language, recently rediscovered, shows that as early as the middle of the fourteenth century, Bonfils taught arithmetic employing a decimal system of his own devising, with rules of operation forming an exponential calculus. The manuscript entitled *Derekh Hilluq* had been listed by an old Hebrew copyist as "A method of division by Rabbi Immanuel. and other topics." This title has now been proved to be a misnomer. The subject matter of *Derekh Hilluq* is not division but the exposition of an arithmetic which consistently employs the decimal system of notation not only for integers but also for fractions. In 1935, through a brilliant piece of research, the error of this misnomer was discovered by Sarton, Editor of ISIS. At his invitation, the task of translating and annotating the manuscript was undertaken by Solomon Gandz. Immanuel's short manuscript was divided by Gandz into six paragraphs. The first three paragraphs dealt with Bonfils' new theory of decimal fractions. The remaining paragraphs, unrelated to the first three, proved to be disconnected fragments of a chapter on the extraction of roots belonging to another work by Bonfils (MS. Hebrew 1081, National Library of Paris).

Derekh Hilluq contains no numerical examples. Bonfils, using no symbols whatever and writing in a fashion common to medieval mathematicians, states his step by step rules for operating, rather than the underlying laws or principles. It is clear, however, that the theory of positive and negative exponents was well known to him. While the proposals made by Bonfils concerning a decimal system lay concealed for centuries in a misnamed manuscript, they were in their time of no little importance, enunciated and taught as they were, in a vital center of commerce and culture, the city of Tarascon, by a man whose works were widely known. Immanuel of Tarascon thus takes his place, as Sarton predicted he would, in the line of the great contributors to the development of the decimal system.

A METHOD OF DIVISION BY RABBI IMMANUEL AND OTHER TOPICS

From *Invention of the Decimal Fractions*

by Solomon Gandz

Introduction (52)

1. *Terminology and Definitions*

Know that the unit is divided into ten parts which are called Primes, and each Prime is divided into ten parts which are called Seconds, and so on into infinity. I also want to call to your attention that I am calling the degrees of the tens Prime Integers, and the hundreds Second Integers, and so on into infinity. The degree of the units, however, I am calling by their name Units, for it is an intermediate between the integers and the fractions. Therefore, if one multiplies units with units the result is units. Furthermore, I am calling the degrees with a higher denominator (53) "Of a higher denominator." I mean by that: I am calling the Thirds, of a higher denominator than the Seconds, for the Thirds are derived from three, while the Seconds come from two. Similarly, the Fourths are of a higher denominator than the Thirds, and the Fifths than the Fourths. And this applies to the integers as well as to the fractions.

Furthermore, when I say: add this denominator to that denominator, or subtract this denominator from that denominator, I mean by that: add the denominator of the Seconds to the denominator of the Thirds, so that the

(52) This heading is found in the Hebrew MS., and may have been applied by Bonfils to the first paragraph containing the terminology and definitions, while paragraphs 2 and 3 were regarded as the text proper. It is possible, however, that all the three paragraphs were intended to form the introduction to a larger text, which became lost or was never written.

(53) Literally *shem,* "name."

THE HEBREW TEXT

MS Hebr 1054 b . National Library - Paris

דרך חלוק לר עמנואל ועא (ועניינים אחרים)

הקדמה

ידע כי האחד נחלק לעשרה חלקים יקראו ראשונים, וכן כל ראשון חולק
לעשרה חלקים יקראו שניים וכן לאין תכלית. וכן אמרתי להסכים כי הנני
קורא למעלות העשרות שלמים ראשונים ולמאות שלמים שניים, וכן לאין
תכלית. אמנם מעלת האחדים אני קורא אותם בשם אחדים, לפי שהוא אמצעי
בין השלמים והשברים, ולזה כשיכפל אחדים באחדים יצאו אחדים. וכן אני קורא
המעלות שהם גדולות השם, גדול השם. רצוני בזה שלישיים אני קורא יותר
גדול השם משניים לפי ששלישיים נגזר משלשה ושניים משנים וכן רביעיים
יותר גדול השם משלישיים, וכן חמישיים מרביעיים. וזה הוא בשלמים ובשברים.
וכן כשאומר חבר שם זה עם שם זה, או גרע שם זה משם זה רצוני בזה, חבר
שם שניים עם שם שלישיים ויהיו חמשיים, ואם שם שניים עם שם שניים יהיו רביעיים.
וכן גרע שם שניים משם שלישיים וישאר ראשונים, ואם שם שניים משם שניים לא
ישאר דבר ויפול במעלת האחדים וזה בשלמים ובשברים. וכאשר תגרע שם
גדול משם קטן כאמרנו נגרע רביעיים משניים [והן בשלמים][1] הן בשברים,
יבוא במעלת השניים לצד האחר. כאמרנו נגרע שם רביעיים בשברים משם
שניים גם כן בשברים, יפול במעלת שלמים שניים. וכן באמרנו זה בשלמים,
ר"ל שנרצה לגרוע שם רביעיים שלמים משם שניים שלמים, יפול בשברים שניים.

§2 שתכפול מספר על מספר ושניהם שלמים או שניהם שברים חבר שם
המדרגות האחד [עם האחר][1] ושם הוא הנכפל, בשלמים אם שניהם
שלמים ובשברים אם שניהם שברים ואם [האחד][1] שלמים והאחר שברים,
[אם הם שוים בשם הנה יכפול[2] הנכפל במעלת האחדים. ואם שם האחד
רב על האחר, גרע הקטן מהגדול ובמספר השם שישאר שם יפול הנכפל,

---

[1] Added by me.

[2] Read יפול.

result will be Fifths, or, the denominator of the Seconds to the denominator of the Seconds, so that there will result Fourths. Or also, subtract the denominator of the Seconds from the denominator of the Thirds and there will remain Primes, or, the denominator of the Seconds from the denominator of the Seconds and nothing will remain, hence it (54) will fall into the degree of the units. And this applies to the integers as well as to the fractions. And if you subtract a large denominator from a small denominator, as when we say: let us subtract Fourths from Seconds, [be it among integers] (55) or among fractions, then it (56) will come into the degree of the Seconds of the opposite direction. For instance, when we say: let us subtract the denominator of the Fourths, among the fractions, from the denominator of the Seconds, also among the fractions, then it falls into the degree of the Second integers. Similarly, if we say the same with regard to the integers, i.e.: if we want to subtract the denominator of the Fourth integers from the denominator of the Second integers, then it falls into the Second fractions (57).

2. *Multiplication*

If you multiply one number with another number, both being integers or both fractions, add the denominator of the degrees of the one [to the other one], and there the product will be: among the integers, if both are integers, and among the fractions, if both are fractions. If, however, [the one] is an integer and the other one a fraction: if they have the same denominator, then the product will fall into the degree of the units. But if the one has a higher denominator than the other one, then subtract the smaller from the higher one, and where the number of

(54) The Quotient.

(55) Added by conjecture.

(56) The Quotient.

(57) Bonfils omits to say how one shall proceed when the denominator of the fraction is to be deducted from the denominator of the integers, or, when an integer is divided by a fraction. But the rule is given below, at the end of § 3, where it is expressed by a somewhat different formula.

the remaining denominator is, there the product falls; among the integers, if the denominator of the integers is higher, or among the fractions, if the denominator of the fractions is higher.

3. *Division*

If you divide one number by another number, both being integers or both fractions, and the denominator of their degree is the same, then the quotient will fall into the degree of the units. For if you subtract the one denominator from the other denominator, nothing remains; hence it falls into the degree of the units. If [the denominator of] the upper (58) is higher than the denominator of the lower one, subtract the denominator of the lower from the denominator of the upper one, and where the number of the remaining denominator is, there the quotient will fall, in the same direction, i.e. among the integers, if it is an integer, or among the fractions, if it is a fraction. If, however, the lower is higher, then subtract the denominator of the upper from the denominator of the lower one, and where the number of the remaining denominator is, there the quotient will fall, in the opposite direction, i.e. among the fractions, if both are integers, or among the integers, if both are fractions. If, however, the one is an integer and the second is a fraction, may their degrees have the same denominator or different denominators then add the denominators of the degrees, and the quotient will fall where the number of the resulting denominator is: among the fractions, if the upper is a fraction, or among the integers, if the upper is an integer.

Terminology

'Elyon, the upper (number, or row), the dividend.
Gera', deduct.
Habber, add.
Haluqqah, the quotient.

(58) The upper number, or row, is the dividend; the lower is the divisor.

Hattekh, melt, reduce a number into the lowest kind of fraction.

Ma'alah, degree; meaning the decimal powers, and also the integers in the sexagesimal fractions.

Madregah, degree, of the decimal powers and of the sexagesimal fractions.

Min ha-sheber, the kind of the fraction.

Nifrad, odd.

Rishonim, Sheniyyim, Primes, Seconds, of the decimal powers and of the sexagesimal fractions.

Shabber, break, reduce a number into the lowest kind of fractions.

Shebarim, fractions.

Shelemim, integers.

Shem, name, denominator. *Gedol ha-shem,* of a higher denominator.

Shoresh, root.

Tahton, the lower (number, or row), the divisor.

Tur, row. The upper row is the dividend, and the lower row is the divisor.

GEORGE BOOLE

(1815-1864)

George Boole, founder of the generalized class-calculus, sometimes called *Boolean algebra* in his honor, was animated throughout his life by a zeal for learning which was fulfilled only through his indefatigable efforts and resolution. Born in Lincoln, England, Boole received such early education as could be obtained partly from his father, a tradesman, who was ingenious in mechanics and exceptionally skilled in elementary mathematics, partly at the national school in Lincoln and partly under private tutelage in Greek and Latin. Some additional training was also afforded to him at a small commercial school in Lincoln. When Boole was sixteen years old his basically friendly nature, gentle manner, his integrity as well as his excellence in scholarship were already apparent and he was employed as a teacher, first in a school in Lincoln and later in another in nearby Waddington. During this period the study of modern languages, French, German and Italian, in addition to ancient Greek and Latin, occupied every moment of his spare time. At the age of twenty, after four years of teaching, Boole established his own school in Lincoln. Here he soon felt the need for further study in mathematics on his own part and from this time on he engaged in extensive research in mathematics, wholly self directed and self taught. The vigorous individuality of his way of thinking, nurtured by independent investigation, yielded not only a thorough knowledge of the subject but also some highly original results.

In 1849, on the recommendation of his friend, Augustus De Morgan, Boole was appointed professor of mathematics at the newly organized Queen's College in Cork, Ireland. In contrast to the privations and discouragements which marked his early years of struggle, the period of his activity at Queen's College was one of brilliant success. He was a popular lecturer. In later years he served as a public examiner for degrees in the Queen's university. His memoirs and treatises were well received. The eminence which he attained was recognized by such awards as the Keith Medal bestowed by the Royal Society of Edinburgh. The L.L.D. degree was conferred upon him by the University of Dublin and the D.C.L. degree by Oxford. In 1855 Boole married Mary Everest, niece of the great surveyor, Sir George Everest, for whom Mt. Everest was named. Their marriage was one of perfect happiness. When Boole died suddenly in 1864 a few days after his exposure in a rainstorm on his way to the college, he was survived by his wife and five daughters. His widow continued to be his admiring disciple after his death, expounding Boole's theories of education as she had learned them from him.

Many valuable memoirs in pure mathematics written by Boole appeared in various journals. His contributions to the theory of algebraic invariants, and to symbolical methods applicable to operative symbols separated from their operands, laid the groundwork on which future theories were built. Two systematic works, The *Treatise on Differential Equations* (1859) and the *Treatise on the Calculus of Finite Differences* (1860), contain original contributions which appeared in papers written and published by him much earlier. In his *The Mathematical Analysis of Logic being an Essay Towards a Calculus of Deductive Reasoning* (1847) and in his *An Investigation of the Laws of Thought on Which are Founded the Mathematical Theories of Logic and Probabilities* (1854), his theory of an algebra or a calculus of classes is constructed almost entirely on foundations originated by him, and these are the works that have brought Boole ever increasing fame.

THE MATHEMATICAL ANALYSIS OF LOGIC

FIRST PRINCIPLES.

Let us employ the symbol 1, or unity, to represent the Universe, and let us understand it as comprehending every conceivable class of objects whether actually existing or not, it being premised that the same individual may be found in more than one class, inasmuch as it may possess more than one quality in common with other individuals. Let us employ the letters X, Y, Z, to represent the individual members of classes, X applying to every member of one class, as members of that particular class, and Y to every member of another class as members of such class, and so on, according to the received language of treatises on Logic.

Further let us conceive a class of symbols x, y, z, possessed of the following character.

The symbol x operating upon any subject comprehending individuals or classes, shall be supposed to select from that subject all the Xs which it contains. In like manner the symbol y, operating upon any subject, shall be supposed to select from it all individuals of the class Y which are comprised in it, and so on.

When no subject is expressed, we shall suppose 1 (the Universe) to be the subject understood, so that we shall have

$$x = x\ (1),$$

the meaning of either term being the selection from the Universe of all the Xs which it contains, and the result of the operation being in common language, the class X, *i. e.* the class of which each member is an X.

From these premises it will follow, that the product xy will represent, in succession, the selection of the class Y, and the selection from the class Y of such individuals of the class X as are contained in it, the result being the class whose members are both Xs and Ys. And in like manner the product xyz will represent a compound operation of which the successive elements are the selection of the class Z, the selection from it of such individuals of the class Y as are contained in it, and the selection from the result thus obtained of all the individuals of the class X which it contains, the final result being the class common to X, Y, and Z.

From the nature of the operation which the symbols x, y, z, are conceived to represent, we shall designate them as elective symbols. An expression in which they are involved will be called an elective function, and an equation of which the members are elective functions, will be termed an elective equation.

It will not be necessary that we should here enter into the analysis of that mental operation which we have represented by the elective symbol. It is not an act of Abstraction according to the common acceptation of that term, because we never lose sight of the concrete, but it may probably be referred to an exercise of the faculties of Comparison and Attention. Our present concern is rather with the laws of combination and of succession, by which its results are governed, and of these it will suffice to notice the following.

1st. The result of an act of election is independent of the grouping or classification of the subject.

Thus it is indifferent whether from a group of objects considered as a whole, we select the class X, or whether we divide the group into two parts, select the Xs from them separately, and then connect the results in one aggregate conception.

We may express this law mathematically by the equation

$$x(u + v) = xu + xv,$$

$u + v$ representing the undivided subject, and u and v the component parts of it.

2nd. It is indifferent in what order two successive acts of election are performed.

Whether from the class of animals we select sheep, and from the sheep those which are horned, or whether from the class of animals we select the horned, and from these such as are sheep, the result is unaffected. In either case we arrive at the class *horned sheep.*

The symbolical expression of this law is

$$xy = yx.$$

3rd. The result of a given act of election performed twice, or any number of times in succession, is the result of the same act performed once.

If from a group of objects we select the Xs, we obtain a class of which all the members are Xs. If we repeat the operation on this class no further change will ensue: in selecting the Xs we take the whole. Thus we have

$$xx = x.$$

or

$$x^2 = x;$$

and supposing the same operation to be n times performed, we have

$$x^n = x,$$

which is the mathematical expression of the law above stated.*

The laws we have established under the symbolical forms

$$x(u + v) = xu + xv \text{ .... (1)},$$
$$xy = yx \text{ .... (2)},$$
$$x^n = x \text{ .... (3)},$$

are sufficient for the basis of a Calculus. From the first of these, it appears that elective symbols are *distributive,* from the second that they are *commutative;* properties which they possess in common with symbols of *quantity,* and in virtue of which, all the processes of common algebra are applicable to the present system. The one and sufficient axiom involved in this application is that equivalent operations performed upon equivalent subjects produce equivalent results.

The third law (3) we shall denominate the index law. It is peculiar to elective symbols, and will be found of great importance in enabling us to reduce our results to forms meet for interpretation.

From the circumstance that the processes of algebra may be applied to the present system, it is not to be inferred that the interpretation of an elective equation will be unaffected by such processes. The expression of a truth cannot be negatived by a legitimate operation, but it may be limited. The equation $y = z$ implies that the classes Y and Z are equivalent, member for member. Multiply it by a factor x, and we have

$$xy = xz,$$

which expresses that the individuals which are common to the classes X and Y are also common to X and Z, and *vice versa.* This is a perfectly legitimate inference, but

* The office of the elective symbol x, is to select individuals comprehended in the class X. Let the class X be supposed to embrace the universe; then, whatever the class Y may be, we have

$$xy = y.$$

The office which x performs is now equivalent to the symbol $+$, in one at least of its interpretations, and the index law (3) gives

$$+^n = +,$$

which is the known property of that symbol.

the fact which it declares is a less general one than was asserted in the original proposition.

OF EXPRESSION AND INTERPRETATION.

1. To express the class, not-X, that is, the class including all individuals that are not Xs.

The class X and the class not-X together make the Universe. But the Universe is 1, and the class X is determined by the symbol x, therefore the class not-X will be determined by the symbol $1 - x$.

Hence the office of the symbol $1 - x$ attached to a given subject will be, to select from it all the not-Xs which it contains.

And in like manner, as the product xy expresses the entire class whose members are both Xs and Ys, the symbol $y(1 - x)$ will represent the class whose members are Ys but not Xs, and the symbol $(1 - x)(1 - y)$ the entire class whose members are neither Xs nor Ys.

2. To express the Proposition, All Xs are Ys.

As all the Xs which exist are found in the class Y, it is obvious that to select out of the Universe all Ys, and from these to select all Xs, is the same as to select at once from the Universe all Xs.

Hence $$xy = x,$$
or $$x(1 - y) = 0, (4).$$

3. To express the Proposition, No Xs are Ys.

To assert that no Xs are Ys, is the same as to assert that there are no terms common to the classes X and Y. Now all individuals common to those classes are represented by xy. Hence the Proposition that No Xs are Ys, is represented by the equation

$$xy = 0, (5).$$

4. To express the Proposition, Some Xs are Ys.

If some Xs are Ys, there are some terms common to the classes X and Y. Let those terms constitute a separate class V, to which there shall correspond a separate elective symbol v, then

$$v = xy, \quad (6).$$

And as v includes all terms common to the classes X and Y, we can indifferently interpret it, as Some Xs, or Some Ys.

5. To express the Proposition, Some Xs are not Ys.

In the last equation write $1 - y$ for y, and we have

$$v = x(1 - y), \quad (7),$$

the interpretation of v being indifferently Some Xs or Some not-Ys.

The above equations involve the complete theory of categorical Propositions, and so far as respects the employment of analysis for the deduction of logical inferences, nothing more can be desired. But it may be satisfactory to notice some particular forms deducible from the third and fourth equations, and susceptible of similar application.

If we multiply the equation (6) by x, we have

$$vx = x^2y = xy \text{ by } (3).$$

Comparing with (6), we find

$$v = vx,$$

or

$$v(1 - x) = 0, \quad (8).$$

And multiplying (6) by y, and reducing in a similar manner, we have

$$v = vy,$$

or

$$v(1 - y) = 0, \quad (9).$$

Comparing (8) and (9),

$$vx = vy = v, \quad (10).$$

And further comparing (8) and (9) with (4), we have as the equivalent of this system of equations the Propositions

$$\left.\begin{array}{l}\text{All Vs are Xs}\\ \text{All Vs are Ys}\end{array}\right\}.$$

The system (10) might be used to replace (6), or the single equation

$$vx = vy, \ (11),$$

might be used, assigning to vx the interpretation, Some Xs, and to vy the interpretation, Some Ys. But it will be observed that this system does not express quite so much as the single equation (6), from which it is derived. Both, indeed, express the Proposition, Some Xs are Ys, but the system (10) does not imply that the class V includes *all* the terms that are common to X and Y.

In like manner, from the equation (7) which expresses the Proposition Some Xs are not Ys, we may deduce the system

$$vx = v(1 - y) = v, \ (12),$$

in which the interpretation of $v(1 - y)$ is Some not-Ys. Since in this case $vy = 0$, we must of course be careful not to interpret vy as Some Ys.

If we multiply the first equation of the system (12), viz.

$$vx = v(1 - y),$$

by y, we have

$$vxy = vy(1 - y);$$

$$\therefore \quad vxy = 0, \ (13),$$

which is a form that will occasionally present itself. It is not necessary to revert to the primitive equation in order to interpret this, for the condition that vx represents Some Xs, shews us by virtue of (5), that its import will be

Some Xs are not Ys,

the subject comprising *all* the Xs that are found in the class V.

Universally in these cases, difference of form implies a difference of interpretation with respect to the auxiliary symbol v, and each form is interpretable by itself.

Further, these differences do not introduce into the Calculus a needless perplexity. It will hereafter be seen that they give a precision and a definiteness to its conclusions, which could not otherwise be secured.

Finally, we may remark that all the equations by which

particular truths are expressed, are deducible from any one general equation, expressing any one general Proposition, from which those particular Propositions are necessary deductions. This has been partially shewn already, but it is much more fully exemplified in the following scheme.

The general equation $x = y$,
implies that the classes X and Y are equivalent, member for member; that every individual belonging to the one, belongs to the other also. Multiply the equation by x, and we have

$$x^2 = xy;$$
$$\therefore x = xy,$$

which implies, by (4), that all Xs are Ys. Multiply the same equation by y, and we have in like manner

$$y = xy;$$

the import of which is, that all Ys are Xs. Take either of these equations, the latter for instance, and writing it under the form

$$(1 - x)y = 0,$$

we may regard it as an equation in which y, an unknown quantity, is sought to be expressed in terms of x. Now it will be shewn when we come to treat of the Solution of Elective Equations (and the result may here be verified by substitution) that the most general solution of this equation is

$$y = vx,$$

which implies that All Ys are Xs, and that Some Xs are Ys. Multiply by x, and we have

$$vy = vx,$$

which indifferently implies that some Ys are Xs and some Xs are Ys, being the particular form at which we before arrived.

For convenience of reference the above and some other results have been classified in the annexed Table, the first column of which contains propositions, the second equations, and the third the conditions of final interpretation. It is to be observed, that the auxiliary equations which are given in this column are not independent: they are implied either in the equations of the second column, or in the condition for the interpretation of v. But it has been thought better to write them separately, for greater ease and convenience. And it is further to be borne in mind, that although three different forms are given for the expression of each of the *particular* propositions, everything is really included in the first form.

TABLE.

The class X	x	
The class not-X	$1 - x$	
All Xs are Ys All Ys are Xs	$x = y$	
All Xs are Ys	$x(1 - y) = 0$	
No Xs are Ys	$xy = 0$	
All Ys are Xs Some Xs are Ys	$y = vx$	$vx =$ some Xs $v(1 - x) = 0.$
No Ys are Xs Some not-Xs are Ys	$y = v(1 - x)$	$v(1 - x) =$ some not-Xs $vx = 0.$
Some Xs are Ys	$v = xy$ or $vx = vy$ or $vx(1 - y) = 0$	$v =$ some Xs or some Ys $vx =$ some Xs, $vy =$ some Ys $v(1 - x) = 0$, $v(1 - y) = 0.$
Some Xs are not Ys	$v = x(1 - y)$ or $vx = v(1 - y)$ or $vxy = 0$	$v =$ some Xs, or some not-Ys $vx =$ some Xs, $v(1 - y) =$ some not-Ys $v(1 - x) = 0$, $vy = 0.$

●

THE LAWS OF THOUGHT

CHAPTER II.

Of signs in general, and of the signs appropriate to the science of logic in particular; also of the laws to which that class of signs are subject.

1. That Language is an instrument of human reason, and not merely a medium for the expression of thought,

is a truth generally admitted. It is proposed in this chapter to inquire what it is that renders Language thus subservient to the most important of our intellectual faculties. In the various steps of this inquiry we shall be led to consider the constitution of Language, considered as a system adapted to an end or purpose; to investigate its elements; to seek to determine their mutual relation and dependence; and to inquire in what manner they contribute to the attainment of the end to which, as coordinate parts of a system, they have respect.

2. The elements of which all language consists are signs or symbols. Words are signs. Sometimes they are said to represent things; sometimes the operations by which the mind combines together the simple notions of things into complex conceptions; sometimes they express the relations of action, passion, or mere quality, which we perceive to exist among the objects of our experience; sometimes the emotions of the perceiving mind. But words, although in this and in other ways they fulfil the office of signs, or representative symbols, are not the only signs which we are capable of employing. Arbitrary marks, which speak only to the eye, and arbitrary sounds or actions, which address themselves to some other sense, are equally of the nature of signs, provided that their representative office is defined and understood. In the mathematical sciences, letters, and the symbols $+$, $-$, $=$, &c., are used as signs, although the term "sign" is applied to the latter class of symbols, which represent operations or relations, rather than to the former, which represent the elements of number and quantity. As the real import of a sign does not in any way depend upon its particular form or expression, so neither do the laws which determine its use. In the present treatise, however, it is with written signs that we have to do, and it is with reference to these exclusively that the term "sign" will be employed. The essential properties of signs are enumerated in the following definition.

Definition.—A sign is an arbitrary mark, having a fixed interpretation, and susceptible of combination with other signs in subjection to fixed laws dependent upon their mutual interpretation.

3. Let us consider the particulars involved in the above definition separately.

(1.) In the first place, a sign is an *arbitrary* mark. It is clearly indifferent what particular word or token we associate with a given idea, provided that the association once made is permanent. The Romans expressed by the word "civitas" what we designate by the word "state." But both they and we might equally well have employed any other word to represent the same conception. Nothing, indeed, in the nature of Language would prevent us from using a mere letter in the same sense. Were this done, the laws according to which that letter would require to be used would be essentially the same with the laws which govern the use of "civitas" in the Latin, and of "state" in the English language, so far at least as the use of those words is regulated by any general principles common to all languages alike.

(2.) In the second place, it is necessary that each sign should possess, within the limits of the same discourse or process of reasoning, a fixed interpretation. The necessity of this condition is obvious, and seems to be founded in the very nature of the subject. There exists, however, a dispute as to the precise nature of the representative office of words or symbols used as names in the processes of reasoning. By some it is maintained, that they represent the conceptions of the mind alone; by others, that they represent things. The question is not of great importance here, as its decision cannot affect the laws according to which signs are employed. I apprehend, however, that the general answer to this and such like questions is, that in the process of reasoning, signs stand in the place and fulfil the office of the conceptions and operations of the mind; but that as those conceptions and operations represent things, and the connexions and relations of things, so signs represent things with their connexions and relations; and lastly, that as signs stand in the place of the conceptions and operations of the mind, they are subject to the laws of those conceptions and operations. This view will be more fully elucidated in the next chapter; but it here serves to explain the third of those particulars involved in the definition of a sign, viz., its subjection to fixed laws of combination depending upon the nature of its interpretation.

4. The analysis and classification of those signs by which the operations of reasoning are conducted will be considered in the following Proposition:

PROPOSITION I.

All the operations of Language, as an instrument of reasoning, may be conducted by a system of signs composed of the following elements, viz.:

1st. *Literal symbols, as x, y, &c., representing things as subjects of our conceptions.*

2nd. *Signs of operation, as $+$, $-$, $\times$, standing for those operations of the mind by which the conceptions of things are combined or resolved so as to form new conceptions involving the same elements.*

3rd. *The sign of identity, $=$.*

And these symbols of Logic are in their use subject to definite laws, partly agreeing with and partly differing from the laws of the corresponding symbols in the science of Algebra.

Let it be assumed as a criterion of the true elements of rational discourse, that they should be susceptible of combination in the simplest forms and by the simplest laws, and thus combining should generate all other known and conceivable forms of language. . . .

6. Now, as it has been defined that a sign is an arbitrary mark, it is permissible to replace all signs of the species above described by letters. Let us then agree to represent the class of individuals to which a particular name or description is applicable, by a single letter, as x. If the name is "men," for instance, let x represent "all men," or the class "men." By a class is usually meant

a collection of individuals, to each of which a particular name or description may be applied; but in this work the meaning of the term will be extended so as to include the case in which but a single individual exists, answering to the required name or description, as well as the cases denoted by the terms "nothing" and "universe," which as "classes" should be understood to comprise respectively "no beings," "all beings." Again, if an adjective, as "good," is employed as a term of description, let us represent by a letter, as y, all things to which the description "good" is applicable, i.e. "all good things," or the class "good things." Let it further be agreed, that by the combination xy shall be represented that class of things to which the names or descriptions represented by x and y are simultaneously applicable. Thus, if x alone stands for "white things," and y for "sheep," let xy stand for "white sheep;" and in like manner, if z stand for "horned things," and x and y retain their previous interpretations, let zxy represent "horned white sheep," i.e. that collection of things to which the name "sheep," and the descriptions "white" and "horned" are together applicable.

Let us now consider the laws to which the symbols x, y, &c., used in the above sense, are subject.

7. First, it is evident, that according to the above combinations, the order in which two symbols are written is indifferent. The expressions xy and yx equally represent that class of things to the several members of which the names or descriptions x and y are together applicable. Hence we have,

$$xy = yx. \qquad (1)$$

In the case of x representing white things, and y sheep, either of the members of this equation will represent the class of "white sheep." There may be a difference as to the order in which the conception is formed, but there is none as to the individual things which are comprehended under it. In like manner, if x represents "estuaries," and y "rivers," the expressions xy and yx will indifferently represent "rivers that are estuaries," or "estuaries that are rivers," the combination in this case being in ordinary language that of two substantives, instead of that of a substantive and adjective as in the previous instance. Let there be a third symbol, as z, representing that class of things to which the term "navigable" is applicable, and any one of the following expressions,

$$zxy, zyx, xyz, \&c.,$$

will represent the class of "navigable rivers that are estuaries."

If one of the descriptive terms should have some implied reference to another, it is only necessary to include that reference expressly in its stated meaning, in order to render the above remarks still applicable. Thus, if x represent "wise" and y "counsellor," we shall have to define whether x implies wisdom in the absolute sense, or only the wisdom of counsel. With such definition the law $xy = yx$ continues to be valid.

We are permitted, therefore, to employ the symbols x, y, z, &c., in the place of the substantives, adjectives, and descriptive phrases subject to the rule of interpretation, that any expression in which several of these symbols are written together shall represent all the objects or individuals to which their several meanings are together applicable, and to the law that the order in which the symbols succeed each other is indifferent.

As the rule of interpretation has been sufficiently exemplified, I shall deem it unnecessary always to express the subject "things" in defining the interpretation of a symbol used for an adjective. When I say, let x represent "good," it will be understood that x only represents "good" when a subject for that quality is supplied by another symbol, and that, used alone, its interpretation will be "good things."

8. Concerning the law above determined, the following observations, which will also be more or less appropriate to certain other laws to be deduced hereafter, may be added.

First, I would remark, that this law is a law of thought,

and not, properly speaking, a law of things. Difference in the order of the qualities or attributes of an object, apart from all questions of causation, is a difference in conception merely. The law (1) expresses as a general truth, that the same thing may be conceived in different ways, and states the nature of that difference; and it does no more than this.

Secondly, As a law of thought it is actually developed in a law of Language, the product and instrument of thought. Though the tendency of prose writing is toward uniformity, yet even there the order of sequence of adjectives absolute in their meaning, and applied to the same subject, is indifferent, but poetic diction borrows much of its rich diversity from the extension of the same lawful freedom to the substantive also. The language of Milton is peculiarly distinguished by this species of variety. Not only does the substantive often precede the adjectives by which it is qualified, but it is frequently placed in their midst. In the first few lines of the invocation to Light, we meet with such examples as the following:

"*Offspring of heaven first-born.*"
"The rising world of *waters dark and deep.*"
"Bright effluence of *bright essence increate.*"

Now these inverted forms are not simply the fruits of a poetic license. They are the natural expressions of a freedom sanctioned by the intimate laws of thought, but for reasons of convenience not exercised in the ordinary use of language.

Thirdly, The law expressed by (1) may be characterized by saying that the literal symbols x, y, z, are *commutative, like the symbols of Algebra.* In saying this, it is not affirmed that the process of multiplication in Algebra, of which the fundamental law is expressed by the equation

$$xy = yx,$$

possesses in itself any analogy with that process of logical combination which xy has been made to represent above; but only that if the arithmetical and the logical process are expressed in the same manner, their symbolical expressions will be subject to the same formal law. The evidence of that subjection is in the two cases quite distinct.

9. As the combination of two literal symbols in the form xy expresses the whole of that class of objects to which the names or qualities represented by x and y are together applicable, it follows that if the two symbols have exactly the same signification, their combination expresses no more than either of the symbols taken alone would do. In such case we should therefore have

$$xy = x.$$

As y is, however, supposed to have the same meaning as x, we may replace it in the above equation by x, and we thus get

$$xx = x.$$

Now in common Algebra the combination xx is more briefly represented by x^2. Let us adopt the same principle of notation here; for the mode of expressing a particular succession of mental operations is a thing in itself quite as arbitrary as the mode of expressing a single idea or operation (II. 3). In accordance with this notation, then, the above equation assumes the form

$$x^2 = x, \qquad (2)$$

and is, in fact, the expression of a second general law of those symbols by which names, qualities, or descriptions, are symbolically represented.

Again: If two classes of things, x and y, be identical, that is, if all the members of the one are members of the other, then those members of the one class which possess a given property z will be identical with those members of the other which possess the same property z. Hence if we have the equation

$$x = y;$$

then whatever class or property z may represent, we have also

$$zx = zy.$$

This is formally the same as the algebraic law:—If both

members of an equation are multiplied by the same quantity, the products are equal.

In like manner it may be shown that if the corresponding members of two equations are multiplied together, the resulting equation is true.

14. Here, however, the analogy of the present system with that of algebra, as commonly stated, appears to stop. Suppose it true that those members of a class x which possess a certain property z are identical with those members of a class y which possess the same property z, it does not follow that the members of the class x universally are identical with the members of the class y. Hence it cannot be inferred from the equation

$$zx = zy,$$

that the equation

$$x = y$$

is also true. In other words, the axiom of algebraists, that both sides of an equation may be divided by the same quantity, has no formal equivalent here. I say no *formal equivalent*, because, in accordance with the general spirit of these inquiries, it is not even sought to determine whether the mental operation which is represented by removing a logical symbol, z, from a combination zx, is in itself analogous with the operation of division in Arithmetic. That mental operation is indeed identical with what is commonly termed Abstraction, and it will hereafter appear that its laws are dependent upon the laws already deduced in this chapter. What has now been shown is, that there does not exist among those laws anything analogous in *form* with a commonly received axiom of Algebra.

But a little consideration will show that even in common algebra that axiom does not possess the generality of those other axioms which have been considered. The deduction of the equation $x = y$ from the equation $zx = zy$ is only valid when it is known that z is not equal to 0. If then the value $z = 0$ is supposed to be admissible in the algebraic system, the axiom above stated ceases to be applicable, and the analogy before exemplified remains at least unbroken.

15. However, it is not with the symbols of quantity generally that it is of any importance, except as a matter of speculation, to trace such affinities. We have seen (II. 9) that the symbols of Logic are subject to the special law,

$$x^2 = x.$$

Now of the symbols of Number there are but two, viz. 0 and 1, which are subject to the same formal law. We know that $0^2 = 0$, and that $1^2 = 1$; and the equation $x^2 = x$, considered as algebraic, has no other roots than 0 and 1. Hence, instead of determining the measure of formal agreement of the symbols of Logic with those of Number generally, it is more immediately suggested to us to compare them with symbols of quantity *admitting only of the values* 0 *and* 1. Let us conceive, then, of an Algebra in which the symbols x, y, z, &c. admit indifferently of the values 0 and 1, and of these values alone.

BRAHMAGUPTA

(b. 598 A.D.)

Brahmagupta, the author of the celebrated astronomical work, the Brahma-sidd'hanta (astronomical system of Brahma), sometimes called the *Brahma-sphuta-sidd'hanta* (correct astronomical system of Brahma), was the chief astronomer of the observatory at Ujjain in the early part of the seventh century. In a period of the history of civilization, when the world was at the nadir of its intellectual development, this illustrious Indian mathematician wrote a work on astronomy and mathematics which was to be studied and repeated word by word for centuries to come. Later Indian writers painstakingly explained each verse of Brahmagupta's text, adding illustrative examples for clarification. In the twelfth century, when Bhascara Acharya was head of the observatory at Ujjain (c. 1150), Brahmagupta's text and the commentaries on it were fully available to him. The *Brahma-sidd'hanta,* written when Brahmagupta was thirty years old, at a date which has been found to be equivalent to 628 A.D., had been preserved through the devotion of copyists and scholars. Through sustained interest and effort, it has survived to our time in almost complete form. Of the twenty-one chapters into which the treatise was originally divided, the first ten were on astronomy. The eleventh chapter was given over to a forceful rejection or correction of views which Brahmagupta regarded as erroneous. Chapter twelve was on arithmetic and mensuration. The next five chapters, in which there are now some serious gaps, were again on astronomy. The subject matter of the eighteenth chapter was mathematical. The next two chapters are missing. The last chapter, the twenty-first, was on spherics. While basing his work on previous treatises, Brahmagupta justified his correction of older writers on the grounds of observation and tradition. "The computation of the planets taught by Brahma," he wrote, "which had become imperfect by great length of time is propounded correct by Brahmagupta, son of Jishnu." * The commentary available to us was written about 860 A.D. by the great scholiast of the *Brahma-sphuta-sidd'hanta,* Chaturveda-Prit'hudaca-Swami, frequently mentioned by Bhascara in his *Sidd'hanta-siromani* as one of the authorities upon whom he depended.

Most of the problems proposed by Brahmagupta in Chapter 12, *Ganitad 'hyaya* (arithmetic and mensuration) and Chapter 18, *Cuttacad'hyaya* (algebra) were related to astronomy. Rather fanciful problem situations were introduced later, in the commentaries. Brahmagupta himself departed at times from the strictly practical problem. "These questions are stated merely

* H. T. Colebrooke, *Algebra with Arithmetic and Mensuration,* translated from the Sanskrit of Brahmagupta and Bhascara, p. xxx.

for gratification," he stated toward the end of his eighteenth chapter. "The proficient may devise a thousand others; or may resolve, by the rules taught, problems proposed by others." ** Among the mathematical topics taught by Brahmagupta were rules for elementary operations with positive and negative numbers, progressions, rational triangles and quadrilaterals, linear functions made squares, and problems solved by indeterminate equations of the first and second degrees. His work, especially in number theory, was followed and developed by a long list of famous mathematicians.

●

BRAHMA-SPHUTA-SIDD'HANTA

Translated from the Sanscrit

by HENRY THOMAS COLEBROOKE.

CHAPTER XII.

ARITHMETIC.

SECTION I.

RULE OF PROPORTION.

1. He, who distinctly and severally knows addition and the rest of the twenty logistics, and the eight determinations including measurement by shadow,[1] is a mathematician.[2]

10. In the rule of three, argument, fruit and requisition [are names of the terms]: the first and last terms must

** Ibid. p. 377.

[1] Addition, subtraction, multiplication, division, square, square-root, cube, cube-root, five [should be, six] rules of reduction of fractions, rule of three terms [direct and inverse,] of five terms, seven terms, nine terms, eleven terms, and barter, are twenty (*paricarman*) arithmetical operations. Mixture, progression, plane figure, excavation, stack, saw, mound, and shadow, are eight determinations (*vyavahara*). CH.

[2] *Ganaca,* a calculator; a proficient competent to the study of the sphere. CH.

be similar.[1] Requisition, multiplied by the fruit, and divided by the argument, is the produce.[2]

SECTION III.

PROGRESSION.

17. The period less one, multiplied by the common difference, being added to the first term, is the amount of the last. Half the sum of the last and first terms is the mean amount: which, multiplied by the period, is the sum of the whole.[1]

18. Add the square of the difference between twice the

---

[1] The middle term is dissimilar. CH.

[2] The rule concerns integers. If there be fractions among the terms, reduce all to the same denominator. CH.

Example: A person gives away a hundred and eight cows in three days; how many kine does he bestow in a year and a month?

Statement: Days 3. Cows 108. Days 390.

Answer: 14040.

Example: A white ant advances eight barley corns less than one fifth part of that amount in a day; and returns the twentieth part of a finger in three days. In what space of time will one, whose progress is governed by these rates of advancing and receding, proceed one hundred *yojanas?*

Example: One bestows an unit on holy men, in the third part of a day; another gives the same alms in half a day; and a third distributes three in five days. In what time, persevering in those rates, will they have given a hundred?

Statement: 1 1 3 And, the rule being observed, 3/1 2/1 3/5.
1/3 1/2 5/1

Reducing these to a common denominator, and summing them, the result is 28/5; the total amount, which all bestow in alms in a day. Then by the rule of three, if so many fifths of an unit be given in one day, in how many will a hundred units be given?

Statement: 28/5 | 1/1 | 100/1. Answer: 17 6/7. CH.

[1] To find the contents of a pile in the form of half the *meru-yantra* [or spindle]. CH.

Example: A stack of bricks is seen, containing five layers, having two bricks at the top, and increasing by three in each layer: tell the whole number of bricks.

Statement: Init. 2; Diff. 3; Per. 5. Answer: 40.

Example: The king bestowed gold continually on venerable priests, during three days and a ninth part, giving one and a half [*bharas*] with a daily increase of a quarter: what were the mean and last terms, and the total?

Statement: Init. 1-1/2; Diff. 1/4; Per. 3-1/9.

Period 28/9, less one, is 19/9; multiplied by the difference, it is 19/36; and added to the first term, becomes 73/36. This is the last term. Added to the first term and halved, it gives 127/72. This is the mean amount: multiplied by the period, it yields the total 889/162; or 5 *bharas,* 9 hundred [*palas*] and 60/80 [of a hundred].

Example: Tell the price of the seventh conch; the first being worth six *panas,* and the rest increasing by a *pana?*

initial term and the common increase, to the product of the sum of the progression by eight times the increase: the square-root, less the foregoing remainder divided by twice the common increase, is the period.*

SECTION IV.

PLANE FIGURE.[1]

TRIANGLE and QUADRILATERAL.

21. The product of half the sides and countersides[2] is the gross area of a triangle and tetragon.[3] Half the sum

---

Statement: Init. 6; Diff. 1; Per. 7. Answer: 12.

Example: A man gave his son-in-law sixteen *panas* the first day; and diminished the present by two a day. If thou be conversant with progression, say how many had he bestowed when the ninth day was past?

Statement: Init. 16; Diff. 2; Per. 9. Answer: 72; received by the son-in-law: or 72 the father-in-law's; being his disbursement.

* The first term, common increase, and total amount, being known, to find the period. CH.

Example: Say how many are the layers in a stack containing a hundred bricks, and having at the summit ten, and increasing by five.

Statement: Init. 10; Com. diff. 5; Per.? Sum 100.

Operation: Twice the initial, 20, less the increase 5, is 15; the square of which is 225. The sum 100, eight (8) and increase 5, multiplied together, make 4000. Add to this the square of the remainder, 225, the total is 4225. Its square-root 65, less the foregoing remainder 15, gives 50; which divided by twice the common increase, 10, yields the period 5.

So in other cases likewise.

[1] Triangles are three; tetragons five, and the circle is the ninth plane figure. Thus triangles are (*sama-tribhuja*) equilateral, (*dwi-sama-tribhuja*) isosceles, and (*vishama-tribhuja*) scalene. Tetragons are (*sama-chaturasra*) equilateral; (*ayata-sama-chaturasra*) oblong with equal sides [two and two]; (*dwi-sama-chaturasra*) having two equal sides; (*tri-sama-chaturasra*) having three sides equal; (*vishama-chaturasra*) having all unequal. CH.

[2] *Bahu-pratibahu,* or *bhuja-pratibhupa* (§23): opposite sides.

[3] Example: What is the area of an equilateral triangle, the side of which is twelve?

Statement: 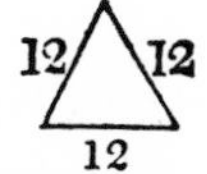

The sum of sides and of countersides, 12 and 24; their moieties 6 and 12; the product of which is 72, the gross area.

Example: What is the area of an isosceles triangle the base of which is ten and the sides thirteen?

Statement: 

The moieties of the sums of opposite sides, 5 and 13; their product 65, the gross area.

Example: What is the area of a scalene triangle, the base of which is fourteen and the sides thirteen and fifteen?

Statement: 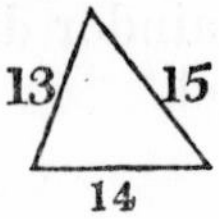 13 15 14 Answer: 98 the gross area.

Example: What is the area of an equilateral tetragon, the side of which is ten?

Statement: 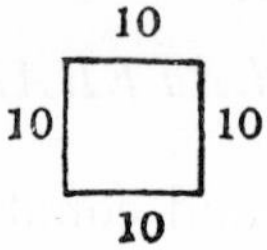 10 10 10 10 Answer: 100, the gross as well as exact area.

Example: What is the area of an oblong, two sides of which are twelve; and two, five?

Statement: 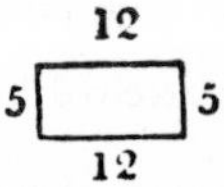 12 5 5 12 Answer: 60, the gross and exact area.

Example: What is the area of a quadrilateral having two equal sides thirteen, the base fourteen, and the summit four?

Statement: 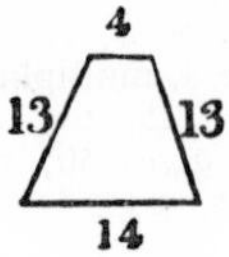 4 13 13 14 Answer: 117 the gross area.

Example: Tell the area of a quadrilateral having three equal sides twenty-five, and base thirty-nine?

Statement: 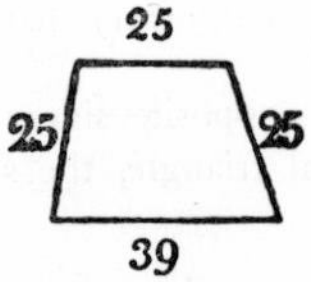 25 25 25 39 Answer: 800 the gross area.

Example: Tell the gross area of a trapezium, of which the base is sixty, the summit twenty-five, and the sides fifty-two and thirty-nine?

Statement: 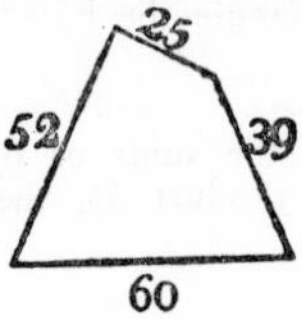 25 52 39 60 Answer: 1933¾ the gross area. CH.

of the sides set down four times, and severally lessened by the sides,[1] being multiplied together, the square-root of the product is the exact area.[2]

22. The difference of the squares of the sides being divided by the base, the quotient is added to and subtracted from the base: the sum and the remainder, divided by two, are the segments. The square-root, extracted from the difference of the square of the side and square of its corresponding segment of the base, is the perpendicular.

30—31. Assuming two triangles within the trapezium, let the diagonals be the bases of them.[3] Then the segments, separately found, are the upper and lower portions formed by the intersection of the diagonals.[4] The

---

[1] The sides of the quadrilateral are severally subtracted from the half of the sum in all four places; but the sides of the triangle are subtracted in three, and the fourth remains as it stood. CH.

[2] Examples as above. Sides of the equilateral triangle 12; the sum 36; its half set down four times 18, 18, 18, 18; which severally lessened by the sides gives 6, 6, 6, 18. The product of those numbers is 3888, the surd root of which is the exact area.

Sides of the isosceles triangle 10, 13, 13; the sum 36. Its half 18, lessened severally by the sides, gives 5, 5, 8, 18. The product whereof is 3600. The square-root of this is the exact area, 60.

Sides of the scalene triangle 14, 13, 15. Half the sum 21, less the sides, gives 7, 8, 6, 21. Product 7056; the root of which is the exact area 84.

The gross area of the equilateral tetragon, as of the oblong, is the same with the exact area.

Sides of the tetragon with two equal sides, 14, 13, 13, 4. The exact area, as found by the rule, is 108.

Sides of the tetragon having three equal sides, 39, 25, 25, 25. Exact area 768.

Sides of the trapezium 60, 52, 39, 25. Exact area 1764. CH.

[3] The greater diagonal is the base of one; and the summit and greater flank are its sides. The least diagonal is the base of the other; and the summit and least flank are the sides. CH.

[4] In the tetragon just now instanced, the scalene triangle with the greater diagonal for base is this

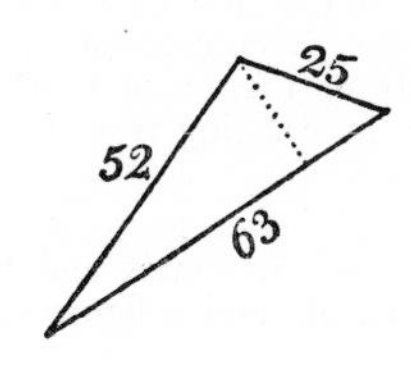

lower portions of the two diagonals are taken for the sides of a triangle; and the base [of the tetragon] for its base. Its perpendicular is the lower portion of the [middle] perpendicular of the tetragon: the upper portion of it is the moiety of the sum of the [extreme] perpendiculars less the lower portion.[1]

32.[2] At the intersection of the diagonals and perpendiculars, the lower segments of the diagonal and of the perpendicular are found by proportion: those lines less these segments are the upper segments of the same. So

---

The segments of its base as found by the rule (§ 22) are 48 and 15. These are respectively the lower and upper portions of the greater diagonal.

The scalene triangle with the less diagonal for base is

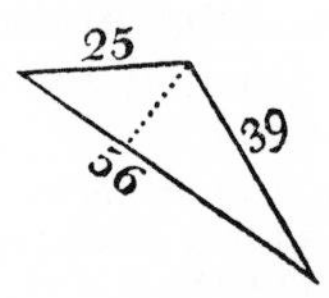

Here the segments, by the same rule (§ 22), are 36 and 20. They are the lower and upper portions of the least diagonal.

Or find the segments of one only: the perpendicular, found by the rule (§ 22) is the upper portion of the second diagonal: and subtracting that from the entire length, the remainder is the lower portion of it. Thus, in the foregoing example, the least segment in the first triangle is 15. Its square 225, subtracted from the square of the least side 625, leaves 400, the root of which is 20. It is the upper portion of the smaller diagonal, and subtracted from the whole length 56, leaves the lower portion 36. CH.

[1] In the same figure, the scalene triangle composed of the two lower segments of the diagonals together with the base is this

Here the perpendicular found by the rule (§ 22) is 28-4/5. It is the lower portion of the mean perpendicular. The greatest and least perpendiculars being 44-4/5 and 37-4/5, the moiety of their sum is 41-3/10. This is the length of the entire mean perpendicular. Subtracting from it its lower segment the residue is its upper segment 12-1/2. CH.

[2] A rule to find the upper and lower portions of the diagonals and perpendiculars cut by the intersection of diagonals and perpendiculars, within a trapezium; also the lines of the needle and a figure of intersection.

in the needle[3] as well as in the (*pata*) intersection [of prolonged sides and perpendiculars].[4]

---

[3] *Suchi,* the needle; the triangle formed by the produced flanks of the tetragon. The section of a cone or pyramid.

Pata, sampata, tripata, intersection; of a prolonged side and perpendicular. The figure formed by such intersection.

[4] Example: In a trapezium the base of which is sixty; one side fifty-two; the other thirty-nine; and the summit twenty-five: the greater diagonal sixty-three; the less, fifty-six: the greater perpendicular forty-five less one fifth; its segments of the base, the greatest thirty-three and three-fifths, the least twenty-six and two-fifths: the least perpendicular thirty-seven and four-fifths; its segments of the base, greatest fifty and two-fifths, least nine and three-fifths: the perpendicular passing through the intersection of the diagonals, forty-one and three-tenths; its segments of the base, greatest thirty-eight and two-fifths, least twenty-one and three-fifths; tell the upper and lower portions of the perpendiculars, the intersections [of prolonged sides and perpendiculars] and the needle.

Here at the intersection of the diagonals, the segments of the greater diagonal, found as before (§ 30), are 48 and 15; those of the less are 36 and 20.

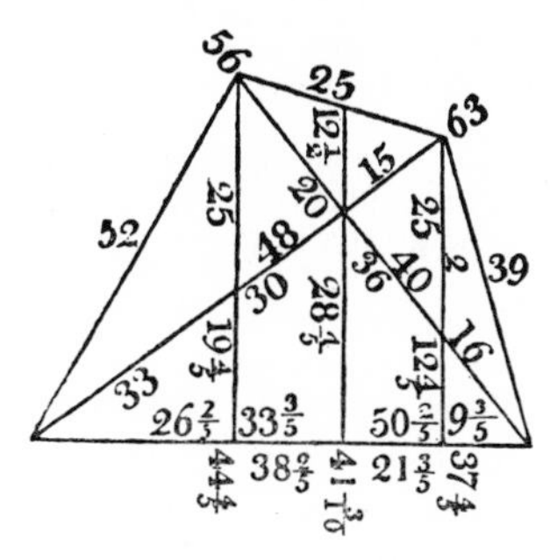

At the junction of the greater diagonal and greater perpendicular; the proportion is as diagonal sixty-three to the complement fifty and two fifths, so, to the segment twenty-six and two-fifths, what? or rendered homogeneous, $\frac{252}{5}$ | 63 | $\frac{132}{5}$. Answer: 33. It is the lower portion of the diagonal. Again, as the same complement is to the least perpendicular, so is the above mentioned segment to what? Statement: $\frac{252}{5}$ | $\frac{189}{5}$ | $\frac{132}{5}$ | Answer: 19-4/5. It is the lower portion of the perpendicular. Subtracting these from the whole diagonal 63 and entire perpendicular 44-4/5, the remainders are the upper segments of the diagonal and perpendicular; 30 and 25.

Next, at the junction of the less diagonal and less perpendicular: as the complement thirty-three and three-fifths is to the diagonal fifty-six, so is the segment nine and three-fifths to what? Statement: 33-3/5 | 56 | 9-3/5 . Answer: 16, the lower portion of the diagonal. So, putting the perpendicular for the middle term, the lower portion of the less perpendicular comes out 12-4/5. By subtraction from the entire diagonal and perpendicular, their upper segments are obtained 40 and 25.

In like manner, for any given question, the solution may be variously devised with the segment of the base for side, the segment of the perpendicular for upright, and the segment of the diagonal for hypotenuse.

39.[1] The height of the mountain, taken into a multiplier arbitrarily put, is the distance of the town. That result being reserved, and divided by the multiplier added to two, is the height of the leap. The journey is equal.[2]

The operation on the needle is next exhibited

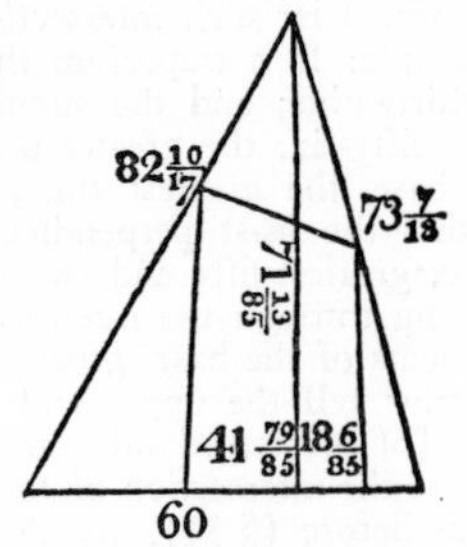

The segments of the base on either side of the perpendicular let fall from the top of the needle come out 41-79/85 and 18-6/85.† With either of these segments the mean perpendicular is found by proportion: if the least segment 9-3/5 give the least perpendicular 37-4/5, what does the segment 18-6/85 give? Answer: 71-13/85. It is the perpendicular let fall from the summit of the needle. In the same manner, with the greater segment, the same length of the perpendicular is deduced.

† The text relative to the method of finding these segments is irretrievably corrupt; and has been therefore omitted in the version.

Next, to find the sides of the needle: As the least perpendicular is to the side thirty-nine, so is the middle perpendicular to what? Statement: 37-4/5 | 39 | 71-13/85. Answer: 73-7/17. Or the side may be found from the segments: thus 9-3/5 |39| 18-6/85. Answer 73-7/17 as before. To find the greater side: As the greater perpendicular is to the side fifty-two, so is the perpendicular of the needle to what? 44-4/5 | 52 | 71-13/85 | . Answer: 82-10/17. Or proportion may be taken with the segments of the base: 26-2/5 | 52 | 41-70/85 | . Answer: 82-10/17, as before. See figure [as above].

[1] Within an oblong tetragon, to describe a figure such, that the sum of the side and one portion of the upright may be equal to the diagonal and remaining portion of the upright: so as the journeys may be equal.—CH. See *Lilavati,* § 154, and *Vija-ganita,* § 126; where the same problem is introduced: substituting, however, in the example, a tree, an ape and a pond, for a hill, a wizard and a town.

[2] Example: On the top of a certain hill live two ascetics. One of them, being a wizard, travels through the air. Springing from the summit of the mountain, he ascends to a certain elevation, and proceeds by an oblique descent, diagonally, to a neighbouring town. The other, walking down the hill, goes by land to the same town. Their journeys are equal. I desire to know the distance of the town from the hill, and how high the wizard rose.

This being proposed, the rule applies; and its interpretation is this: any elevation of the mountain is put; and is multiplied by an arbitrarily assumed multiplier: the product is the distance of the town from the mountain. Then divide this reserved quantity by the multiplier added to two, the quotient is the number of *yojanas* of the wizard's ascent. The sum of the hill's elevation and wizard's ascent is the upright; the distance of the town from the mountain is the side: the square-root of the sum of their squares is the diagonal (hypotenuse): it is the oblique interval between the town and the summit of the rise.

41. In a circle the chord is the square-root of the diameter less the arrow taken into the arrow and multiplied by four.[1] The square of the chord divided by four times the arrow, and added to the arrow, is the diameter.[2]

Thus, let the height of the mountain be twelve. This, multiplied by an arbitrarily assumed multiplier four, 12 by 4, makes 48. It is the distance of the town from the hill. This divided by the multiplier added to two, 48 by 6, gives 8. It is the ascent. Here the upright is 20: its square is 400. The side is 48; the square of which is 2304. The sum of these squares is 2704; and its square-root 52. The semirectangle is thus found. Here also

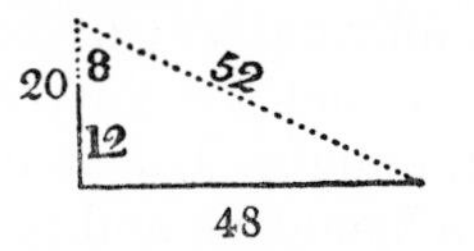

the sum of the side and lower portion of the upright is 60, the journey of one of the ascetics: and the upper portion added to the hypotenuse is that of the other, likewise 60.

[1] Example: Within a circle, the diameter of which is ten, in the place where the arrow is two, what is the chord?

Diameter 10: less the arrow 2; remains 8. This multiplied by the arrow makes 16; which multiplied by 4, gives 64: the square-root of which is 8. See figure

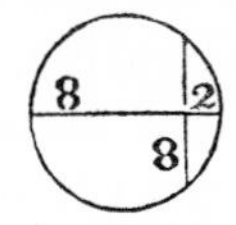

The principle of the rule for finding the square of the chord (in the construction of tabular sines) is here to be applied. But the square is in this place multiplied by four, because the entire chord is required. CH.

[2] Example: Chord 8. Its square 64, divided by four times the arrow 2, viz. 8; gives the quotient 8: to which adding the arrow, the sum is 10.

Example 2d: A bambu, eighteen cubits high, was broken by the wind. Its tip touched the ground at six cubits from the root. Tell the length of the segments of the bambu.

Statement: Length of the bambu 18. It is the diameter less the least arrow.* The ground from the root, to the point where the tip fell, is 6: it is the semichord. Its square is 36. This is equal to the diameter less the arrow multiplied by the arrow. Dividing it by the diameter less the arrow, viz. 18, the quotient is 2. It is the arrow. Adding this to the diameter less the arrow, the sum is the diameter, 20. Half of this, 10, is the semidiameter. It is the upper portion of the bambu and is the hypotenuse. Subtracted from eighteen, it leaves the upright, or lower portion of the bambu, 8. The side is the interval between the root and tip, 6. The point of fracture of the bambu is the centre of the circle. See figure

* What is termed by us "diameter less the arrow," is by ARYA-BHATTA denominated the greater arrow. For he says, 'In a circle the product of the arrows is equal to the square of the semichord of both arcs.' CH.

CHAPTER XVIII.

SECTION II.

*ALGORITHM.**

31. Rule for addition of affirmative and negative quantities and cipher: § 19. The sum of two affirmative quantities is affirmative; of two negative is negative; of an affirmative and a negative is their difference; or, if they be equal, nought. The sum of cipher and negative is negative; of affirmative and nought is positive; of two ciphers is cipher.

32—33. Rule for subtraction: § 20—21. The less is to be taken from the greater, positive from positive; negative from negative. When the greater, however, is subtracted from the less, the difference is reversed. Negative, taken from cipher, becomes positive; and affirmative, becomes negative. Negative, less cipher, is negative; positive, is positive; cipher, nought. When affirmative is to be subtracted from negative, and negative from affirmative, they must be thrown together.

34. Rule for multiplication: §22. The product of a negative quantity and an affirmative is negative; of two negative, is positive; of two affirmative, is affirmative. The product of cipher and negative, or of cipher and affirmative, is nought; of two ciphers, is cipher.

35—36. Rule for division: § 23—24. Positive, divided by positive, or negative by negative, is affirmative. Cipher, divided by cipher, is nought. Positive, divided by negative, is negative. Negative, divided by affirmative, is negative. Positive, or negative, divided by cipher, is a fraction with that for denominator:[1] or cipher divided by negative or affirmative.[2]

[36 Concluded.] Rule for involution and evolution:

---

* *Shat-trinsat-paricarman.* Thirty-six operations or modes of process. See Arithm. § 1. *Vijgan.* § 3.

[1] *Tach-ch'heda,* having that for denominator: having, in this instance, cipher for denominator, to a finite quantity for numerator. See *Vij.-gan.* § 16.

[2] Is in like manner expressed by a fraction having a finite denominator to a cipher for numerator.

§24. The square of negative or affirmative is positive; of cipher, is cipher. The root of a square is such as was that from which it was [raised].[3]

78. Rule: To find a quantity such, that, being severally multiplied by two multipliers, and having unity added in each instance, both sums may afford square roots: §46. The sum of the multiplier, being multiplied by eight, and divided by the square of their difference, is the quantity [sought]. The two multipliers, tripled and added to the opposite, and divided by the difference, are the roots.[1]

79. Question 33. The residue of seconds of the moon, severally multiplied by seventeen, and by thirteen, and having one added, [becomes in both instances] a square. Solving [this problem] within a year [the proficient is] a mathematician.

Here the multipliers are 17 and 13. Their sum 30: multiplied by eight, 240. Difference of the multipliers 4: its square 16. Quotient of the division, 15: it is the number [sought]; and it is the residue of the seconds of the moon.

To find the roots: multipliers 17, 13; multiplied by three, 51, 39: added to the reciprocals, 56, 64. Divided by the difference of the multipliers 4, the roots come out 14, 16.

80. Rule: §47. A square, with another square added and subtracted, being multiplied by the quotient of the sum of that sum and difference divided by the square of half their difference, produces numbers, of which both the sum and difference are squares; as also the product with one added to it.[2]

---

[3] The root is to be taken either negative or affirmative, as best answers for the further operations. COM.

[1] The proposed multipliers are to be added together: and the sum, being multiplied by eight, and divided by the square of the difference of these multipliers, is the quantity [sought]. How are the roots found? The author proceeds to reply: multiplying the multipliers severally by three, add to the two products the opposite multiplier respectively. Then dividing by the difference of the multipliers, the quotients are the roots. COM.

[2] Some square of an arbitrary number is to be set down; and the square of another arbitrary number is to be added in one place and subtracted in another. The sum of these two quantities is divided by the square of half their difference: the quotient is their multiplier. Multiplied by it, they are the numbers sought: of which if the sum be taken, it is a square; if the difference, it also is square; if the product with unity added, this again is square. COM.

81. Question 34. The residue of minutes of the sun on Wednesday, having the residue of seconds on Thursday added and subtracted, yields in both instances an exact square; and so does the product with one added. A person solving [this problem] within a year is a mathematician.

Here let an assumed square be 16; with another square, as 4, added and subtracted, 20 and 12: sum of these 32. Divided by the square of half the difference of these quantities, namely 16, the quotient is their multiplier, 2. Multiplied by it, the two quantities come out 40, 24. The first is residue of minutes of the sun, 40. Hence, as before, the number of [elapsed] days is deduced, 3385. The second is residue of seconds of the sun, 24: whence the number of days, 27. Adding five times the divisor, 5480, the number of [elapsed] days on Thursday comes out 5509. So, by virtue of suppositions, manifold answers may be obtained.

82. Rule: To find a quantity, such that having two given numbers added, or else subtracted, the results may be exact squares: § 48. The difference of the numbers, by addition or subtraction of which the quantity becomes a square, is divided by an arbitrary number and has it added or subtracted: the square of half the result, having the greater number added or subtracted, is the quantity which answers in the case of addition or subtraction.[1]

83. Question 35. Making the residue of minutes of the sun on a Wednesday, with the addition of twelve and of sixty-three, and with the subtraction of sixty and of eight,

---

[1] Of the two quantities, the addition of which makes the quantity in question an exact square, or the subtraction of which does so, the difference is in every case to be taken. This step is common to both methods. Dividing the difference then by an arbitrary number; the quotient must have added to it the same arbitrary number; if addition were given by the question: but, if subtraction were so, the same quotient must have the arbitrary number subtracted. Then the quantity resulting in either case is to be halved; and the half, to be squared. [From which subtracting the greater number, the remainder is the quantity which answers*] if the condition were addition: but, if it were subtraction, the square of the moiety appertaining to the case being added to the greater number, the sum is the quantity sought. COM.

* The original is deficient: but may be thus supplied from comparison of the text, and of the example as wrought.

an exact square; [the proficient solving the problem] within a year is a mathematician.

Two questions are here proposed. The numbers, which are to be added to the quantity, are separated, 12, 63. Their difference, 51; divided by an arbitrary number, as 3, gives 17; with the same added, since addition is in question, the sum is 20: its moiety, 10; the square of which is 100. The greater of the two additive quantities is 63. Subtracting this, the result is the quantity sought, 37. With either twelve or sixty-three added, it is an exact square.

In the example of subtraction; the two numbers which are to be subtracted to make a square, are 60, 8. Their difference, divided by an arbitrary number, namely two, yields 26: less the arbitrary number, leaves 24: its moiety 12; the square of which is 144. Here the greater of the two subtractive quantities is 60. This added to the square is 204. It is the quantity, which lessened by sixty, affords a square root; or by eight. It is the residue of minutes of the sun. Hence, as before, the number of [elapsed] days on Wednesday, is to be deduced.

In like manner, by virtue of suppositions, manifold answers may be obtained.

84. Rule: §49. The sum of the numbers, the addition and subtraction of which makes the quantity a square, being divided by an arbitrarily assumed number, has that assumed number taken from the quotient: the square of half the remainder, with the subtractive number added to it, is the quantity [sought].[1]

85. Question 36. Making the residue of seconds of the sun on Wednesday, with ninety-three added, or with sixty-seven subtracted, an exact square, [a proficient

[1] If a pair of quantities equal or unequal be given such, that a quantity, which lessened by the first, is an exact square, is also a square when increased by the second; then the two proposed quantities are to be added together; and their sum is to be divided by some arbitrary number. From the quotient subtracting the same arbitrary number, the half of the remainder is taken: and the square of that moiety, added to the number the subtraction of which renders the quantity in question a square, is in every case the quantity sought. COM.

solving this problem] within a year [is] a mathematician.

Here the subtractive number is 67; the additive number, 93: their sum, 160: divided by an assumed number 4, makes 40: less the assumed number, leaves 36; the half of which is 18: its square, 324: added to the subtractive quantity 67, the quantity is found 391. It is the residue of seconds of the sun.

GEORG CANTOR

(1845—1918)

Georg Ferdinand Ludwig Philipp Cantor, whose theory of transfinite numbers and whose contributions to the theory of sets was to usher in a new epoch in the development of mathematics, was born in St. Petersburg (Leningrad), Russia, in 1845. His father, Georg Waldemar Cantor had, as a youth, emigrated from Copenhagen, Denmark, to St. Petersburg, where he had become a successful merchant. His mother, Maria Bohm Cantor, came of a family well known in the fields of music and art. In 1856, the father contracted a pulmonary illness and, in search of a less inclement climate, the family moved to Germany. At about this time, young Georg's mathematical talents became evident but the boy's desire to devote himself to mathematics ran counter to his father's wish that he study engineering. The tensions generated by this opposition of aims were relieved at last when the elder Cantor recognized the depth and sincerity of his son's choice of a career. Just before entering upon his university training, Georg received permission to pursue his mathematical studies and he replied to his father in a highly emotional letter. The letter contained more than words of thanks. It painted a picture in broad strokes of a devoted son and a conscientious personality, modest and at the same time hopeful and very ardently desirous of proving himself worthy.

Cantor studied at Zurich, Berlin and Gottingen, where he was greatly influenced by Kummer, by Kronecker and especially by Weierstrass. In 1867, he received his degree at Berlin, and as his father, who had died in 1863, had left him well provided for, he was ready to embark on what he undoubtedly believed was to be a tranquil life-work in the calm and peaceful atmosphere of university halls. It was his destiny, however, to be led through his quiet and erudite researches to a field of mathematics so new and so strange to his contemporaries that its immediate effect was completely disturbing. Instead of sedate honors, his innovations brought him misunderstanding, disappointment, controversy, discouragement and illness. The post Cantor wanted most, an appointment at the University of Berlin, was never to be his. He taught for a time at a girls' school. He was examined for and received a license to teach children. In 1669, he was appointed Privat-dozent at the University of Halle, and this assignment was the beginning of a teaching career at Halle which was to last for more than forty years.

The basic concepts of Cantor's theory of transfinite numbers began to be clear to him as early as 1871. In 1874, he published his first paper on the theory of sets. In 1883, his famous *Grundlagen einer allgemeinen Mannigfaltigkeitslehre* appeared, in which he distinguished between the "improper" and "proper" mathematical infinite, developing the theory of the latter, the transfinite numbers. A violent storm of protest against this work was led by Kronecker and Poincare. Their criticisms effectively discouraged many mathematicians from even attempting to understand Cantor's novel concepts. However, the support given him by Dedekind, Mittag-Leffler and others, though it was less noisy and aggressive, was the more understanding and the more fruitful. In the early twentieth century, academic honors were awarded to Cantor in Italy, England and Denmark as well as in Germany. However, academic honors and recognition could not stem the nervous breakdown which first beset him in 1884 and recurred from time to time to the end of his life. Cantor died in the psychiatric clinic at Halle in 1918.

A new generation of mathematicians, turning their attention to subtle points which Cantor had not settled, have given themselves to the study and development of his theories. Now widely accepted, Cantor's novel concepts lie firmly imbedded in the bases of mathematical analysis.

•

CONTRIBUTIONS TO THE FOUNDING OF THE THEORY OF TRANSFINITE NUMBERS

Translated by Philip E. B. Jourdain

(First Article)

§1

The Conception of Power or Cardinal Number

By an "aggregate" (*Menge*) we are to understand any collection into a whole (*Zusammenfassung zu einem Ganzem*) M of definite and separate objects *m* of our intuition or our thought. These objects are called the "elements" of M.

In signs we express this thus:

(1) $$M = \{m\}.$$

We denote the uniting of many aggregates M, N, P,

. . ., which have no common elements, into a single aggregate by

(2) $$(M, N, P, \ldots).$$

The elements of this aggregate are, therefore, the elements of M, of N, of P, . . ., taken together.

We will call by the name "part" or "partial aggregate" of an aggregate M any other aggregate M_1 whose elements are also elements of M.

If M_2 is a part of M_1 and M_1 is a part of M, then M_2 is a part of M.

Every aggregate M has a definite "power," which we will also call its "cardinal number."

We will call by the name "power" or "cardinal number" of M the general concept which, by means of our active faculty of thought, arises from the aggregate M when we make abstraction of the nature of its various elements *m* and of the order in which they are given.

[482] We denote the result of this double act of abstraction, the cardinal number or power of M, by

(3) $$\overline{\overline{M}}.$$

Since every single element *m*, if we abstract from its nature, becomes a "unit," the cardinal number $\overline{\overline{M}}$ is a definite aggregate compose of units, and this number has existence in our mind as an intellectual image or projection of the given aggregate M.

We say that two aggregates M and N are "equivalent," in signs

(4) $$M \sim N \quad \text{or} \quad N \sim M,$$

if it is possible to put them, by some law, in such a relation to one another that to every element of each one of them corresponds one and only one element of the other. To every part M_1 of M there corresponds, then, a definite equivalent part N_1 of N, and inversely.

If we have such a law of co-ordination of two equivalent aggregates, then, apart from the case when each of them consists only of one element, we can modify this law in many ways. We can, for instance, always take care that to a special element m_0 of M a special element

n_0 of N corresponds. For if, according to the original law, the elements m_0 and n_0 do not correspond to one another, but to the element m_0 of M the element n_1 of N corresponds, and to the element n_0 of N the element m_1 of M corresponds, we take the modified law according to which m_0 corresponds to n_0 and m_1 to n_1 and for the other elements the original law remains unaltered. By this means the end is attained.

Every aggregate is equivalent to itself:

(5) $$M \sim M.$$

If two aggregates are equivalent to a third, they are equivalent to one another; that is to say:

(6) from $M \sim P$ and $N \sim P$ follows $M \sim N$.

Of fundamental importance is the theorem that two aggregates M and N have the same cardinal number if, and only if, they are equivalent: thus,

(7) from $M \sim N$ we get $\overline{\overline{M}} = \overline{\overline{N}}$,

and

(8) from $\overline{\overline{M}} = \overline{\overline{N}}$ we get $M \sim N$.

Thus the equivalence of aggregates forms the necessary and sufficient condition for the equality of their cardinal numbers.

[483] In fact, according to the above definition of power, the cardinal number $\overline{\overline{M}}$ remains unaltered if in the place of each of one or many or even all elements m of M other things are substituted. If, now, $M \sim N$, there is a law of co-ordination by means of which M and N are uniquely and reciprocally referred to one another; and by it to the element m of M corresponds the element n of N. Then we can imagine, in the place of every element m of M, the corresponding element n of N substituted, and, in this way, M transforms into N without alteration of cardinal number. Consequently

$$\overline{\overline{M}}=\overline{\overline{N}}.$$

The converse of the theorem results from the remark that between the elements of M and the different units of its cardinal number M a reciprocally univocal (or biunivocal) relation of correspondence subsists. For, as we saw, $\overline{\overline{M}}$ grows, so to speak, out of M in such a way that from every element m of M a special unit of $\overline{\overline{M}}$ arises. Thus we can say that

$$(9) \qquad M \sim \overline{\overline{M}}.$$

In the same way $N \sim \overline{\overline{N}}$. If then $\overline{\overline{M}} = \overline{\overline{N}}$, we have, by (6), $M \sim N$.

We will mention the following theorem, which results immediately from the conception of equivalence. If M, N, P, . . . are aggregates which have no common elements, M′, N′, P′, . . . are also aggregates with the same property, and if

$$M \sim M', N \sim N', P \sim P', \ldots,$$

then we always have

$$(M, N, P, \ldots) \sim (M', N', P', \ldots).$$

§ 2

"Greater" and "Less" with Powers

If for two aggregates M and N with the cardinal numbers $\mathfrak{a} = \overline{\overline{M}}$ and $\mathfrak{b} = \overline{\overline{N}}$, both the conditions:

(*a*) There is no part of M which is equivalent to N,

(*b*) There is a part N_1 of N, such that $N_1 \sim M$,

are fulfilled, it is obvious that these conditions still hold if in them M and N are replaced by two equivalent aggregates M′ and N′. Thus they express a definite relation of the cardinal numbers a and b to one another.

[484] Further, the equivalence of M and N, and thus the equality of a and b, is excluded; for if we had $M \sim N$, we would have, because $N_1 \sim M$, the equivalence $N_1 \sim N$, and then, because $M \sim N$, there would exist a part M_1 of M such that $M_1 \sim M$, and therefore we should have $M_1 \sim N$; and this contradicts the condition (*a*).

Thirdly, the relation of a to b is such that it makes impossible the same relation of b to a; for if in (*a*) and (*b*) the parts played by M and N are interchanged, two conditions arise, contradictory to the former ones.

We express the relation of a to b characterized by (*a*) and (*b*) by saying: a is "less" than b or b is "greater" than a; in signs

(1) $\quad a<b \quad \text{or} \quad b>a.$

We can easily prove that,

(2) if $a<b$ and $b<c$, then we always have $a<c$.

Similarly, from the definition, it follows at once that, if P_1 is part of an aggregate P, from $a<\overline{\overline{P}}_1$ follows $a<\overline{\overline{P}}$ and from $\overline{\overline{P}}<b$ follows $\overline{\overline{P}}_1<b$.

We have seen that, of the three relations

$$a=b, \; a<b, \; b<a,$$

each one excludes the two others. On the other hand, the theorem that, with any two cardinal numbers a and b, one of those three relations must necessarily be realized, is by no means self-evident and can hardly be proved at this stage.

Not until later, when we shall have gained a survey over the ascending sequence of the transfinite cardinal numbers and an insight into their connexion, will result the truth of the theorem:

A. If a and b are any two cardinal numbers, then either $a=b$ or $a<b$ or $a>b$.

From this theorem the following theorems, of which, however, we will here make no use, can be very simply derived:

B. If two aggregates M and N are such that M is equivalent to a part N_1 of N and N to a part M_1 of M, then M and N are equivalent;

C. If M_1 is a part of an aggregate M, M_2 is a part of the aggregate M_1, and if the aggregates M and M_2 are equivalent, then M_1 is equivalent to both M and M_2;

D. If, with two aggregates M and N, N is equivalent neither to M nor to a part of M, there is a part N_1 of N that is equivalent to M;

E. If two aggregates M and N are not equivalent, and there is a part N_1 of N that is equivalent to M, then no part of M is equivalent to N.

[485] § 3

The Addition and Multiplication of Powers

The union of two aggregates M and N which have no

common elements was denoted in §1, (2), by (M, N). We call it the "union-aggregate (*Vereinigungsmenge*) of M and N."

If M′ and N′ are two other aggregates without common elements, and if M ∼ M′ and N ∼ N′, we saw that we have

$$(M, N) \sim (M', N').$$

Hence the cardinal number of (M, N) only depends upon the cardinal numbers $\overline{\overline{M}}=a$ and $\overline{\overline{N}}=b$.

This leads to the definition of the sum of a and b. We put

(1) $$a+b=\overline{\overline{(M, N)}}.$$

Since in the conception of power, we abstract from the order of the elements, we conclude at once that

(2) $$a+b=b+a;$$

and, for any three cardinal numbers a, b, c, we have

(3) $$a+(b+c)=(a+b)+c.$$

We now come to multiplication. Any element *m* of an aggregate M can be thought to be bound up with any element *n* of another aggregate N so as to form a new element (*m*, *n*); we denote by (M.N) the aggregate of all these bindings (*m*, *n*), and call it the "aggregate of bindings (*Verbindungsmenge*) of M and N." Thus

(4) $$(M.N) = \{(m, n)\}.$$

We see that the power of (M.N) only depends on the powers $\overline{\overline{M}}=a$ and $\overline{\overline{N}}=b$; for, if we replace the aggregates M and N by the aggregates

$$M' = \{m'\} \quad \text{and} \quad N' = \{n'\}$$

respectively equivalent to them, and consider *m*, *m′* and *n*, *n′* as corresponding elements, then the aggregate

$$(M' . N') = \{(m', n')\}$$

is brought into a reciprocal and univocal correspondence with (M.N) by regarding (*m*, *n*) and (*′m*, *n′*) as corresponding elements. Thus

(5) $$(M' . N') \sim (M . N).$$

We now define the product a.b by the equation

(6) $$a.b=\overline{\overline{(M.N)}}.$$

[486] An aggregate with the cardinal number a.b may

also be made up out of two aggregates M and N with the cardinal numbers a and b according to the following rule: We start from the aggregate N and replace in it every element n by an aggregate $M_n \sim M$; if, then, we collect the elements of all these aggregates M_n to a whole S, we see that

$$(7) \qquad S \sim (M . N),$$

and consequently

$$\overline{\overline{S}} = a . b.$$

For, if, with any given law of correspondence of the two equivalent aggregates M and M_n, we denote by m the element of M which corresponds to the element m_n of M_n, we have

$$(8) \qquad S = \{m_n\};$$

and thus the aggregates S and (M.N) can be referred reciprocally and univocally to one another by regarding m_n and (m, n) as corresponding elements.

From our definitions result readily the theorems:

$$(9) \qquad a . b = b . a,$$
$$(10) \qquad a .(b . c) = (a . b) . c,$$
$$(11) \qquad a(b+c) = ab+ac;$$

because:

$$(M . N) \sim (N . M),$$
$$(M . (N. P)) \sim ((M . N) . P),$$
$$(M . (N, P)) \sim ((M . N), (M . P)).$$

Addition and multiplication of powers are subject, therefore, to the commutative, associative, and distributive laws.

§4

The Exponentiation of Powers

By a "covering of the aggregate N with elements of the aggregate M," or, more simply, by a "covering of N with M," we understand a law by which with every element n of N a definite element of M is bound up, where one and the same element of M can come repeatedly into application. The element of M bound up with n is, in a way, a one-valued function of n, and may be denoted by $f(n)$; it is called a "covering function of n." The corresponding covering of N will be called $f(\mathrm{N})$.

[487] Two coverings $f_1(\mathrm{N})$ and $f_2(\mathrm{N})$ are said to be equal if, and only if, for all elements n of N the equation

$$(1) \qquad f_1(n)=f_2(n)$$

is fulfilled, so that if this equation does not subsist for even a single element $n=n_0$, $f_1(\mathrm{N})$ and $f_2(\mathrm{N})$ are characterized as different coverings of N. For example, if m_0 is a particular element of M, we may fix that, for all n's

$$f(n)=m_0;$$

this law constitutes a particular covering of N with M. Another kind of covering results if m_0 and m_1 are two different particular elements of M and n_0 a particular element of N, from fixing that

$$f(n_0)=m_0$$
$$f(n)=m_1,$$

for all n's which are different from n_0.

The totality of different coverings of N with M forms a definite aggregate with the elements $f(\mathrm{N})$; we call it the "covering-aggregate (*Belegungsmenge*) of N with M" and denote it by $(\mathrm{N} \mid \mathrm{M})$. Thus:

$$(2) \qquad (\mathrm{N} \mid \mathrm{M}) = \{f(\mathrm{N})\}.$$

If $\mathrm{M} \sim \mathrm{M}'$ and $\mathrm{N} \sim \mathrm{N}'$, we easily find that

$$(3) \qquad (\mathrm{N} \mid \mathrm{M}) \sim (\mathrm{N}' \mid \mathrm{M}').$$

Thus the cardinal number of $(\mathrm{N} \mid \mathrm{M})$ depends only on the cardinal numbers $\overline{\overline{\mathrm{M}}}=\mathfrak{a}$ and $\overline{\overline{\mathrm{N}}}=\mathfrak{b}$; it serves us for the definition of $\mathfrak{a}^{\mathfrak{b}}$:

$$(4) \qquad \mathfrak{a}^{\mathfrak{b}}=\overline{\overline{(\mathrm{N} \mid \mathrm{M})}}.$$

For any three aggregates, M, N, P, we easily prove the theorems:

$$(5) \qquad ((\mathrm{N} \mid \mathrm{M}) \,.\, (\mathrm{P} \mid \mathrm{M})) \sim ((\mathrm{N}, \mathrm{P}) \mid \mathrm{M}),$$
$$(6) \qquad ((\mathrm{P} \mid \mathrm{M}) \,.\, (\mathrm{P} \mid \mathrm{N})) \sim (\mathrm{P} \mid (\mathrm{M} \,.\, \mathrm{N})),$$
$$(7) \qquad (\mathrm{P} \mid (\mathrm{N} \mid \mathrm{M})) \sim ((\mathrm{P} \,.\, \mathrm{N}) \mid \mathrm{M}),$$

from which, if we put $\overline{\overline{\mathrm{P}}}=\mathfrak{c}$, we have, by (4) and by paying attention to § 3, the theorems for any three cardinal numbers, a, b, and c:

$$(8) \qquad \mathfrak{a}^{\mathfrak{b}} \cdot \mathfrak{a}^{\mathfrak{c}} = \mathfrak{a}^{\mathfrak{b}+\mathfrak{c}},$$

$$(9) \qquad \mathfrak{a}^{\mathfrak{c}} \cdot \mathfrak{b}^{\mathfrak{c}} = (\mathfrak{a} \cdot \mathfrak{b})^{\mathfrak{c}},$$

$$(10) \qquad (\mathfrak{a}^{\mathfrak{b}})^{\mathfrak{c}} = \mathfrak{a}^{\mathfrak{b} \cdot \mathfrak{c}}.$$

[488] We see how pregnant and far-reaching these simple formulae extended to powers are by the following example. If we denote the power of the linear continuum X (that is, the totality X of real numbers x such that $x \geqq$ and $\leqq 1$) by $\mathfrak{o}$, we easily see that it may be represented by, amongst others, the formula:

$$(11) \qquad \mathfrak{o} = 2^{\aleph_0},$$

where § 6 gives the meaning of $\aleph_0$. In fact, by (4), $2^{\aleph}$ is the power of all representations

$$(12) \qquad x = \frac{f(1)}{2} + \frac{f(2)}{2^2} + \ldots + \frac{f(\nu)}{2^\nu} + \ldots$$

(where $f(\nu) = 0$ or 1)

of the numbers x in the binary system. If we pay attention to the fact that every number x is only represented once, with the exception of the numbers $x = \frac{2\nu+1}{2^\mu} < 1$, which are represented twice over, we have, if we denote the "enumerable" totality of the latter by $\{s_\nu\}$,

$$2^{\aleph_0} = \overline{\overline{(\{s_\nu\}, X)}}.$$

If we take away from X any "enumerable" aggregate $\{t_\nu\}$ and denote the remainder by X_1, we have:

$$X = (\{t_\nu\}, X_1) = (\{t_{2\nu-1}\}, \{t_{2\nu}\}, X_1),$$

$$(\{s_\nu\}, X) = (\{s_\nu\}, \{t_\nu\}, X_1),$$

$$\{t_{2\nu-1}\} \sim \{s_\nu\}, \quad \{t_{2\nu}\} \sim \{t_\nu\}, \quad X_1 \sim X_1;$$

$$X \sim (\{s_\nu\}, X),$$

and thus (§ 1)

$$2^{\aleph_0} = \overline{\overline{X}} = \mathfrak{o}.$$

From (11) follows by squaring (by § 6, (6))

$$\mathfrak{o} \cdot \mathfrak{o} = 2^{\aleph_0} \cdot 2^{\aleph_0} = 2^{\aleph_0 + \aleph_0} = 2^{\aleph_0} = \mathfrak{o},$$

and hence, by continued multiplication by $\mathfrak{o}$,

$$(13) \qquad \mathfrak{o}^{\nu} = \mathfrak{o},$$

where ν is any finite cardinal number.

If we raise both sides of (11) to the power* $\aleph_0$ we get

$$\mathfrak{o}^{\aleph_0} = (2^{\aleph_0})^{\aleph_0} = 2^{\aleph_0 \cdot \aleph_0}.$$

But since, by § 6, (8), $\aleph_0 \cdot \aleph_0 = \aleph_0$, we have

$$(14) \qquad \mathfrak{o}^{\aleph_0} = \mathfrak{o}.$$

The formulae (13) and (14) mean that both the ν-dimensional and the $\aleph_0$-dimensional continuum have the power of the one-dimensional continuum. Thus the whole contents of my paper in Crelle's *Journal*, vol. lxxxiv, 1878,† are derived purely algebraically with these few strokes of the pen from the fundamental formulae of the calculation with cardinal numbers.

§ 6

The Smallest Transfinite Cardinal Number Aleph-Zero

Aggregates with finite cardinal numbers are called "finite aggregates," all others we will call "transfinite aggregates" and their cardinal numbers "transfinite cardinal numbers."

The first example of a transfinite aggregate is given by the totality of finite cardinal numbers ν; we call its cardinal number (§ 1) "Aleph-zero" and denote it by $\aleph_0$; thus we define

$$(1) \qquad \aleph_0 = \overline{\overline{\{\nu\}}}.$$

* [In English there is an ambiguity.]
† [See Section V of the Introduction.]

That $\aleph_0$ is a *transfinite* number, that is to say, is not equal to any finite number μ, follows from the simple fact that, if to the aggregate $\{\nu\}$ is added a new element e_0, the union-aggregate $(\{\nu\}, e_0)$ is equivalent to the original aggregate $\{\nu\}$. For we can think of this reciprocally univocal correspondence between them: to the element e_0 of the first corresponds the element 1 of the second, and to the element ν of the first corresponds the element $\nu + 1$ of the other. By § 3 we thus have

$$\aleph_0 + 1 = \aleph_0. \quad (2)$$

But we showed in § 5 that $\mu + 1$ is always different from μ, and therefore $\aleph_0$ is not equal to any finite number μ.

The number $\aleph_0$ is greater than any finite number μ:

$$\aleph_0 > \mu. \quad (3)$$

[493] This follows, if we pay attention to § 3, from the three facts that $\mu = \overline{\overline{(1, 2, 3, \ldots, \mu)}}$, that no part of the aggregate $(1, 2, 3, \ldots, \mu)$ is equivalent to the aggregate $\{\nu\}$, and that $(1, 2, 3, \ldots, \mu)$ is itself a part of $\{\nu\}$.

On the other hand, $\aleph_0$ is the least transfinite cardinal number. If a is any transfinite cardinal number different from $\aleph_0$, then

$$\aleph_0 < \mathfrak{a}. \quad (4)$$

This rests on the following theorems:

A. Every transfinite aggregate T has parts with the cardinal number $\aleph_0$.

Proof.—If, by any rule, we have taken away a finite number of elements $t_1, t_2, \ldots, t_{\nu-1}$, there always remains the possibility of taking away a further element t_ν. The aggregate $\{t_\nu\}$, where ν denotes any finite cardinal number, is a part of T with the cardinal number $\aleph_0$, because $\{t_\nu\} \sim \{\nu\}$ (§ 1).

B. If S is a transfinite aggregate with the cardinal number $\aleph_0$, and S_1 is any transfinite part of S, then $\overline{\overline{S_1}} = \aleph_0$.

From A and B the formula (4) results, if we have regard to § 2.

From (2) we conclude, by adding 1 to both sides,

$$\aleph_0 + 2 = \aleph_0 + 1 = \aleph_0,$$

and, by repeating this

$$(5) \qquad \aleph_0 + \nu = \aleph_0.$$

We have also

$$(6) \qquad \aleph_0 + \aleph_0 = \aleph_0.$$

The equation (6) can also be written

$$\aleph_0 \,.\, 2 = \aleph_0;$$

and, by adding $\aleph_0$ repeatedly to both sides, we find that

$$(7) \qquad \aleph_0 \,.\, \nu = \nu \,.\, \aleph_0 = \aleph_0.$$

We also have

$$(8) \qquad \aleph_0 \,.\, \aleph_0 = \aleph_0.$$

Proof.—By (6) of § 3, $\aleph_0 \,.\, \aleph_0$ is the cardinal number of the aggregate of bindings

$$\{(\mu, \nu)\}$$

where μ and ν are any finite cardinal numbers which are independent of one another. If also λ represents any finite cardinal number, so that $\{\lambda\}$, $\{\mu\}$, and $\{\nu\}$ are only different notations for the same aggregate of all finite numbers, we have to show that

$$\{(\mu, \nu)\} \sim \{\lambda\}.$$

Let us denote $\mu + \nu$ by p; then p takes all the numerical values 2, 3, 4, . . ., and there are in all $p - 1$ elements (μ, ν) for which $\mu + \nu = p$, namely:

$$(1, p-1),\ (2, p-2),\ \ldots,\ (p-1, 1).$$

In this sequence imagine first the element (1, 1), for which $p = 2$, put, then the two elements for which $p = 3$, then the three elements for which $p = 4$, and so on. Thus we get all the elements (μ, ν) in a simple series:

(1, 1); (1, 2), (2, 1); (1, 3),(2, 2), (3, 1); (1, 4), (2, 3), . . .,

and here, as we easily see, the element (μ, ν) comes at the λth place, where

$$(9) \qquad \lambda = \mu + \frac{(\mu + \nu - 1)(\mu + \nu - 2)}{2}.$$

The variable λ takes every numerical value 1, 2, 3, . . ., once. Consequently, by means of (9), a reciprocally univocal relation subsists between the aggregates $\{\nu\}$ and $\{(\mu, \nu)\}$.

[495] If both sides of the equation (8) are multiplied by $\aleph_0$, we get $\aleph_0^3 = \aleph_0^2 = \aleph_0$, and, by repeated multiplications by $\aleph_0$, we get the equation, valid for every finite cardinal number ν:

$$(10) \qquad \aleph_0^\nu = \aleph_0.$$

The theorems E and A of § 5 lead to this theorem on finite aggregates:

C. Every finite aggregate E is such that it is equivalent to none of its parts.

This theorem stands sharply opposed to the following one for transfinite aggregates:

D. Every transfinite aggregate T is such that it has parts T_1 which are equivalent to it.

Proof.—By theorem A of this paragraph there is a part $S = \{t_\nu\}$ of T with the cardinal number $\aleph_0$. Let $T = (S, U)$, so that U is composed of those elements of T which are different from the elements t_ν. Let us put $S_1 = \{t_{\nu+1}\}$, $T_1 = (S_1, U)$; then T_1 is a part of T, and, in fact, that part which arises out of T if we leave out the single element t_1. Since $S \sim S_1$, by theorem B of this paragraph, and $U \sim U$, we have, by § 1, $T \sim T_1$.

In these theorems C and D the essential difference between finite and transfinite aggregates, to which I referred in the year 1877, in volume lxxxiv [1878] of Crelle's *Journal*, p. 242, appears in the clearest way.

After we have introduced the least transfinite cardinal number $\aleph_0$ and derived its properties that lie the most readily to hand, the question arises as to the higher cardinal numbers and how they proceed from $\aleph_0$. We shall show that the transfinite cardinal numbers can be arranged according to their magnitude, and, in this order, form, like the finite numbers, a "well-ordered aggregate" in an extended sense of the words. Out of $\aleph_0$ proceeds, by a definite law, the next greater cardinal number $\aleph_1$, out of this by the same law the next greater $\aleph_2$, and so on. But even the unlimited sequence of cardinal numbers

$$\aleph_0, \aleph_1, \aleph_2, \ldots, \aleph_\nu, \ldots$$

does not exhaust the conception of transfinite cardinal number. We will prove the existence of a cardinal number which we denote by $\aleph_w$ and which shows itself to be the next greater to all the numbers $\aleph_\nu$; out of it proceeds in the same way as $\aleph_1$ out of $\aleph$ a next greater $\aleph_{w+1}$, and so on, without end.

[496] To every transfinite cardinal number a there is a next greater proceeding out of it according to a unitary law, and also to every unlimitedly ascending well-ordered aggregate of transfinite cardinal number, {a}, there is a next greater proceeding out of that aggregate in a unitary way.

For the rigorous foundation of this matter, discovered in 1882 and exposed in the pamphlet *Grundlagen einer allgemeinen Mannichfaltigkeitslehre* (Leipzig, 1883) and in volume xxi of the *Mathematische Annalen,* we make use of the so-called "ordinal types" . . .

ARTHUR CAYLEY

(1821—1895)

Arthur Cayley, a prolific writer in mathematics, through whose fertile imagination and genius, new and vital branches of modern mathematics were created, was born at Richmond, Surrey, England, on August 16, 1821. His family was of old origin, dating back to William the Conqueror. In 1829, his father, a merchant in the Russian trade, on retiring from business, returned to England and thus Cayley's early education was begun in England. Indications of his mathematical genius were so impressive that Cayley, who had been intended for a place in his father's former business, was sent instead to Cambridge. He was a distinguished student from the first. In 1842 he was chosen Senior Wrangler without the viva voce tests which were a customary part of the Tripos. Cayley was called to the Bar in 1848, but his chief interest continued to be in mathematics and he always reserved a substantial portion of his time for study and research in this field. In the fourteen years during which he practiced law, Cayley wrote between two hundred and three hundred mathematical papers. Many of his most famous memoirs belong to this period. These include memoirs on quantics, contributions to the theory of symmetric functions of the roots of an equation, calculations connected with planetary and lunar theories, reports on theoretical dynamics and his important work on matrices. Although he was the author of only one book, *A Treatise on Elliptic Functions,* Cayley published more than eight hundred papers which appeared in a steady stream throughout his life.

In 1863 Cayley was elected to the newly constituted Sadlerian Professorship of Pure Mathematics at Cambridge. He married Susan Moline that same year and settled in Cambridge to a life of serenity, devoting himself to mathematical research and the quiet round of activity in the University. Cayley was highly respected for his fair mindedness and the soundness of his judgment. He was frequently called upon by the University and the scientific societies for his opinion on legal matters. In 1881 he accepted an invitation to lecture at Johns Hopkins University where his friend Sylvester was professor of mathematics. Apart from this interlude, his tenure at Cambridge was uninterrupted until his retirement in 1892. His health failed gradually and he died on January 26, 1895.

Numerous honors were conferred upon Cayley at home and on the continent by universities and academies of science, in recognition of his many fundamental contributions to modern pure mathematics. Cayley belonged to the group of mathematicians who, working from a small number of fundamental concepts, developed modern algebraic and geometrical systems. Cayley is credited with the invention of an n-dimensional geometry.

He was the founder, with Sylvester, of the theory of invariants. The theory of matrices, extensively developed within the last hundred years, was originated by Cayley in his famous paper, *A Memoir on the Theory of Matrices,* published in the *Philosophical Transactions of the Royal Society of London* in 1858. Almost every branch of pure mathematics was enriched by his contributions.

A MEMOIR ON THE THEORY OF MATRICES.

[From the *Philosophical Transactions of the Royal Society of London,* vol. cxlviii. *for the year,* 1858, pp. 17—37. Received December 10, 1857,—Read January 14, 1858.]

The term matrix might be used in a more general sense, but in the present memoir I consider only square and rectangular matrices, and the term matrix used without qualification is to be understood as meaning a square matrix; in this restricted sense, a set of quantities arranged in the form of a square, e.g.

$$\left(\begin{array}{ccc} a, & b, & c \\ a', & b', & c' \\ a'', & b'', & c'' \end{array}\right|$$

is said to be a matrix. The notion of such a matrix arises naturally from an abbreviated notation for a set of linear equations, viz. the equations

$$X = ax + by + cz,$$
$$Y = a'x + b'y + c'z,$$
$$Z = a''x + b''y + c''z,$$

may be more simply represented by

$$(X, Y, Z) = \left(\begin{array}{ccc} a, & b, & c \\ a', & b', & c' \\ a'', & b'', & c'' \end{array}\right)(x, y, z),$$

and the consideration of such a system of equations leads to most of the fundamental notions in the theory of matrices. It will be seen that matrices (attending only to those of the same order) comport themselves as single quantities; they may be added, multiplied or compounded together, &c.: the law of the addition of matrices is precisely similar to that for the addition of ordinary algebraical quantities; as regards their multiplication (or composition), there is the peculiarity that matrices are not in general convertible; it is nevertheless possible to form the powers (positive or negative, integral or fractional) of a matrix, and thence to arrive at the notion of a rational and integral function, or generally of any algebraical function, of a matrix. I obtain the remarkable theorem that any matrix whatever satisfies an algebraical equation of its own order, the coefficient of the highest power being unity, and those of the other powers functions of the terms of the matrix, the last coefficient being in fact the determinant; the rule for the formation of this equation may be stated in the following condensed form, which will be intelligible after a perusal of the memoir, viz. the determinant, formed out of the matrix diminished by the matrix considered as a single quantity involving the matrix unity, will be equal to zero. The theorem shows that every rational and integral function (or indeed every rational function) of a matrix may be considered as a rational and integral function, the degree of which is at most equal to that of the matrix, less unity; it even shows that in a sense, the same is true with respect to any algebraical function whatever of a matrix. One of the applications of the theorem is the finding of the general expression of the matrices which are convertible with a given matrix. The theory of rectangular matrices appears much less important than that of square matrices, and I have not entered into it further than by showing how some of the notions applicable to these may be extended to rectangular matrices.

1. For conciseness, the matrices written down at full length will in general be of the order 3, but it is to be understood that the definitions, reasonings, and conclusions apply to matrices of any degree whatever. And when two or more matrices are spoken of in connexion with each other, it is always implied (unless the contrary is expressed) that the matrices are of the same order.

2. The notation

$$\begin{array}{l} (\; a\;, \quad b\;, \quad c \;\;)\!(x,\; y,\; z) \\ \left| \begin{array}{ccc} a', & b', & c' \\ a'', & b'', & c'' \end{array} \right| \end{array}$$

represents the set of linear functions

$$((a,\, b,\, c\,)\!(x,\, y,\, z),\;\; (a',\, b',\, c'\,)\!(x,\, y,\, z),\;\; (a'',\, b'',\, c''\,)\!(x,\, y,\, z)),$$

so that calling these (X, Y, Z), we have

$$(X,\; Y,\; Z) = \begin{array}{l} (\; a\;, \quad b\;, \quad c \;\;)\!(x,\; y,\; z) \\ \left| \begin{array}{ccc} a', & b', & c' \\ a'', & b'', & c'' \end{array} \right| \end{array}$$

and, as remarked above, this formula leads to most of the fundamental notions in the theory.

3. The quantities (X, Y, Z) will be identically zero, if all the terms of the matrix are zero, and we may say that

$$\begin{array}{l} (\; 0, \quad 0, \quad 0 \;) \\ \left| \begin{array}{ccc} 0, & 0, & 0 \\ 0, & 0, & 0 \end{array} \right| \end{array}$$

is the matrix zero.

Again, (X, Y, Z) will be identically equal to (x, y, z), if the matrix is

$$\begin{pmatrix} 1, & 0, & 0 \\ 0, & 1, & 0 \\ 0, & 0, & 1 \end{pmatrix}$$

and this is said to be the matrix unity. We may of course, when for distinctness it is required, say, the matrix zero, or (as the case may be) the matrix unity *of such an order*. The matrix zero may for the most part be represented simply by 0, and the matrix unity by 1.

4. The equations

$$(X,\ Y,\ Z) = \begin{pmatrix} a, & b, & c \\ a', & b', & c' \\ a'', & b'', & c'' \end{pmatrix}(x,\ y,\ z),\quad (X',\ Y',\ Z') = \begin{pmatrix} \alpha, & \beta, & \gamma \\ \alpha', & \beta', & \gamma' \\ \alpha'', & \beta'', & \gamma'' \end{pmatrix}(x,\ y,\ z)$$

give

$$(X+X',\ Y+Y',\ Z+Z') = \begin{pmatrix} a+\alpha, & b+\beta, & c+\gamma \\ a'+\alpha', & b'+\beta', & c'+\gamma' \\ a''+\alpha'', & b''+\beta'', & c''+\gamma'' \end{pmatrix}(x,\ y,\ z)$$

and this leads to

$$\begin{pmatrix} a+\alpha, & b+\beta, & c+\gamma \\ a'+\alpha', & b'+\beta', & c'+\gamma' \\ a''+\alpha'', & b''+\beta'', & c''+\gamma'' \end{pmatrix} = \begin{pmatrix} a, & b, & c \\ a', & b', & c' \\ a'', & b'', & c'' \end{pmatrix} + \begin{pmatrix} \alpha, & \beta, & \gamma \\ \alpha', & \beta', & \gamma' \\ \alpha'', & \beta'', & \gamma'' \end{pmatrix}$$

as a rule for the addition of matrices; that for their subtraction is of course similar to it.

5. A matrix is not altered by the addition or subtraction of the matrix zero, that is, we have $M \pm 0 = M$.

The equation $L = M$, which expresses that the matrices L, M are equal, may also be written in the form $L - M = 0$, i.e. the difference of two equal matrices is the matrix zero.

6. The equation $L = -M$, written in the form $L + M = 0$, expresses that the sum of the matrices L, M is equal to the matrix zero, the matrices so related are said to be *opposite* to each other; in other words, a matrix the

terms of which are equal but opposite in sign to the terms of a given matrix, is said to be opposite to the given matrix.

7. It is clear that we have $L + M = M + L$, that is, the operation of addition is commutative, and moreover that $(L + M) + N = L + (M + N) = L + M + N$, that is, the operation of addition is also associative.

8. The equation

$$(X, Y, Z) = \left(\begin{array}{ccc} a, & b, & c \\ a', & b', & c' \\ a'', & b'', & c'' \end{array}\right)(mx, my, mz).$$

written under the forms

$$(X, Y, Z) = m\left(\begin{array}{ccc} a, & b, & c \\ a', & b', & c' \\ a'', & b'', & c'' \end{array}\right)(x, y, z) = \left(\begin{array}{ccc} ma, & mb, & mc \\ ma', & mb', & mc' \\ ma'', & mb'', & mc'' \end{array}\right)(x, y, z)$$

gives

$$m\left(\begin{array}{ccc} a, & b, & c \\ a', & b', & c' \\ a'', & b'', & c'' \end{array}\right) = \left(\begin{array}{ccc} ma, & mb, & mc \\ ma', & mb', & mc' \\ ma'', & mb'', & mc'' \end{array}\right)$$

as the rule for the multiplication of a matrix by a single quantity. The multiplier m may be written either before or after the matrix, and the operation is therefore commutative. We have it is clear $m\,(L + M) = mL + mM$, or the operation is distributive.

9. The matrices L and mL may be said to be similar to each other; in particular, if $m = 1$, they are equal, and if $m = -1$, they are opposite.

10. We have, in particular,

$$m\left(\begin{array}{ccc} 1, & 0, & 0 \\ 0, & 1, & 0 \\ 0, & 0, & 1 \end{array}\right) = \left(\begin{array}{ccc} m, & 0, & 0 \\ 0, & m, & 0 \\ 0, & 0, & m \end{array}\right)$$

or replacing the matrix on the left-hand side by unity, we may write

$$m = \left(\begin{array}{ccc} m, & 0, & 0 \\ 0, & m, & 0 \\ 0, & 0, & m \end{array}\right);$$

the matrix on the right-hand side is said to be the single quantity m considered as *involving the matrix unity.*

11. The equations

$$(X, Y, Z) = \left(\begin{array}{ccc} a, & b, & c \\ a', & b', & c' \\ a'', & b'', & c'' \end{array}\right) \between (x, y, z), \quad (x, y, z) = \left(\begin{array}{ccc} \alpha, & \beta, & \gamma \\ \alpha', & \beta', & \gamma' \\ \alpha'', & \beta'', & \gamma'' \end{array}\right) \between (\xi, \eta,$$

give

$$(X, Y, Z) = \left(\begin{array}{ccc} A, & B, & C \\ A', & B', & C' \\ A'', & B'', & C'' \end{array}\right) \between (\xi, \eta, \zeta) = \left(\begin{array}{ccc} a, & b, & c \\ a', & b', & c' \\ a'', & b'', & c'' \end{array}\right) \between \left(\begin{array}{ccc} \alpha, & \beta, & \gamma \\ \alpha', & \beta', & \gamma' \\ \alpha'', & \beta'', & \gamma'' \end{array}\right) \between (\xi, \eta, \zeta),$$

and thence, substituting for the matrix

$$\left(\begin{array}{ccc} A, & B, & C \\ A', & B', & C' \\ A'', & B'', & C'' \end{array}\right)$$

its value, we obtain

$$\left(\begin{array}{ccc} (a, b, c \between \alpha, \alpha', \alpha''), & (a, b, c \between \beta, \beta', \beta''), & (a, b, c \between \gamma, \gamma', \gamma'') \\ (a', b', c' \between \alpha, \alpha', \alpha''), & (a', b', c' \between \beta, \beta', \beta''), & (a', b', c' \between \gamma, \gamma', \gamma'') \\ (a'', b'', c'' \between \alpha, \alpha', \alpha''), & (a'', b'', c'' \between \beta, \beta', \beta''), & (a'', b'', c'' \between \gamma, \gamma', \gamma'') \end{array}\right) = \left(\begin{array}{c} a, b, c \\ a', b', c' \\ a'', b'', c'' \end{array}\right) \between \left(\begin{array}{c} \alpha, \beta, \\ \alpha', \beta', \\ \alpha'', \beta'', \end{array}\right.$$

as the rule for the multiplication or composition of two matrices. It is to be observed, that the operation is not a commutative one; the component matrices may be distinguished as the first or further component matrix, and the second or nearer component matrix, and the rule of composition is as follows, viz. any *line* of the compound matrix is obtained by combining the corresponding *line* of the first or further component matrix successively with the several *columns* of the second or nearer compound matrix.

[We may conveniently write

$$\begin{array}{c|ccc} & (\alpha,\ \alpha',\ \alpha''), & (\beta,\ \beta',\ \beta''), & (\gamma,\ \gamma',\ \gamma'') \\ \hline (a\ ,\ b\ ,\ c\ ) & ,, & ,, & ,, \\ (a',\ b',\ c') & ,, & ,, & ,, \\ (a'',\ b'',\ c'') & ,, & ,, & ,, \end{array}$$

to denote the left-hand side of the last preceding equation.]

12. A matrix compounded, either as first or second component matrix, with the matrix zero, gives the matrix zero. The case where any of the terms of the given matrix are infinite is of course excluded.

13. A matrix is not altered by its composition, either as first or second component matrix, with the matrix unity. It is compounded either as first or second component matrix, with the single quantity m considered as involving the matrix unity, by multiplication of all its terms by the quantity m: this is in fact the before-mentioned rule for the multiplication of a matrix by a single quantity, which rule is thus seen to be a particular case of that for the multiplication of two matrices.

14. We may in like manner multiply or compound together three or more matrices: the order of arrangement of the factors is of course material, and we may distinguish them as the first or furthest, second, third, &c., and last or nearest component matrices: any two consecutive factors may be compounded together and replaced by a single matrix, and so on until all the matrices are compounded together, the result being independent of the particular mode in which the composition is effected; that is, we have $L \,.\, MN = LM \,.\, N = LMN$, $LM \,.\, NP = L \,.\, MN \,.\, P$, &c., or the operation of multiplication, although, as already remarked, not commutative, is associative.

15. We thus arrive at the notion of a positive and integer power L^p of a matrix L, and it is to be observed that the different powers of the same matrix are convertible. It is clear also that p and q being positive in-

tegers, we have $L^p \,.\, L^q = L^{p+q}$, which is the theorem of indices for positive integer powers of a matrix.

16. The last-mentioned equation, $L^p \,.\, L^q = L^{p+q}$, assumed to be true for all values whatever of the indices p and q, leads to the notion of the powers of a matrix for any form whatever of the index. In particular, $L^p \,.\, L^0 = L^p$ or $L^0 = 1$, that is, the 0th power of a matrix is the matrix unity. And then putting $p = 1$, $q = -1$, or $p = -1$, $q =$ v, we have $L \,.\, L^{-1} = L^{-1} \,.\, L = 1$; that is, L^{-1}, or as it may be termed the inverse or reciprocal matrix, is a matrix which, compounded either as first or second component matrix with the original matrix, gives the matrix unity.

17. We may arrive at the notion of the inverse or reciprocal matrix, directly from the equation

$$(X,\ Y,\ Z) = \left(\begin{array}{|ccc|} a, & b, & c \\ a', & b', & c' \\ a'', & b'', & c'' \end{array}\right)\!\!)(\, x,\ y,\ z),$$

in fact this equation gives

$$(x,\ y,\ z) = \left(\begin{array}{|ccc|} A, & A', & A'' \\ B, & B', & B'' \\ C, & C', & C'' \end{array}\right)\!\!)(\, X,\ Y,\ Z) = \left(\left(\begin{array}{|ccc|} a, & b, & c \\ a', & b', & c' \\ a'', & b'', & c'' \end{array}\right)^{-1}\right)\!\!)(\, X,\ Y,\ Z),$$

and we have, for the determination of the coefficients of the inverse or reciprocal matrix, the equations

$$\left(\begin{array}{|ccc|} A, & A', & A'' \\ B, & B', & B'' \\ C, & C', & C'' \end{array}\right)\!\!)(\! \left(\begin{array}{|ccc|} a, & b, & c \\ a', & b', & c' \\ a'', & b'', & c'' \end{array}\right) = \left(\begin{array}{|ccc|} 1, & 0, & 0 \\ 0, & 1, & 0 \\ 0, & 0, & 1 \end{array}\right),$$

$$\left(\begin{array}{|ccc|} a, & b, & c \\ a', & b', & c' \\ a'', & b'', & c'' \end{array}\right)\!\!)(\! \left(\begin{array}{|ccc|} A, & A', & A'' \\ B, & B', & B'' \\ C, & C', & C'' \end{array}\right) = \left(\begin{array}{|ccc|} 1, & 0, & 0 \\ 0, & 1, & 0 \\ 0, & 0, & 1 \end{array}\right),$$

which are equivalent to each other, and either of them is by itself sufficient for the complete determination of the inverse or reciprocal matrix. It is well known that if ∇ denote the determinant, that is, if

$$\nabla = \begin{vmatrix} a, & b, & c \\ a', & b', & c' \\ a'', & b'', & c'' \end{vmatrix}$$

then the terms of the inverse or reciprocal matrix are given by the equations

$$A = \frac{1}{\nabla}\begin{vmatrix} 1, & 0, & 0 \\ 0, & b', & c' \\ 0, & b'', & c'' \end{vmatrix}, \qquad B = \frac{1}{\nabla}\begin{vmatrix} 0, & 1, & 0 \\ a', & 0, & c' \\ a'', & 0, & c'' \end{vmatrix}, \text{ \&c.}$$

or what is the same thing, the inverse or reciprocal matrix is given by the equation

$$\begin{pmatrix} a, & b, & c \\ a', & b', & c' \\ a'', & b'', & c'' \end{pmatrix}^{-1} = \frac{1}{\nabla}\begin{pmatrix} \partial_a\nabla, & \partial_{a'}\nabla, & \partial_{a''}\nabla \\ \partial_b\nabla, & \partial_{b'}\nabla, & \partial_{b''}\nabla \\ \partial_c\nabla, & \partial_{c'}\nabla, & \partial_{c''}\nabla \end{pmatrix}$$

where of course the differentiations must in every case be performed as if the terms *a, b*, &c. were all of them independent arbitrary quantities.

18. The formula shows, what is indeed clear *a priori*, that the notion of the inverse or reciprocal matrix fails altogether when the determinant vanishes: the matrix is in this case said to be indeterminate, and it must be understood that in the absence of express mention, the particular case in question is frequently excluded from consideration. It may be added that the matrix zero is indeterminate; and that the product of two matrices may be zero, without either of the factors being zero, if only the matrices are one or both of them indeterminate.

19. The notion of the inverse or reciprocal matrix once established, the other negative integer powers of the original matrix are positive integer powers of the inverse or reciprocal matrix, and the theory of such negative integer powers may be taken to be known. The

theory of the fractional powers of a matrix will be further discussed in the sequel.

20. The positive integer power L^m of the matrix L may of course be multiplied by any matrix of the same degree: such multiplier, however, is not in general convertible with L; and to preserve as far as possible the analogy with ordinary algebraical functions, we may restrict the attention to the case where the multiplier is a single quantity, and such convertibility consequently exists. We have in this manner a matrix cL^m, and by the addition of any number of such terms we obtain a rational and integral function of the matrix L.

21. The general theorem before referred to will be best understood by a complete development of a particular case. Imagine a matrix

$$M = \left(\begin{array}{|cc|} a, & b \\ c, & d \end{array}\right),$$

and form the determinant

$$\left|\begin{array}{cc} a - M, & b \\ c & , d - M \end{array}\right|,$$

the developed expression of this determinant is

$$M^2 - (a+d)\,M^1 + (ad - bc)\,M^0\,;$$

the values of M^2, M^1, M^0 are

$$\left(\begin{array}{|cc|} a^2 + bc\;, & b\,(a+d) \\ c\,(a+d), & d^2 + bc \end{array}\right),\quad \left(\begin{array}{|cc|} a, & b \\ c, & d \end{array}\right),\quad \left(\begin{array}{|cc|} 1, & 0 \\ 0, & 1 \end{array}\right),$$

and substituting these values the determinant becomes equal to the matrix zero, viz. we have

$$\left|\begin{array}{cc} a - M, & b \\ c & , d - M \end{array}\right| = \left(\begin{array}{|cc|} a^2 + bc\;, & b\,(a+d) \\ c\,(a+d), & d^2 + bc \end{array}\right) - (a+d)\left(\begin{array}{|cc|} a, & b \\ c, & d \end{array}\right) + (ad - bc)\left(\begin{array}{|c} 1, \\ 0, \end{array}\right.$$

$$= \left(\begin{array}{|cc|} (a^2 + bc) - (a+d)\,a + (ad - bc), & b\,(a+d) - (a+d)\,b \\ c\,(a+d) - (a+d)\,c & , d^2 + bc - (a+d)\,d + ad - bc \end{array}\right) = \left(\begin{array}{|c} 0, \\ 0, \end{array}\right.$$

that is

$$\left|\begin{array}{cc} a - M, & b \\ c & , d - M \end{array}\right| = 0,$$

where the matrix of the determinant is

$$\begin{pmatrix} a, & b \\ c, & d \end{pmatrix} - M \begin{pmatrix} 1, & 0 \\ 0, & 1 \end{pmatrix}$$

that is, it is the original matrix, diminished by the same matrix considered as a single quantity involving the matrix unity. And this is the general theorem, viz. the determinant, having for its matrix a given matrix less the same matrix considered as a single quantity involving the matrix unity, is equal to zero.

22. The following symbolical representation of the theorem is, I think, worth noticing: let the matrix M, considered as a single quantity, be represented by $\tilde{M}$, then writing 1 to denote the matrix unity, $\tilde{M} . 1$ will represent the matrix M, considered as a single quantity involving the matrix unity. Upon the like principles of notation, $\tilde{1} . M$ will represent, or may be considered as representing, simply the matrix M, and the theorem is

$$\text{Det.}\ (\tilde{1} . M - \tilde{M} . 1) = 0.$$

23. I have verified the theorem, in the next simplest case of a matrix of the order 3, viz. if M be such a matrix, suppose

$$M = \begin{pmatrix} a, & b, & c \\ d, & e, & f \\ g, & h, & i \end{pmatrix},$$

then the derived determinant vanishes, or we have

$$\begin{vmatrix} a-M, & b & , c \\ d & , e-M, & f \\ g & , h & , i-M \end{vmatrix} = 0,$$

or expanding

$$M^3 - (a+e+i)\,M^2 + (ei+ia+ae-fh-cg-bd)\,M$$
$$-\,(aei+bfg+cdh-afh-bdi-ceg) = 0;$$

but I have not thought it necessary to undertake the

labour of a formal proof of the theorem in the general case of a matrix of any degree.

24. If we attend only to the general form of the result, we see that any matrix whatever satisfies an algebraical equation of its own order, which is in many cases the material part of the theorem.

25. It follows at once that every rational and integral function, or indeed every rational function of a matrix, can be expressed as a rational and integral function of an order at most equal to that of the matrix, less unity. But it is important to consider how far or in what sense the like theorem is true with respect to irrational functions of a matrix. If we had only the equation satisfied by the matrix itself, such extension could not be made; but we have besides the equation of the same order satisfied by the irrational function of the matrix, and by means of these two equations, and the equation by which the irrational function of the matrix is determined, we may express the irrational function as a rational and integral function of the matrix, of an order equal at most to that of the matrix, less unity; such expression will however involve *the coefficients of the equation satisfied by the irrational function,* which are functions (in number equal to the order of the matrix) of the terms, assumed to be unknown, of the irrational function itself. The transformation is nevertheless an important one, as reducing the number of unknown quantities from n^2 (if n be the order of the matrix) down to n. To complete the solution, it is necessary to compare the value obtained as above, with the assumed value of the irrational function, which will lead to equations for the determination of the n unknown quantities.

36. Two matrices such as

$$\left(\begin{array}{cc} a, & b \\ c, & d \end{array}\right), \quad \left(\begin{array}{cc} a, & c \\ b, & d \end{array}\right),$$

are said to be formed one from the other by transposition, and this may be denoted by the symbol tr.; thus we may write

$$\begin{pmatrix} a, & c \\ b, & d \end{pmatrix} = \text{tr.} \begin{pmatrix} a, & b \\ c, & d \end{pmatrix}.$$

The effect of two successive transpositions is of course to reproduce the original matrix.

37. It is easy to see that if M be any matrix, then

$$(\text{tr. } M)^p = \text{tr. } (M^p),$$

and in particular,

$$(\text{tr. } M)^{-1} = \text{tr. } (M^{-1}).$$

38. If L, M be any two matrices,

$$\text{tr. } (LM) = \text{tr. } M . \text{ tr. } L,$$

and similarly for three or more matrices, L, M, N, &c.,

$$\text{tr. } (LMN) = \text{tr. } N . \text{ tr. } M . \text{ tr. } L, \text{ \&c.}$$

40. A matrix such as

$$\begin{pmatrix} a, & h, & g \\ h, & b, & f \\ g, & f, & c \end{pmatrix}$$

which is not altered by transposition, is said to be symmetrical.

41. A matrix such as

$$\begin{pmatrix} 0, & \nu, & -\mu \\ -\nu, & 0, & \lambda \\ \mu, & -\lambda, & 0 \end{pmatrix}$$

which by transposition is changed into its opposite, is said to be skew symmetrical.

42. It is easy to see that any matrix whatever may be expressed as the sum of a symmetrical matrix, and a skew symmetrical matrix; thus the form

$$\begin{pmatrix} a \ , & h+\nu, & g-\mu \\ h-\nu, & b \ , & f+\lambda \\ g+\mu, & f-\lambda, & c \end{pmatrix}$$

which may obviously represent any matrix whatever of

the order 3, is the sum of the two matrices last before mentioned.

43. The following formulae, although little more than examples of the composition of transposed matrices, may be noticed, viz.

$$\begin{pmatrix} a, & b \\ c, & d \end{pmatrix} \begin{pmatrix} a, & c \\ d, & b \end{pmatrix} = \begin{pmatrix} a^2+b^2, & ac+bd \\ ac+bd, & c^2+d^2 \end{pmatrix}$$

which shows that a matrix compounded with the transposed matrix gives rise to a symmetrical matrix. It does not however follow, nor is it the fact, that the matrix and transposed matrix are convertible. And also

$$\begin{pmatrix} a, & c \\ b, & d \end{pmatrix} \begin{pmatrix} a, & b \\ c, & d \end{pmatrix} \begin{pmatrix} a, & c \\ b, & d \end{pmatrix} = \begin{pmatrix} a^3+bcd+a(b^2+c^2), & c^3+abd+c(a^2+d^2) \\ b^3+acd+b(a^2+d^2), & d^3+abc+d(b^2+c^3) \end{pmatrix}$$

which is a remarkably symmetrical form. It is needless to proceed further, since it is clear that

$$\begin{pmatrix} a, & c \\ b, & d \end{pmatrix} \begin{pmatrix} a, & b \\ c, & d \end{pmatrix} \begin{pmatrix} a, & c \\ b, & d \end{pmatrix} \begin{pmatrix} a, & b \\ c, & d \end{pmatrix} = \left(\begin{pmatrix} a, & c \\ b, & d \end{pmatrix} \begin{pmatrix} a, & b \\ c, & d \end{pmatrix} \right)^2.$$

44. In all that precedes, the matrix of the order 2 has frequently been considered, but chiefly by way of illustration of the general theory; but it is worth while to develop more particularly the theory of such matrix. I call to mind the fundamental properties which have been obtained, viz. it was shown that the matrix

$$M = \begin{pmatrix} a, & b \\ c, & d \end{pmatrix},$$

satisfies the equation

$$M^2 - (a+d)M + ad - bc = 0,$$

and that the two matrices

$$\begin{pmatrix} a, & b \\ c, & d \end{pmatrix}, \quad \begin{pmatrix} a', & b' \\ c', & d' \end{pmatrix},$$

will be convertible if

$$a' - d' : b' : c' = a - d : b : c,$$

and that they will be skew convertible if

$$a + d = 0, \quad a' + d' = 0, \quad aa' + bc' + b'c + dd' = 0,$$

the first two of these equations being the conditions in order that the two matrices may be respectively periodic of the second order to a factor *pres.*

45. It may be noticed in passing, that if L, M are skew convertible matrices of the order 2, and if these matrices are also such that $L^2 = -1$, $M^2 = -1$, then putting $N = LM = -ML$, we obtain

$$L^2 = -1, \quad M^2 = -1, \quad N^2 = -1,$$
$$L = MN = -NM, \quad M = NL = -NL, \quad N = LM = -ML,$$

which is a system of relations precisely similar to that in the theory of quaternions.

CHANG TSANG

(d. 152 B.C.)

Chang Tsang was a distinguished soldier, statesman and scholar of ancient China, who flourished in the second century B.C. He was the author of the greatest mathematical work of antiquity, the *K'iu-ch'ang Suan-shu,* or *Kew-chang-swan-shuh* (Arithmetical Rules in Nine Sections), a restoration of a vastly older work of the same name. Chang began his career in the service of his country as a civil servant. Later, he fought brilliantly in the wars of the first Han emperor, Liu Pang, gaining great fame for his remarkable military exploits. During the ensuing peaceful years, Chang served again as an able and loyal official of the government, rising to the position of chief minister in 176 B.C., an office which he held until his death in 152 B.C. During his tenure as chief minister, Chang's fame increased through his distinguished service in the financial administration of the government. He was held in the highest esteem, however, for his learning in the fields of mathematics, astronomy and astrology. Chang is said to have been more than one hundred years old when he died.

Chang Tsang's mathematical work, the *K'iu-ch'ang Suan-shu,* was based on fragments of the earlier *K'iu-ch-ang* which had escaped the book burning ordered by Ch'in Shih Huang-ti (Ts'in Shih Huang-ti) in the latter part of the third century B.C. At that time, despite the knowledge that four hundred scholars had been buried alive for protesting against the book burning, and despite the continuing threat of dire penalties for failure to obey the order for the destruction of the proscribed books, there were individuals who secretly clung to and preserved some fragments of the ancient books. When the ban on these books was lifted by the second emperor of the Han, a diligent search was made for any works that may have survived the conflagration. Gradually, piece by piece, remnants of the old works came out of hiding, and in the light of these fragments, Chang Tsang reconstructed the ancient text. The rules of arithmetic contained in the old text were the mathematical rules taught by the Royal Tutor of the Chou dynasty at a time which was ancient even in Chang's day. Tradition places the origin of the early work in the third millennium B.C. The text of Chang Tsang's work, as we possess it, was compiled from items extracted from the encyclopaedia *Yung lo ta tien,* which was written in the fifteenth century. Edited and re-edited with extreme care, Chang Tsang's ancient mathematical classic has been published many times.

Chang Tsang's *K'iu-ch'ang Suan-shu* contains two hundred and forty-six problems classified into nine groups or sections. Each section is headed by a stanza giving an accurate and concisely stated general rule for solving the problems in the section. Among the topics involved in the problems, are proportion, the extraction of square and cube roots, partnership, plane mensuration, solid mensuration, and the right triangle. Frequent use is made of the rule of false position. The *K'iu-ch'ang Suan-shu* is the earliest mathematical work in which mention is made of negative numbers.

●

ARITHMETICAL RULES IN NINE SECTIONS

From *Chinese Researches*

by Alexander Wylie

From Chang Tsang *Kew-chang-swan-shuh*, "Arithmetical Rules of the Nine Sections."—Suppose there are a number of rabbits and pheasants confined in a cage, in all 35 heads and 94 feet: required the number of each? Ans. 23 pheasants, 12 rabbits.

A number of men bought a number of articles, neither of which are known; it is only known that if each man paid 8 cash, there would be a surplus of 3 cash; and if each man paid 7 cash, there would be a deficiency of 4 cash; required the respective numbers? Ans. 7 men, 53 articles.

. . .—Equations. This section is remarkable as containing an exposition of the use of the terms *ching*, "plus" and *foo*, "minus." In a series of 18 problems it gives the method of ascertaining the value of unknown quantities from certain conditions of combination, depending on the number of terms in the equation. The following is one of the simplest examples:—If 5 oxen and 2 sheep cost 10 taels of gold, and 2 oxen and 5 sheep cost 8 taels, what are the prices of the oxen and sheep respectively? Ans. Each ox 1 tael and 13 twenty-first parts; each sheep, 20 twenty-first parts of a tael.

In the following examples let a represent the base, b the altitude and c the hypothenuse.† 1. Given the difference of altitude and hypothenuse, and the base; to find the hypothenuse.

$$(a^2 - \overline{c-b}^2) \div 2\overline{c-b} \text{ Ex.}$$

There is a pool 10 feet square, with a reed growing in the centre, which rises a foot above the surface; when drawn towards the shore it reaches exactly to the brink of the pool; what is the depth of water? Ans. 12 feet. 2. Another method.

$$(a^2 + \overline{c-b}^2) \div 2\overline{c-b} \text{ Ex.}$$

On opening a two-leaved door, when the inner edge of the leaves are a foot from the door frame, there is an opening of 2 inches between the leaves; what is the width of the door? Ans. Each leaf 72½ inches. 3. Another method.

$$a^2 \div \overline{c-b} + c - b \text{ Ex.}$$

A chain suspended from an upright post has a length of 2 feet lying on the ground, and on being drawn out to its full length, so as just to touch the ground, the end is found to be 8 feet from the post; what is the length of the chain? Ans. 17 feet. . . . 5. Given the sum of the altitude and hypothenuse, and the base, to find the altitude.

$$\frac{b + c - a^2 \div \overline{b + c}}{2} \text{ Ex.}$$

There is a bamboo 10 feet high, the upper end of which being broken down on reaching the ground, the tip is just 3 feet from the stem; what is the height to the break? Ans. feet 4 and 11 twentieths.

What is the diameter of the largest circle that can be inscribed within a right-angled triangle, the two short sides of which are respectively 8 and 15. Ans. 6.

† Algebraic symbols are used here for the sake of brevity; it is not meant to imply that these are in the original.

From *The Development of Mathematics in China and Japan*

by Yoshio Mikami

"While a good runner walks 100 paces (or a), a bad runner goes 60 paces (or b). Now the latter goes 100 paces (or c) in advance of the former, who then pursues the other. In how many paces will the two come together?"

The answer is: $a \times c \div (a - b) = 250$ paces.

"A hare runs 100 paces (a) ahead of a dog. The latter pursues the former for 250 paces (b), when the two are 30 paces (c) apart. In how many further paces will the dog overtake the hare?"

The answer is: $cb \div (a - c) = 107 \frac{1}{7}$ paces.

"When buying things in companionship, if each gives 8 pieces, the surplus is 3; if each gives 7, the deficiency is 4. It is required to know the number of persons and the price of the things bought."

"When buying hens in companionship, if each gives 9, then 11 will be surplus; and if each gives 6, then 16 will be the deficiency. What will be the number of persons and the price of the hens?"

These problems are equivalent to the solution of the equation

$$y = ax - b \text{ and } y = a'x + b'.$$

The rule for solution is given as follows:

"Arrange the rates (a and a') forwarded by the partners in buying things. What surpasses (b), or is deficient (b'), be each arranged below these rates, and then cross multiply with them. Add the products together, and one gets the *shih*. The surplus and deficiency being added, make the *fa*. If fractional, first make both members equidenominated. Then the *shih* and the *fa* being divided by the difference of the rates, the quotients represent the price of the things bought and the number of persons, respectively."

According to this rule we first form the arrangement (1), from which by cross multiplication follows (2); and then by addition we have (3). Thus

$$(1)\quad \begin{matrix} a & a' \\ b & b', \end{matrix} \qquad (2)\quad \begin{matrix} ab' & a'b \\ b & b', \end{matrix} \qquad (3)\quad \begin{matrix} ab' + a'b \\ b + b'. \end{matrix}$$

And now we have to take price $= \dfrac{a'b + ab'}{a - a'}$, persons $= \dfrac{b + b'}{a - a'}$.

A second rule for the same case, which is this: "Add the surplus and deficiency, which makes the *shih.* The difference of the rates is the *fa.* The *shih,* divided by the *fa,* gives the number of persons. Multiply it by the rates and subtract the surplus or add the deficiency, when we get the price of the things."

"Of two water-weeds, the one grows 3 feet and the other one foot on the first day. The growth of the first becomes every day half of that of the preceding day, while the other grows twice as much as on the day before. In how many days will the two grow to equal heights?"

The answer is $2\frac{6}{13}$ days, when both grow to the same height of 4 feet and $8\frac{6}{13}$ decimal parts.

"There are three classes of corn, of which three bundles of the first class, two of the second and one of the third make 39 measures. Two of the first, three of the second and one of the third make 34 measures. And one of the first, two of the second and three of the third make 26 measures. How many measures of grain are contained in one bundle of each class?"

"Rule. Arrange the 3, 2 and 1 bundles of the three classes and the 39 measures of their grains at the right. Arrange other conditions at the middle and at the left."

The arrangement then takes the form shown in the accompanying diagram.

1	2	3	1st class
2	3	2	2nd ,,
3	1	1	3rd ,,
26	34	39	measures

The text proceeds "With the first class in the right column multiply currently the middle column, and directly leave out."

This means to subtract the terms in the right column as often as possible from the corresponding terms of the middle column thus multiplied.

1	0	3	1st class
2	5	2	2nd ,,
3	1	1	3rd ,,
26	24	39	measures

"Again multiply the next, and directly leave out."

0	0	3	1st class
4	5	2	2nd ,,
8	1	1	3rd ,,
39	24	39	measures

"Then with what remains of the second class in the middle column, directly leave out".

That is, the 2nd class from the left column is to be eliminated by applying the process as above described. The result is as shown here.

36	third class
99	measures

"Of the quantities that do not vanish, make the upper

the *fa,* the divisor, and the lower the *shih,* the dividend, i. e., the dividend for the third class.

"To find the second class, with the divisor multiply the measure in the middle column and leave out of it the dividend for the third class. The remainder, being divided by the number of bundles of the second class, gives the dividend for the 2nd class.

"To find the first class, also with the divisor multiply the measures in the right column and leave out from it the dividends for the third and second classes. The remainder being divided by the number of bundles of the first class, gives the dividend for the first class.

"Divide the dividends of the three classes by the divisor, and we get their respective measures."

The answer is given as 9¼, 4¼, and 2¾ measures of grain, respectively.

"There are three kinds of corn. The grains contained in two, three and four bundles, respectively, of these three classes of corn, are not sufficient to make a whole measure. If however we add to them one bundle of the 2nd, 3rd, and 1st classes, respectively, then the grains would become full one measure in each case. How many measures of grain does then each one bundle of the different classes contain?"

The answer is given as $\frac{9}{25}$, $\frac{7}{25}$, $\frac{4}{25}$ measures of the three classes.

The "Nine Sections" explains as to the treatment of the positive and negative quantities thus:

"When the equi-named (or equally signed) quantities are to be subtracted and the different named are to be added (in their absolute values), if a positive quantity has no opponent, make it negative; and if a negative has no opponent, make it positive. When the different named are to be subtracted and the same named are to be added (in absolute values), if a positive quantity has no opponent, make it positive; and if a negative has no opponent, make it negative."

GEOFFREY CHAUCER

(1340?—1400)

Geoffrey Chaucer, first great poet to write extensively in the English language, was also a superb master of English prose. His works, immediately popular, have been celebrated by all the generations of readers from his day to the present, for the dramatic clarity of the story they tell and for the breadth of human nature they portray. In addition to his acute observations on life and the vivid touches which make his characters spring alive Chaucer's poetry exhibits his magnificent power in poetical techniques and verse forms. Deeply learned in Latin, French and Italian literature, he introduced and embodied in his English compositions, many technical features of style and form which had hitherto been known only in the older languages. His prose writings include only one scientific work, *A Treatise on the Astrolabe* (1391). Intended primarily as a text book of instruction for his "litell son Lowys" whose attainments in Latin had not reached the proficiency required for current Latin expositions, the *Treatise* was written in "plain English words" superbly accommodated to the scientific needs of clarity, directness and accuracy. The prologue of the *Treatise,* moreover, is an excellent example of Chaucer's graceful and flowing prose style, and of his incomparable felicity in arousing in his readers the pleasant sense of personal, sole discovery of the author's meaning and matchless charm.

Geoffrey Chaucer was born in London about 1340, and most of his life was spent in that city. His career was twofold, divided between writing and his service to the royal family, the periods of his greatest activity in the latter capacity being the least productive of literary works. His first employment in the service of the royal family was probably obtained through the intercession of his father, John Chaucer, a vintner, who is known to have been in attendance on King Edward III as early as 1338. The household account books (1357) of Princess Elizabeth, wife of Lionel, Duke of Clarence (third son of Edward III), contain items relating to the purchase of clothes and other articles for Geoffrey Chaucer, serving in that household as a page. Toward the end of the first phase of the Hundred Years' War, Chaucer took part in the one military adventure of his life. Serving in the English army that invaded France in 1359, he was unfortunately taken prisoner, but was released some months later on the payment by King Edward of 16 Pds. toward his ransom. When his patron Lionel died in 1368, Chaucer entered the service of the next brother, John of Gaunt, Duke of Lancaster, and his fortunes thereafter were closely connected to those of the House of Lancaster. Chaucer's wife, Philippa, was the sister of Katherine, widow of Sir Hugh de Swynford. Katherine was governess to John of

Gaunt's children, later becoming his mistress, and in 1396, his wife. For more than twenty years Chaucer served in various civil and diplomatic offices. Diplomatic missions of the highest importance were entrusted to him and were the occasions of his journeys to the distant cities of Genoa, Pisa and Florence. Through his fees as the Comptroller of the Customs for the port of London, pensions and other income, Chaucer appears generally to have prospered, although there are records which indicate some periods of hardship.

Nothing more has been learned concerning Chaucer's son whose importunities at the age of ten led to the purchase of the portable Arabian astrolabe described in the *Treatise.* Chaucer states that his claim in this work is not for originality, but only for his selection of the most reliable authorities on the subject, for the accuracy of his instruction and for rendering it accessible in the English language. For the *Conclusions* of Part II, and for the methods of *Umbra Recta* for finding the height of an accessible object and of *Umbra Versa* for finding the height of an inaccessible object, Chaucer drew heavily upon the Latin manuscript of the *Compositio et Operatio Astrolabii,* by Messahalla, many copies of which are extant. The five parts which Chaucer projected for his work do not all seem to have been completed. The first two parts of Chaucer's *A Treatise on the Astrolabe* and the supplement soon became and still remain a standard work on the construction and the uses of the astrolabe.

•

TREATISE ON THE ASTROLABE.

From *Chaucer and Messahalla on the Astrolabe.*

by Robert T. Gunther

Bread and milk for children.

Little Lewis my son, I have perceived well by certain signs thy ability to learn sciences touching numbers and proportions; and I also consider thy earnest prayer specially to learn the Treatise of the Astrolabe. Then forasmuch as a philosopher saith, 'he wrappeth him in his friend, who condescendeth to the rightful prayers of his friend,' therefore I have given thee an astrolabe for our horizon, composed for the latitude of Oxford, upon which, by means of this little treatise, I purpose to teach thee a certain number of conclusions appertaining to the same instrument. I say certain conclusions, for three reasons.

The first is this: understand that all the conclusions that have been found, or possibly might be found in so noble an instrument as an astrolabe, are not known perfectly to any mortal man in this region, as I suppose.

Another reason is this: that truly, in any treatise of the astrolabe that I have seen, there are some conclusions that will not in all things perform their promises. And some of them are too hard for thy tender age of ten years to understand.

I will show thee this treatise, divided into five parts, under full easy rules and in plain English words; for Latin thou knowest as yet but little, my little son. But nevertheless, these true conclusions are sufficient for thee in English, as they are in Greek for noble Greek scholars, and in Arabic for Arabians, and in Hebrew for Jews, and in Latin for the Latin folk, for they have written them first out of other different languages, in their own tongue, that is to say, in Latin. And God knows, that in all these languages, and in many more, these conclusions have been sufficiently learned and taught, though by diverse rules, just as diverse paths lead diverse folk the right way to Rome. Now I will meekly pray every discreet person that readeth or heareth this little treatise, to have my rude inditing and my superfluity of words excused, for two causes. The first, that curious inditing and hard sentences are at once too difficult for a child to learn. And the second, that indeed it seems better to me to write a good sentence twice unto a child, rather than that he forget it once. And Lewis, if I show thee in my easy English as true conclusions touching this matter, and not only as true but as many and as subtle conclusions as are shown in Latin in any common treatise of the astrolabe, grant me the more thanks; and pray God save the King, who is lord of this language, and all that are true to him and obey him, each in his degree, the more and the less. But consider well, that I do not claim to have found this work by my own labour or ingenuity, I am but an unlearned compiler of the labour of old astrologians. I have translated it into English only for thy instruction; and with this sword shall I slay envy.

The first part of this treatise will rehearse the figures and the parts of thy astrolabe, so that thou mayest have the greater knowledge of thy own instrument.

The second part will teach thee to work the exact practice of the aforesaid conclusions, as far and as exactly as may be showed in so small and portable an instrument. For every astrologian well knows that the smallest fractions are not shown in so small an instrument, as they are in subtle tables calculated on purpose.

The third part will contain diverse tables of longitudes and latitudes of fixed stars for the astrolabe, and tables of declinations of the sun, and tables of longitudes of cities and of towns; both for the regulation of a clock and to find the meridian altitude, and many another notable conclusion, in accordance with the calendars of the reverend scholars, friar John Somer and friar Nicholas Lenne.[1]

The fourth part will be a theory to explain the moving of the celestial bodies with the causes. In particular it will show a table of the exact moving of the moon from hour to hour, every day and in every sign, after thy almanac; after which table there follows an explanation, sufficient to teach both the manner of the working of that same conclusion, and to know in our horizon the degree of the zodiac with which the moon rises in any latitude, and the arising of any planet in accordance with its latitude from the ecliptic line.

---

[1] Somer's Calendar was calculated for 140 years from 1367. Lynn's for 76 years from 1387.

The fifth part will be an introduction according to the rules of our doctors, in which thou mayest learn a great part of the general rules of theory in astrology. In this fifth part thou wilt find tables of equations of 'houses' for the latitude of Oxford; and table of dignities of planets, and other useful things, if God and his mother, the maid, will grant more than I promise.

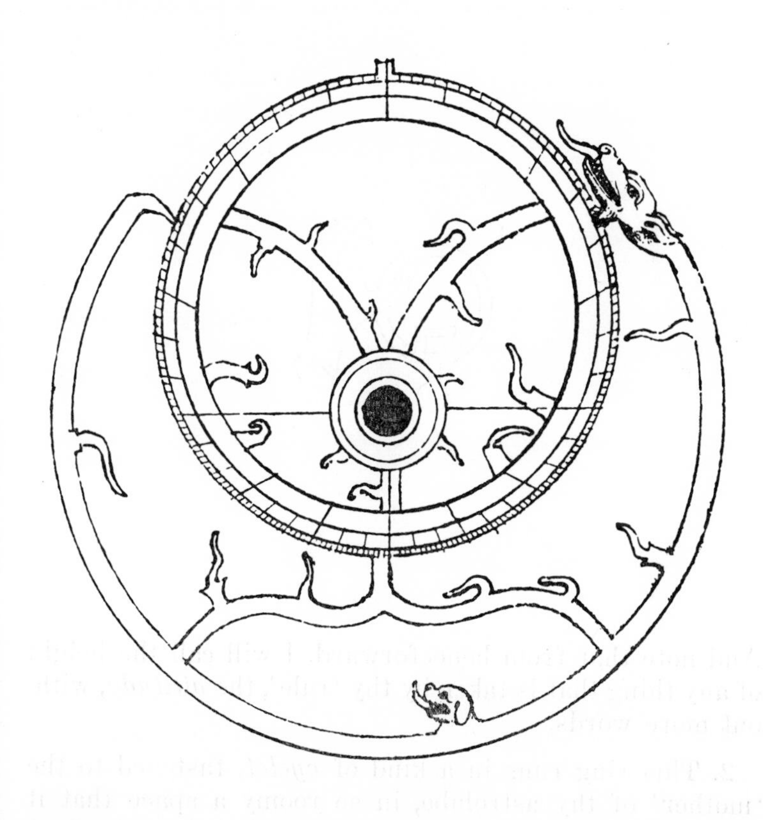

Thy zodiak of þin astrelabye ys schapen as a com
pas which þat conteneþ a large brede as after the
quantite of þin astrelabye. in ensample þat þe zodiak in
heuene ys ymagyned to ben a superfice conteynynge a

THE RETE OF CHAUCER'S ASTROBE. MS. Rawlinson D. 913.

PART I.

Here beginneth the Description of the Astrolabe.

1. Thy astrolabe hath a *ring* to put on the thumb of thy right hand when taking the height of things.

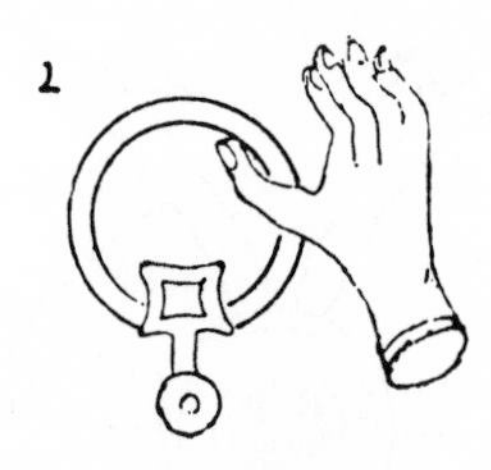

And note that from henceforward, I will call the height of any thing that is taken by thy 'rule', the *altitude,* without more words.

2. This ring runs in a kind of *eyelet,* fastened to the 'mother' of thy astrolabe, in so roomy a space that it does not prevent the instrument from hanging plumb.

3. The *mother* of thy astrolabe is a very thick plate, hollowed out with a large cavity, which receives within it the thin *plates,* marked for different climates, and thy *rete,* shaped like a net or the web of a spider. For more explanation, lo here the figure:

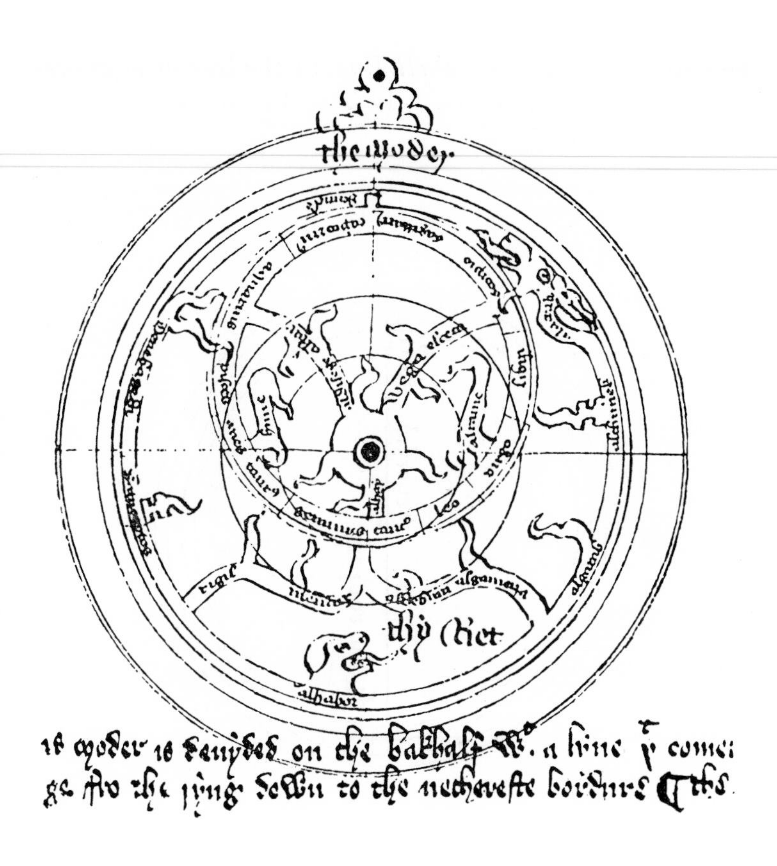

FIGURE SHOWING THE RETE LYING IN THE MOTHER.

Like the other text-figures it has been taken from Ms. Cambridge Rd. 3.53, *and is obviously from the same source as the Rete, with the head of the Dogstar, Alhabor, reversed.*

4. This mother is divided on the backhalf with a line, which descends from the ring down to the lowest border. This line, from the aforesaid ring to the centre of the large cavity in the middle, is called the *south line*, or the *line meridional*. And the remainder of this line down to

the border is called the *north line*, or the *line of midnight*. And for more explanation, lo here the figure:

4

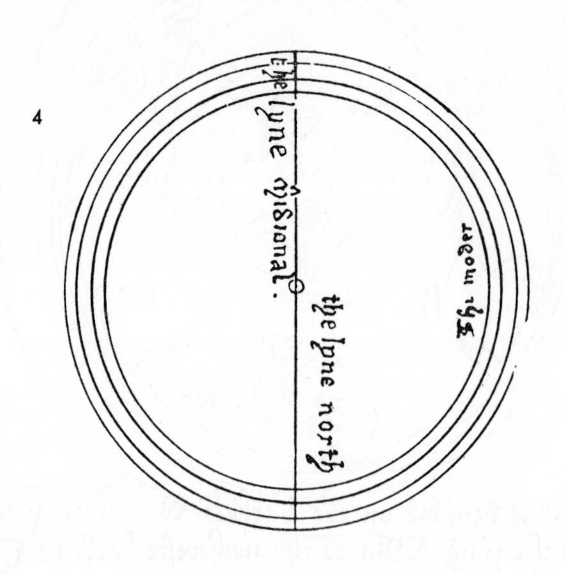

5. At right angles to the meridional line, there crosses it another line of the same length from east to west. This, from a little cross + in the border to the centre of the large cavity, is called the *east line*, or *line oriental*; and the remainder of the line from the aforesaid + to the border, is called the *west line*, or *line occidental*. Now hast thou here the 4 quarters of thy astrolabe, divided according to the 4 principal quarters of the compass, or quarters of the firmament. And for more explanation, lo here thy figure:

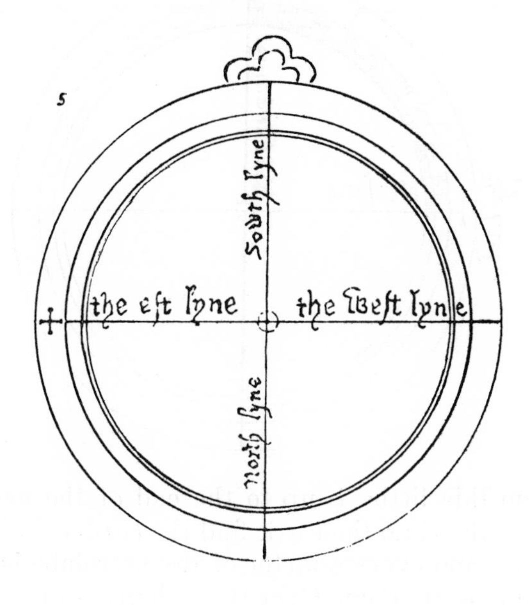

6. The east side of thy astrolabe is called the right side, and the west side is called the left side. Forget not this, little Lewis. Put the ring of thy astrolabe upon the thumb of thy right hand, and then its right side will be towards thy left side, and its left side will be towards thy right side; take this as a general rule, as well on the back as on the hollow side. Upon the end of the east line, as I first said, is marked a little +, which is always regarded as the beginning of the first degree in which the sun rises. And for more explanation, lo here the figure:

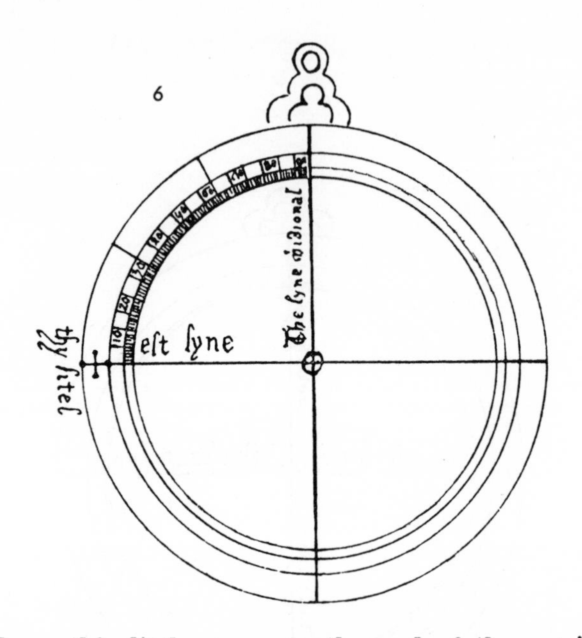

7. From this little + up to the end of the meridional line, under the ring, thou wilt find the *border divided into* 90 *degrees*; and every quarter of thy astrolabe is divided in the same proportion. Over these degrees are numbers, and the degrees are divided into fives as shown by long lines between. The space between the long lines containeth a mile-way.[1] And every degree of the border contains 4 minutes, that is to say, minutes of an hour. And for more explanation, lo here the figure:

[*The Figure is similar to the figure drawn above*].

8. Under the circle of these degrees are written the *names of the* 12 *Signs,* as Aries, Taurus, Gemini, Cancer, Leo, Virgo, Libra, Scorpio, Sagittarius, Capricornus, Aquarius, Pisces; and the numbers of the degrees of the Signs are written in Arabic numerals above, and with long divisions, from 5 to 5, divided from the time that the Sign entereth unto the last end. But understand well, that these degrees of Signs are each of them considered

[1] The time it takes to walk a mile.

to be of 60 minutes, and every minute of 60 seconds, and so forth into small fractions infinite, as saith Alkabucius,[1] and therefore, know well, that a degree of the border containeth 4 minutes, and a degree of a Sign containeth 60 minutes; remember this. And for more explanation, lo here thy figure:

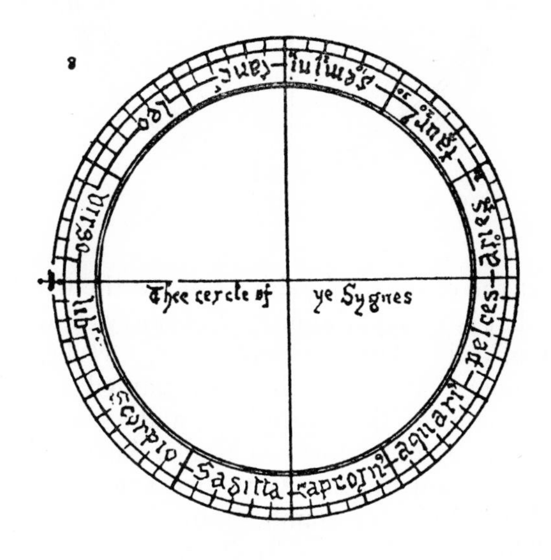

9. Next follows the *Circle of the Days,* in number 365 that are numbered as are the degrees, and divided also by long lines from 5 to 5; and the numbers under that circle are written in Arabic numerals. And for more explanation, lo here thy figure:

---

[1] Abdilazi Alchabitius, *Introductorium ad scientiam judicialem astronomiae,* printed 1473.

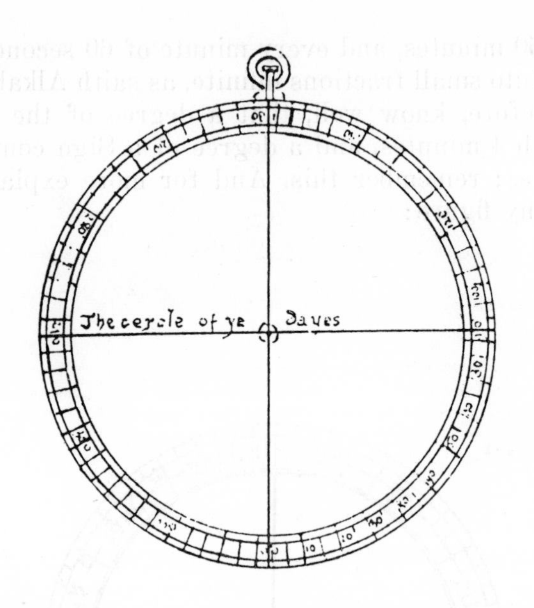

10. Next the circle of the days follows the *Circle of the Months*; that is to say, January, February, March, April, May, June, July, August, September, October, November, December. These months were named amongst the Arabians, some for their prophets, and some by statutes of lords, some by other lords of Rome. Also, as it pleased Julius Caesar and Caesar Augustus, some months were composed of different numbers of days, as July and August. Then hath January 31 days, February 28, March 31, April 30, May 31, June 30, July 31, August 31, September 30, October 31, November 30, December 31. Nevertheless, although Julius Caesar took 2 days out of February and put them in his month of July,[1] and Augustus Caesar called the month of August after his own name and ordained it of 31 days; yet trust well, that the sun never dwelleth on that account more or less in one sign than in another.

11. Then follow the names of the *Holydays* in the cal-

[1] This is not right. Julius Caesar added 2 days to January, August, and December, and 1 day to April, June, September, and November.

endar, and next them the letters of the a. b. c. on which they fall. And for more explanation, lo here thy figure:[2]

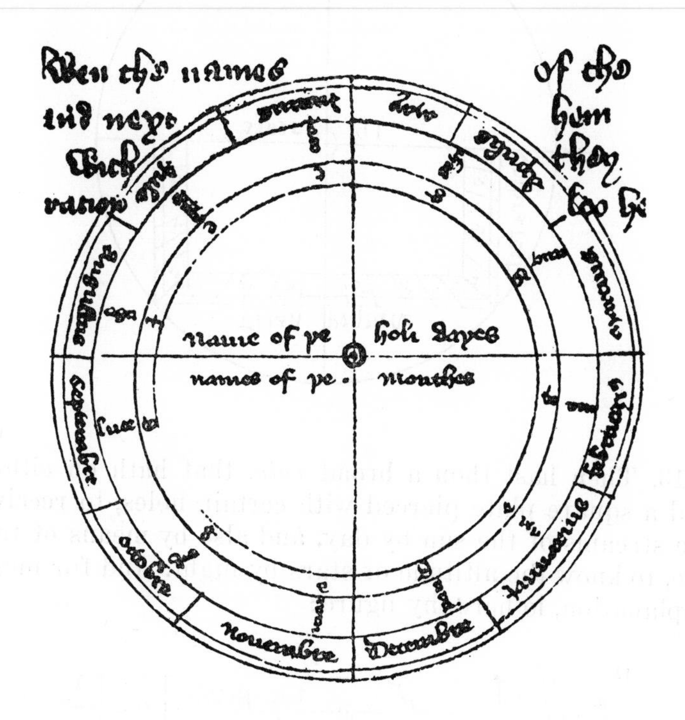

12. Next to the aforesaid circle of the a. b. c., and under the crossline is marked a *scale,* like 2 measuring-rules or else like ladders, that serveth by its 12 points and its divisions for full many a subtle conclusion. Of this aforesaid scale, the part from the cross-line to the right angle, is called *umbra versa,* and the nether part is called *umbra recta,* or else *umbra extensa.*[1] And for more explanation, lo here the figure:

[2] The Festivals marked in the figure are those of St. Paul (Jan. 25), Purification (Feb. 2), Annunciation (March 25), Invention of the Cross (May 3), St. John Baptist (June 24), St. James (July 25), St. Lawrence (Aug. 10)?, Nativity B.V.M. (Sept. 8), St. Luke (Oct. 18), All Souls (Nov. 2), Conception B.V.M. (Dec. 8). But the scribe has put them in the wrong months.

[1] The names are transposed in the original MS. and in the figure.

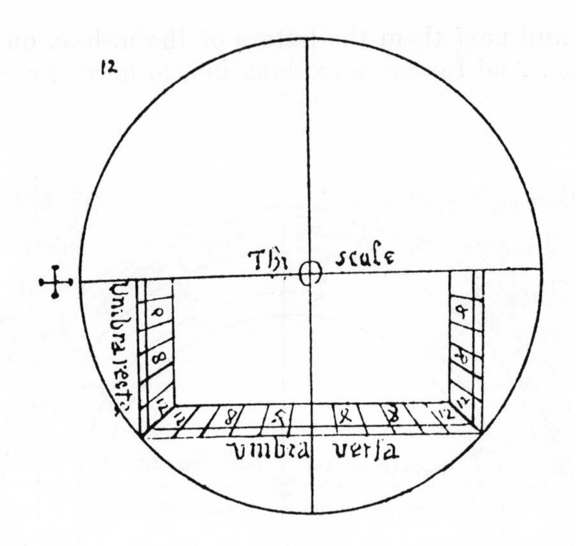

13. Then hast thou a broad *rule*, that hath on either end a square plate pierced with certain holes, to receive the streams of the sun by day, and also by means of thy eye, to know the altitude of stars by night. And for more explanation, lo here thy figure:

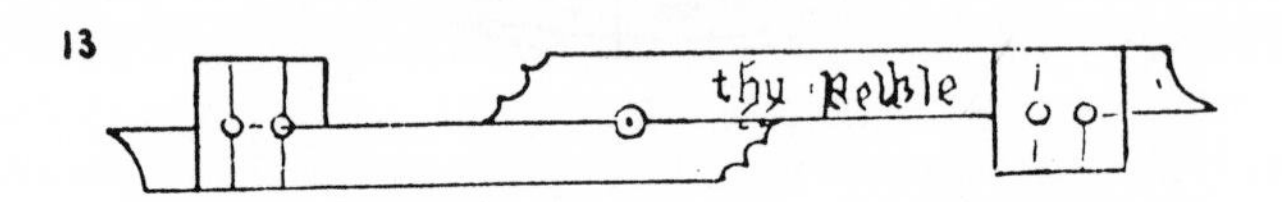

14. Then is there a large *pin* like an axle-tree, that goeth through the hole, and holdeth the tables of the climates and the rete in the cavity of the mother. Through this pin there goeth a little *wedge*, called the *horse*, which compresses all the parts in a heap; the pin which resembles an axle-tree, is imagined to be the pole arctic (north pole) in thy astrolabe. And for the more explanation, lo here thy figure:

15. The hollow side of thy astrolabe is also divided with a long cross into 4 *quarters* from east to west, from south to north, from right side to left side, as is the back-side. And for the more explanation, lo here thy figure:

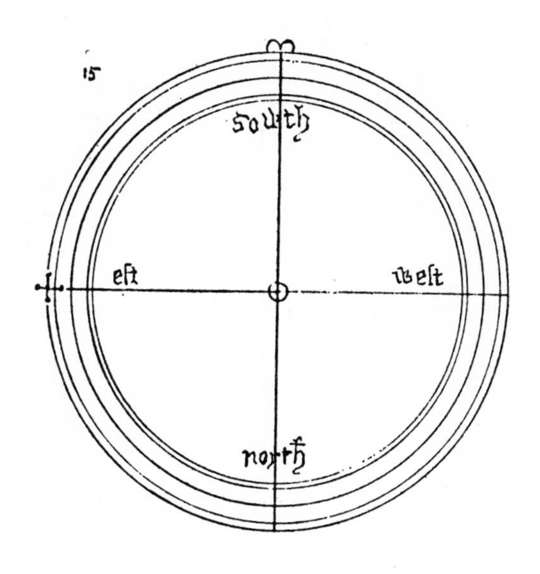

16. The border of the hollow-side is divided from the point of the east line to the point of the south line under the ring, into 90 *degrees*; and every quarter is divided by that same proportion. So too is the back-side divided, and that amounteth to 360 *degrees*. And understand well, that degrees of this border correspond with, and are concentric to, the degrees of the equinoctial, that is divided into the same number as is every other circle in the high heaven. This same border is also divided with 23 capital letters and a small cross + above the south line, so as to show the 24 *equal* hours of the clock; and, as I have said, 5 of these degrees make a mile-way, and 3 mile-ways make an hour. And every degree of this border contains 4 minutes of time, and every minute

contains 60 seconds. Now have I told thee twice, and for more explanation, lo here the figure:

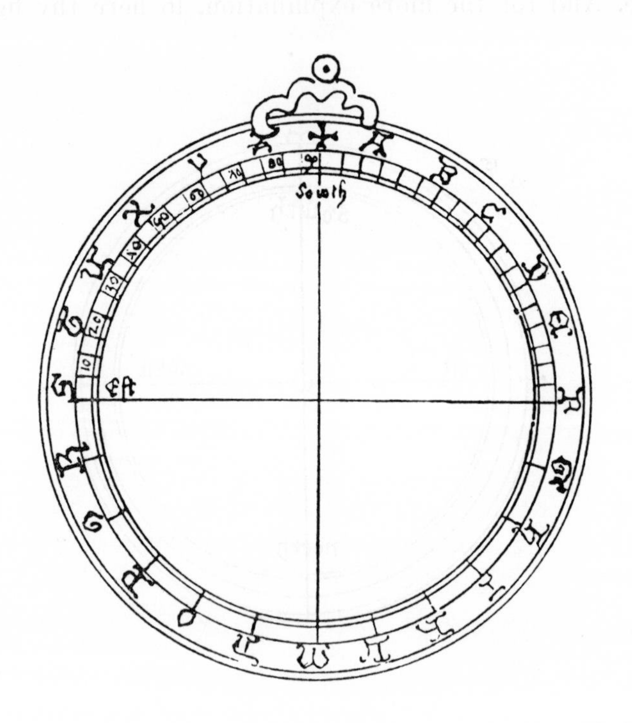

17. The *plate* under thy rete is marked with 3 principal circles; of which the least is called the *Circle of Cancer,* because that the head of Cancer, or the beginning of the Sign of Cancer in the rete, turneth evermore concentric upon this same circle. In this head of Cancer is the greatest declination northward of the sun. And therefore is it called the solstice of summer; which declination, according to Ptolemy is 23 degrees and 50 minutes, as well in Cancer as in Capricorn. This sign of Cancer is called the *tropic* of summer, from *tropos,* that is to say a turning, for then beginneth the sun to pass away from us; and for the more explanation, lo here the figure:

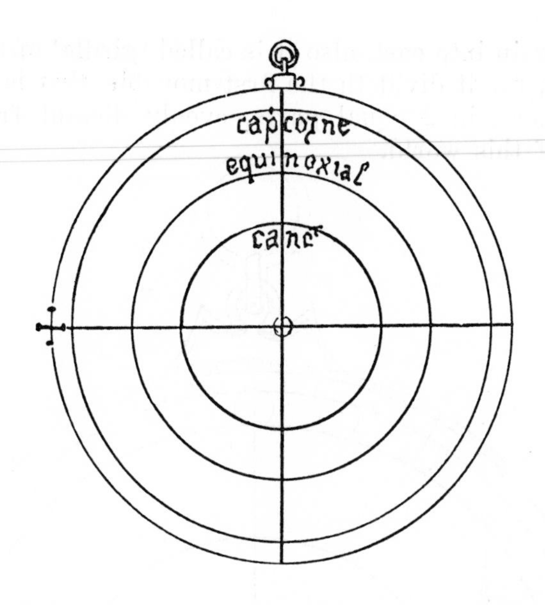

The middle circle in wideness, of these 3, is called the *Equinoctial Circle,* upon which turns evermore the heads of Aries and Libra. And understand well, that evermore this equinoctial circle turns exactly from very east to very west; as I have shown thee in the solid sphere. This same circle is called also the weigher, *equator,* of the day, for when the sun is in the heads of Aries and Libra, then are the days and the nights equal in length in all the world. And therefore are these two signs called the *equinoxes.* And all that moveth within the heads of these Aries and Libra, their moving is called northward, and all that moveth without these heads, their moving is called southward as from the equinoctial. Take heed of these latitudes north and south, and forget it not. By the equinoctial circle the 24 hours of the clock are considered; for [evermore] the arising of 15 degrees of the equinoctial maketh an equal hour of the clock. This equinoctial is called the girdle of the *first moving,* or else of the *angulus primi motus vel primi mobilis.* And note, that first moving is called 'moving' of the first movable of the 8th sphere, which motion is from east to west, and after again into east, also it is called 'girdle' of the first moving, for it divideth the first movable, that is to say, the sphere, in 2 equal parts, evenly distant from the poles of this world.

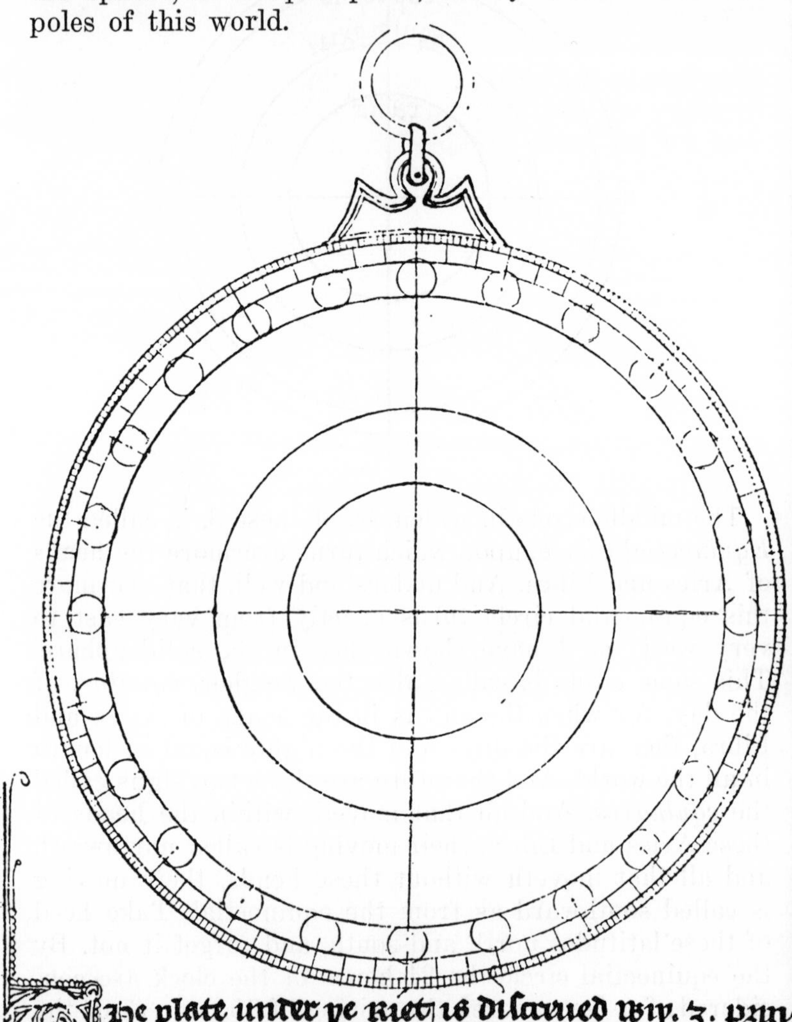

The plate under ye riet is discriued wiþ. 3. prin
cipal cercles. Of which leeste ys cleped ye cercle of
canc. by cause þat ye hed of canc turneþ eu'mo con
centrik upon ye same cercle. In þis hed of canc is

ALTERNATIVE FIGURE OF
THE MOTHER OF CHAUCER'S ASTROLABE.
MS. Rawlinson D. 913.

The widest of these 3 principal circles is called the *Circle of Capricorn,* because that the head of Capricorn turneth evermore concentric upon the same circle, in the head of Capricorn is the greatest declination southward of the sun, and therefore is it called the *solstice of winter.* This sign of Capricorn is also called the *tropic of winter* for then beginneth the sun to come again towards us. And for the more explanation, lo here thy figure:

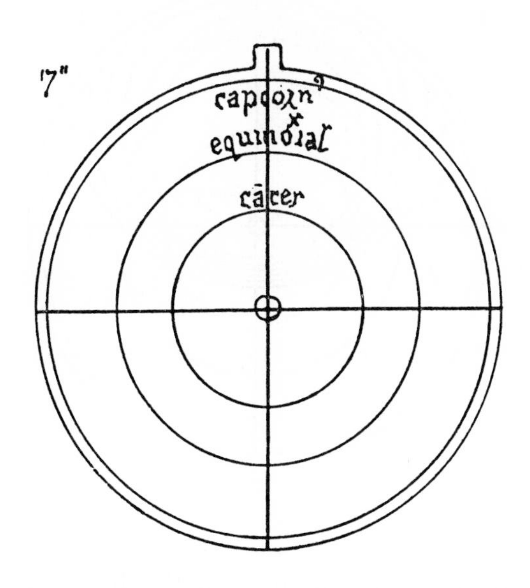

18. Upon this aforesaid plate are drawn certain circles [of altitude] that are called *Almicanteras,* some of which seem perfect circles, and some seem imperfect. The centre that standeth amidst the narrowest circle is called the *zenith;* and the lowest circle, or the first circle, is called the *horizon,* that is to say, the circle that divides the two hemispheres, i.e. the part of the heaven above the earth, and the part beneath. These almicanteras are

compounded by 2 and 2 [or are two degrees apart], but some other astrolabes have the almicanteras divided by one degree, others by two, and others by 3 degrees according to the size of the astrolabe. The aforesaid zenith is imagined to be the point exactly over the crown of thy head, and also the zenith is the exact pole of the horizon in every region. And for more explanation, lo here thy figure:

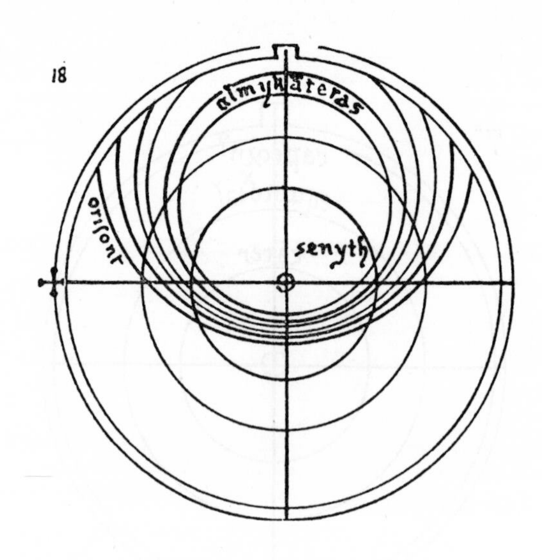

19. From this zenith, as it seemeth, there comes a kind of crooked lines like the claws of a spider, or else like the work of a woman's caul, crossing the almicanteras at right angles. These lines or divisions are called *azimuths*. They divide the horizon of thy astrolabe into 24 divisions. And serve to indicate the directions of the firmament, and to other conclusions, such as the position of the cenith[1] of the sun and of every star. And for more explanation, lo here thy figure:

[1] The cenith (*not* zenith) was the 'point of the horizon denoting the sun's place in azimuth' (Skeat) In the figure the 18 azimuth lines have been carelessly sketched: they should be symmetrical and 24 in number.

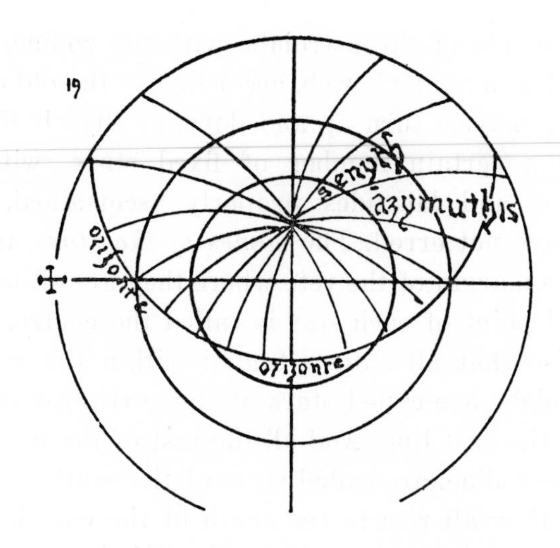

20. Next the azimuths, under the Circle of Cancer, there are 12 oblique divisions, much like to the shape of the azimuths; they show the spaces of the *hours of planets.* And for more explanation, lo here thy figure:

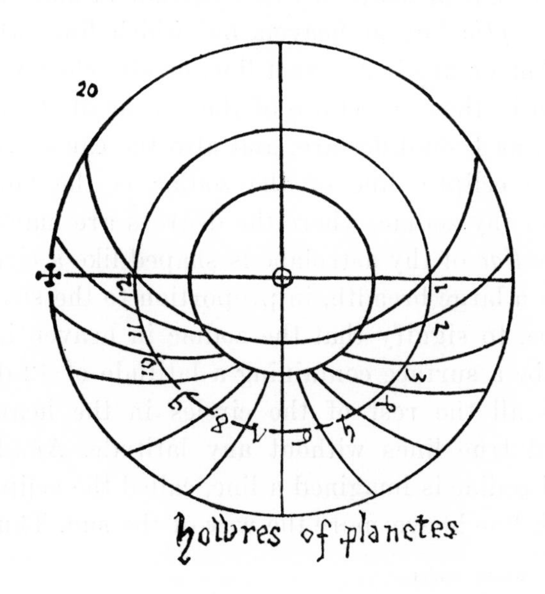

21. The *rete* of thy astrolabe with thy zodiac, shaped like a net or a spider's web, according to the old description, thou mayest turn up and down as thyself liketh. It contains a certain number of fixed stars, with their longitudes and latitudes properly ascertained, if the maker have not erred. The *names of the stars* are written in the margin of the rete where they are situate; and the small point of each star is called the centre. Understand also that all stars situated within the zodiac of thy astrolabe are called stars of the north, for they rise north of the east line. And all the rest of the fixed stars, out of the zodiac, are called stars of the south; but I say not that they all rise to the south of the east line; witness one, Aldebaran and Algomeisa. Understand generally this rule, that those stars that are called stars of the north rise sooner than the degree of their longitude; and all the stars of the south rise later than the degree of their longitude; that is to say, the fixed stars in thy astrolabe. The measure of this longitude of stars is taken in the *ecliptic line* of heaven, on[1] which line, when the sun and moon are in an exact line, or else closely bordering upon it, then an eclipse of the sun or of the moon is possible, as I shall declare, and also the cause why. But truly the ecliptic line of the zodiac is the outermost border of thy zodiac, where the degrees are marked.

The *zodiac* of thy astrolabe is shaped like a circle that contains a large breadth, in proportion to the size of thy astrolabe, to signify that the zodiac in heaven is imagined to be a surface containing a latitude of 12 degrees, whereas all the rest of the circles in the heaven are imagined true lines without any latitude. Amidst this celestial zodiac is imagined a line, called the ecliptic line, on which line is evermore the way of the sun. Thus there

[1] Chaucer wrote 'under.'

are 6 degrees of the zodiac on one side of the line, and 6 degrees on the other. In the rete of an astrolabe the zodiac band represents the 6 degrees of the zodiac on the northern side of the ecliptic line. The zodiac is divided into 12 principal divisions, dividing the 12 signs. And, for the accuracy of thy astrolabe, every small division in a sign is divided by two degrees and two; I mean degrees containing 60 minutes. And this aforesaid heavenly zodiac is called the circle of the signs, or the circle of the beasts, for 'zodia' in the Greek language means 'beasts' in the Latin tongue. And in the zodiac are the 12 *signs* that have names of beasts; either because when the sun enters into any of the signs, he taketh the property of such beasts; or else because the stars that are fixed there are disposed in signs of beasts, or shaped like beasts; or else, when the planets are under these signs, they act upon us by their influence, operations and effects like to the operations of beasts. And understand also, that when a hot planet comes into a hot sign, then its heat increaseth; and if a planet be cold, then its coldness diminisheth, because of the hot sign. And by this conclusion thou mayest take example in all the signs, be they moist or dry, movable or fixed; reckoning the quality of the planet as I first said.

And each of these 12 signs hath respect to a certain part of the body of a man and hath it in subjection; as Aries hath thy head, and Taurus thy neck and thy throat, Gemini thy armholes and thy arms, and so forth; as shall be shown more plainly in the 5th part of this treatise. This zodiac, which is part of the 8th sphere, cuts across the Equinoctial; and crosses it again in equal parts, of which one half declineth southward, and the other northward, as the *Treatise of the Sphere* plainly declareth. And for more explanation, lo here thy figure:

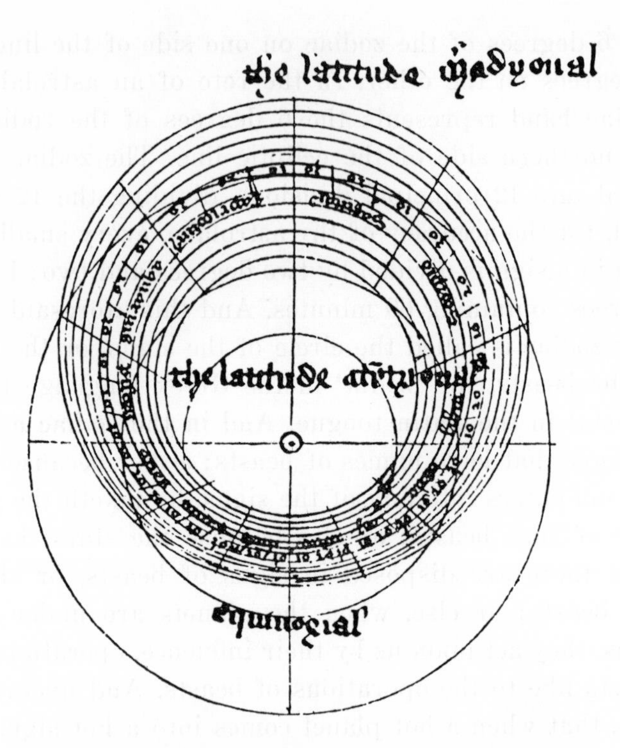

22. Then thou hast a *label*, that is shaped like a rule, save that it is straight and hath no plates with holes at the ends; but by the point of the aforesaid label, thou wilt calculate thy equations in the border of thy astrolabe, as by thy almury. And for more declaration, lo here thy figure:

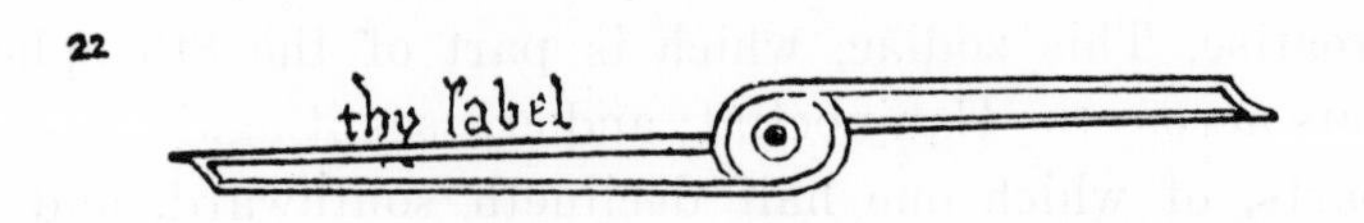

23. Thy *almury* is called the denticle of Capricorn or else the calculator. It is situate fixed in the head of Cap-

ricorn, and it serveth for many a necessary conclusion in equations of things, as shall be shown. And for the more declaration, lo here thy figure:

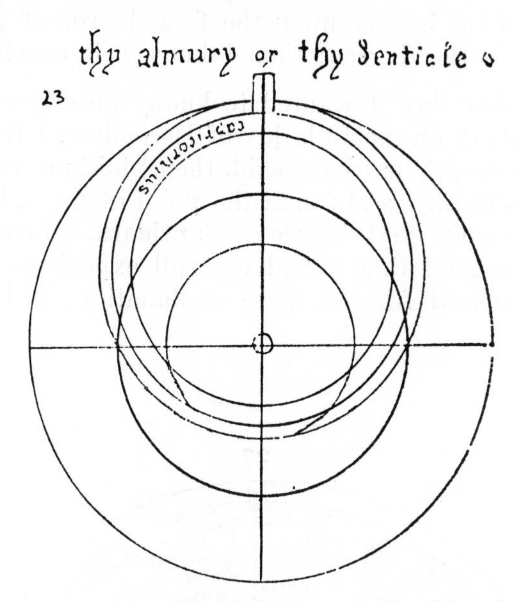

Her endith the Description of the Astrelabie.

PART II.

Her bygynnen the Conclusions of the Astrelabie.

1. To find the degree in which the sun is day by day, after her[1] course about.

Ascertain the day of thy month, and lay thy rule upon that day, then the true point of thy rule will sit in the border, on the degree of thy sun.

Example as thus: In the year of our Lord 1391, on the 12th day of March[2] at midday, I wished to know the

[1] The sun was of the feminine gender in Anglo-Saxon.

[2] Chaucer's dates are about 8 days behind ours, e.g. his March 12 is our March 21.

degree of the sun. I sought in the back-half of my astrolabe, and found the circle of the days, which I know by the names of the months written under the circle. Then I laid my rule over the said day, and found the point of my rule in the border upon the first degree of Aries, a little within the degree; thus I know this conclusion.

On another day, I wanted to know the degree of my sun at midday on the 13th day of December; I found the day of the month as I have said, then I laid my rule upon the said 13th day, and found the point of my rule in the border upon the first degree of Capricorn, a little within the degree. And then I had the full experience of this conclusion; and for the more explanation, lo here thy figure:

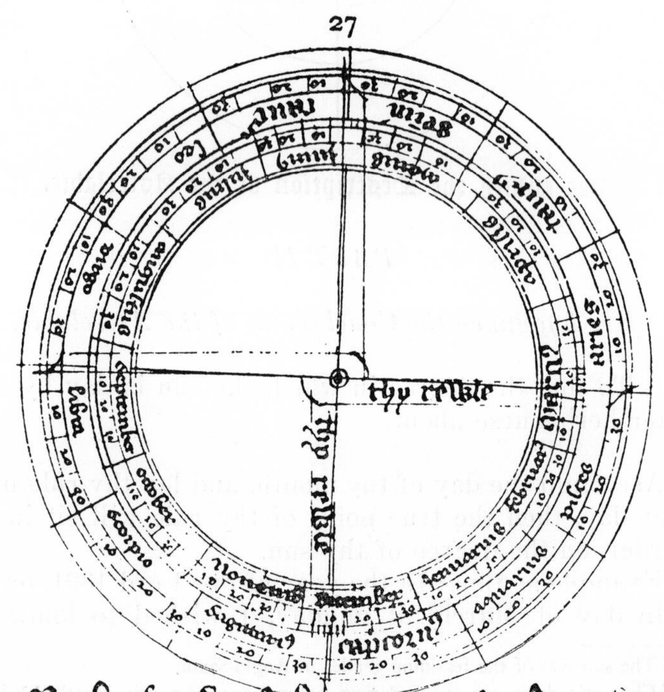

2. To find the altitude of the sun, or of other celestial bodies.

Put the ring of thy astrolabe upon thy right thumb and turn thy left side against the light of the sun. And move thy rule up and down till the streams of the sun shine through both holes of thy rule. Then look to see how many degrees thy rule is raised from the little cross upon thy east line, and take there the altitude of thy sun. In this same wise thou mayest find by night the altitude of the moon, or of bright stars. This chapter is so general, that there needeth no more explanation; but forget it not. And for the more explanation, lo here thy figure:

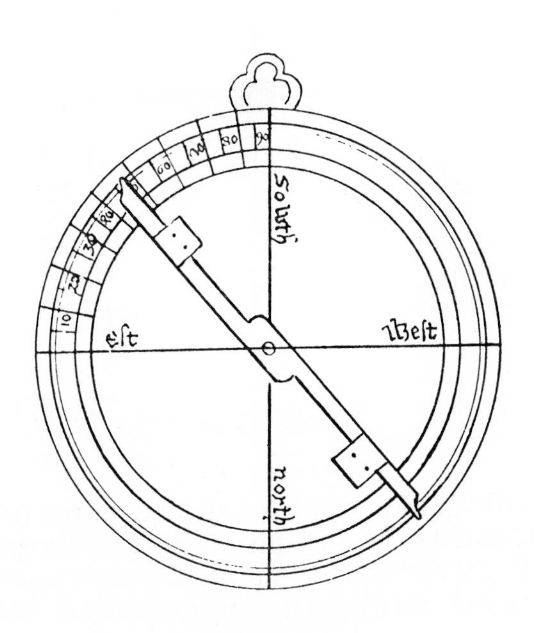

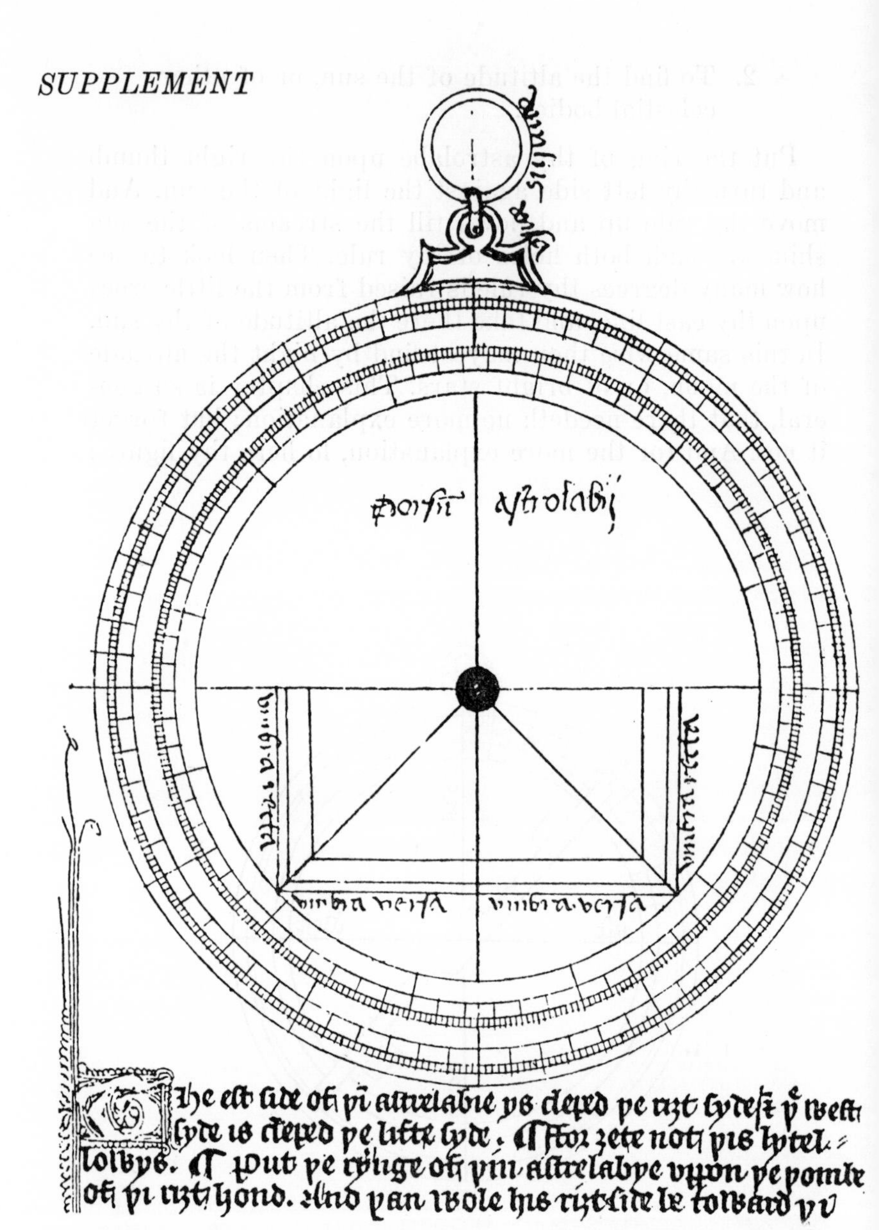

BACK OF CHAUCER'S ASTROLABE. M.S. Rawlinson D. 9B.

The names of the shadow scales, *umbra, recta* and *umbra versa,* have been transposed in this figure.

41. Umbra Recta.

[*St. John's Coll. Cambridge MS.*]

If it so be that thou willt work by *umbra recta,* and canst get to the base of the tower, thou shalt work in this manner:—

Take the altitude of the tower by both holes so that the rule lies even on a point. For example: [Suppose] I see him [the top of the tower] at the point of 4; I then measure the space between myself and the tower and find it 20 feet; then I say that as 4 is to 12, right so is the space between thee and the tower to the height of the tower. 4 is a third part of 12, so is the space between thee and the tower a third part of the height of the tower. Then thrice 20 feet is the height of the tower, with the addition of [the height of] thy person to thine eye. And this rule is general for *umbra recta* from the point of 1 to 12. And if thy rule fall upon 5, then the space between thee and the tower is five-twelfths of the height of the tower, with the addition of thine own height.

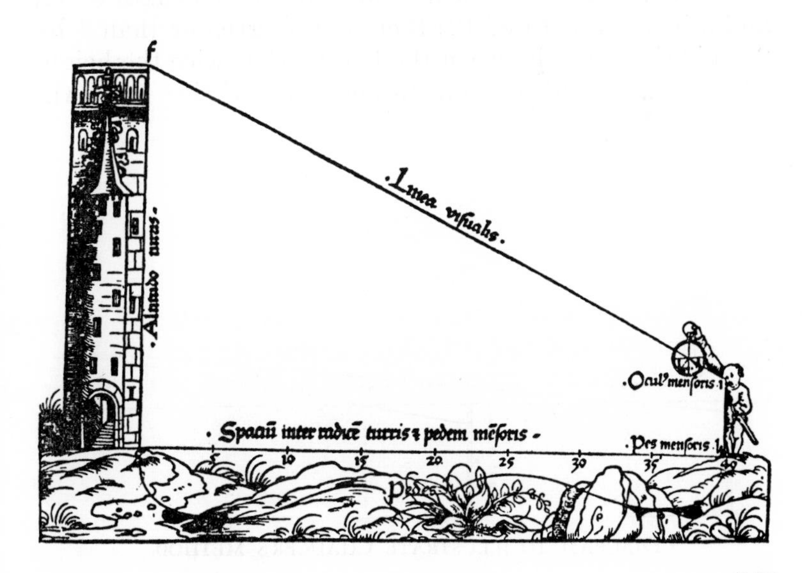

42. Umbra Versa.

Another method of working is by *umbra versa,* if so be that thou canst not get to the base of the tower. I see him [the top of the tower] through the number of 1 [on the scale], and I set a mark at my foot. Then I go nearer to the tower and look at him through the point of 2, and there I set another mark. I then consider the ratio of 1 to 12, and find that [1 goes into 12] 12 times; and I consider the ratio of 2 to 12, and thou wilt find it to be 6 times. Then thou willt find that as 12 is more than 6 by the number of 6, so is the space between the two marks the space of 6 times the height [you wish to measure]. And note that at the first altitude of 1, thou settest a mark, and again when thou sawest it at 2, thou settest another mark, and thou findest [the space] between the two marks to be 60 feet; then thou willt find that 10 is the sixth part of 60. Hence 10 feet is the height of the tower.

For other points, if it [the rule] fall in *umbra versa,* as thus: suppose it fell upon 2, and at the second [sighting] upon 3, then thou willt find that 2 is one-sixth of 12, and 3 is one-fourth of 12; then as 6 is greater than 4 by 2, so is the space between the two marks twice the height of the tower, and if the difference were thrice, then will

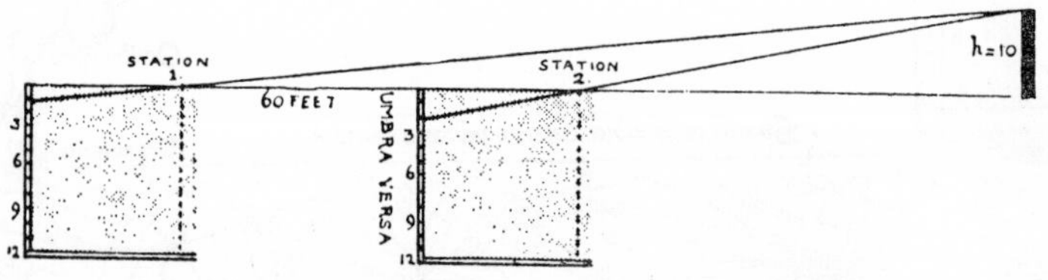

DIAGRAM TO ILLUSTRATE CHAUCER'S METHOD.

it be 3 times; and thus thou mayest proceed from 2 to 12; and if it be 4, 4 times, or 5, 5 times and *sic de ceteris*.

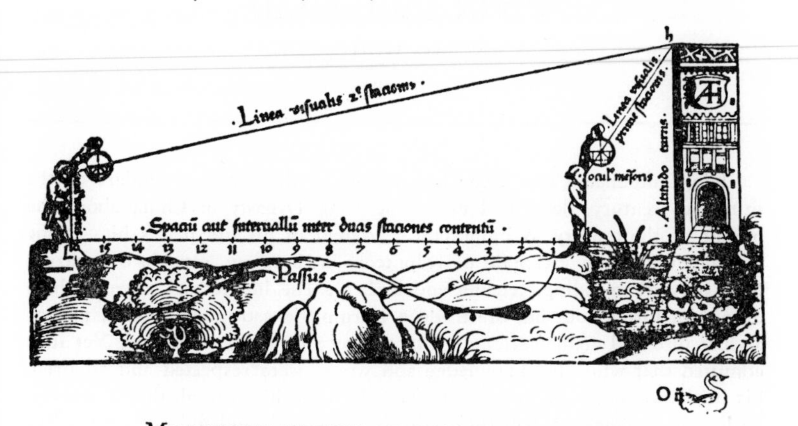

MEASURING HEIGHT OF INACCESSIBLE TOWER.
After Stoffler 1524.

CH'IN CHIU-SHAO

(c. 1250)

Ch'in Chiu-Shao (Tsin Keu-Chaou), one of the greatest scholars of the thirteenth century, flourished under the Sung Dynasty in China about the middle of the century. A biographical account of his life places him at the age of seventeen as a captain of volunteers in the army, capable of amazing feats of skill in riding, fencing and archery. The intellectual talents which drew him throughout his life to deep learning in astronomy, music, poetry, architecture and mathematics were in evidence from his childhood. Yet it is admitted that while his knowledge and works were respected and admired, his brilliance and superiority in every field made him proud, that moreover, he loved extravagance, had little faith in his friends and did not always live up to the highest ideals of character. From Ch'in's own writing we learn that although he had escaped the hazards of military combat unscathed, ten long years of suffering the ravages of illness brought him to the depths of despair. Not until his faith enabled him to acknowledge and bow to the inevitability of fate was his torment alleviated. Then, as he resumed his studies he also recovered his vigor. Devoting himself completely to the study of mathematics, Ch'in retired into seclusion where he wrote his most important work, the *Su-shu Chiu-chang* ("Nine Sections of the Art of Numbers" or "Nine Sections of Mathematics"). When he had fully recovered, Ch'in returned to the service of the Sung government. During the period 1253–1258 he served in the region bordering the Yang-tse River. Later he became governor of Ch'iung Chou. His last appointment under the Sung was as governor of Mei Chou. Ch'in was serving in this office when he died.

Ch'in Chiu-Shao's *Su-shu Chiu-chang* or *Su-hsiao Chiu-chang* is not a reworking or redevelopment of the old *K'iu-ch'ang Suan-shu* ("Arithmetic in Nine Sections"). The problems in Ch'in's works are grouped in nine sections but the classifications are not the same as in the older work. The title given to the work by Ch'in is said by some to have been merely *Sh-shu* or *Su-hsiao.* The present text of Ch'in's treatise, including his preface with its autobiographical notes, has been obtained from a copy made by Chang Ch'i-mei in 1646. Chang Ch'i-mei's sources go back to the *Yuan-lo Tai-tien* (Yuan-lo Great Collections). The eighty one problems of Ch'in's *Su-shu* include both determinate and indeterminate types. In addition to some traditional Chinese problems there are also problems whose sources are astronomy, land surveying, state service, commerce and military science. The *Su-shu* is distinguished for its advance in algebraic techniques. It contains a detailed description of the Chinese method, *Tai-yen ch'iu-i-shu* or *Ta-yen* ("Great Extension"), for solving indeterminate problems. It also presents the method for solving determinate equations, which was called *Lih-tien-yuen-yih* ("Setting Up the Celestial Monad"). Here, the unknown quantity is taken as the celestial element or monad and the principle of place values for algebraic terms is employed. Many illustrations are given of the Chinese method known as *Ling-lung-kae-fang* ("Harmoniously Alternating Evolution") for finding the roots of numerical equations. Positive and negative numbers are written by Ch'in in red and black ink respectively, corresponding to the red and black bamboo computing rods. Ch'in's procedure in his *Ling-lung-kae-fang* involves place values for algebraic terms and is remarkably like Horner's method of the early nineteenth century.

●

NINE SECTIONS OF THE ART OF NUMBERS

From *Chinese Researches*

by Alexander Wylie

In examining the productions of the Chinese one finds considerable difficulty in assigning the precise date for the origin of any mathematical process; for on almost every point, where we consult a native author, we find references to some still earlier work on the subject. The high veneration with which it has been customary for them to look upon the labours of the ancients, has made them more desirous of elucidating the works of their predecessors than of seeking fame in an untrodden path; so that some of their most important formulae have reached the state in which we now find them by an almost innumerable series of increments. One of the most remarkable of these is the *Ta-yen,* "Great Extension," a rule for the resolution of indeterminate problems. This rule is met with in embryo in Sun Tsze's Arithmetical Classic under the name of *Wuh-puh-chi-soo,* "Unknown Numerical Quantities," where after a general statement in four lines of rhyme the following question is proposed:—

Given an unknown number, which when divided by 3, leaves a remainder of 2; when divided by 5, it leaves 3; and when divided by 7, it leaves 2; what is the number? Ans. 23.

This is followed by a special rule for working out the problem, in terms sufficiently concise and elliptical, to elude the comprehension of the casual reader:—

Dividing by 3 with a remainder of 2, set down 140; dividing by 5 with a remainder of 3, set down 63; dividing by 7 with a remainder of 2, set down 30; adding these sums together gives 233, from which subtract 210, and the remainder is the number required.

A more general note succeeds:—

For 1 obtained by 3, set down 70; for 1 obtained by 5, set down 21; for 1 obtained by 7, set down 15; when the sum is 106 or above subtract 105 from it, and the remainder is the number required.

In tracing the course of this process we find it gradually becoming clearer till towards the end of the Sung dynasty, when the writings of Tsin Keu-chaou put us in full possession of the principles, and enables us to unravel the meaning of the above mysterious assemblage of numerals. Applying the principles of the *Ta-yen* as there laid down:—Multiplying together the three divisors 3, 5 and 7, gives 105 for the *Yen-moo,* "Extension Parent." Divide this by the *Ting-moo,* "Fixed Parent," 7, the quotient 15 is the *Yen-soo,* "Extension Number." Divide this again by 7, and there is an overplus of 1, which is the *Ching-suh,* "Multiplying Term;" by which multiply the Extension Number 15, and the product 15 is the *Yung-soo,* "Use Number," or as it is given above,—*for* 1 *obtained* by 7, *set down* 15. Divide the Extension Parent 105 by the Fixed Parent 5, and the quotient 21 is the Extension Number. Divide this again by 5, and the overplus 1 is the Multiplying Term. Multiply the Extension Number 21 by this, and the product 21 is the Use Number; which is given above,—*for* 1 *obtained by* 5, *set down* 21. Divide the Extension Parent 105 by the Fixed Parent 3, and the quotient 35 is the Extension Number. Divide this again by 3, and there is a *Ke,* "Remainder" of 2. This Remainder being more than unity is then submitted to a subsidiary process termed *Kiu-yih,* "Finding Unity," which is the alternate division of the Extension Parent and Remainder by each other, till the remainder is reduced to 1; the result in the present instance is 2, which is the Multiplying Term; by which multiply the Extension Number, and the product 70 is the Use Number, which is the meaning of the sentence,—*for* 1 *obtained by* 3, *set down* 70. Having thus obtained the several Use Numbers multiply the corresponding original remainders by these:—

$70 \times 2 = 140$; $21 \times 3 = 63$; $15 \times 2 = 30$; add these numbers together as stated in the rule, and the sum is 233, from which subtract as many times the Parent Number 105 as it will admit, which making 210 the remainder is 23, the number required.

But it is in the "Nine Sections of the Art of Numbers" by Tsin Keu-chaou that we have the most full and explicit details on this subject. Here we have the various applications of this theory worked out at great length; the first problem being to find a solution of a passage in the Yih King treating of the origin of the divining numbers:—

Qu. In the Yih King it is said:—'The Great Extension Number is 50, and the Use Number is 49.' Again it is said:—'It is divided into 2, to represent the 2 spheres; 1 is suspended to represent the 3 powers; they are drawn out by 4, to represent the 4 seasons; three changes complete a symbol, and eighteen changes perfect the diagram.' What is the rule for the Extension and what are the several numbers?

The 4 cardinal numbers—1 the senior male, 2 the junior female, 3 the junior male and 4 the junior female—are used to start with as the Origin Numbers. In a second row, opposite each number respectively, is placed the product of the other three.

Origin Numbers	1	2	3	4
Extension Numbers	24	12	8	6

The sum of these lower numbers gives 50, the *Great Extension Number* alluded to in the text of the Yih King: 50 being an even number and consequently unsuitable for the Use Number, the Origin Numbers are severally taken in pairs and common divisors sought: where this is obtained the number which gives an odd quotient is divided by it, but the other is not. The result of this last operation gives the Fixed Parent Numbers, and the Extension Numbers are obtained the same as before.

Fixed Parents	1	1	3	4
Extension Numbers	12	12	4	3

Subtract from the respective Extension Numbers as many of the corresponding Fixed Parents as they will admit, so as always to leave some remainder.

Fixed Parents	1	1	3	4
Remainders	1	1	1	3

The three Remainders 1 become the respective Multiplying Terms, and submitting the last Remainder 3 to the process for Finding Unity, the Multiplying Term 3 is obtained. By these four terms multiply the respective Extension Numbers, and the Expansion Use Numbers are obtained.

Fixed Parents	1	1	3	4
Expansion Use	12	12	4	9

The second Origin Number 2 having been reduced 1 at the beginning, once the Extension Parent 12 is consequently added to the second Expansion Number, and the Expansion Numbers then become the Fixed Use Numbers, and stand as follows:—

Origin Numbers	1	2	3	4
Fixed Use Numbers	12	24	4	9

The four upper numbers here are those employed in drawing the divining straws. The sum of the four lower numbers is 49, which is denominated the *Use Number* in the text of the Yih King, being the number of the straws used in divination. These 49 divining straws being divided at random between the two hands, one hand containing an even number, the other must contain odd. In the present instance the left hand is supposed to hold the odd number 33, though unknown by the enquirer. In drawing them out by 1 at a time, as it is known there must be a remainder of 1, the number 1 is suspended at first, as it is said in the text, 1 *is suspended to represent the* 3 *powers*. The straws are then drawn in so many successive operations by 2, 3 and 4 at a time, which give respectively the remainders 1, 3 and 1, and these are now put down in three parcels. Making the suspended 1, the first parcel, we have then the following numbers:—

Use Numbers	12	24	4	9
Parcels	1	1	3	1

Multiply these parcels by the respective Use Numbers and the Full Numbers are obtained.

Full Numbers	12	24	12	9

Adding together these 4 numbers gives 57, from which subtract the Extension Parent 12 as many times as it will admit, and there is a remainder of 9, which make the dividend, and divide it by 3 the Extension Measure, when the quotient 3 is the junior male, and represents the single stroke symbol.

In this number by changing the odd number in the left hand different symbols might be obtained. 1, representing two whole strokes; 2, representing one broken stroke; 3, one whole stroke; and 4, one whole and one broken stroke. Such was the means employed in former times for diving into futurity; the various diagrams of Fo-he being thus obtained were supposed to set forth the destiny of enquirers. Some knowledge of the Yih King is necessary to enable one to understand these diagrams, which are evidently the relics of a very ancient system of divination.

The 2nd problem is to find the epoch of conjunction of the terms of concurrent cycles of time. The question is given as follows:—

Let the solar year be equal to 365¼ days, the moon's revolution 29-499/940 days, and the *Kea-tsze* 60 days. Suppose in the year A.D. 1246, the 53rd day of the *Kea-tsze* or sexagenary cycle of days is the 1st of the 11th month; the 57th day of the *Kea-tsze* is the winter solstice or 1st day of the solar year; and the 1st day of the *Kea-tsze* is the 9th day of the month. Required the time between two conjunctions of the commencement of these three cycles; also the time that has already elapsed, and how much has yet to run. *Ans.* The time between two conjunctions, 18,240 years: 225,600 months: 6,662,160 days: number of years already past 9,163: number of years unexpired, 9,077.

The 9th problem is as follows:—

A report being raised that 3 rice bins each containing the same amount have been robbed, the original quantity is not known, but it is found that in the left hand one there is still 1 *ho* left; in the middle one, there is 1 *shing* 4 *ho* left; in the right hand one there is 1 *ho* remaining; the thieves being caught, A confesses that he took a horse-ladle at night and filled it several times out of the left hand bin, putting the contents in a bag; B confesses having hastily taken a wooden shoe several times full, out of the middle bin; C says he took a bowl and filled it successively out of the right hand bin. Examining the three vessels the horse-ladle is found to contain 1 *shing* 9 *ho,* the wooden shoe, 1 *shing* 7 *ho,* and the bowl, 1 *shing* 2 *ho.* What is the amount of rice lost, and how much did each take? Ans. Lost, 9 *shih* 5 *tow* 6 *shing* 3 *ho.* Stolen by A, 3 *shih* 1 *tow* 9 *shing* 2 *ho;* B, 3 *shih* 1 *tow* 7 *shing* 9 *ho;* C, 3 *shih* 1 *tow* 9 *shing* 2 *ho.*

At the close of the 13th century, we find a grand step made toward the theory of analysis, in the publication of the *Lih-tien-yuen-yih,* "Setting up the Celestial Monad," a new branch of arithmetic, which may with propriety be termed the Chinese algebra.

In the *Tien-yuen-yih,* unity is employed as the representative of an unknown number; this being combined with an extension of the theory of local value, in order to represent the successive powers of the Monad or unknown number. The Monad has the character *Yuen* written by the side of it, to distinguish its place in the column. Immediately below the Monad is the place for the natural number, which is marked by the character *Tai,* implying that it is the place of *Tai-kieh,* or extreme limit. Immediately above the Monad is the square; next above is the cube; again above, the fourth power, and so on upwards *ad infinitum.* Thus the equation $x^3+15x^2+66x-360=0$ would be written—

1 Cube of Monad.
15 Square of Monad.
66 Monad.
—360 Natural Number.

The cube, square, &c., are all indicated by their relative position with respect to *Tai,* the characters being used only to express coefficients.

One example taken from a great number in Tsin's work, will best illustrate this. It is required to extract the root of $-x^4 + 1534464x^2-526727677600$, or to find the value of x.

720 *Shang.* Value of x, the Monad.
—526727577600 *Shih.*
—14940217600
14940217600
0 *Fang.*
731124800
776249600
747010880
1534464 *Shang-lien.*
1044464
64464
—1405536
—1461936

0	*Hia-lien.*
—700	
—1400	
—2100	
—2800	
—2820	
—1	*Yu*
—1	

In the above example, the several terms are set down with the Chinese names *Shih, Fang,* &c., against them, the units in each being 2 places more to the left than in the term above it, because there is found to be 3 figures in the root. The first figure of the root being 7, is set down at the top. The *Yu*—1 is then multiplied by this 7, and the product added to the *Hia-lien* 0, regard being had to the place in the column, which gives—700; the *Hia-lien*—700 is then multiplied by 7, the product being added to the *Shang-lien* 1534464, still preserving the same place in the column, gives 1044464; again this is multiplied by 7, and the product added to the *Fang* 0, gives 731124800; this multiplied by 7 and the product combined with the *Shih,* leaves—14940217600, &c. The second figure in the root being found to be 2, the same process is repeated, moving all the terms to the right 1, 2, 3, &c. places.

CHOU KUNG

(c. 1100 B.C.)

Chou Kung (also Chow Kung), the illustrious Duke of Chou, was a statesman, military genius and mathematician who flourished in China toward the end of the twelfth century B.C. Capable of prodigious bursts of energy, he was of inestimable service in establishing his brother Wu Wang as the first emperor of the Chou Dynasty. After Wu's death, he served as regent during the minority of the second emperor. The period of Chou Kung's activity in the early years of the Chou Dynasty remained a model and an ideal for succeeding generations. Though the Chou lasted almost a thousand years, no period or reign throughout this entire time has been described in terms of greater approbation by historians of the nation, than the regency of the sagacious Chou Kung.

Chou Kung is accepted as the author of the first dialogue contained in the *Chou-Pi* (also *Chow-pei,* or *Chou-pei Suan-king*), one of the oldest of the ancient Chinese scientific treatises. Written in two parts, it deals principally with the calendrical problems, and thus, with astronomy and mathematics. The first dialogue, as recorded, takes place between Chou Kung and a nobleman of the defeated Shang Dynasty. The questions and answers provide us with intimations of the level of mathematical learning attained in China by the twelfth century B.C. Clearly, we have evidence here of interest in and also knowledge of mensurational geometry, the principle of the Pythagorean theorem, elements of trigonometry basic to indirect measurement, and some instruments for astronomical measurements. The astronomical-mathematical material of the *Chou-Pi* formed the basis of Chinese works written more than a thousand years later.

CHOU-PI
(CHOW-PI)

From *Chinese Researches*

by ALEXANDER WYLIE

The *Chow-pi,* Thigh-bone of Chow.* The translation is given here of the first section, which forms an epitome of the whole:—

"1. Formerly Chow Kung addressing Shang Kaou, said:—I have heard it said my lord that you are famous at numbers; may I venture to ask you how the ancient Fo-hi established the degrees of the celestial sphere? There are no steps by which one may ascend the heavens, and it is impracticable to take a rule and measure the extent of the earth; I wish to ask then how he ascertained these numbers? 2. Shang Kaou replied:—The art of numbering originates in the circle and quadrangle. 3. The circle is derived from the quadrangle. 4. The quadrangle originates in the right angle.† 5. The right angle originates in the multiplication of the nine digits. 6. Hence, separating a right angle into its component parts, if the base be equal to 3, and the altitude to 4, a line connecting the farther extremities will be 5. 7. Square the external dimensions, and half the amount will give the area of the triangle. 8. Add together all the sides, and the result will equal the sum of 3, 4 and 5. 9. The square of the hypotheneuse being 25, is equal to the squares of the two short sides of the triangle. 10. Thus the means by which Yu restored order throughout the empire was by following out the principles of these numbers. 11. Chow Kung exclaimed:—How truly great is

* The name which at first sight appears a little *outré,* receives its explanation from the two characters Keu-koo used to designate the base and altitude of a triangle, and which mean originally the Leg and Thigh. It may call to mind also a similar device in our English term, Napier's Bones.

† The term right angle is used here to designate the *keu-koo,* two short sides of a right angle triangle.

the theory of numbers! May I ask what is the principle of the use of the rectangle? 12. Shang-kaou replied:— The plane rectangle is formed by uninclined straight lines. 13. The direct rectangle is used for observing heights. 14. The reversed rectangle is used for fathoming depths. 15. The flat rectangle is used for ascertaining distances. 16. By the revolution of the rectangle the circle is formed. 17. By the junction of rectangles the square is formed. 18. The square pertains to earth, the circle belongs to heaven, heaven being round and the earth square. 19. The numbers of the square being the standard, the dimensions of the circle are deduced from the square. 20. The circular plate is employed to represent heaven; the celestial colours are blue and black, the terrestrial are yellow and red; the circular plate is formed according to the celestial numbers; it is blue and black outside, red and yellow inside, in order to represent the celestial and terrestrial stations. 21. Therefore he who understands the earth is a wise man; he who comprehends the heavens is a sage. This knowledge begins with the straight line; the straight line is a component part of the rectangle, and the numbers of the rectangle are applicable to the construction of all things. 22. Chow Kung exclaimed, Excellent indeed!"

CHU CHI-CHIEH

(c. 1300)

Chu Chi-chieh (Choo Shi-ki, also Chu Shih-chieh), a Chinese mathematician of remarkable talent, whose works formed a link between the mathematics of China and Japan, was a teacher who wandered over many areas of China earning his livelihood by giving public lessons in mathematics to pupils who gathered about him. He was the author of two great mathematical treatises, one written in 1299 and the other in 1303. The first, *Suan-hsaio Chi-meng* (Introduction to Mathematical Studies) was a compendium of two hundred and fifty nine problems with their detailed solutions. This work with its skillful employment of the method of the celestial element or monad, explicit rules of operations with positive and negative numbers, and an improved table for use with the abacus, brought Chinese algebra of this period to the high point of its power. The *Suan-hsaio Chi-meng* was reprinted in Korea in 1660 and an edition by the great Japanese mathematician Takebe containing his commentaries, was published in 1690. Chu Chi-chieh's treatise was thus directly connected with the advance of mathematics in Japan where his methods were studied and developed by Japanese mathematicians in the seventeenth century and later.

In the second of Chu Chi-chieh's treatises, the *Sze-yuen yuh-kien* ("Precious Mirror of the Four Origins," or "Precious Mirror of the Four Elements"), he tabulated in triangular form the binomial coefficients as far as the eighth power. The *Precious Mirror* contained two hundred and eighty eight problems, some requiring an elaborate four monad process and others involving the extraction of roots. Chu Chi-chieh's achievements are all the more striking when it is remembered that his operations were carried out entirely by the use of calculating rods or pieces.

PRECIOUS MIRROR OF THE FOUR ORIGINS

From *Chinese Researches*

by Alexander Wylie

At the beginning of the work of Choo Shi-ki, the following table of the "Ratio of the *Liens* in the involution of numbers, up to the 8th power," is given; not as anything new, however, for it is denominated the "*ancient method;*" but at what time it was first discovered, we have no sufficient date to determine:—

1 Original sum.
1 1 Factors.
1 2 1 Square.
1 3 3 1 Cube.
1 4 6 4 1 Biquadrate.
1 5 10 10 5 1 5th Power.
1 6 15 20 15 6 1 6th Power.
1 7 21 35 35 21 7 1 7th Power.
1 8 28 56 70 56 28 8 1 8th Power.

Choo Shi-ki published his *Sze-yuen-yuh-kien,* "Precious Mirror of the Four Origins," about the year 1303; in which he makes a decided step in advance of his contemporaries, by using the Monad for known as well as unknown quantities. Four several Monads are used, which are styled respectively, Heaven, Earth, Man and Thing. The three first are generally (not necessarily) employed to designate known quantities, and the last, *Wuh,* "Thing"* for the unknown quantity. Here again we must yield precedence to the Chinese, for until the time of Vieta, who lived in the 16th century, arbitrary representations of numbers were never used in Europe

* "The Persians and Arabs employed the word answering to 'thing' in their language for the unknown quantity, and the Italians adopted the word 'cosa' for the same purpose: hence algebra came to be called the *Regola de la Cosa,* in Italy, and the *Cossike Art* in England." Penny Cyclopaedia, vol. 1, p. 325. The coincidence here is curious.

for anything but quantities sought. The *Tien-yuen,* or Heaven, is written below *Tai,* the powers increasing as they descend; Earth is written on the left side of *Tai,* the powers increasing as they recede from *Tai* in a lateral direction; Man is written on the right side, the powers increasing towards the right; and Thing is written above, the powers increasing as they ascend.

Thus the four simple Monads or $a + b + c + x$ are written in the following form[1]:—

```
    1
1   *   1
    1
```

The square of the above, or $a^2 + 2ab + 2ac + 2ax + b^2 + 2bc + 2bx + c^2 + 2cx + x^2$, is as follows:—

```
          1
      2   0   2
            2
  1   0   *   0   1
        2
      2   0   2
          1
```

A very little practice is sufficient to render any one perfectly familiar with the several terms of this algorithm. The left being the side for the Earth Monad or b, the 1 removed 2 stages from *Tai* is b^2; in the next column, the upper 2 standing opposite the place for the Thing Monad, signifies twice the product of Earth and Thing, or $2bx$; the lower 2 standing opposite the place for the Heaven Monad, signifies twice the product of Heaven and Earth, or $2ab$; the 2 standing diagonally against *Tai,* indicates twice the product of Earth and Man, the 2 Monads in the same horizontal line, or $2bc$; the other diagonal 2 above *Tai* is twice the product of Heaven and Thing, or $2ax$, &c. The operations connected with this formula are as simple as in the *Tien-yuen,* except it be with regard to multiplication, and even in that, the apparent intricacy is more imaginary than real,

[1]Ed. note: An asterisk occupies the position of the original character *Tai.*

the several columns being taken separately and the products added together afterwards. The process of amalgamation and reduction is carried on till all the columns are gradually reduced to one, when the root is extracted the same as before.

From *The Development of Mathematics in China and Japan*

by Yoshio Mikami

Some of the problems solved by the method of the four elements are:

"There is a right triangle whose area is 30 square paces. Given the sum of the two sides to be 17 paces, it is required to find the sum of the first side and the hypotenuse."

Here the sum of the first side and the hypotenuse is represented by the heaven element and the first side by the earth element. "These operations being carried out for the heaven and earth elements", the author writes, "the final equation will be found to be

$$-3600 - 3706x - 71x^2 + 34x^3 - x^4 = 0\text{''}.$$

"There is a right triangle whose area is 30 square paces. Given the sum of the two sides to be 17 paces, it is required to find the sum of the second side and the hypotenuse."

For this problem the rule is given thus: "Take the heaven element for the sum of the second side and the hypotenuse; take the earth element for the second side. These operations being carried out for the heaven and earth elements, the final equation will be obtained to be

$$3600 + 3706x + 71x^2 - 34x^3 + x^4 = 0.\text{''}$$

"There is a right triangle, of which the product of the second side and the sum of the 'five differences' is equal to the sum of the hypotenuse square and the product of the first side and the hypotenuse; and the quotient of the sum of the 'five sums' by the first side is equal to the difference of the second side square and the difference of the first side and the hypotenuse. It is required to find the 'yellow magnitude' plus the three sides."

Here an explanation is needful. If we designate the three sides of the right triangle by a, b, c, where the last represents the hypotenuse, the "yellow magnitude" spoken of in the above is $a + b - c$, and the "five sums" and the "five differences" are

$$a + b, a + c, b + c, a + (a + b), b + (a + b);$$
$$b - a, c - a, c - b, c - (b - a), (a + b) - c.$$

Chu's consideration of this problem is only too brief, but we shall reproduce what he says, because it is of the deepest interest in the history of the Chinese mathematics. Says he:

"Take the heaven element for the first side, the earth element for the second side, the man element for the hypotenuse, and the thing element for the quantity sought for. And operating with these four elements we get the equations[1]):

—2	*	1
0	1	0

(a),

0	4	*	4
—1	0	2	1
0	0	—1	0

(b),

1	0	*	0	—1
0	0	0	0	0
0	0	1	0	0

(c)

0	—1	0
2	*	0
0	2	0

(d).

"Operating with these four equations so as to effect elimination, and exchanging the thing element with the

1) If we denote the four elements by x, y, z, u, these equations will be expressed by

(a) $x - 2y + z = 0$,
(b) $2x - x^2 + 4y - xy^2 + 4z + xz = 0$,
(c) $x^2 + y^2 - z^2 = 0$,
(d) $2x + 2y - u = 0$.

heaven element we get the equations (α) and (β)[2], of which (β) will be taken for the left column. From these we get the equation (γ)[3], which we take to the right column. From the two inside columns (when (β) and (γ) are arranged side by side on the left and right), and from the two outside columns, by multiplication we get

$$\underset{(\alpha)}{\boxed{\begin{array}{cccc} 2 & -8 & 28 & * \\ 0 & -1 & 6 & -2 \\ 0 & 0 & 0 & -1 \end{array}}}, \qquad \underset{(\beta)}{\boxed{\begin{array}{cc} -7 & * \\ 0 & 2 \end{array}}}, \qquad \underset{(\gamma)}{\boxed{\begin{array}{cc} 0 & 294 \\ 8 & 3 \\ 0 & -4 \end{array}}}$$

the expressions (δ) and (ϵ)[1], and subtracting these from each other and dividing the result by 3, we obtain the equation (ζ).[2] Evolving it according to the square root-extraction, we obtain $x = 14$ paces, which is the required answer."

$$(\delta)\boxed{\begin{array}{r} 0 \\ 0 \\ 16 \end{array}}, \qquad (\epsilon)\boxed{\begin{array}{r} -2058 \\ -21 \\ 28 \end{array}}, \qquad (\zeta)\boxed{\begin{array}{r} -686 \\ -7 \\ 4 \end{array}}.$$

●

SUAN-HSIAO CHI-MENG

(Introduction to Mathematical Studies)

From *A History of Japanese Mathematics*

by DAVID EUGENE SMITH and YOSHIO MIKAMI

Chu Chi-chieh also gives, in the *Suan-hsiao Chi-meng,*

---

2) (α) $-2x - x^2 + 28y + 6xy - 8y^2 - xy^2 + 2y^3 = 0$,
(β) $2x - 7y = 0$.

3) $294 + 3x - 4x^2 + 8xy = 0$.

1) (δ) $16x^2$, (ϵ) $-2058 - 21x + 28x^2$. Here of course the factor y is understood as rejected.

2) $-686 - 7x + 4x^2 = 0$.

rules for the treatment of negative numbers. The following translations are as literal as the circumstances allow:

"When the same-named diminish each other, the different-named should be added together.[1] If then there is no opponent for a positive term, make it negative; and for a negative, make it positive."[2]

"When the different-named diminish each other the same-named should be added together. If then there is no opponent for a positive, make it positive; and for a negative, make it negative."[3]

"When the same-named are multiplied together, the product is made positive. When the different-named are multiplied together, the product is made negative."

---

[1] This is intended to mean that when $(+4) - (+3) = +(4-3)$, then $(+4) - (-3)$ should be $+4+3$.

[2] That is, $0 - (+4) = -4$, and $0 - (-4) = +4$.

[3] When $(+p) - (-q) = +p + q$, then $(-p) - (+q) = -(p+q)$. Also, $0 + (+4) = +4$, and $0 + (-4) = -4$.

GABRIEL CRAMER

(1704-1752)

Gabriel Cramer, an eminent Swiss mathematician, widely known among students of mathematics for his rule for solving systems of equations by determinants, was born in Geneva on July 31, 1704. He belonged to an ancient Holstein family known first in Strassburg, and then in Geneva, where his father and grandfather were beloved physicians. Cramer was educated at the University of Geneva at a time when that institution was renowned for its great teachers. When he was barely twenty years old, his capacity was well recognized at the University and in 1724 he was given an appointment there as a professor of mathematics. In 1727 he took a two year leave for travel during which time he made the acquaintance of Jean Bernoulli in Basel and thereby began his long and fruitful association with the Bernoulli family. Returning to Geneva after travelling to England, Holland and France, Cramer resumed his professional duties. A skillful researcher in mathematics, Cramer wrote many memoirs in the development of topics in mathematics and his writings appeared in various scientific journals. Gabriel Cramer was the first outstanding scholar who set aside his own investigations for the purpose of seriously undertaking the laborious and often thankless work of editing and publishing the writings of others. His publications, such as the work of Jean Bernoulli, and his two volume edition of the correspondence between Leibniz and Jean Bernoulli remain invaluable sources for historical research in the field of mathematics.

Cramer's greatest mathematical work, *Introduction to the Analysis of Algebraic Curves* (1750) containing the famous "Cramer's Rule" mentioned above, was written while his health was failing. At this time, a severe fall suffered when his carriage accidently overturned, rendered his condition worse. Seeking aid toward his recovery, he went to the south of France late in 1751. However, he survived only a short time and died in Bagnols near Nisme on January 4, 1752.

INTRODUCTION TO THE ANALYSIS OF ALGEBRAIC CURVES

by Gabriel Cramer

Professor of Philosophy and Mathematics of the Academies and Royal Societies of London, Berlin, Montpellier and the Academy of the Institute of Bologna. Published in Geneva by Cramer Bros. and Cl. Philibert, 1750.

Translated by Henrietta O. Midonick.

Chapter III

The number of coefficients a, b, c, d, e, etc. in every general equation is the same as the number of its terms. But the number of these coefficients can be diminished by one because the second member of each equation is zero and consequently the entire first member can be divided by any one of the coefficients. If, for example, we divide the entire first member by the coefficient of the highest power of y or x, then after the division, this term will have the number one, exactly, as its coefficient.

Thus, dividing the general equation of the first order

$$a + by + cx = 0$$

by c, we reduce it to $\frac{a}{c} + \frac{b}{c} y + x = 0$

where, in addition to unity, the coefficient of x, there are but two coefficients $\frac{a}{c}$ and $\frac{b}{c}$.

Accordingly, if v is an exponent of any order whatsoever, the number of coefficients of the general equation of this order will be $\frac{1}{2} vv + \frac{3}{2} v$, which is the sum of the arithmetical progression 2 + 3 + 4 + 5 + etc., where the difference is 1, the first term 2 and the number of terms v.*

From this it follows that a curve of order v can always be passed through $\frac{1}{2} vv + \frac{3}{2} v$ given points, that is, any curve of order v is determined and its equation given when there are $\frac{1}{2} vv + \frac{3}{2} v$ fixed points through which it must pass.

Thus a curve of the first order is determined by two given points; a curve of the second order by 5; one of the third order by 9; one of the fourth by 14; one of the fifth order by 20, and so on.

Only one example is required for the demonstration.**

Let A, B, C, D and E be five given points through which a curve of the second order is to be passed. Draw

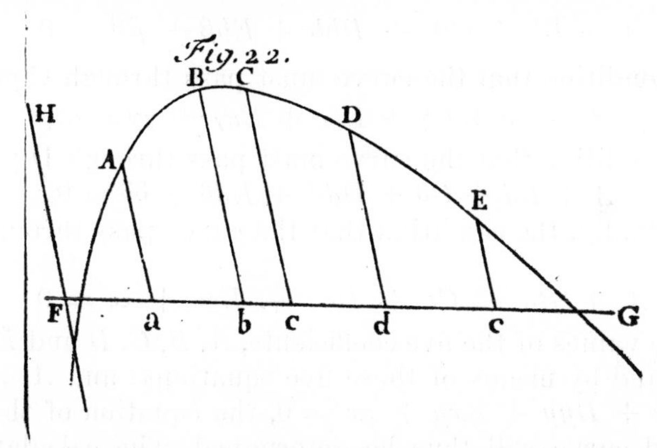

any two lines FG and FH through a point F. Take F as the origin and the two lines FG and FH as the axes. Then draw Aa, Bb, Cc, Dd and Ee, the ordinates of the given points. These ordinates as well as the abscissas Fa, Fb, Fc, Fd and Fe will be given values. Denote Aa by a,

* Stirling, *Lineae tertii Ordinis,* etc., p. 3 ff.
** Stirling, *Lineae tertii Ordinis,* etc., p. 69.
Newton, *Arithmetica universalis.* Problem LXI.

Bb by b, Cc by c, Dd by d, Ee by e and Fa by α, Fb by β, Fc by γ, Fd by δ, Fe by ϵ, and take

$$A + By + Cx + Dyy + Exy + xx = 0$$

as the equation of the second order which must pass through the given points A, B, C, D and E. The problem is thus reduced to finding the values of the five unknown coefficients, A, B, C, D, E. Now, to do this, we have five equations. For, since the curve passes through the point A, Fa (α) must be the abscissa corresponding to the ordinate aA (a). Hence, if α is a value of x, a is the corresponding value of y. Substituting α for x and a for y in the equation $A + By + Cx + Dyy + Exy + xx = 0$, the condition that the curve must pass through A is expressed by the equation

$$A + Ba + C\alpha + Daa + Ea\alpha + \alpha\alpha = 0.$$

The condition that the curve must pass through B similarly yields

$$A + Bb + C\beta + Dbb + Eb\beta + \beta\beta = 0.$$

The condition that the curve must pass through C yields

$$A + Bc + C\gamma + Dcc + Ec\gamma + \gamma\gamma = 0.$$

The condition that the curve must pass through D yields

$$A + Bd + C\delta + Ddd + Ed\delta + \delta\delta = 0.$$

And finally, the condition that the curve pass through E yields

$$A + Be + C\epsilon + Dee + Ee\epsilon + \epsilon\epsilon = 0$$

The values of the five coefficients, A, B, C, D and E can be found by means of these five equations; and $A + By + Cx + Dyy + Exy + xx = 0$, the equation of the required curve will thus be determined. The calculations involved in the solution would in fact be very long*; but it is not necessary to carry out the solution in order to convince oneself that it is always possible to pass a curve of the second order through five given points, A, B, C,

* The science of algebra has given us the means of shortening the calculations. I believe I have found a rule for this purpose, which is very easy and general, given any number of equations and a like number of unknowns, none of which is above the first degree. It will be found in *Appendix* No. 1.

D and E, and in general, to pass a curve of order v through $\frac{1}{2} vv + \frac{3}{2} v$ given points. It will suffice merely to observe that every point provides an equation and that one can determine as many coefficients as there are equations. Thus, $\frac{1}{2} vv + \frac{3}{2} v$ points determine $\frac{1}{2} vv + \frac{3}{2} v$ coefficients. This means that all the coefficients contained in the general equation of a curve of order v (See preceding section.) can be determined.

As the unknowns *A, B, C, D* and *E* in these equations never go above the first degree, the solution of the problem will always be possible and no exception or limitation can be introduced through imaginary roots. For the coefficients are determined without any necessity whatsoever for the extraction of a root, the sole operation by which imaginary roots can be introduced into a calculation. However, it may happen that some of the coefficients will be zero. In that case the equation of the curve will contain a smaller number of terms. Or it may happen that some of the coefficients may prove to be infinite and consequently the terms affected by these coefficients would alone constitute the whole equation, the other terms vanishing in comparison with them. Or some of the coefficients may remain undetermined and in that case it will be possible to pass an infinity of curves of the same order through the given points.

If finding the actual equation of the curve passing through a number of given points is required, the calculations may be shortened by taking one of the points, A, for example, as the origin (Plate III, fig. 23). Since the abscissa and ordinate are zero at this point, both α and a

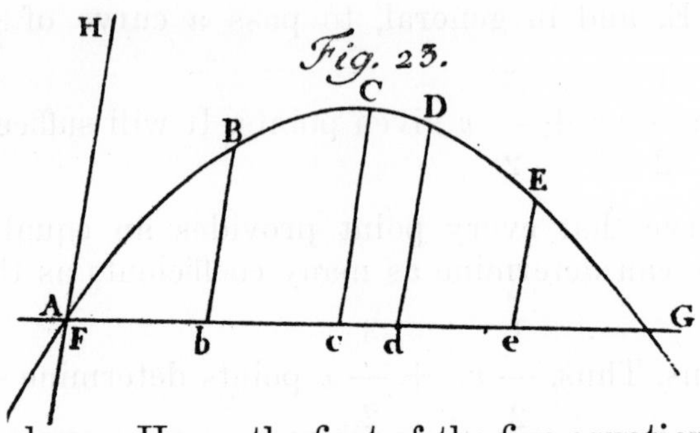

will equal zero. Hence the first of the five equations above reduces to $A = 0$, and the other four equations become

$$\begin{aligned}
Bb + C\beta + Dbb + E\beta b \quad + \beta\beta &= 0\\
Bc + C\gamma + Dcc + Ec\gamma \quad + \gamma\gamma &= 0\\
Bd + C\delta + Ddd + Ed\delta \quad + \delta\delta &= 0\\
Be + C\epsilon + Dee + Ee\epsilon \quad + \epsilon\epsilon &= 0
\end{aligned}$$

from which we derive

$$B = \frac{\beta\gamma de(\beta-\gamma)(\delta e-d\varepsilon)-\beta c\delta e(\beta-\delta)(\gamma e-c\varepsilon)+\beta d\varepsilon(\beta-\varepsilon)(\gamma d-c\delta)-b\gamma\delta e(\gamma-\delta)(\beta e-b\varepsilon) + \gamma d\varepsilon(\gamma-\varepsilon)(\beta d-b\delta)-\delta\varepsilon(\delta-\varepsilon)(\beta c-b\gamma)}{(\beta c-b\gamma)(\delta e-d\varepsilon)(bc+de)-(\beta d-b\delta)(\gamma e-c\varepsilon)(bd+ce)+(\beta e-b\varepsilon)(\gamma d-c\delta)(be+cd)}$$

$$C = -\frac{(\beta\beta c-b\gamma\gamma)(\delta e-d\varepsilon)de-(\beta\beta d-b\delta\delta)(\gamma e-c\varepsilon)ce+(\beta\beta e-b\varepsilon\varepsilon)(\gamma d-c\delta)cd+(\gamma\gamma d-c\delta\delta)(\beta e-b\varepsilon)be -(\gamma\gamma e-c\varepsilon\varepsilon)(\beta d-b\delta)bd+(\delta\delta e-d\varepsilon\varepsilon)(\beta c-b\gamma)bc}{(\beta c-b\gamma)(\delta e-d\varepsilon)(bc+de)-(\beta d-b\delta)(\gamma e-c\varepsilon)(bd+ce)+(\beta e-b\varepsilon)(\gamma d-c\delta)(be+cd)}$$

$$D = \frac{(\beta c-b\gamma)(\delta e-d\varepsilon)(\beta\gamma+\delta\varepsilon)-(\beta d-b\delta)(\gamma e-c\varepsilon)(\beta\delta+\gamma\varepsilon)+(\beta e-b\varepsilon)(\gamma d-c\delta)(\beta\varepsilon+\gamma\delta)}{(\beta c-b\gamma)(\delta e-d\varepsilon)(bc+de)-(\beta d-b\delta)(\gamma e-c\varepsilon)(bd+ce)+(\beta e-b\varepsilon)(\gamma d-c\delta)(be+cd)}$$

$$E = \frac{(\beta c-b\gamma)(\delta e-d\varepsilon)(\beta c+b\gamma+\delta e+d\varepsilon)-(\beta d-b\delta)(\gamma e-c\varepsilon)(\beta d+b\delta+\gamma e+c\varepsilon)+(\beta e-b\varepsilon)(\gamma d-c\delta)(\beta e+b\varepsilon+\ldots}{(\beta c-b\gamma)(\delta e-d\varepsilon)(bc+de)-(\beta d-b\delta)(\gamma e-c\varepsilon)(bd+ce)+(\beta e-b\varepsilon)(\gamma d-c\delta)(be+cd)}$$

But the work can be considerably shortened again by drawing lines (Plate III, fig. 24) from A to each of the

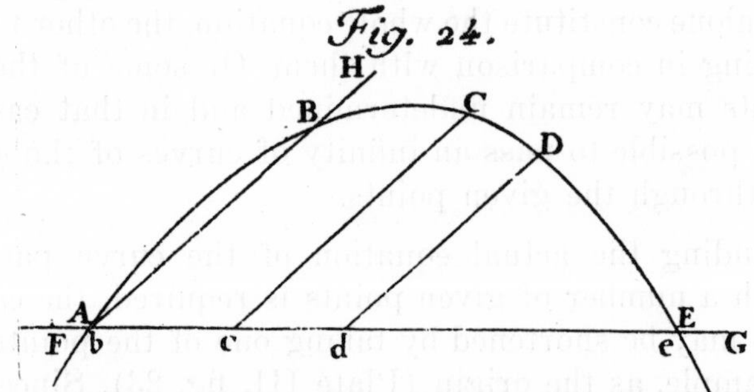

Lower left portion of Plate III, Cramer, *Introduction to the Analysis of Algebraic Curves.*

given points B and E, taking AB as the axis of the ordinates and AE as the axis of the abscissas. Then with the abscissa (β) of zero value, corresponding to the ordinate AB (b) and the ordinate (e) of zero value, corresponding to the abscissa AE (ϵ), the values of B, C, D and E are reduced to

$$B = -\frac{b\gamma\delta(d(\epsilon-\gamma) - (\epsilon-\delta)c)}{cd(\gamma(b-d) - (b-c)\delta)}$$

$$C = -\frac{cd\epsilon(\gamma(b-d) - (b-c)\delta)}{cd(\gamma(b-d) - (b-c)\delta)} = -\epsilon$$

$$D = +\frac{\gamma\delta(d(\epsilon-\gamma) - (\epsilon-\delta)c)}{cd(\gamma(b-d) - (b-c)\delta)} = -\frac{B}{b}$$

$$E = +\frac{c\delta(b-c)(\epsilon-\delta) - \gamma d(b-d)(\epsilon-\gamma)}{cd(\gamma(b-d) - (b-c)\delta)}$$

APPENDIX

On the Elimination of Unknowns.

If a problem involves several unknowns whose relations are so complicated, that several equations are required to express them, the values of the unknowns may be found by eliminating all of the unknowns except one. The single remaining unknown combined with the known quantities will yield a *final equation*. If the problem is determinate, the *final equation* will produce as a first result, the value of the aforesaid unknown, and then, by means of it, the values of all the remaining unknowns.

Algebra provides infallible rules for the success of this procedure, provided that one has the patience to follow them. However, the calculations become extremely long when the number of equations and unknowns is excessively large. . . . The purpose of the two items following is to remove these disadvantages.

NO. I

Let z, y, x, v, etc., represent several unknowns. Take as many equations as there are unknowns; let the equations involving the unknowns, be:

$$\begin{aligned}
A^1 &= Z^1 z + Y^1 y + X^1 x + V^1 v + \&c. \\
A^2 &= Z^2 z + Y^2 y + X^2 x + V^2 v + \&c. \\
A^3 &= Z^3 z + Y^3 y + X^3 x + V^3 v + \&c. \\
A^4 &= Z^4 z + Y^4 y + X^4 x + V^4 v + \&c. \\
&\&c.
\end{aligned}$$

where the letters A^1, A^2, A^3, A^4, etc., denote the first member (assumed to be known) of the first, second, third, fourth, etc., equations, respectively, and not the powers of A, as ordinarily. Similarly, Z^1, Z^2, etc. are the coefficients of z in the first, second, etc., equations, Y^1, Y^2, etc., are the coefficients of y, X^1, X^2, etc., are the coefficients of x, and V^1, V^2, etc., of v in the first, second, etc., equations, and so on.

Granting this notation, if there is but one equation, and the only unknown is z, we will have $z = \frac{A^1}{Z^1}$. If there are two equations and two unknowns, z and y, we will find

$$z = \frac{A^1Y^2 - A^2Y^1}{Z^1Y^2 - Z^2Y^1}, \text{ and } \qquad y = \frac{Z^1A^2 - Z^2A^1}{Z^1Y^2 - Z^2Y^1}.$$

If there are three equations and three unknowns z, y, and x, we will find

$$z = \frac{A^1Y^2X^3 - A^1Y^3X^2 - A^2Y^1X^3 + A^2Y^3X^1 + A^3Y^1X^2 - A^3Y^2X}{Z^1Y^2X^3 - Z^1Y^3X^2 - Z^2Y^1X^3 + Z^2Y^3X^1 + Z^3Y^1X^2 - Z^3Y^2X}$$

$$y = \frac{Z^1A^2X^3 - Z^1A^3X^2 - Z^2A^1X^3 + Z^2A^3X^1 + Z^3A^1X^2 - Z^3A^2X}{Z^1Y^2X^3 - Z^1Y^3X^2 - Z^2Y^1X^3 + Z^2Y^3X^1 + Z^3Y^1X^2 - Z^3Y^2X}$$

$$x = \frac{Z^1Y^2A^3 - Z^1Y^3A^2 - Z^2Y^1A^3 + Z^2Y^3A^1 + Z^3Y^1A^2 - Z^3Y^2A}{Z^1Y^2X^3 - Z^1Y^3X^2 - Z^2Y^1X^3 + Z^2Y^3X^1 + Z^3Y^1X^2 - Z^3Y^2X}$$

An inspection of these formulas yields the following general rule: If there are n equations and n unknowns, the value of each unknown will be found by forming n

fractions each having the same denominator; the number of terms in the denominator will be the same as the number of different possible arrangements of n distinct objects, taken n at a time; each term of the denominator will be composed of the letters $ZYXV$, etc., always written in the same order, but with the first n natural numbers as exponents (actually merely indices written as superscripts) distributed among the letters in every possible way. Thus, if there are three unknowns, the denominator will consist of ($1 \times 2 \times 3 =$) 6 terms, each composed of the three letters ZYX to which the sets of indices 123, 132, 213, 231, 312, 321 are successively applied. The sign + or — is assigned to each term in accordance with the following rule: If, within the same term, any index is followed by a smaller index, either immediately or with other indices intervening, I shall call this an alteration or an inversion. The number of inversions must be counted for each term. If the number of inversions in a term is even or zero, the sign of the term will be +; if the number of inversions in a term is odd, the sign of the term will be —. For example in the term $Z^1Y^2V^3$, there is no inversion. Hence the sign of this term is +. The sign of the term $Z^3Y^1X^2$ is also +, because there are two inversions in the order of its indices, 3 preceding 1, and 3 preceding 2. But the term $Z^3Y^2X^1$, which has three inversions, 3 preceding 2, 3 preceding 1, and 2 preceding 1, takes the sign —.

The denominator common to the expression for the value of each unknown having been thus formed, the value of z will be obtained by assigning to this denominator a numerator formed by changing Z to A in every term of the denominator. The value of y is likewise a fraction which has the same denominator, its numerator being the quantity obtained by changing Y to A in every term of the denominator. The values of the other unknowns are found by a similar procedure.

Generally speaking, the problem is determinate. But there may be some special cases where it is indeterminate and others where it becomes impossible. This occurs when the denominator common to the unknowns proves to be equal to zero, as, for example, if there are only two equations, the denominator $Z^1Y^2 - Z^2Y^1 = 0$ or if there are three unknowns, the denominator

$$Z^1Y^2Z^3 - Z^1Y^3X^2 - Z^2Y^1X^3 + Z^2Y^3X^1 + Z^3Y^1X^2 - Z^3Y^2X^1 = 0$$

and so on. Now, if the quantities A^1, A^2, A^3, etc., are such that the numerators are also zero, the problem is indeterminate. For the fractions which must yield the values of the unknowns are then $\frac{0}{0}$ and indeterminate. But if the quantities A^1, A^2, A^3, etc., are such that while the denominator common to all unknowns is equal to zero, all the numerators, or some of them are not zero, then the problem is impossible, or at least, the quantities required for the solution of the problem are either all infinite or some of them are. For example, if we have two equations, $2 = 3z - 2y$ and $5 = 6z - 4y$, it will be found that $z = \frac{2}{0}$ and $y = \frac{3}{0}$. Hence z and y are infinite magnitudes which are in the ratio of 2 to 3. Solving for the unknowns by the ordinary methods, we should stumble into the absurd statement $\frac{2}{3} = \frac{5}{6}$. For, the first equation gives $z = \frac{2}{3}y + \frac{2}{3}$ and the second gives $z = \frac{4}{6}y + \frac{5}{6}$. Hence, $\frac{2}{3}y + \frac{2}{3} = \frac{4}{6}y + \frac{5}{6}$, which is absurd if z and y are finite quantities. However, if they are infinite, it may be said without absurdity that $z = \frac{2}{3}y + \frac{2}{3}$ and at the same time, that $z = \frac{2}{3}y + \frac{5}{6}$, because the finite quantities $\frac{2}{3}$ and $\frac{5}{6}$ are insignificant in comparison with the infinite quantities z and $\frac{2}{3}y$, and the two equations $z = \frac{2}{3}y + \frac{2}{3}$ and $z = \frac{2}{3}y + \frac{5}{6}$ both reduce to $z = \frac{2}{3}y$, which contains no contradiction.

AUGUSTUS De MORGAN

(1806—1871)

Augustus De Morgan, one of the greatest teachers of mathematics of all time, possessed a rare combination of profound insight, good humor and originality. Born in Madura, India, he was educated at private schools, entering Trinity College, Cambridge at the age of sixteen. An excellent student, he nevertheless failed to qualify for his M. A. degree because of his conscientious objection to the religious tests required of candidates for the degree at Cambridge at that time. In 1828 he received an appointment as professor of mathematics in the newly established London University. His highly informative lectures hold a unique position in university teaching for their lively extemporaneous delivery and sparkling interest. The lustre of his reputation was enhanced by his whimsy and love of the unexpected, clearly evidenced in his *Budget of Paradoxes,* by his gentle nature, and his genius for logical presentation and lucidity of expression. Extremely independent in mind and spirit, De Morgan encouraged genuine aptitude wherever it appeared. Increasingly liberal as he grew older, he became more sympathetic towards women's rights and he lectured to women's classes without charge.

De Morgan's texts and treatises on algebra, trigonometry, differential and integral calculus, on the calculus of variations, and on probability, charmingly written in a leisurely style, remain valuable sources to this day for students who wish to acquire mathematical techniques and basic understanding. Many of his writings appeared in periodicals, learned journals and encyclopaedias, where they were in great demand. A variety of his works, some of which are great treatises in mathematics and logic, may be found in the Cambridge Philosophical Society Transactions, in Lardner's Cyclopaedia, in the Encyclopaedia Metropolitana, in the Quarterly Journal of Education, in the Penny Encyclopaedia and others.

In 1837 De Morgan married Sophia Elizabeth Frend. Their home in Chelsea, enlivened by their five children, became the center of a large circle of friends who shared their intellectual and artistic interests. Prominent among these was George Boole who side by side with De Morgan pioneered in the development of symbolic logic. *De Morgan's Formal Logic* appeared in the same year (1847) as Boole's work on the algebra of logic. Both works were concerned with an algebra or calculus of classes. In 1860 De Morgan published his *Syllabus of a Proposed System of Logic* in which he constructed a similar calculus of relations. The two dually related theorems of the algebra of classes (De Morgan's Laws) first enunciated by him in 1847, were clearly presented again in his article *On the Syllogism, No. III, and On Logic in General* (1864). De Morgan laid great stress on the need and value of symbolism in logic. Through the power of his personal magnetism and the popularity of his numerous publications he was a stimulating force in the development of mathematics and logic.

●

ON THE SYLLOGISM, NO. III AND ON LOGIC IN GENERAL

SECTION I. *General Considerations.*

The syllogism itself is the web of an argument, on which the tapestry of thought is woven; the *primed* canvas on which the picture is painted. The logician presents it to the world as the tapestry or the picture: he does this in effect by the position he makes it occupy; for he sends the primed canvas to the exhibition. And the world does not see that, though the syllogism be a mere canvas, it stands to the thinker in a very different position from that in which the canvas stands to the painter. Call the historian or the moralist a practised artist at a thousand a year, and I am well content that his structure of the canvas shall be valued at ten shillings a week: it would not hurt my argument if it were valued at a half-penny. For the painter can and does delegate the preparation of the canvas; the historian cannot *put out* his logic. He must do it himself as he goes on; and he must do it well, or his whole work is spoiled.

I will take an example from one of the unusual forms of syllogism. Say "The time is past in which the transmission of news can be measured by the speed of animals or even of steam; for the telegraph is not approached by either.'' Is this a syllogism? Many would say it is not; but wrongly. Throw out the *charges,* the modal reference to past falsehood and present truth, the advantage of the telegraph, its *superior* speed, the reference to progress conveyed in *even*—and we rub off the whole design of the picture. But the ground which carried the design is a syllogism. In old form it is *Darapti,* awkwardly.

All telegraph speed is (not steam speed)
All telegraph speed is (not animal speed)
Therefore Some (not animal speed) is (not steam speed).

In the system which admits contraries it is a syllogism with two negative premises, and a form of conclusion unknown to Aristotle: it is, in the symbols I use, the deduction of)(from)·()·(

No animal speed is telegraph speed
No steam speed is telegraph speed
Therefore Some speed is neither animal nor steam speed.

When this is presented, a person would naturally ask, What then? The answer to this question is seen when the charges are restored, and the sentence takes its proper place in the whole argument.

V. A great objection has been raised to the employment of mathematical symbols: and it seems to be taken for granted that any symbols used by me must be mathematical. The truth is that I have not made much use of symbols actually employed in algebra; and the use which I have made is in one instance seriously objectionable, and must be discontinued. But it has been left to me to discover this mistake, into which I was led, as I shall shew, by the ordinary school of logicians. If A and B be the premises of a syllogism, and C the conclusion, the representation $A + B = C$ is faulty in two points. The premises are compounded, not aggregated; and AB should have been written: the relation of joint premises to conclusion is that (speaking in extension) of contained and containing, and $AB < C$ should have been the symbol. Nevertheless, $A + B = C$, with all its imperfections, made a suggestion of remarkable character to an inventive friend of mine: while $AB < C$ was both a *suggestio veri* and a *suppressio falsi* to myself. For these things see the second part of this paper.

As to symbols in general, it is not necessary to argue in their favour: mine or better ones will make their way, under all the usual difficulties of new language. There was a time when logic had more peculiar symbols than algebra. Every system of signs, before it has become familiar, as we all remember when we look back to ABC, is repulsive, difficult, unmeaning, full of signs of difference which are practical synonyms* by combination of want of comprehension with ignorance of the want. But it is too certain to need argument that the separation of form and matter requires as many symbols as there are separations. . . .

SECTION 2. *First Elements of a System of Logic.*

XXII. A *name* is a sign by which we distinguish one object, process, or product of thought from another.

A name has four applications: two *objective,* signs of what the mind can (be it right or wrong in so doing) conceive to exist though thought were annihilated; two *subjective,* signs of what the mind cannot but conceive to be annihilated with thought. (§ VI.)

The objective applications are:—first, to individual *objects* external to the mind; secondly, to individual notions attaching to or connected with objects, called *qualities,* which are said *and thought* to inhere in the objects. The object itself is but a compound of qualities.

* A Cambridge tutor of high reputation was once trying to familiarise a beginner with the difference between na and a^n. After repeated illustration, he asked the pupil whether he saw the point. "Thank you very much, Mr. ——" was the answer; "I now see perfectly what you mean: but, Mr. ——, between ourselves, now, and speaking candidly, ***don't*** you think it's a ***needless refinement.***"

The *quality* is, in logic, any appurtenance whatever: thus to be called Caesar is a quality.

The subjective applications are:—to designate *class,* collection of objects having similar qualities, or put into one notion by some similar *class-mark;* and a class may consist of one individual only, if only one have the mark: secondly, to designate *attribute,* the class-name of *quality,* the notion of quality in the mind.

Class and *attribute* are two modes of thinking many in the manner of one; two reductions of plurality to unity. The class *man* is one notion in the mind, the receptacle of many individuals: the attribute *human* is also one in thought, being the notion derived from similar qualities possessed by many individuals. *Class* is a noun of multitude, but not a multitude of nouns, nor even one noun selected from a multitude.

Quality, as a class name, may be distributed over any number of individuals. But it has a division peculiar to itself. As merely an appurtenant notion, it may be the compound of several notions. And similarly, attribute may be the compound of several attributes.

In grammar, class is often a substantive capable of designating the individual also, and used in both ways, as man, the man Plato. Quality is often an adjective, as *human;* attribute is often an abstract substantive, as *humanity,* which cannot designate an individual. Language would be more perfect if these distinctions were made by inflexion in all cases: logic would do well to think of introducing such* words as X-ic and X-ity.

The class is an aggregate of individuals; the individual is a compound of qualities; the attribute is a compound of attributes.

Objective names, representing objects and qualities, were once called names of *first intention* or *first notions,*

* The boldest symbolic word ever made was proposed—I think in print, but I cannot find the reference and I am not sure—by one of the young analysts (I speak of 1813, or thereabouts) who first cultivated the continental analysis in England. It was such as 'iso-x-ical,' to signify that in which x has always one value. Thus every circle which has its centre at the origin is iso-$(x^2 + y^2)$-ical. When the crude form is not too complicated, the word might be useful.

as being used according to the mind's first *bent* towards names. Subjective names, representing classes and attributes, were names of *second intention*, or *second notions*. Thus, 'every crow is black' considered merely as a collation of cases, is of first intention: but 'the class crow has the attribute black' is of second intention. Nevertheless, the first sentence, spoken or written, may be thought under the second form. (§ XII.)

Logic is the science and art, the theory and practice, of the form of thought, the law of its action, the working of its machinery; independently of the matter thought on. It considers different kinds of matter only when, if ever, and so far as, they necessitate different forms of thought. It must deal with names, and therefore should deal with all the forms of thought demanded in the four uses of names. It has no right to reject any use of a name: for every such use appertains to a form of thought. (§§ II, III.)

Logic considers both first and second intentions, because both are forms of thought; but the first chiefly as leading to the second: and in both it considers *quae non debentur rebus secundum se, sed secundum esse quod habent in anima*. That is, logic belongs to psychology, not to metaphysics.

It is not to be assumed that the practice of the logic of first intentions is the common property of mankind, and that second intentions form a science to which the student is to be led. The actual form of thought is an unanalysed mixture of first and second intention, with the latter in decided predominance.

A name may be formed from other names as follows. First, by *extension*, symbolised in X = (A, B, C) where the *aggregate* X includes as much as can be spoken of under each and all of the *aggregants* A, B, C. Secondly, by *intension*, symbolised in X = A-B-C, or ABC, where the *compound* X includes *no more than* can be spoken of under *all* the *component* names A, B, C. Thirdly, by combinations of the two.

Increase of extension is generally diminution of intension, never increase: and diminution of extension is generally increase of intension, never diminution. And *vice versa.*

The disjunctive particle, *or,* expresses aggregation: 'either A or B' means 'in the class (A, B).'

Class is most connected with extension, and attribute with intension. Extended attribute is merely class of qualities, and there is some effective use in the distinction between class and its subdivisions on the one hand, and the whole class-mark and its subdivision into qualities on the other hand. These two forms of thought, though closely related, must not be confounded with the relations arising out of comparison of extension and intension. (§ VIII.)

Aggregation of the impossible does not destroy the notion; composition of the impossible does. (§ X.)

The universe is the whole sphere of thought within which the matter in hand is contained: usually not the whole possible universe of thought, but a limited portion of it. In the last syllogism of § IV, the universe is *speed of transmission of news.* The universe being U, the class X introduces with itself the class not-X (or x). Let X and x be called *contraries* or *contradictories* (I make no distinction between these words). It is understood that every class is only *part* of the universe. The symbol (X, x) is equivalent to U: in extension, it contains everything; in intension, it belongs to everything. Thus A, if in the universe, is in (X, x); and A is A-(X, x) aggregate of A-X and A-x. The universe is the maximum of extension, and the minimum of intension. (§ IX.)

The contrary of an aggregate is the compound of the contraries of the aggregants: the contrary of a compound is the aggregate of the contraries of the components. Thus (A, B) and AB have ab and (a, b) for contraries.

XXIII. When two objects, qualities, classes, or attributes, viewed together by the mind, are seen under some connexion, that connexion is called a *relation.* To make very perfect parallelism, we should say that *relation* may be either of the four: that a boat towed by a ship, for instance, has the tow-rope for an *object* of relation. But relation, for all useful logical purposes, is a word of second intention, used only of class and attribute.

A *proposition* is the presentation of two names under a relation. A *judgment* is the sentence of the mind upon a proposition, true, false, more or less probable. The distinction of judgments, other than the simple *true* or *false,* is referred to the theory of probabilities, as a matter of practical convenience. The absolute exclusion of this distinction from logic is an error: the difference between certainty and uncertainty is of the form of thought; the amount of uncertainty is of the matter of this form. Full belief is a logical whole, which is divided into parts in the theory of probabilities: and the division of a logical whole into parts is of logic, whether it be convenient or not to treat it in the same book which treats the syllogism.

The distinction of *subject* and *predicate* is the distinction between the *notion in relation* and the *notion to which it is in relation.*

Every relation has its counter-relation, or *converse* relation: thus if X be in the relation A to Y, Y is therefore in some relation B to X: and A and B are converse relations, and the propositions are converse propositions. Every proposition has its converse, of meaning identical with itself.

When a relation is its own converse, the *proposition* is said to be *convertible*: meaning that the converse exhibits no change of relation. It is the *terms* (subject and predicate) which are convertible, strictly speaking.

When X has a relation (A) to that which has a relation (B) to Y, X has to Y a *combined* relation: the *combinants* are A and B. Relations have both extension and intension. Thus, to take one of those *relations* which have appropriated the word in common life, the relation of *first-cousin* is the *aggregate* of son of uncle, daughter of uncle, son of aunt, daughter of aunt. The relation of the minister to the crown is the *compound* of *subordinate* and *adviser.*

XXIV. Certain relations take precedence of all others, because they are presented by the notion of naming, and spring out of its purpose, if indeed they do not themselves constitute the purpose. They may be called *onomatic* or *onymatic* (*nominative* and *nominal* being engaged).

The excessive importance of these relations has enabled them to drive all others out of common logic, on the pretext of every other relation being expressible in terms of these: as must be the case, since these relations exist wherever names exist which apply to the same object.

The onymatic relations, to which in *this* paper I confine myself, are those of *whole and part* in the two aspects of *containing and contained* and *compounded and component;* and also the relations which the notion of contraries, and the notion of true and false, introduce in connexion with them.

Subordinate to, and necessarily compounded in, the notion of whole and part, is that of *more and less,* in the matter of which are the incidents of *quantity.* But *more and less* is only a component of *whole and part,* in the form of thought: and except as such component, is of no logical import. Thus *infusorium* is no doubt a larger class than *man,* and no doubt for reasons: but if we knew the extent of superiority, and the reasons, neither would be of any logical effect, for our present purpose; because the more and less is not that of containing and contained, and the relation is not onymatic.

The distinction of *aggregation* and *composition* is the most important distinction in the subdivisions of logic. Our knowledge does not suffice to define it by full description: we can only illustrate it. To the mathematician we may say that it has the distinctive character of $a + b$ and ab: to the chemist, of mechanical mixture and chemical combination: to the lawyer it appears in the distinction between 'And be it further enacted' and 'provided always.'

RENE DESCARTES

(1596—1650)

Rene Descartes, celebrated philosopher and mathematician of the seventeenth century, was a descendant of old line lesser nobility or landed gentry on both sides of his family. The title of Seigneur du Perron which came to him through a small estate inherited from his mother, was sometimes used to distinguish him from his older brother, but Rene appears not to have cared to be addressed by this title. From 1604 to 1612, Rene Descartes was a student at the newly established Jesuit College of La Fleche. A frail child, he was permitted some special privileges (such as being excused from early rising), and thus gently cared for, he proved to be an excellent student in all the usual scholastic studies, though he showed a marked preference for mathematics. A year spent at home after leaving La Fleche was followed by a short, wild year in Paris. Then, suddenly and almost in concealment, he returned to his studies. During this period, he was encouraged in his philosophical and mathematical investigations by the mathematician Mydorge and by Marin Mersenne, who had formerly been a pupil at La Fleche. He also studied at the university of Poitier where he received a degree in law in 1616. In 1618, Descartes entered the service of Prince Maurice of Orange, whose army encampment at Breda served as an officers' training ground for young men of the nobility of all the countries of Europe. Later, Descartes fought under Maximilian I, elector and duke of Bavaria. For about ten or twelve years, Descartes crisscrossed the whole of Europe, having, as he said in his *Discourse on Method,* " . . . abandoned the study of letters and resolved no longer to seek any other science than the knowledge of myself and the book of the world." He settled at last in Holland where, in a rising tide of economic, artistic and intellectual development, civil and religious freedom and personal security were found to a degree unequalled anywhere else in the world. "What other place could you choose in all the world," he wrote to Balzac in 1631, "where all the comforts of life and all the curiosities that can be desired are so easy to find as here? What other country where you can enjoy such perfect liberty, where you can sleep with more security, where there are always armies afoot for our protection, where poisonings, treacheries, calumnies are less known, and where there has survived more of the innocence of our forefathers?"

When Descartes arrived in Holland he had already achieved an established reputation as a philosopher and scientist. The twenty-one years of fruitful meditation and writing in Holland raised him to the position of world leadership in both fields. Most of his published works were written in Holland. By means of voluminous correspondence carried on either directly, or through

Mersenne and Clersellier of Paris as intermediaries, he maintained contact with all the great intellectual figures of his time. However, life in Holland was by no means a sedentary retreat for him uninterrupted by travel. Excellent Dutch roads made all parts of the country accessible to him and, attracted by the beauty of the land, he made frequent use of this mobility, writing enthusiastically of his travels. In 1631, Descartes made a swift trip to England, and in 1634, another to Denmark. He revisited France three times, in 1644, 1647 and 1648, in response to invitations from Princess Elizabeth, daughter of the Winter King, Frederick V. In the fall of 1649, he sailed to Sweden to gratify Queen Christina's ambition for the intellectual development of her country as well as her personal desire to learn his philosophy at first hand. Descartes arrived at Stockholm in October, 1649. His health had never been robust, and there he succumbed to the rigors of an exceptionally cold northern winter. He died on February 11, 1650.

Descartes' *Discourse on Method* contained his creative theory of perception. Its importance for mathematics lies, first, in his use of mathematical method for the construction of his general methodology, and, second, in his creation of new mathematical procedures in the course of his illustration of the application of his general methodology to the field of mathematics. Three essays were appended to Descartes' *Discourse on Method: La Dioptrique, Les Meteores* and *La Geometrie.* Each was intended as an illustration of the practical usefulness of Descartes' methodology in advancing scientific knowledge. In the third of the essays, *La Geometrie,* Descartes proposed to show how easily his *Method* yielded the solution of a problem considered difficult by ancient mathematicians as well as by moderns, selecting a problem for which no complete solution had heretofore been offered by any one. In carrying out this purpose, Descartes introduced an improved mathematical notation, made advances in the theory of equations, used for the first time, the highly significant method of restating a geometrical problem in algebraic form and then solving it algebraically, and thereby earned for himself the title of founder of analytic geometry.

●

DISCOURSE ON METHOD

translated by John Veitch

PART I.

Good sense is, of all things among men, the most equally distributed; for every one thinks himself so abundantly provided with it, that those even who are the most difficult to satisfy in everything else, do not usually desire a larger measure of this quality than they already possess. And in this it is not likely that all are mistaken: the conviction is rather to be held as testifying that the power of judging aright and of distinguishing Truth from Error, which is properly what is called Good Sense or Reason, is by nature equal in all men; and that the diversity of our opinions, consequently, does not arise from some being endowed with a larger share of Reason than others, but solely from this, that we conduct our thoughts along different ways, and do not fix our attention on the same objects. For to be possessed of a vigorous mind is not enough; the prime requisite is rightly to apply it.

From my childhood, I have been familiar with letters; and as I was given to believe that by their help a clear and certain knowledge of all that is useful in life might be acquired, I was ardently desirous of instruction. But as soon as I had finished the entire course of study, at the close of which it is customary to be admitted into the order of the learned, I completely changed my opinion. For I found myself involved in so many doubts and errors, that I was convinced I had advanced no farther in all my attempts at learning, than the discovery at every turn of my own ignorance. And yet I was studying in one of the most celebrated Schools in Europe, in which I thought there must be learned men, if such were anywhere to be found. I had been taught all that others learned there; and not contented with the sciences actually taught us, I had, in addition, read all the books that had fallen into my hands, treating of such branches as are esteemed the most curious and rare. I knew the judgment which others had formed of me; and I did not find that I was considered inferior to my fellows, although there were among them some who were already marked out to fill the places of our instructors. And, in fine, our age appeared to me as flourishing, and as fertile in powerful minds as any preceding one. I was thus led to take the liberty of judging of all other men by myself, and of concluding that there was no science in existence that was of such a nature as I had previously been given to believe.

I still continued, however, to hold in esteem the studies of the Schools. I was aware that the Languages taught in them are necessary to the understanding of the writings of the ancients; that the grace of Fable stirs the mind; that the memorable deeds of History elevate it; and, if read with discretion, aid in forming the judgment; that the perusal of all excellent books is, as it were, to interview with the noblest men of past ages, who have written them, and even a studied interview, in which are discovered to us only their choicest thoughts; that Eloquence has incomparable force and beauty; that Poesy has its ravishing graces and delights; that in the Mathematics there are many refined discoveries eminently suited to gratify the inquisitive, as well as further all the arts and lessen the labor of man; that numerous highly useful precepts and exhortations to virtue are contained in treatises on Morals; that Theology points out the path to heaven; that Philosophy affords the means of discoursing with an appearance of truth on all matters, and commands the admiration of the more simple; that Jurisprudence, Medicine, and the other Sciences, secure for their cultivators honors and riches; and, in fine, that it is useful to bestow some attention upon all, even upon those abounding the most in superstition and error, that we may be in a position to determine their real value, and guard against being deceived.

. . .I was especialy delighted with the Mathematics, on account of the certitude and evidence of their reasonings: but I had not as yet a precise knowledge of their true use; and thinking that they but contributed to the advancement of the mechanical arts, I was astonished that foundations, so strong and solid, should have had no loftier superstructure reared on them. . . .

Among the branches of Philosophy, I had, at an earlier period, given some attention to Logic, and among those of the Mathematics to Geometrical Analysis and Algebra, —three Arts or Sciences which ought, as I conceived, to contribute something to my design. But, on examination, I found that, as for Logic, its syllogisms and the majority of its other precepts are of avail rather in the communication of what we already know, or even as the Art of Lully, in speaking without judgment of things of which we are ignorant, than in the investigation of the unknown; and although this Science contains indeed a number of correct and very excellent precepts, there are, nevertheless, so many others, and these either injurious or superfluous, mingled with the former, that it is almost quite as difficult to effect a severance of the true from the false as it is to extract a Diana or a Minerva from a rough block of marble. Then as to the Analysis of the ancients and the Algebra of the moderns, besides that they embrace only matters highly abstract, and, to appearance, of no use, the former is so exclusively restricted to the consideration of figures, that it can exercise the Understanding only on condition of greatly fatiguing the Imagination; and, in the latter, there is so complete a subjection to certain rules and formulas, that there results an art full of confusion and obscurity calculated to embarrass, instead of a science fitted to cultivate the mind. By these considerations I was induced to seek some other Method which would comprise the advantages of the three and be exempt from their defects. And as a multitude of laws often only hampers justice, so that a state is best governed when, with few laws, these are rigidly administered; in like manner, instead of the great number of precepts of which Logic is composed, I believed that the four following would prove perfectly sufficient for me, provided I took the firm and unwavering resolution never in a single instance to fail in observing them.

The FIRST was never to accept anything for true which I did not clearly know to be such; that is to say, carefully to avoid precipitancy and prejudice, and to comprise nothing more in my judgment than what was presented to my mind so clearly and distinctly as to exclude all ground of doubt.

The SECOND, to divide each of the difficulties under examination into as many parts as possible, and as might be necessary for its adequate solution.

The THIRD, to conduct my thoughts in such order that, by commencing with objects the simplest and easiest to know, I might ascend by little and little, and, as it were, step by step, to the knowledge of the more complex; assigning in thought a certain order even to those objects which in their own nature do not stand in a relation of antecedence and sequence.

At the LAST, in every case to make enumerations so complete, and reviews so general, that I might be assured that nothing was omitted.

The long chains of simple and easy reasonings by means of which geometers are accustomed to reach the conclusions of their most difficult demonstrations, had led me to imagine that all things, to the knowledge of which man is competent, are mutually connected in the same way, and that there is nothing so far removed from us as to be beyond our reach, or so hidden that we cannot discover it, provided only we abstain from accepting the false for the true, and always preserve in our thoughts the order necessary for the deduction of one truth from another. And I had little difficulty in determining the objects with which it was necessary to commence, for I was already persuaded that it must be with the simplest and easiest to know, and considering that of all those who have hitherto sought truth in the Sciences, the mathematics alone have been able to find any demonstrations, that is, any certain and evident reasons, I did not doubt but that such must have been the rule of their investigations. I resolved to commence, therefore, with the examination of the simplest objects, not anticipating, however, from this any other advantage than that to be found in accustoming my mind to the love and nourishment of truth, and to a distaste for all such reasonings as were unsound. But I had no intention on that account of attempting to master all the particular Sciences commonly denominated Mathematics: but observing that, however different their objects, they all agree in considering only the various relations or proportions subsisting among those objects, I thought it best for my purpose to consider these proportions in the most general form possible, without referring them to any objects in particular, except such as would most facilitate the knowledge of them, and without by any means restricting them to these, that afterward I might thus be the better able to apply them to every other class of objects to which they are legitimately applicable. Perceiving further, that in order to understand these relations I should sometimes have to consider them one by one, and sometimes only to bear them in mind, or embrace them in the aggregate, I thought that, in order the better to consider them individually, I should view them as subsisting between straight lines, than which I could find no objects more simple, or capable of being more distinctly represented to my imagination and senses; and on the other hand, that in order to retain them in the memory, or embrace an aggregate of many, I should express them by certain characters the briefest possible. In this way I believed that I could borrow all that was best both in Geometrical Analysis and in Algebra, and correct all the defects of the one by help of the other.

And, in point of fact, the accurate observance of these few precepts gave me, I take the liberty of saying, such ease in unraveling all the questions embraced in these two sciences, that in the two or three months I devoted to their examination, not only did I reach solutions of questions I had formerly deemed exceedingly difficult, but even as regards questions of the solution of which I continued ignorant, I was enabled, as it appeared to me, to determine the means whereby, and the extent to which, a solution was possible; results attributable to the circumstance that I commenced with the simplest and most general truths, and that thus each truth discovered was a rule available in the discovery of subsequent ones. Nor in this perhaps shall I appear too vain, if it be considered that, as the truth on any particular point is one, whoever apprehends the truth, knows all that on that point can be known. The child, for example, who has been instructed in the elements of Arithmetic, and has made a particular addition, according to rule, may be assured that he has found, with respect to the sum of the numbers before him, all that in this instance is within the reach of human genius. Now, in conclusion, the Method which teaches adherence to the true order, and an exact enumeration of all the conditions of the thing sought includes all that gives certitude to the rules of Arithmetic.

But the chief ground of my satisfaction with this Method was the assurance I had of thereby exercising my reason in all matters, if not with absolute perfection, at least with the greatest attainable by me: besides, I was conscious that by its use my mind was becoming gradually habituated to clearer and more distinct conceptions of its objects; and I hoped also, from not having restricted this Method to any particular matter, to apply it to the difficulties of the other Sciences, with not less success than to those of Algebra.

●

THE GEOMETRY OF RENE DESCARTES

Translated by
David Eugene Smith and Marcia L. Latham

BOOK I

Problems the Construction of Which Requires Only Straight Lines and Circles

Any problem in geometry can easily be reduced to such terms that a knowledge of the lengths of certain

LA GEOMETRIE.

LIVRE PREMIER.

Des problesmes qu'on peut construire sans y employer que des cercles & des lignes droites.

TOus les Problesmes de Geometrie se peuuent facilement reduire a tels termes, qu'il n'est besoin par aprés que de connoistre la longeur de quelques lignes droites, pour les construire.

Et comme toute l'Arithmetique n'est composée, que de quatre ou cinq operations, qui sont l'Addition, la Soustraction, la Multiplication, la Diuision, & l'Extraction des racines, qu'on peut prendre pour vne espece de Diuision : Ainsi n'a-t'on autre chose a faire en Geometrie touchant les lignes qu'on cherche, pour les preparer a estre connuës, que leur en adiouster d'autres, ou en oster, Oubien en ayant vne, que ie nommeray l'vnité pour la rapporter d'autant mieux aux nombres, & qui peut ordinairement estre prise a discretion, puis en ayant encore deux autres, en trouuer vne quatriesme, qui soit à l'vne de ces deux, comme l'autre est a l'vnité, ce qui est le mesme que la Multiplication ; oubien en trouuer vne quatriesme, qui soit a l'vne de ces deux, comme l'vnite

Commēt le calcul d'Arithmetique se rapporte aux operations de Geometrie.

Pp est

straight lines is sufficient for its construction.[1] Just as arithmetic consists of only four or five operations, namely, addition, subtraction, multiplication, division and the extraction of roots, which may be considered a kind of division, so in geometry, to find lines it is merely necessary to add or subtract other lines; or else, taking one line which I shall call unity in order to relate it as closely as possible to numbers, and which can in general be chosen arbitrarily, and having given two other lines, to find a fourth line which shall be to one of the given lines as the other is to unity (which is the same as multiplication); or, again, to find a fourth line which is to one of the given lines as unity is to the other (which is equivalent to division); or, finally, to find one, two, or several mean proportionals between unity and some other line (which is the same as extracting the square root, etc., of the given line.)[3] And I shall not hesitate to introduce these arithmetical terms into geometry, for the sake of greater clearness.

For example, let AB be taken as unity, and let it be required to multiply BD by BC. I have only to join the points A and C, and draw DE parallel to CA; then BE is the product of BD and BC.

If it be required to divide BE by BD, I join E and D,

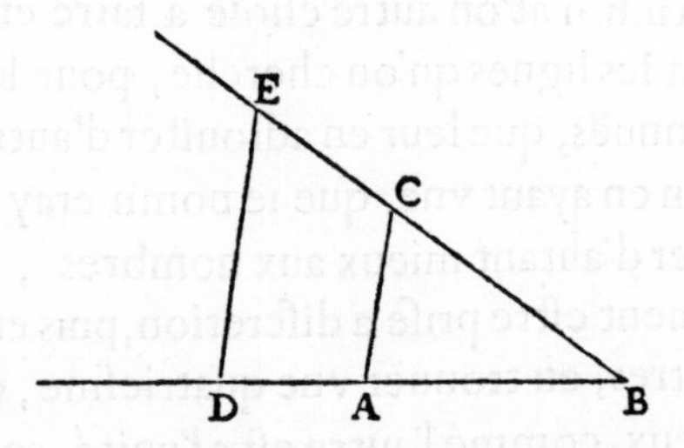

[1] Large collections of problems of this nature are contained in the following works: Vincenzo Riccati and Girolamo Saladino, *Institutiones Analyticae*, Bologna, 1765; Maria Gaetana Agnesi, *Istituzioni Analitiche*, Milan, 1748; Claude Rabuel, *Commentaries sur la Geometrie de M. Descartes*, Lyons, 1730 (hereafter referred to as Rabuel); and other books of the same period or earlier.

[3] While in arithmetic the only exact roots obtainable are those of perfect powers, in geometry a length can be found which will represent exactly the square root of a given line, even though this line be not commensurable with unity. Of other roots, Descartes speaks later.

and draw AC parallel to DE; then BC is the result of the division.

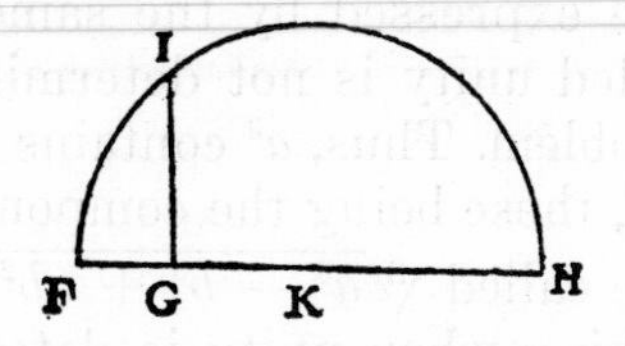

If the square root of GH is desired, I add, along the same straight line, FG equal to unity; then, bisecting FH at K, I describe the circle FIH about K as a center, and draw from G a perpendicular and extend it to I, and GI is the required root. I do not speak here of cube root, or other roots, since I shall speak more conveniently of them later.

Often it is not necessary thus to draw the lines on paper, but it is sufficient to designate each by a single letter. Thus, to add the lines BD and GH, I call one a and the other b, and write $a + b$. Then $a - b$ will indicate that b is subtracted from a; ab that a is multiplied by b; $\frac{a}{b}$ that a is divided by b; aa or a^2 that a is multiplied by itself; a^3 that this result is multiplied by a, and so on, indefinitely.[4] Again, if I wish to extract the square root of $a^2 + b^2$, I write $\sqrt{a^2 + b^2}$; if I wish to extract the cube root of $a^3 - b^3 + ab^2$, I write $\sqrt[3]{a^3 - b^3 + ab^2}$, and similarly for other roots.[5] Here it must be observed that by a^2, b^3, and similar expressions, I ordinarily mean only simple lines, which, however, I name squares, cubes, etc.,

[4] Descartes uses a^3, a^4, a^5, a^6, and so on, to represent the respective powers of a, but he uses both aa and a^2 without distinction. For example, he often has $aabb$, but he also uses $\frac{3a^2}{4b^2}$.

[5] Descartes writes: $\sqrt{C.a^3 - b^3 + abb}$.

so that I may make use of the terms employed in algebra.[6]

It should also be noted that all parts of a single line should always be expressed by the same number of dimensions, provided unity is not determined by the conditions of the problem. Thus, a^3 contains as many dimensions as ab^2 or b^3, these being the component parts of the line which I have called $\sqrt[3]{a^3 - b^3 + ab^2}$. It is not, however, the same thing when unity is determined, because unity can always be understood, even where there are too few dimensions; thus, if it be required to extract the cube root of $a^2b^2 - b$, we must consider the quantity a^2b^2 divided once by unity, and the quantity b multiplied twice by unity.[7]

Finally, so that we may be sure to remember the names of these lines, a separate list should always be made as often as names are assigned or changed. For example, we may write, $AB = 1$, that is AB is equal to 1;[8] $GH = a$, $BD = b$, and so on.

If, then, we wish to solve any problem, we first suppose the solution already effected,[9] and give names to all the lines that seem needful for its construction,— to those that are unknown as well as to those that are known.

---

[6] At the time this was written, a^2 was commonly considered to mean the surface of a square whose side is a, and b^3 to mean the volume of a cube whose side is b; while b^4, b^5, . . . were unintelligible as geometric forms. Descartes here says that a^2 does not have this meaning, but means the line obtained by constructing a third proportional to 1 and a, and so on.

[7] Descartes seems to say that each term must be of the third degree, and that therefore we must conceive of both a^2b^2 and b as reduced to the proper dimension.

[8] Descartes writes, AB ∝ 1. He seems to have been the first to use this symbol. Among the few writers who followed him, was Hudde (1633-1704). It is very commonly supposed that ∝ is a ligature representing the first two letters (or diphthong) of "aequare." See, for example, M. Aubry's note in W. W. R. Ball's *Recreations Mathematiques et Problemes des Temps Anciens et Modernes,* French edition, Paris, 1909, Part III, p. 164.

[9] This plan, as is well known, goes back to Plato. It appears in the work of Pappus as follows: "In analysis we suppose that which is required to be already obtained, and consider its connections and antecedents, going back until we reach either something already known (given in the hypothesis), or else some fundamental principle (axiom or postulate) of mathematics." *Pappi Alexandrini Collectiones quae supersunt e libris manu scriptis edidit Latina interpellatione et commentariis instruxit Fredericus Hultsch,* Berlin, 1876-1878; vol. II, p. 635 (hereafter referred to as Pappus).

Then, making no distinction between known and unknown lines, we must unravel the difficulty in any way that shows most naturally the relations between these lines, until we find it possible to express a single quantity in two ways.[11] This will constitute an equation, since the terms of one of these two expressions are together equal to the terms of the other.

We must find as many such equations as there are supposed to be unknown lines; but if, after considering everything involved, so many cannot be found, it is evident that the question is not entirely determined. In such a case we may choose arbitrarily lines of known length for each unknown line to which there corresponds no equation.

If these are several equations, we must use each in order, either considering it alone or comparing it with the others, so as to obtain a value for each of the unknown lines; and so we must combine them until there remains a single unknown line[14] which is equal to some known line, or whose square, cube, fourth power, fifth power, sixth power, etc., is equal to the sum or difference of two or more quantities, one of which is known, while the others consist of mean proportionals between unity and this square, or cube, or fourth power, etc., multiplied by other known lines. I may express this as follows:

$$z = b,$$
$$\text{or } z^2 = -az + b^2,$$
$$\text{or } z^3 = az^2 + b^2z - c^3,$$
$$\text{or } z^4 = az^3 - c^3z + d^4, \textit{ etc.}$$

That is, z, which I take for the unknown quantity, is equal to b; or, the square of z is equal to the square of b diminished by a multiplied by z; or, the cube of z is equal to a multiplied by the square of z, plus the square of b multiplied by z, diminished by the cube of c; and similarly for the others.

---

[11] That is, we must solve the resulting simultaneous equations.

[14] That is, a line represented by $x, x^2, x^3, x^4, \ldots$

Thus, all the unknown quantities can be expressed in terms of a single quantity, whenever the problem can be constructed by means of circles and straight lines, or by conic sections, or even by some other curve of degree not greater than the third or fourth.

But I shall not stop to explain this in more detail, because I should deprive you of the pleasure of mastering it yourself, as well as of the advantage of training your mind by working over it, which is in my opinion the principal benefit to be derived from this science. Because, I find nothing here so difficult that it cannot be worked out by any one at all familiar with ordinary geometry and with algebra, who will consider carefully all that is set forth in this treatise.[18]

---

[18] In the Introduction to the 1637 edition of *La Geometrie,* Descartes made the following remark: "In my previous writings I have tried to make my meaning clear to everybody; but I doubt if this treatise will be read by anyone not familiar with the books on geometry, and so I have thought it superfluous to repeat demonstrations contained in them." See *Oeuvres de Descartes,* edited by Charles Adam and Paul Tannery, Paris, 1897-1910, vol. VI, p. 368. In a letter written to Mersenne in 1637 Descartes says: "I do not enjoy speaking in praise of myself, but since few people can understand my geometry, and since you wish me to give you my opinion of it, I think it well to say that it is all I could hope for, and that in *La Dioptrique* and *Les Meteores,* I have only tried to persuade people that my method is better than the ordinary one. I have proved this in my geometry, for in the beginning I have solved a question which, according to Pappus, could not be solved by any of the ancient geometers.

"Moreover, what I have given in the second book on the nature and properties of curved lines, and the method of examining them, is, it seems to me, as far beyond the treatment in the ordinary geometry, as the rhetoric of Cicero is beyond the a, b, c of children. . . .

"As to the suggestion that what I have written could easily have been gotten from Vieta, the very fact that my treatise is hard to understand is due to my attempt to put nothing in it that I believed to be known either by him or by any one else. . . . I begin the rules of my algebra with what Vieta wrote at the very end of his book, *De emendatione aequationum*. . . . Thus, I begin where he left off." *Oeuvres de Descartes, publiees par Victor Cousin,* Paris, 1824, Vol. VI, p. 294 (hereafter referred to as Cousin).

In another letter to Mersenne, written April 20, 1646, Descartes writes as follows: "I have omitted a number of things that might have made it (the geometry) clearer, but I did this intentionally, and would not have it otherwise. The only suggestions that have been made concerning changes in it are in regard to rendering it clearer to readers, but most of these are so malicious that I am completely disgusted with them." Cousin, Vol. IX, p. 553.

In a letter to the Princess Elizabeth, Descartes says: "In the solution of a geometrical problem I take care, as far as possible, to use as lines of reference parallel lines or lines at right angles; and I use no theorems except those which assert that the sides of similar triangles are proportional, and that in a right triangle the square of the hypotenuse is equal to the sum of the squares of the sides. I do not hesitate to introduce several unknown quantities, so as to reduce the question to such terms that it shall depend only on these two theorems." Cousin, Vol. IX, p. 143.

BOOK II

On the Nature of Curved Lines

The ancients were familiar with the fact that the problems of geometry may be divided into three classes, namely, plane, solid, and linear problems. This is equivalent to saying that some problems require only circles and straight lines for their construction, while others require a conic section and still others require more complex curves. I am surprised, however, that they did not go further, and distinguish between different degrees of these more complex curves, nor do I see why they called the latter mechanical, rather than geometrical.

In their treatment of the conic sections they did not hesitate to introduce the assumption that any given cone can be cut by a given plane. Now to treat all the curves which I mean to introduce here, only one additional assumption is necessary, namely, two or more lines can be moved, one upon the other, determining by their intersection other curves. This seems to me in no way more difficult.

It is true that the conic sections were never freely received into ancient geometry, and I do not care to undertake to change names confirmed by usage; nevertheless, it seems very clear to me that if we make the usual assumption that geometry is precise and exact, while mechanics is not; and if we think of geometry as the science which furnishes a general knowledge of the measurement of all bodies, then we have no more right to exclude the more complex curves than the simpler ones, provided they can be conceived of as described by a continuous motion or by several successive motions, each motion being completely determined by those which precede; for in this way an exact knowledge of the magnitude of each is always obtainable.

I think the best way to group together all such curves and then classify them in order, is by recognizing the fact that all points of those curves which we may call "geometric," that is, those which admit of precise and exact measurement, must bear a definite relation[77] to all points of a straight line, and that this relation must be expressed by means of a single equation.[78]

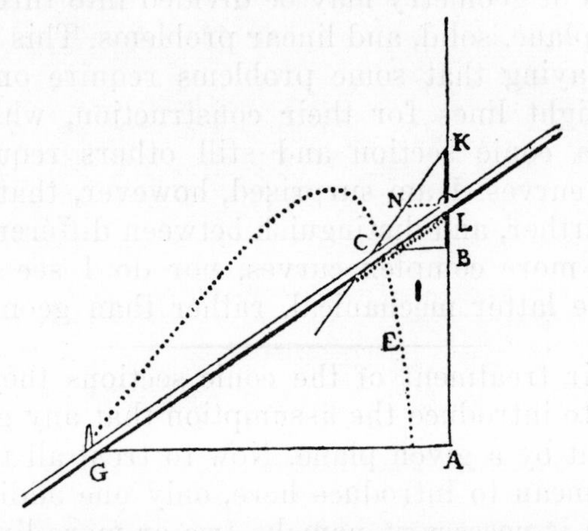

Suppose the curve EC to be described by the intersection of the ruler GL and the rectilinear plane figure CNKL, whose side KN is produced indefinitely in the direction of C, and which, being moved in the same plane in such a way that its side[82] KL always coincides with some part of the line BA (produced in both directions), imparts to the ruler GL a rotary motion about G (the ruler being hinged to the figure CNKL at L).[83] If I wish to find out to what class this curve belongs, I choose a straight line, as AB, to which to refer all its points, and in AB I choose a point A at which to begin the investigation.[84] I say "choose this and that," because we are

[77] That is, a relation exactly known, as, for example, that between two straight lines in distinction to that between a straight line and a curve, unless the length of the curve is known.

[78] It will be recognized at once that this statement contains the fundamental concept of analytic geometry.

[82] "Diametre."

[83] The instrument thus consists of three parts, (1) a ruler AK of indefinite length, fixed in a plane: (2) a ruler GL, also of indefinite length, fastened to a pivot, in the same plane, but not on AK; and (3) a rectilinear figure BKC, the side KC being indefinitely long, to which the ruler GL is hinged at L, and which is made to slide along the ruler GL.

[84] That is, Descartes uses the point A as origin, and the line AB as axis of abscissas. He uses parallel ordinates, but does not draw the axis of ordinates.

free to choose what we will, for, while it is necessary to use care in the choice in order to make the equation as short and simple as possible, yet no matter what line I should take instead of AB the curve would always prove to be of the same class, a fact easily demonstrated.[85]

Then I take on the curve an arbitrary point, as C, at which we will suppose the instrument applied to describe the curve. Then I draw through C the line CB parallel to GA. Since CB and BA are unknown and indeterminate quantities, I shall call one of them y and the other x. To the relation between these quantities I must consider also the known quantities which determine the description of the curve, as GA, which I shall call a; KL, which I shall call b; and NL parallel to GA, which I shall call c. Then I say that as NL is to LK, or as c is to b, so CB, or y, is to BK, which is therefore equal to $\frac{b}{c}y$. Then BL is equal to $\frac{b}{c}y - b$, and AL is equal to $x + \frac{b}{c}y - b$. Moreover, as CB is to LB, that is, as y is to $\frac{b}{c}y - b$, so AG or a is to LA or $x + \frac{b}{c}y - b$. Multiplying the second by the third, we get $\frac{ab}{c}y - ab$ equal to

$$xy + \frac{b}{c}y^2 - by,$$

which is obtained by multiplying the first by the last. Therefore, the required equation is

$$y^2 = cy - \frac{cx}{b}y + ay - ac.$$

---

[85] That is, the nature of a curve is not affected by a transformation of coordinates.

From this equation we see that the curve EC belongs to the first class, it being, in fact, a hyperbola.[86]

If in the instrument used to describe the curve we substitute for the rectilinear figure CNK this hyperbola or some other curve of the first class lying in the plane CNKL, the intersection of this curve with the ruler GL will describe, instead of the hyperbola EC, another curve, which will be of the second class.

Thus, if CNK be a circle having its center at L, we shall describe the first conchoid of the ancients, while if we use a parabola having KB as axis we shall describe the curve which, as I have already said, is the first and simplest of the curves required in the problem of Pappus, that is, the one which furnishes the solution when five lines are given in position.

BOOK III

On the Construction of Solid and Super Solid Problems.

Every equation can have[184] as many distinct roots (values of the unknown quantity) as the number of dimensions of the unknown quantity in the equation.[185] Suppose, for example, $x = 2$ or $x - 2 = 0$, and again, $x = 3$, or $x - 3 = 0$. Multiplying together the two equations $x - 2 = 0$ and $x - 3 = 0$, we have $x^2 - 5x + 6 = 0$, or $x^2 = 5x - 6$. This is an equation in which x has the value 2 and at the same time[186] x has the value 3. If we next make $x - 4 = 0$ and multiply this by $x^2 - 5x + 6 = 0$, we have $x^3 - 9x^2 + 26\,x - 24 = 0$ another equation, in which x, having three dimensions, has also three values, namely, 2, 3, and 4.

---

[86] Cf. Briot and Bouquet, *Elements of Analytical Geometry of Two Dimensions,* trans. by J. H. Boyd, New York, 1896, p. 143.

The two branches of the curve are determined by the position of the triangle CNKL with respect to the directrix AB. See Rabuel, p. 119.

[184] It is worthy of note that Descartes writes "can have" ("peut-il y avoir"), not "must have," since he is considering only real positive roots.

[185] That is, as the number denoting the degree of the equation.

[186] "Tout ensemble,"—not quite the modern idea.

It often happens, however, that some of the roots are false[187] or less than nothing. Thus, if we suppose x to represent the defect[188] of a quantity 5, we have $x + 5 = 0$ which, multiplied by $x^3 - 9x^2 + 26x - 24 = 0$, yields $x^4 - 4x^3 - 19x^2 + 106x - 120 = 0$, an equation having four roots, namely three true roots, 2, 3, and 4, and one false root, 5.[189]

It is evident from the above that the sum[190] of an equation having several roots is always divisible by a binomial consisting of the unknown quantity diminished by the value of one of the true roots, or plus the value of one of the false roots. In this way,[191] the degree of an equation can be lowered.

On the other hand, if the sum of the terms of an equation[192] is not divisible by a binomial consisting of the unknown quantity plus or minus some other quantity, then this latter quantity is not a root of the equation. Thus the[193] above equation $x^4 - 4x^3 - 19x^2 + 106x - 120 = 0$ is divisible by $x - 2$, $x - 3$, $x - 4$ and $x + 5$,[194] but is not divisible by x plus or minus any other quantity. Therefore the equation can have only the four roots, 2, 3, 4, and 5.[195] We can determine also the number of true and false roots that any equation can have, as follows:[196]

---

187 "Racines fausses," a term formerly used for "negative roots." Fibonacci, for example, does not admit negative quantities as roots of an equation. *Scritti de Leonardo Pisano,* published by Boncompagni, Rome, 1857. Cardan recognizes them, but calls them "æstimationes falsæ" or "fictæ," and attaches no special significance to them. See Cardan, *Ars Magna,* Nurnberg, 1545, p. 2. Stifel called them "Numeri absurdi," as also in Rudolff's Coss, 1545.

188 "Le defaut." If $x = -5$, -5 is the "defect" of 5, that is, the remainder when 5 is subtracted from zero.

189 That is, three positive roots, 2, 3, and 4, and one negative root, -5.

190 "Somme," the left member when the right member is zero; that is, what we represent by $f(x)$ in the equation $f(x) = 0$.

191 That is, by performing the division.

192 "Si la somme d'un equation."

193 First member of the equation. Descartes always speaks of dividing the equation.

194 Incorrectly given as $x - 5$ in some editions.

195 Where 5 would now be written -5. Descartes neither states nor explicitly assumes the fundamental theorem of algebra, namely, that every equation has at least one root.

196 This is the well known "Descartes's Rule of Signs." It was known however, before his time, for Harriot had given it in his *Artis analyticae praxis,* London, 1631. Cantor says Descartes may have learned it from Cardan's writings, but was the first to state it as a general rule. See Cantor, Vol. II(1) pp. 496 and 725.

An equation can have as many true roots as it contains changes of sign, from + to — or from — to +; and as many false roots as the number of times two + signs or two — signs are found in succession.

Thus, in the last equation, since $+x^4$ is followed by $-4x^3$, giving a change of sign from + to —, and $-19x^2$ is followed by $+106x$ and $+106x$ by -120, giving two more changes, we know there are three true roots; and since $-4x^3$ is followed by $-19x^2$ there is one false root.

It is also easy to transform an equation so that all the roots that were false shall become true roots, and all those that were true shall become false. This is done by changing the signs of the second, fourth, sixth, and all even terms, leaving unchanged the signs of the first, third, fifth, and other odd terms. Thus, if instead of

$$+x^4-4x^3-19x^2+106x-120=0$$

we write

$$+x^4+4x^3-19x^2-106x-120=0$$

we get an equation having one true root, 5, and three false roots, 2, 3, and 4.[197]

[197] In absolute value.

DIOPHANTUS

(c. 250 A.D.)

Diophantus of Alexandria, an ancient Greek mathematician, was the author of one of the greatest mathematical treatises of ancient times, the *Arithmetica*, a masterly exposition of algebraic analysis, so thorough and complete in its time, that all previous works in its field ceased to be of interest and passed into oblivion. In the *Arithmetica,* moreover, algebraic methods advanced to a peak of achievement which was not to be surpassed before the sixteenth century. The pronounced influence exerted by Diophantus upon the development of algebra in the Late Renaissance began in a flurry of activity centering around the rediscovery of a manuscript of his work in 1570. In 1572, Bombelli published his *Algebra* containing many problems taken from the *Arithmetica.* While Bombelli's translation of the problems was excellent, he was not careful to state which problems in his *Algebra* were his own and which had come from Diophantus. A Latin translation of the *Arithmetica* written by Xylander (William Holzmann) appeared in 1574. In 1585, Simon Stevin published a French version of the first four books of the *Arithmetica.* In 1621, Bachet de Meziriac published an edition of the *Arithmetica* which contained the Greek text as well as his Latin translation. Bachet's edition was made famous by the notes written in the margin of a copy of his book by Fermat (publ. 1670). Since that day, Fermat's notes have stirred the speculative instincts of mathematicians, have stimulated a prodigious output in the theory of numbers, and nevertheless, still offer problems which continue to be completely baffling.

The few details of the personal life of Diophantus available to us are all contained in his epitaph as quoted in the *Anthologia Graecia.* It is said to have been composed shortly after his death by a close friend who shared Diophantus's love of an algebraic problem. The epitaph states that a sixth of Diophantus's life was spent in childhood, that after a twelfth more had elapsed he grew a beard, that when a seventh more had passed he married, and that five years later his son was born; the son lived to half his father's age and four years after the son's death the father died. We learn in this way that Diophantus lived to the age of eighty-four. It is generally believed that he lived in the third century A.D., since neither Nicomachus (c. 100 A.D.) nor Theon of Smyrna (c. 130 A.D.) make any mention of him, and on the other hand, he is quoted by Theon of Alexandria (c. 365). The commentary on his work written by Hypatia (d. 415), daughter of Theon of Alexandria, is the ultimate source of all extant manuscripts and translations of the *Arithmetica.*

The *Arithmetica* was originally written in thirteen books. Hypatia's commentary extends only to the first six books. The remainder of the work was probably lost before the tenth century. Mathematical notation clearly had its beginnings in the *Arithmetica* where Diophantus employed symbols to represent operations or quantities occurring repeatedly in his solutions. No substantial improvement over his essentially abbreviative symbolism was invented until Vieta's time (c. 1580). In the *Arithmetica,* Diophantus dealt with a wide variety of problems. Some were solved by determinate equations, others by indeterminate equations, the latter type being by far the more numerous. His clear mastery of this area of mathematics, the impressive variety of his clever devices for effecting his solutions, and his comprehensive presentation have made his name descriptive of this type of analysis. Diophantine analysis is the name of a branch of the theory of numbers which is concerned with the rational solutions of indeterminate problems (Diophantine problems) involving one or more indeterminate equations (Diophantine equations) of the first, second or higher degrees.

●

THE ARITHMETICA

From *Diophantus of Alexandria*

by Sir Thomas L. Heath

BOOK I

PRELIMINARY

Dedication.

"Knowing, my most esteemed friend Dionysius, that you are anxious to learn how to investigate problems in numbers, I have tried, beginning from the foundations on which the science is built up, to set forth to you the nature and power subsisting in numbers.

"Perhaps the subject will appear rather difficult, inasmuch as it is not yet familiar (beginners are, as a rule, too ready to despair of success); but you, with the impulse of your enthusiasm and the benefit of my teaching, will find it easy to master; for eagerness to learn, when seconded by instruction, ensures rapid progress."

"All numbers are made up of some multitude of units, so that it is manifest that their formation is subject to no limit."

Definitions.

A *square* ($=x^2$) is δύναμις ("power"), and its sign is a Δ with Y superposed, thus Δ^Y.

A *cube* ($=x^3$) is κύβος, and its sign K^Y.

A *square-square* ($=x^4$) is δυναμοδύναμις[1], and its sign is $\Delta^Y\Delta$.

A *square-cube* ($=x^5$) is δυναμόκυβος, and its sign ΔK^Y.

A *cube-cube* ($=x^6$) is κυβόκυβος, and its sign $K^Y K$.

"It is, from the addition, subtraction or multiplication of these numbers or from the ratios which they bear to one another or to their own sides respectively that most arithmetical problems are formed" . . . "each of these numbers . . . is recognised as an element in arithmetical inquiry."

"But the number which has none of these characteristics, but *merely has in it an indeterminate multitude of units* (πλῆθος μονάδων ἀόριστον) *is called* ἀριθμός, *'number,' and its sign is* ς $[=x]$."

"And there is also another sign denoting that which is invariable in determinate numbers, namely the unit, the sign being M with o superposed, thus $\overset{o}{M}$."

Thus

from ἀριθμός $[x]$ we derive the term ἀριθμοστόν $[=1/x]$
,, δύναμις $[x^2]$,, ,, δυναμοστόν $[=1/x^2]$
,, κύβος $[x^3]$,, ,, κυβοστόν $[=1/x^3]$
,, δυναμοδυναμις $[x^4]$,, ,, δυναμοδυναμοστόν $[=1/x^4]$
,, δυναμόκυβος $[x^5]$,, ,, δυναμοκυβοστόν $[=1/x^5]$
,, κυβόκυβος $[x^6]$,, ,, κυβοκυβοστόν $[=1/x^6]$,

and each of these has the same sign as the corresponding original species, but with a distinguishing mark

Thus $\Delta^{Y\chi} = 1/x^2$, just as $\gamma^\chi = 1/3$

Sign of Subtraction (*minus*).

"*A minus multiplied by a minus makes a plus*[1]; *a minus multiplied by a plus makes a minus; and the sign of a minus is a truncated Ψ turned upside down: thus* ⋔."

"It is well that one who is beginning this study should have acquired practice in the addition, subtraction and multiplication of the various species. He should know how to add positive and negative terms with different coefficients to other terms[1], themselves either positive or likewise partly positive and partly negative, and how to subtract from a combination of positive and negative terms other terms either positive or likewise partly positive and partly negative.

"Next, if a problem leads to an equation in which certain terms are equal to terms of the same species but with different coefficients, it will be necessary to subtract like from like on both sides, until one term is found equal to one term. If by chance there are on either side or on both sides any negative terms, it will be necessary to add the negative terms on both sides, until the terms on both sides are positive, and then again to subtract like from like until one term only is left on each side.

"This should be the object aimed at in framing the hypotheses of propositions, that is to say, to reduce the equations, if possible, until one term is left equal to one term; *but I will show you later how, in the case also where two terms are left equal to one term, such a problem is solved.*"

PROBLEMS

1. To divide a given number into two having a given difference.

[1] The literal rendering would be "A wanting multiplied by a wanting makes a forthcoming." The word corresponding to *minus* is λεῖψις ("wanting"): when it is used exactly as our *minus* is, it is in the dative λείψει, but there is some doubt whether Diophantus himself used this form.

[1] εἶδος, "species," is the word used by Diophantus throughout.

Given number 100, given difference 40.

Lesser number required x. Therefore

$$2x + 40 = 100,$$

$$x = 30.$$

The required numbers are 70, 30.

2. To divide a given number into two having a given ratio.

Given number 60, given ratio 3:1.

Two numbers x, $3x$. Therefore $x = 15$.

The numbers are 45, 15.

26. Given two numbers, to find a third number which, when multiplied into the given numbers respectively, makes one product a square and the other the side of that square.

Given numbers 200, 5; required number x.

Therefore $200x = (5x)^2$, and

$$x = 8.$$

27. To find two numbers such that their sum and product are given numbers.

Necessary condition. The square of half the sum must exceed the product by a square number.

Given sum 20, given product 96.

$2x$ the difference of the required numbers.

Therefore the numbers are $10 + x$, $10 - x$.

Hence $100 - x^2 = 96$.

Therefore $x = 2$, and

the required numbers are 12, 8.

28. To find two numbers such that their sum and the sum of their squares are given numbers.

Necessary condition. Double the sum of their squares

must exceed the square of their sum by a square. ἔστι δὲ καὶ τοῦτο πλασματικόν[1].

Given sum 20, given sum of squares 208.
Difference $2x$.
Therefore the numbers are $10 + x$, $10 - x$.
Thus $200 + 2x^2 = 208$, and $x = 2$.

The required numbers are 12, 8.

29. To find two numbers such that their sum and the difference of their squares are given numbers.

Given sum 20, given difference of squares 80.
Difference $2x$.
The numbers are therefore $10 + x$, $10 - x$.

$$\text{Hence}\quad (10 + x)^2 - (10 - x)^2 = 80,$$
$$\text{or } 40x = 80, \text{ and } x = 2.$$

The required numbers are 12, 8.

30. To find two numbers such that their difference and product are given numbers.

Necessary condition. Four times the product together with the square of the difference must give a square. ἔστι δὲ καὶ τοῦτο πλασματικόν.

Given difference 4, given product 96.
$2x$ the sum of the required numbers.
Therefore the numbers are $x + 2$, $x - 2$; accordingly $x^2 - 4 = 96$, and $x = 10$.

The required numbers are 12, 8.

[1] There has been controversy as to the meaning of this difficult phrase. Xylander, Bachet, Cossali, Schulz, Nesselmann, all discuss it. Xylander translated it by "effictum aliunde." Bachet of course rejects this, and, while leaving the word untranslated, maintains that it has an active rather than a passive signification; it is, he says, not something "made up" (effictum) but something "a quo aliud quippiam effingi et plasmari potest," "from which something else can be made up," and this he interprets as meaning that from the conditions to which the term is applied, combined with the solutions of the respective problems in which it occurs, the rules for solving mixed quadratics can be evolved. Of the two views I think Xylander's is nearer the mark. πλασματικόν should apparently mean "of the nature of a πλάσμα," just as δραματικόν means something connected with or suitable for a drama; and πλάσμα means something "formed" or "moulded." Hence the expression would seem to mean "this is of the nature of a formula," with the implication that the formula is not difficult to make up or discover. Nesselmann, like Xylander, gives it much this meaning, translating it "das lässt sich aber bewerkstelligen." Tannery translates πλασματικόν by "formativum."

31. To find two numbers in a given ratio and such that the sum of their squares also has to their sum a given ratio.

Given ratios 3:1 and 5:1 respectively.

Lesser number x.

Therefore $10x^2 = 5 . 4x$, whence $x = 2$, and

the numbers are 2, 6.

32. To find two numbers in a given ratio and such that the sum of their squares also has to their difference a given ratio.

Given ratios 3:1 and 10:1.

Lesser number x, which is then found from the equation $10x^2 = 10 . 2x$.

Hence $x = 2$, and

the numbers are 2, 6.

BOOK II

6. To find two numbers having a given difference and such that the difference of their squares exceeds their difference by a given number.

Necessary condition. The square of their difference must be less than the sum of the said difference and the given excess of the difference of the squares over the difference of the numbers.

Difference of numbers 2, the other given number 20.

Lesser number x. Therefore $x + 2$ is the greater, and $4x + 4 = 22$.

Therefore $x = 4\frac{1}{2}$, and

the numbers are $4\frac{1}{2}$, $6\frac{1}{2}$.

7. To find two numbers such that the difference of

their squares is greater by a given number than a given ratio of their difference[2]. [*Difference assumed.*]

Necessary condition. The given ratio being 3:1, the square of the difference of the numbers must be less than the sum of three times that difference and the given number.

Given number 10, difference of required numbers 2.

Lesser number x. Therefore the greater is $x + 2$,

$$\text{and } 4x + 4 = 3 \cdot 2 + 10.$$

Therefore $x = 3$, and

the numbers are 3, 5.

8. To divide a given square number into two squares[3].

---

[2] Here we have the identical phrase used in Euclid's *Data* the difference of the squares is τῆς ὑπεροχῆς αὐτῶν δοθέντι ἀριθμῷ μείζων ἢ ἐν λόγῳ, literally "greater than their difference by a given number (more) than in a (given) ratio," by which is meant "greater by a given number than a given proportion or fraction of their difference."

[3] It is to this proposition that Fermat appended his famous note in which he enunciates what is known as the "great theorem" of Fermat. The text of the note is as follows:

"On the other hand it is impossible to separate a cube into two cubes, or a biquadrate into two biquadrates, or generally *any power except a square into two powers with the same exponent.* I have discovered a truly marvellous proof of this, which however the margin is not large enough to contain."

Did Fermat really possess a proof of the general proposition that $x^m + y^m = z^m$ cannot be solved in rational numbers where m is any number > 2? As Wertheim says, one is tempted to doubt this, seeing that, in spite of the labours of Euler, Lejeune-Dirichlet, Kummer and others, a general proof has not even yet been discovered. Euler proved the theorem for $m = 3$ and $m = 4$, Dirichlet for $m = 5$, and Kummer, by means of the higher theory of numbers, produced a proof which only excludes certain particular values of m, which values are rare, at all events among the smaller values of m; thus there is no value of m below 100 for which Kummer's proof does not serve. (I take these facts from Weber and Wellstein's *Encyclopädie der Elementar-Mathematik*, 1_2, p. 284, where a proof of the formula for $m = 4$ is given.)

It appears that the Göttingen Academy of Sciences has recently awarded a prize to Dr A. Wieferich, of Münster, for a proof that the equation $x^p + y^p = z^p$ cannot be solved in terms of positive integers not multiples of p, if $2^p - 2$ is not divisible by p^2. "This surprisingly simple result represents the first advance, since the time of Kummer, in the proof of the last Fermat theorem" (*Bulletin of the American Mathematical Society*, February 1910).

Fermat says ("Relation des nouvelles découvertes en la science des nombres," August 1659, *Oeuvres*, II. p. 433) that he proved that *no cube is divisible into two cubes* by a variety of his method of *infinite diminution* (*descente infinie* or *indéfinie*) different from that which he employed for other negative or positive theorems;

Given square number 16.

x^2 one of the required squares. Therefore $16 - x^2$ must be equal to a square.

Take a square of the form[1] $(mx - 4)^2$, m being any integer and 4 the number which is the square root of 16, *e.g.* take $(2x - 4)^2$, and equate it to $16 - x^2$.

Therefore $4x^2 - 16x + 16 = 16 - x^2$,

or $5x^2 = 16x$, and $x = 16/5$.

The required squares are therefore 256/25, 144/25.

9. To divide a given number which is the sum of two squares into two other squares[2].

Given number $13 = 2^2 + 3^2$.

As the roots of these squares are 2, 3, take $(x + 2)^2$ as the first square and $(mx - 3)^2$ as the second (where m is an integer), say $(2x - 3)^2$.

Therefore $(x^2 + 4x + 4) + (4x^2 + 9 - 12x) = 13$,

or $\quad 5x^2 + 13 - 8x = 13$.

Therefore $x = 8/5$, and

the required squares are 324/25, 1/25.

10. To find two square numbers having a given difference.

---

[1] Diophantus' words are: "I form the square from any number of ἀριθμοί *minus* as many units as there are in the side of 16." It is implied throughout that m must be so chosen that the result may be *rational* in Diophantus' sense, *i.e.* rational and positive.

[2] Diophantus' solution is substantially the same as Euler's (*Algebra*, tr. Hewlett, Part II. Art. 219), though the latter is expressed more generally.

Required to find xy, such that

$$x^2 + y^2 = f^2 + g^2.$$

If $x \gtrless f$, then $y \lessgtr g$.

Put therefore $\quad x = f + pz, \quad y = g - qz$:

hence $\quad 2fpz + p^2z^2 - 2gqz + q^2z^2 = 0$,

and $\quad z = \dfrac{2gq - 2fp}{p^2 + q^2}$,

so that $\quad x = \dfrac{2gpq + f(q^2 - p^2)}{p^2 + q^2}, \quad y = \dfrac{2fpq + g(p^2 - q^2)}{p^2 + q^2}$,

in which we may substitute all possible numbers for p, q.

Given difference 60.

Side of one number x, side of the other x *plus* any number the square of which is not greater than 60, say 3.

Therefore $(x + 3)^2 - x^2 = 60$;

$x = 8\frac{1}{2}$, and

the required squares are $72\frac{1}{4}$, $132\frac{1}{4}$.

11. To add the same (required) number to two given numbers so as to make each of them a square.

(1) Given numbers 2, 3; required number x.

Therefore

$$\left.\begin{array}{l} x+2 \\ x+3 \end{array}\right\} \text{ must both be squares.}$$

This is called a double-equation (διπλοϊσότης).

To solve it, *take the difference between the two expressions and resolve it into two factors*[1]; in this case let us say 4, $\frac{1}{4}$.

Then *take either*

(*a*) *the square of half the difference between these factors and equate it to the lesser expression,*

or (*b*) *the square of half the sum and equate it to the greater.*

In this case (*a*) the square of half the difference is 225/64.

Therefore, $x + 2 = 225/64$, and $x = 97/64$, the squares being 225/64, 289/64.

Taking (*b*) the square of half the sum, we have $x + 3 = 289/64$, which gives the same result.

(2) To avoid a double-equation,

first find a number which when added to 2, or to 3, gives a square.

Take *e.g.* the number $x^2 - 2$, which when added to 2 gives a square.

Therefore, since this same number added to 3 gives a square,

$$x^2 + 1 = \text{a square} = (x - 4)^2, \text{ say,}$$

[1] Here, as always, the factors chosen must be suitable factors, *i.e.* such as will lead to a "rational" result, in Diophantus' sense.

the number of units in the expression (in this case 4) being so taken that the solution may give $x^2 > 2$.

Therefore $x = 15/8$, and

the required number is 97/64, as before.

12. To subtract the same (required) number from two given numbers so as to make both remainders squares.

Given numbers 9, 21.

Assuming $9 - x^2$ as the required number, we satisfy one condition, and the other requires that $12 + x^2$ shall be a square.

Assume as the side of this square x *minus* some number the square of which > 12, say 4.

Therefore $(x - 4)^2 = 12 + x^2$,

and $x = \frac{1}{2}$.

The required number is then $8\frac{3}{4}$.

[Diophantus does not reduce to lowest terms, but says $x = 4/8$ and then subtracts 16/64 from 9 or 576/64.]

BOOK III

6. To find three numbers such that their sum is a square and the sum of any pair is a square.

Let the sum of all three be $x^2 + 2x + 1$, sum of first and second x^2, and therefore the third $2x + 1$; let sum of second and third be $(x - 1)^2$.

Therefore the first $= 4x$, and the second $= x^2 - 4x$.

But first + third = square,

that is, $6x + 1 =$ square $= 121$, say.

Therefore $x = 20$, and

the numbers are 80, 320, 41.

[An alternative solution, obviously interpolated, is practically identical with the above except that it takes the square 36 as the value of $6x + 1$, so that $x = 35/6$, and the numbers are $140/6 = 840/36$, 385/36, 456/36.]

7. To find three numbers in A.P. such that the sum of any pair gives a square.

First find three square numbers in A.P. and such that half their sum is greater than any one of them. Let x^2, $(x + 1)^2$ be the first and second of these; therefore the third is $x^2 + 4x + 2 = (x - 8)^2$, say.

Therefore $x = 62/20$ or $31/10$;
and we may take as the numbers 961, 1681, 2401.
We have now to find three numbers such that the sums of pairs are the numbers just found.
The sum of the three $= 5043/2 = 2521\frac{1}{2}$, and the three numbers are $120\frac{1}{2}$, $840\frac{1}{2}$, $1560\frac{1}{2}$.

10. To find three numbers such that the product of any pair of them added to a given number gives a square.

Let the given number be 12. Take a square (say 25) and subtract 12. Take the difference (13) for the product of the first and second numbers, and let these numbers be $13x$, $1/x$ respectively.

Again subtract 12 from another square, say 16, and let the difference (4) be the product of the second and third numbers.

Therefore the third number $= 4x$.

The third condition gives $52x^2 + 12 =$ a square; now $52 = 4 . 13$, and 13 is not a square; but, if it were a square, the equation could easily be solved[1].

Thus we must find two numbers to replace 13 and 4 such that their product is a square, while either $+ 12$ is also a square.

Now the product is a square if both are squares; hence we must find two squares such that either $+ 12 =$ a square.

---

[1] The equation $52x^2 + 12 = u^2$ can in reality be solved as it stands, by virtue of the fact that it has one obvious solution, namely $x = 1$. Another solution is found by substituting $y + 1$ for x, and so on. The value $x = 1$ itself gives (13, 1, 4) as a solution of the problem.

"This is easy[2] and, as we said, it makes the equation easy to solve."

The squares 4, ¼ satisfy the condition.

19. To find four numbers such that the square of their sum *plus* or *minus* any one singly gives a square.

Since, in any right-angled triangle,
(sq. on hypotenuse) ± (twice product of perps.) = a square, we must seek four right-angled triangles [in rational numbers] having the same hypotenuse,
or we must find a square which is divisible into two squares in four different ways; and "we saw how to divide a square into two squares in an infinite number of ways." [II. 8]

Take right-angled triangles in the smallest numbers, (3, 4, 5) and (5, 12, 13); and multiply the sides of the first by the hypotenuse of the second and *vice versa.*

This gives the triangles (39, 52, 65) and (25, 60, 65); thus 65^2 is split up into two squares in *two* ways.

Again, 65 is "naturally" divided into two squares in two ways, namely into $7^2 + 4^2$ and $8^2 + 1^2$, "which is due to the fact that 65 is the product of 13 and 5, each of which numbers is the sum of two squares."

Form now a right-angled triangle[1] from 7, 4. The sides are $(7^2 - 4^2, 2 \cdot 7 \cdot 4, 7^2 + 4^2)$ or (33, 56, 65).

---

[2] We have to find two pairs of squares differing by 12. (*a*) If we put $12 = 6 \cdot 2$, we have

$$\left\{\frac{1}{2}(6 - 2)\right\}^2 + 12 = \left\{\frac{1}{2}(6 + 2)\right\}^2,$$

and 16, 4 are squares differing by 12, or 4 is a square which when added to 12 gives a square. (*b*) If we put $12 = 4 \cdot 3$, we find $\left\{\frac{1}{2}(4 - 3)\right\}^2$ or $\frac{1}{4}$ to be a square which when added to 12 gives a square.

[1] If there are two numbers p, q to "form a right-angled triangle" from them means to take the numbers $p^2 + q^2$, $p^2 - q^2$, $2pq$. These are the sides of a right-angled triangle, since

$$(p^2 + q^2)^2 = (p^2 - q^2)^2 + (2pq)^2.$$

Similarly, forming a right-angled triangle from 8, 1, we obtain $(2 \cdot 8 \cdot 1, 8^2 - 1^2, 8^2 + 1^2)$ or 16, 63, 65.

Thus 65^2 is split into two squares in *four* ways.

Assume now as the sum of the numbers $65x$ and

as first number $2 \cdot 39 \cdot 52x^2 = 4056x^2$,
" second " $2 \cdot 25 \cdot 60x^2 = 3000x^2$,
" third " $2 \cdot 33 \cdot 56x^2 = 3696x^2$,
" fourth " $2 \cdot 16 \cdot 63x^2 = 2016x^2$,

the coefficients of x^2 being four times the areas of the four right-angled triangles respectively.

The sum $12768x^2 = 65x$, and $x = \frac{65}{12768}$.

The numbers are

$$\frac{17136600}{163021824}, \quad \frac{12675000}{163021824}, \quad \frac{15615600}{163021824}, \quad \frac{8517600}{163021824}.$$

BOOK IV

29. To find four square numbers such that their sum added to the sum of their sides makes a given number[1].

Given number 12.

Now $x^2 + x + \frac{1}{4} =$ a square.

Therefore the sum of four squares + the sum of their sides + 1 = the sum of four other squares = 13, by hypothesis.

---

[1] On this problem Bachet observes that Diophantus appears to assume, here and in some problems of Book V., that any number not itself a square is the sum of two or three or four squares. He adds that he has verified this statement for all numbers up to 325, but would like to see a scientific proof of the theorem. These remarks of Bachet's are the occasion for another of Fermat's famous notes: "I have been the first to discover a most beautiful theorem of the greatest generality, namely this: Every number is either a triangular number or the sum of two or three triangular numbers; every number is a square or the sum of two, three, or four squares; every number is a pentagonal number or the sum of two, three, four or five pentagonal numbers; and so on *ad infinitum,* for hexagons, heptagons and any polygons whatever, the enunciation of this general and wonderful theorem being varied according to the number of the angles. The proof of it, which depends on many various and abstruse mysteries of numbers, I cannot give here; for I have decided to devote a separate and complete work to this matter and thereby to advance arithmetic in this region of inquiry to an extraordinary extent beyond its ancient and known limits."

Unfortunately the promised separate work did not appear. The theorem so far as it relates to squares was first proved by Lagrange (*Nouv. Memoires de l'Acad. de Berlin*, annee 1770, Berlin 1772, pp. 123-133; *Oeuvres,* III, pp. 189-201), who followed up results obtained by Euler. Cf. also Legendre, *Zahlentheorie,* tr. Maser, I pp 212 sqq. Lagrange's proof is set out as shortly as possible in Wertheim's Diophantus, pp. 324-330. The theorem of Fermat in all its generality was proved by Cauchy (*Oeuvres,* II*e* serie, Vol. VI. pp. 320-353); cf. Legendre, *Zahlentheorie*, tr. Maser, II, pp. 332 sqq.

Therefore we have to divide 13 into four squares; then, if we subtract ½ from each of their sides, we shall have the sides of the required squares.

$$\text{Now } 13 = 4 + 9 = \left(\frac{64}{25} + \frac{36}{25}\right) + \left(\frac{144}{25} + \frac{81}{25}\right),$$

and the sides of the required squares are

11/10, 7/10, 19/10, 13/10,

the squares themselves being

121/100, 49/100, 361/100, 169/100.

30. To find four squares such that their sum *minus* the sum of their sides is a given number.

Given number 4.

Now $x^2 - x + 1/4 =$ a square.

Therefore (the sum of four squares) — (sum of their sides) + 1 = the sum of four other squares = 5, by hypothesis.

Divide 5 into four squares, as

9/25, 16/25, 64/25, 36/25.

The sides of these squares *plus* ½ in each case are the sides of the required squares.

Therefore sides of required squares are

11/10, 13/10, 21/10, 17/10,

and the squares themselves

121/100, 169/100, 441/100, 289/100.

31. To divide unity into two parts such that, if given numbers are added to them respectively, the product of the two sums gives a square.

Let 3, 5 be the numbers to be added; x $1 - x$ the parts of 1.

Therefore $(x + 3)(6 - x) = 18 + 3x - x^2 =$ a square $= 4x^2$, say;

thus $18 + 3x = 5x^2$, *which does not give a rational result.*

Now 5 comes from a square + 1; and, in order that the equation may have a rational solution, we must substitute for the square taken (4) a square such that

(the square + 1) . 18 + $(3/2)^2 =$ a square.

Put $(m^2 + 1)\,18 + 2\frac{1}{4} =$ a square,
or $72m^2 + 81 =$ a square $= (8m + 9)^2$, say,
and $m = 18,\ m^2 = 324$.
Hence we must put
$$(x + 3)(6 - x) = 18 + 3x - x^2 = 324x^2.$$
Therefore[1] $325x^2 - 3x - 18 = 0$,
$$x = 78/325 = 6/25,$$
and $\left(\frac{6}{25}, \frac{19}{25}\right)$ is a solution.

BOOK V

29. To find three squares such that the sum of their squares is a square.

Let the squares be x^2, 4, 9 respectively[1].
Therefore $x^4 + 97 =$ a square $= (x^2 - 10)^2$, say; whence $x^2 = 3/20$.
If the ratio of 3 to 20 were the ratio of a square to a square, the problem would be solved; but it is not.
Therefore *I have to find two squares* (p^2, q^2, *say*) *and a number* (m, *say*) *such that* $m^2 - p^4 - q^4$ *has to* $2m$ *the ratio of a square to a square.*
Let $p^2 = z^2$, $q^2 = 4$ and $m = z^2 + 4$.
Therefore $m^2 - p^4 - q^4 = (z^2 + 4)^2 - z^4 - 16 = 8z^2$.
Hence $8z^2/(2z^2 + 8)$, or $4z^2/(z^2 + 4)$, must be the ratio of a square to a square.
Put $z^2 + 4 = (z + 1)^2$, say;
therefore $z = 1\frac{1}{2}$, and the squares are $p^2 = 2\frac{1}{4}$, $q^2 = 4$, while $m = 6\frac{1}{4}$;
or, if we take 4 times each, $p^2 = 9$, $q^2 = 16$, $m = 25$.
Starting again, we put for the squares x^2, 9, 16;

---

[1] Observe the solution of a mixed quadratic equation.

[1] "Why," says Fermat, "does not Diophantus seek *two* fourth powers such that their sum is a square? This problem is in fact impossible, as by my method I am in a position to prove with all rigour." It is probable that Diophantus knew the fact without being able to prove it generally. That neither the sum nor the difference of two fourth powers can be a square was proved by Euler (*Commentationes arithmeticae*, I. pp. 24 sqq., and *Algebra*, Part II, c. XIII.).

then the sum of the squares $= x^4 + 337 = (x^2 - 25)^2$, and $x = 12/5$.

The required squares are 144/25, 9, 16.

30. [The enunciation of this problem is in the form of an epigram, the meaning of which is as follows.]

A man buys a certain number of measures of wine, (χόες) some at 8 drachmas, some at 5 drachmas each. He pays for them a *square* number of drachmas; and if we add 60 to this number, the result is a square, the side of which is equal to the whole number of measures. Find how many he bought at each price.

Let $x =$ the whole number of measures; therefore $x^2 - 60$ was the price paid, which is a square $= (x - m)^2$, say.

Now 1/5 of the price of the five-drachma measures + 1/8 of the price of the eight-drachma measures $= x$;

so that $x^2 - 60$, the total price, has to be divided into two parts such that 1/5 of one + 1/8 of the other $= x$.

We cannot have a real solution of this unless

$x > 1/8\ (x^2 - 60)$ and $< 1/5\ (x^2 - 60)$.

Therefore $\quad 5x < x^2 - 60 < 8x$.

(1) Since $\quad x^2 > 5x + 60$,

$x^2 = 5x +$ a number greater than 60,

whence x is *not less than* 11.

(2) $\quad x^2 < 8x + 60$

or $\quad x^2 = 8x +$ some number less than 60,

whence x is *not greater than* 12.

Therefore $\quad 11 < x < 12$.

Now (from above) $x = (m^2 + 60)/2m$;

therefore $22m < m^2 + 60 < 24m$.

Thus (1) $22m = m^2 +$ (some number less than 60), and therefore m is *not less than* 19.

(2) $24m = m^2 +$ (some number greater than 60), and therefore m is *less than* 21.

Hence we put $m = 20$, and

$$x^2 - 60 = (x - 20)^2,$$

so that $x = 11\frac{1}{2}$, $x^2 = 132\frac{1}{4}$, and $x^2 - 60 = 72\frac{1}{4}$.

Thus we have to divide $72\frac{1}{4}$ into two parts such that 1/5 of one part *plus* 1/8 of the other $= 11\frac{1}{2}$.

Let the first part be $5z$.

Therefore 1/8 (second part) $= 11\frac{1}{2} - z$,

or second part $= 92 - 8z$;

therefore $5z + 92 - 8z = 72\frac{1}{4}$;

and $z = 79/12$.

Therefore the number of five-drachma χόες $= 79/12$.
Therefore the number of eight-drachma " $= 59/12$.

BOOK VI

18. To find a right-angled triangle such that the area added to the hypotenuse gives a cube, while the perimeter is a square.

Area x, hypotenuse some cube *minus* x, perpendiculars x, 2.

Therefore we have to find a cube which, when 2 is added to it, becomes a square.

Let the side of the cube be $m - 1$.

Therefore $m^3 - 3m^2 + 3m + 1 =$ a square $= (1\frac{1}{2}m + 1)^2$, say.

Thus $m = 21/4$, and the cube $= (17/4)^3 = 4913/64$.

Put now x for the area, x, 2 for the perpendiculars, and $4913/64 - x$ for the hypotenuse;

and x is found from the equation $(4913/64 - x)^2 = x^2 + 4$.

[$x = 24121185/628864$, and the triangle is (2, 24121185/628864, 24153953/628864).]

19. To find a right-angled triangle such that its area added to one of the perpendiculars gives a square, while the perimeter is a cube.

Make a right-angled triangle from some indeterminate odd number[2], say $2x + 1$;

then the altitude $= 2x + 1$, the base $= 2x^2 + 2x$, and the hypotenuse $= 2x^2 + 2x + 1$.

Since the perimeter = a cube,

$4x^2 + 6x + 2 = (4x + 2)(x + 1) =$ a cube;

and, if we divide all the sides by $x + 1$, we have to make $4x + 2$ a cube.

Again, the area + one perpendicular = a square.

Therefore $\frac{2x^3 + 3x^2 + x}{(x + 1)^2} + \frac{2x + 1}{x + 1} =$ a square;

that is, $\frac{2x^3 + 5x^2 + 4x + 1}{x^2 + 2x + 1} = 2x + 1 =$ a square.

But $4x + 2 =$ a cube;

therefore we must find a cube which is double of a square; this is of course 8.

Therefore $4x + 2 = 8$, and $x = 1\frac{1}{2}$.

The required triangle is (8/5, 15/5, 17/5).

20. To find a right-angled triangle such that the sum of its area and one perpendicular is a cube, while its perimeter is a square.

Proceeding as in the last problem, we have to make

$$\left.\begin{array}{l} 4x + 2 \text{ a square} \\ 2x + 1 \text{ a cube} \end{array}\right\}.$$

We have therefore to seek a square which is double of a cube; this is 16, which is double of 8.

Therefore $4x + 2 = 16$, and $x = 3\frac{1}{2}$.

The triangle is (16/9, 63/9, 65/9).

[2] This is the method of formation of right-angled triangles attributed to Pythagoras. If m is any odd number, the sides of the right-angled triangle formed therefrom are m, $\frac{1}{2}(m^2 - 1)$, $\frac{1}{2}(m^2 + 1)$, for $m^2 + [\frac{1}{2}(m^2 - 1)]^2 = [\frac{1}{2}(m^2 + 1)]^2$. Cf. Proclus, *Comment. on Eucl.* 1. (ed. Friedlein), p. 428, 7 sqq., etc.etc.

ALBRECHT DURER

(1471—1528)

The letters, manuscripts and printed works of Albrecht Durer, greatest of German artists, reflect the spirit, philosophy, keen perception and theoretical interests of this true Renaissance genius. He was the third of eighteen children born to Albrecht Durer, a goldsmith of Magyar stock, who settled in Nuremberg in 1455. Except for some interludes of travel, Albrecht's entire life was spent in Nuremberg, a city of growing importance, to which, for decades, persons of outstanding ability in all fields had been drawn, through the cross currents in the religious, commercial and political life of Europe. Nuremberg of the fifteenth century possessed two great prerequisites for cultural development, a paper mill and numerous printing presses manned by skilled printers. In addition to the books and pamphlets issuing from her presses, the products of her master craftsmen, watchmakers, bell-founders, builders of organs, glass painters and so on, were in widespread demand. Most important of all were the goldsmiths, whose works of art, coins and seals were kept to a certain standard of purity in the precious metals of which they were fashioned. Direct commercial and banking ties connected Nuremberg to all the principal cities of Europe. In this hard driving community, Albrecht Durer rose from obscure and humble origins to become one of its leading citizens and one of the first of his class to gain acceptance at the highest level in aristocratic and intellectual circles, wholly on the strength of his extraordinary achievements.

"And when I had learned reading and writing," Durer wrote, "my father took me from school and taught me the goldsmith's trade." Nevertheless, his chief interest was in painting and in 1486 he was apprenticed to the finest painter in Nuremberg, Michael Wolgemut, in whose studio numerous woodcuts for book illustrations were also produced. In 1490 the customary *"wanderjahre"* followed, during which Durer learned the art of copper engraving in the Schongauer studio at Colmar. Recalled to Nuremberg in 1494 he married pretty Agnes Frey, 15 years old. The marriage had previously been arranged by their parents. Nothing has been found in Durer's writings to indicate that the marriage was a happy one. We learn that his wife kept his accounts efficiently, but portraits of her rather give an impression of petulance. Durer's lifelong friend, Pirkheimer, wrote of her as avaricious, and the true cause of her husband's death through her incessant demands. This harsh judgment of her has been explained by some as the bitter outcry of a grief stricken man, inconsolable in his loss of a deeply loved and vastly admired friend. As a member of the inner circle of Pirkheimer's friends, and as a friend of Lazarus Spengler, writer and leader in the local reform movement, Durer came to enjoy the association and friendship of the leading political, religious and intellectual figures of his time. He was court painter and protege of Emperor Maximilian I, and later he became court painter to Maximilian's successor, Charles V. Deeply religious, he was a friend and supporter of Martin Luther. Through his great friend Erasmus, Durer made the acquaintance of many of the leading scientists and mathematicians of the world. Fragments of his correspondence with them, showing his keen interest in mathematics, survive. A prolific artist, Durer netted a modest estate from the sale of his paintings, his engravings on wood and copper, his watercolors, his altar pieces, book illustrations and illuminations, even though, as his writings indicate, payments were frequently hard to collect.

In 1505, on the occasion of his second trip to Italy, Durer came as a distinguished artist with an important commission. He was well received both as an artist and as a gentleman. This marked not only the emerging maturity of his art, but also the beginning of the vigorous development of his theoretical interest in measurement, perspective and proportion. Convinced that mastery of these subjects was fundamental to the improvement and advance of artistic achievement, he diligently pursued the study of these branches of mathematics, ingeniously applying the theoretical principles learned here to the practice of the artistic professions. Durer also devoted a great deal of time to basic theoretical geometry. The culmination of many years of persistent effort in research was the publication (1525) of his first literary work, the *Unterweysung der Messung mit dem Zirkel und Richtscheyt* ("Instruction in the Art of Mensuration with Compass and Rule"). Durer's "Art of Mensuration" is a treatise on descriptive geometry founded largely on Euclid. It contains numerous geometrical figures and unusual curves devised by Durer, as well as his original paper folding methods for the construction of geometrical solids. Durer's *Etliche Unterricht zu Befestigung der Stett, Schloss und Flecken,* on the art of fortification, appeared in 1527, and his *Vier Bucher von menschlichen Proportion,* on human proportion, was published in 1528 (posthumously). A great teacher as well as an incomparable artist, Durer wrote in German for the instruction of German youth. In accomplishing his immediate aim, the improvement of artistic methods and practices, he also contributed to the development of the German language and to the spread of scientific knowledge among the great numbers of people to whom Latin was not available. Durer's books were immediately popular all over Europe and soon were translated into Latin, French, Italian, Portuguese and Dutch.

INSTRUCTION IN THE ART OF MENSURATION

From *The Writings of Albrecht Durer*

Translated by William M. Conway

"The Teaching of Measurement with the rule and compass, in lines, and solids, put together and brought into print with accompanying figures by Albrecht Durer, for the use of all lovers of art, in the year 1525."

"To my very dear Master and friend, Herr Wilibald Pirkheimer, I, Albrecht Durer, wish health and happiness.

Gracious Master and friend. Heretofore many talented scholars in our German land have been taught the art of painting, without any foundation and almost according to mere every-day rule-of-thumb. Thus they have grown up in ignorance, like a wild unpruned tree. And, though some of them have acquired a free hand by continuous practice, so that it cannot be denied that their work has been done skillfully, yet, instead of being grounded upon principle, it has merely been made according to their tastes. If, however, painters of understanding and artists worthy of the name were to see so rash a work, they would scorn the blindness of these fellows, and that not without justice. For, to one who really knows, nothing is more unpleasant to see in a picture than fundamental error, however carefully the details may be painted. That such painters have found satisfaction in their errors is only because they have not learnt the Art of Measurement, without which no one can either be or become a master of his craft. But that again has been the fault of their masters, who themselves were ignorant of this art.

Considering, however, that this is the true foundation

for all painting, I have proposed to myself to propound the elements for the use of all eager students of Art, and to instruct them how they may employ a system of *Measurement with Rule and Compass,* and thereby learn to recognise the real Truth, seeing it before their eyes. Thus they will not only acquire a delight in and love towards art, but attain an increasingly correct understanding of it. And they will not be misled by those now amongst us who, in our own day, revile the Art of Painting and say that it is servant to Idolatry. For a Christian would no more be led to superstition by a picture or effigy than an honest man to commit murder because he carries a weapon by his side. He must indeed be an unthinking man who would worship picture, wood, or stone. A picture therefore brings more good than harm, when it is honourably, artistically, and well made.

In what honour and respect these arts were held by the Greeks and Romans the old books sufficiently prove. And, although in the course of time the arts were lost, and remained lost for more than a thousand years, they were once more brought to light by the Italians, two centuries ago. For arts very quickly disappear, but only with difficulty and after a long time can they be rediscovered.

Therefore I hope that no man of understanding will censure this project and teaching of mine, for it is well meant and will be useful to all who study art. It will not alone be serviceable to painters, but also to goldsmiths, sculptors, stone-masons, joiners, and all who require measurements. No one indeed is obliged to avail himself of this doctrine of mine, but I am sure that whosoever does adopt it will not only thereby gain a firm grounding, but, arriving by daily practice at a better comprehension of it, will pursue the search and discover far more than I now point out.

Knowing, as I do, gracious Master and friend, that you are a lover of all the arts, and for the great affection and friendship I bear towards you, I have dedicated this book to you. Not that I think thereby to render you any great or important service, but I hope to give some evidence and measure of my good will towards you. For though I cannot benefit you with my works, my heart has none the less been always ready to render back a return for your favours and the love you cherish towards me."

"Euclid, that most acute man, put together the groundwork of Geometry. Whoever well understandeth the same hath no need of this here following writing. It has been written only for lads and such as have none to instruct them aright."

"Seeing that it is useful for stone-masons, painters, and joiners to know how to set up a common sun-dial on towers, houses, and walls, I will here write somewhat thereof." . . . "Builders, painters, and others sometimes have to show writing on high walls, and so it is needful for them to know how to form their letters correctly."

From *The Mathematics of Great Amateurs*

by JULIAN L. COOLIDGE

This space curve does not lie on a cylinder, nor yet on a cone, but makes one turn around a cylinder and one around a cone, which stands on top of it. The azimuth θ shall run from 0° to 120°, the height shall be given by

$$z = a \tan \frac{\theta}{24}.$$

For the first turn, the horizontal projection on the (X, Y) plane is $r = b$; for the second turn we have the much more complicated form

$$r = b\left[\frac{\tan 30^\circ - \tan\dfrac{\theta}{24}}{\tan 30^\circ - \tan 15^\circ}\right]$$

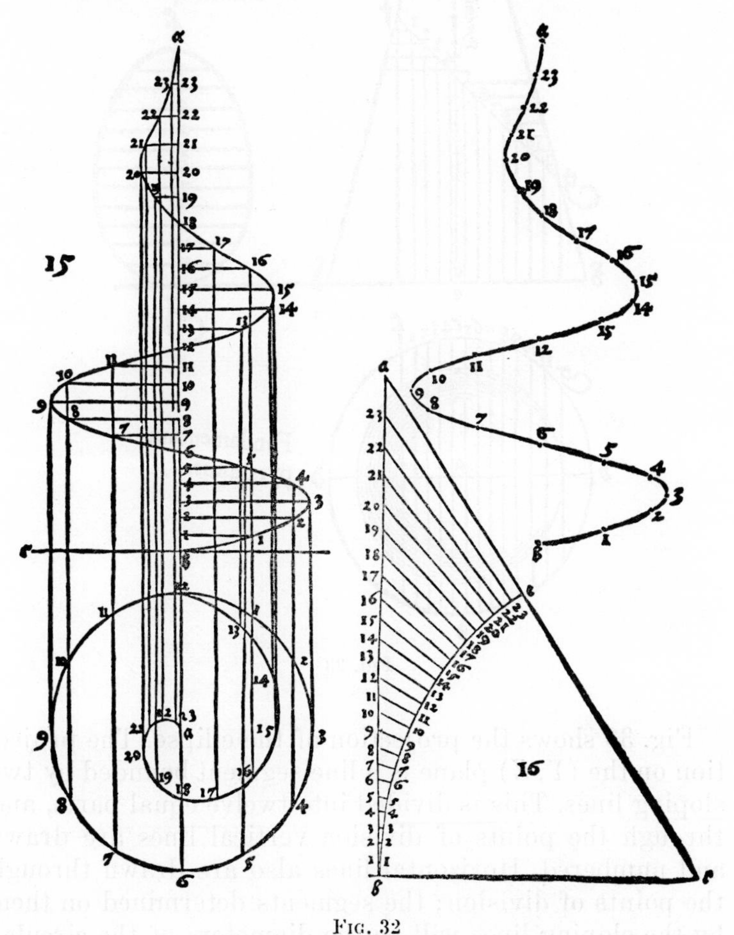

FIG. 32
A DURER SPACE CURVE

The horizontal projection on the (Y, Z) plane is

$$y = r \sin \theta.$$

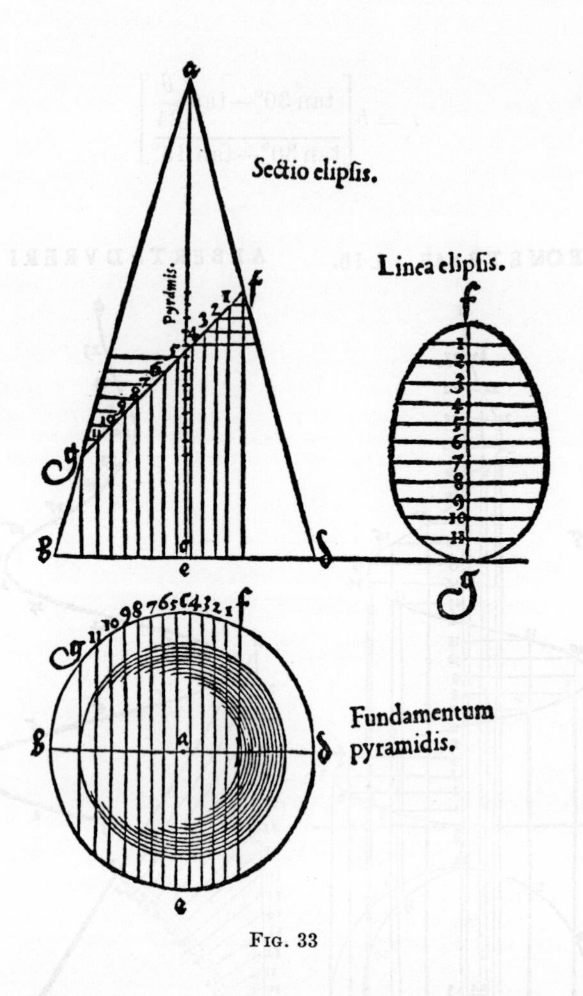

FIG. 33

Fig. 33 shows the projection of the ellipse. The projection on the (Y, Z) plane is a line segment bounded by two sloping lines. This is divided into twelve equal parts, and through the points of division vertical lines are drawn and numbered. Horizontal lines also are drawn through the points of division; the segments determined on them by the sloping lines will be the diameters of the circular sections which horizontal planes cut from the cone. We draw in the (X, Y) plane a series of circles with these diameters, and when that is folded down to lie on the (Y, Z) plane we have a series of concentric circles just below the figure in the (Y, Z) plane. Where each of these circles meets the vertical line with the same number will be the folded-down projection of a point of the ellipse. We have in this way a rather unshapely projection of the original curve. However, Durer does not draw it in, but rather constructs the curve itself. The original line segment has the length of the major axis. This we set upright to the right of the figure, and divide into twelve equal parts. Through each point of division we draw a double ordinate equal to the diameter of the corresponding horizontal circle.

Figure 34 (page 336) illustrates an even more complicated sort of twisting space-curve. This lies on three cylinders of revolution, each tangent to the next along a vertical element. The intersections with the (X, Y) plane, the vertical projection of the curve, are three tangent circles, which are treated as two spirals. . . .

The middle circle is tangent to the two others at points where $Y = 0$.

We start on the smallest circle at a point, not a point of contact, where $Y = 0$, and divide into six equal parts numbered 1 to 6; we pass then to the middle circle, continuing around in the same sense of rotation and in a half-turn take twelve equal parts numbered 7 to 18. Continuing always to turn in the same sense we pass to the largest circle and make a complete circuit with equal parts numbered 19 to 42, then around the other half of the middle circle with parts numbered 43 to 54, and lastly on the smallest circle with parts numbered 55 to 60. The space curve is wound in this order, so that it goes around each imaginary cylinder once. To write its equations we suppose r_1, r_2, r_3, the radii of the three circles, the azimuth θ. We also choose an arbitrary angle α which looks like 60° in the figure, and the height of the column h. If, then, the point numbered n have the azi-

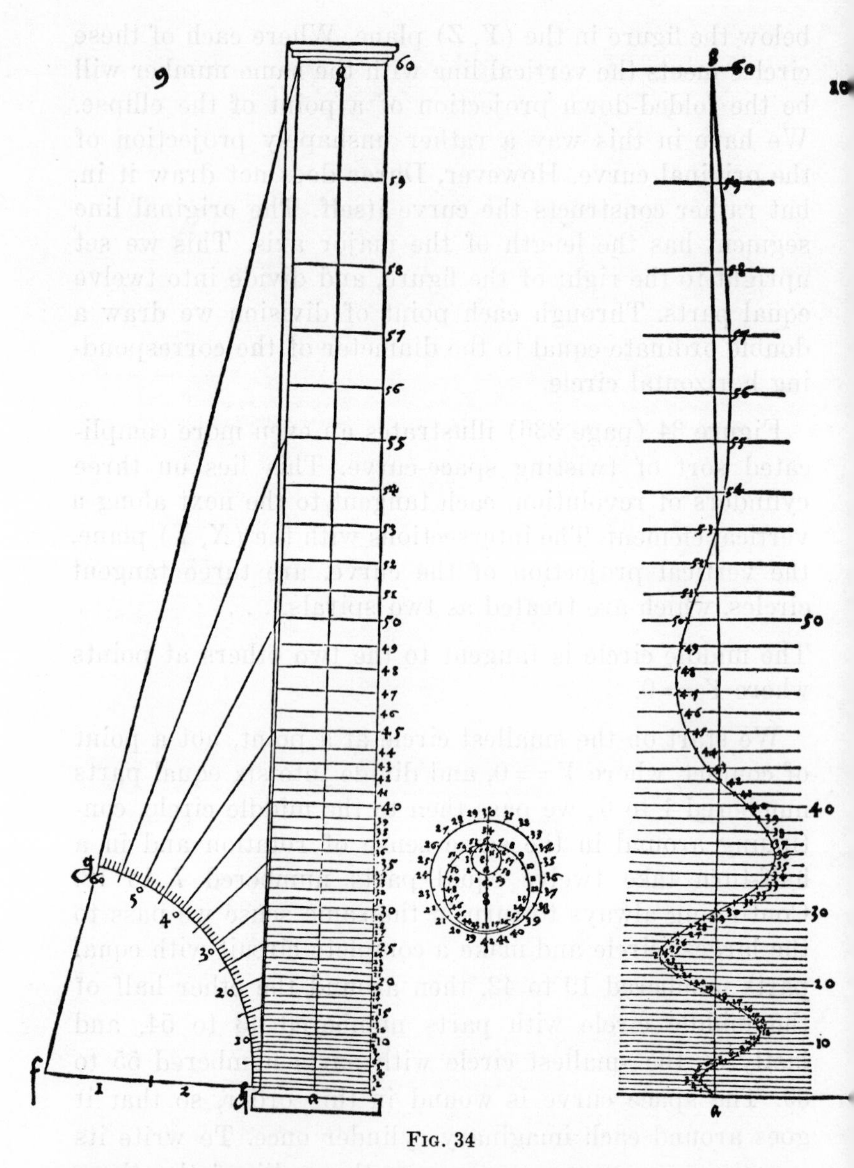

Fig. 34

muth θ, which will depend on whether the semicircle is divided into six parts or twelve, we have

$$y = r_i \sin \theta; \qquad z = \frac{h \tan(n\alpha/60)}{\tan \alpha} \cdot$$

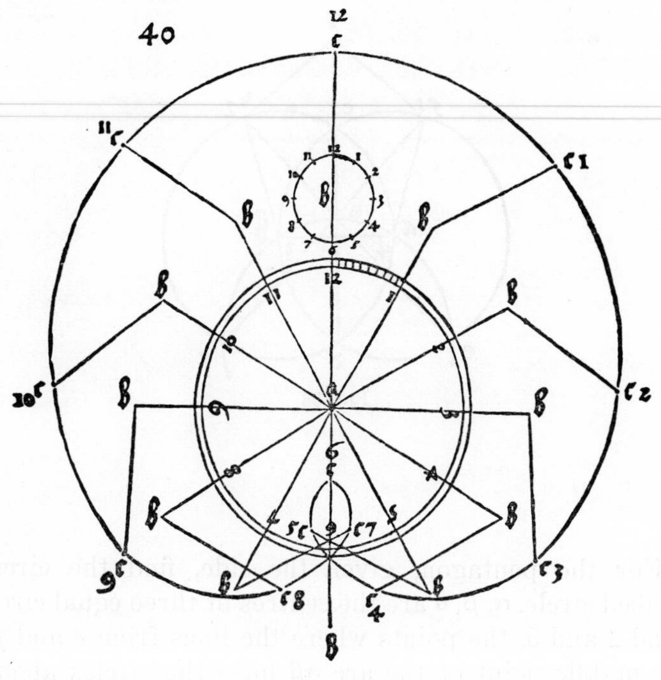

FIG. 35

Durer paid some attention to classical geometrical problems as well as to plane curves of his own devising. Here is his construction for a heart-shaped curve of the fourth order, drawn with a double ruler so constructed that one part makes twice the angle with the horizontal that the other does

$$ab = r; \qquad bc = p;$$

$$x = r\cos\theta + p\cos 2\theta; \qquad y = r\sin\theta + p\sin 2\theta;$$

$$x^2 + y^2 = r^2 + p^2 + 2rp\cos\theta;$$

$$2p(x+p) = [x^2+y^2-(r^2+p^2)]\left[1+\frac{1}{r^2}\{x^2+y^2-(r^2+p^2)\}\right].$$

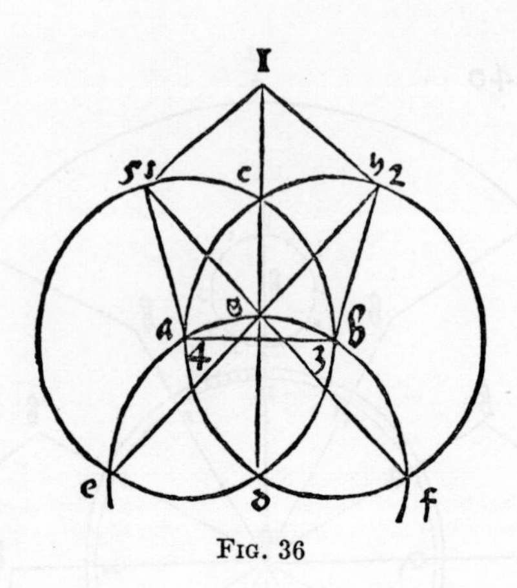

Fig. 36

For the pentagon, given the side, find the circumscribed circle. α, β, δ are the centres of three equal circles. Find 2 and 5, the points where the lines from e and f to the middle point of the arc $\alpha\beta$ meet the circles about α and β. He takes 5α, $\alpha\beta$, $\beta 2$ as three sides of the pentagon. This leads to the approximation

$$\sin 27^\circ = 2 \sin 60^\circ \sin 15^\circ,$$

$$0{\cdot}454 = 0{\cdot}448.$$

Amusing construction appears at the beginning of his Book IV to construct regular solids by paper folding. This is the usual procedure taught to-day in our schools; so far as I can make out it is original with Durer.†

I reproduce his picture for the icosahedron in Fig. 37.

† Cantor[1], vol. ii, p. 466.

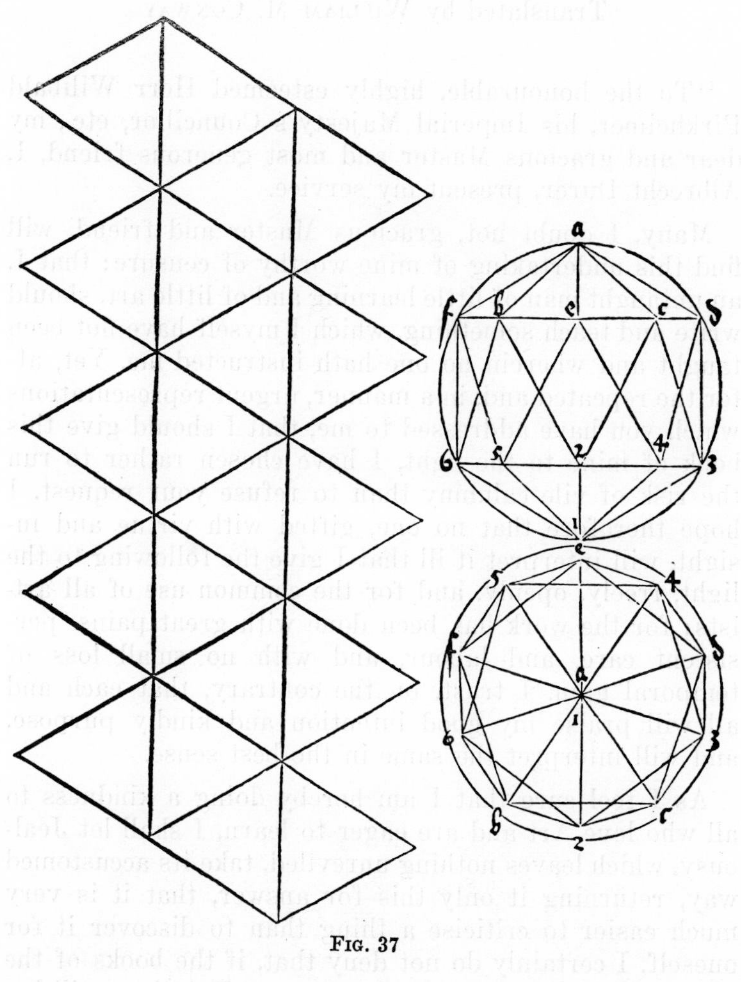

Fig. 37

FOUR BOOKS ON HUMAN PROPORTION

From *The Writings of Albrecht Durer*

Translated by William M. Conway

"To the honourable, highly esteemed Herr Wilibald Pirkheimer, his Imperial Majesty's Councillor, etc., my dear and gracious Master and most generous friend, I, Albrecht Durer, present my service.

Many, I doubt not, gracious Master and friend, will find this undertaking of mine worthy of censure; that I, an untaught man of little learning and of little art, should write and teach something, which I myself have not been taught and wherein no one hath instructed me. Yet, after the repeated and, in a manner, urgent representations which you have addressed to me, that I should give this book of mine to the light, I have chosen rather to run the risk of vile calumny than to refuse your request. I hope therefore that no one, gifted with virtue and insight, will interpret it ill that I give the following to the light, freely, openly, and for the common use of all artists; for the work has been done with great pains, persistent care, and labour, and with no small loss of temporal gain. I trust, on the contrary, that each and all will praise my good intention and kindly purpose, and will interpret the same in the best sense.

As I feel sure that I am hereby doing a kindness to all who love Art and are eager to learn, I shall let Jealousy, which leaves nothing unreviled, take its accustomed way, returning it only this for answer, that it is very much easier to criticise a thing than to discover it for oneself. I certainly do not deny that, if the books of the Ancients, who wrote about the Art of Painting, still lay before our eyes, my design might be open to the false interpretation that I thought to find out something better than what was known unto them. These books however have been totally lost in the lapse of time; so I cannot be justly blamed for publishing my opinions and discoveries in writing, for that is exactly what the Ancients did. If other competent men are thereby induced to do the like, our descendants will have something which they may add to and improve upon, and thus the Art of Painting may in time advance and reach its perfection.

No one need blindly follow this theory of mine, as though it were quite perfect, for human nature has not yet so far degenerated, that another man can not discover something better. So each may use my teaching as long as it seems good to him or until he finds something better. Where he is not willing to accept it, he may well hold that this doctrine was not written for him but for others who are willing.

That must be a strangely dull head which never trusts itself to find out anything fresh, but only travels along the old path, simply following others and not daring to reflect for itself. For it beseems each Understanding, in following another, not to despair of, itself also, discovering something better. If that is done, there remaineth no doubt but that, in time, this Art will again reach the perfection it attained amongst the Ancients. For it is evident that, though the German painters are not a little skilful with the hand and in the use of colours, they have as yet been wanting in the arts of measurement, perspective, and other like matters. It is therefore to be hoped that, if they learn these also and gain skill by knowledge and knowledge by skill, they will in time allow no other nation to take the prize before them.

Without proportion no figure can ever be perfect, even though it be made with all possible diligence. There is of course no need for all figures, especially quite little ones, to be constructed according to the canon, for that would involve too much labour. If however a man has a thorough knowledge of the canon and is well practised in the use of it, he will afterwards be able to make every figure so much the more easily, and without reference to the canon.

In order that this teaching of mine might be better understood I have already published a book about Measurements, that is to say of lines, planes, bodies, and the like, without knowledge of which this my theory cannot be completely understood. It is therefore necessary for all who would try this art that they be well instructed in Measurements and know how to draw a plan and elevation of anything, in the manner in daily use amongst skilful stonemasons; otherwise they will not be able thoroughly to grasp my teaching.

No one should allow himself to be deterred from this study because he does not at once understand the whole, for what is quite easy can be no very high art, but what is full of art calls for diligence, pains, and labour, before it can be understood and fixed in the memory.

If a work be incorrectly designed, however great the care and diligence spent on it, the labour is still in vain. If on the contrary it is rightly drawn, it cannot be condemned by anyone however simply it be finished.

I intend in these lessons to write only about the bounding outlines of forms and figures, and how to draw them from point to point. I shall say nothing at all about the parts within. Neither is this the place to write about such matters as the antiquity of this art, its first discoverer, the respect and honour in which it was held by the Greeks and Romans, or how it should be used in the education of a good Painter or Workman. Whoever desireth to know about these matters should read Pliny and Vitruvius, where he will find enough information.

Considering, dear Sir, that I cannot make the work itself a token of my esteem and affection towards you, I have dedicated it to you, intending thereby to acknowledge the many proofs of love, friendship, and goodwill, which you have given me so often and so long. I hope that hereby this book will acquire in you, noble Sir, a protector against ill reports. Confidently beseeching you to take it under your protection and ever to remain my gracious Master and helper, I continue eager to serve you whenever I may be able."

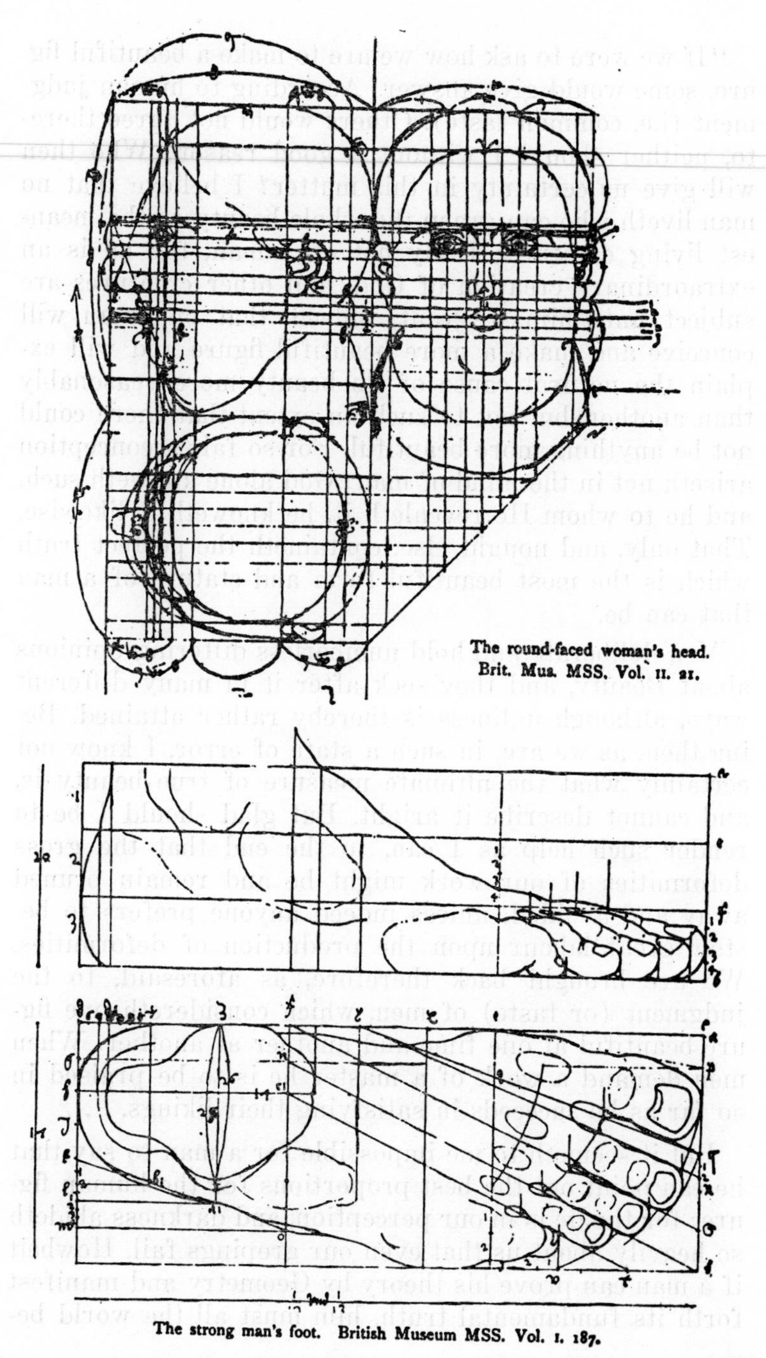

The round-faced woman's head.
Brit. Mus. MSS. Vol. II. 21.

The strong man's foot. British Museum MSS. Vol. I. 187.

"If we were to ask how we are to make a beautiful figure, some would give answer: According to human judgment (i.e. common taste). Others would not agree thereto, neither should I without a good reason. Who then will give us certainty in this matter? I believe that no man liveth who can grasp the whole beauty of the meanest living creature; I say not of a man, for he is an extraordinary creation of God, and other creatures are subject unto him. I grant, indeed, that one man will conceive and make a more beautiful figure and will explain the natural cause of its beauty more reasonably than another, but not to such an extent that there could not be anything more beautiful. For so fair a conception ariseth not in the mind of man; God alone knoweth such, and he to whom He revealeth it, he knoweth it likewise. That only, and nought else, containeth the perfect truth which is the most beautiful form and stature of a man that can be.

Men deliberate and hold numberless differing opinions about Beauty, and they seek after it in many different ways, although ugliness is thereby rather attained. Being then, as we are, in such a state of error, I know not certainly what the ultimate measure of true beauty is, and cannot describe it aright. But glad should I be to render such help as I can, to the end that the gross deformities of our work might be and remain pruned away and avoided, unless indeed anyone prefers to bestow great labour upon the production of deformities. We are brought back therefore, as aforesaid, to the judgment (or taste) of men, which considereth one figure beautiful at one time and another at another. When men demand a work of a master he is to be praised in so far as he succeeds in satisfying their likings. . . .

But it seemeth to me impossible for a man to say that he can point out the best proportions for the human figure; for the lie is in our perception, and darkness abideth so heavily about us that even our gropings fail. Howbeit if a man can prove his theory by Geometry and manifest forth its fundamental truth, him must all the world believe, for so is one compelled. And it were easy to hold such an one for endowed of God to be a master in such matters; and the demonstrations of his reasons are to be listened to with eagerness and still more gladly are his works to be beheld.

Because now we cannot altogether attain unto perfection, shall we therefore wholly cease from our learning? By no means. Let us not take unto ourselves thoughts fit for cattle. For evil and good lie before men, wherefore it behoveth a rational man to choose the good. In order therefore that we may approach unto the knowledge of how a good figure should be made, we must first order the whole figure well and nobly with all its limbs, and we must see next that every limb, regarded in itself, be made aright in all smallest as in greatest things, if so be that thus we may draw forth a part of the beauty given unto us and come so much the nearer to the perfect end. So then, as aforesaid, a man is one whole, made up of many parts, and as each of these parts hath its own proper form, so much equal care be given to all. Anything whereby they might be marred, that same must be shunned, and the true, natural character of each part must be very carefully maintained, neither must we swerve therefrom if we can help it.

. . . He therefore who, by a right understanding, hath attained a good style, hath it ever in his power to make something good, as far as that is possible to us; yet he will do so still better if he study from the life. But to make a good thing is impossible for the unpractised hand, for these things come not by chance. . . .

A man who hath not learnt anything about this art before, and who desireth to make a beginning from this book must read it with great diligence and learn to understand what he readeth; and, taking a little at a time, he must practise himself well in the same, until he can do it, and only then must he go on to do something else. For the understanding must begin to grow side by side with skill, so that the hand have power to do what the will in the understanding commands. By such means certainty of art and skill waxeth with the time; and these two must advance together, for the one is nought without the other. Further, it must be noted that though a common man knows the better from the worse, yet no man can perfectly judge a picture (in point of execution) except an understanding artist who hath often accomplished the like in his work.

Now a man might say: Who will devote continual labour and trouble, with consuming of much time, thus in tedious wise to measure out a single figure, seeing moreover that it often happeneth that he must make, it may be, twenty or thirty different figures in a short time? In answer to which, I do not mean that a man should at all times construct everything by measurements; but if thou hast well learnt the theory of measurements and attained understanding and skill in it, so that thou canst make a thing with free certainty of hand, and knowest how to do each thing aright, then it is not always needful always to measure everything, for the art which thou hast acquired giveth thee a good eye-measure, and the practised hand is obedient. And thus the power of art driveth away error from thy work and restraineth thee from making falsehood; for her thou knowest, and by thy knowledge thou art preserved from despair and become skilful in thy work so that thou makest no false touch or stroke. And this skill bringeth it to pass that thou hast no need to think, if thy head is full stored with Art. And thus thy work appeareth artistic, charming, powerful, free, and good, and will receive manifold praise because rightness is infused into it.

But if thou lackest a true foundation it is impossible for thee to make aught aright and well. And although thou hadst the most skilful freedom of hand in the world, that is rather a slavery when it leads thee astray. Wherefore there must be no freedom without art, and art is lost without skill; so that, as aforesaid, the two must go together. It is therefore needful that a man learn to measure right artfully. He that can do so well maketh wonderful things. The human figure cannot be outlined with rule or compass, but must be drawn from point to point, as above explained; and without a true canon this cannot in any wise be done aright.

It might come to pass that a man, who wanted to use this above written 'canon of a figure' in some large work, might go wrong through his own want of skill, and then might lay the blame upon me, saying that my rules were right for small things but they were misleading for large works. Such however cannot be the case, for the small cannot be right and the large wrong, or the small bad and the large good, neither can the matter be divided in this wise. For a circle, whether small or large, abideth round, and so it is with a square. Each proportion therefore remaineth unaltered whether the scale be large or small, even as in music, a note answereth to its octave, the one high the other low, yet both are the same note."

"A good figure cannot be made without industry and care; it should therefore be well considered before it is begun, so that it be correctly made. For the lines of its form cannot be traced by compass or rule, but must be drawn by the hand from point to point, so that it is easy to go wrong in them. And for such figures great attention should be paid to human proportions, and all their kinds should be investigated. I hold that the more nearly and accurately a figure is made to resemble a man, so much the better will the work be. If the best parts, chosen from many well-formed men, are united in one figure, it will be worthy of praise. But some are of another opinion and discuss how men *ought* to be made. I will not argue with them about that. I hold Nature for master in such matters and the fancy of man for delusion. The Creator fashioned men once for all as they *must* be, and I hold that the perfection of form and beauty is contained in the sum of all men. That man will I rather follow, who can extract this perfection aright, than one who invents some new body of proportions, not to be found amongst men. For the human figure must, once for all, remain different from those of other creatures, let them do with it what else they please. If I, however, were here to be attacked upon this point, namely, that I myself have set up strange proportions for figures, about that I will not argue with anyone. Nevertheless they are not really inhuman, I only exaggerate them so that all may see my meaning in them. Let anyone, who thinks that I alter the human form too much or too little, take care to avoid my error and to follow nature. There are many different kinds of men in various lands; whoso travels far will find this to be so and see it before his eyes. We are considering about the most beautiful human figure conceivable, but the Maker of the world knows how that should be. Even if we succeed well we do but approach towards it somewhat from afar. For we ourselves have differences of perception, and the vulgar who follow only their own taste usually err. Therefore I will not advise anyone to follow me, for I only do what I can, and that is not enough even to satisfy myself."

* * * * * * * *

"He now who trieth and followeth this my teaching, first giving figures a right proportion according to the canon, then arranging them orderly, laying out the outlines, giving the effect of depth by perspective, and so artistically drawing his picture or whatever it may be, will soon find out of how great service it will be unto him, and doubtless will discover much more than is here shown or handled. Notwithstanding that this my doctrine may be considered in some points difficult, it is nevertheless true; for what is hard to understand cannot be learnt without diligence and toil.

And herewith, gracious Master, I shall for this time bring my writing to an end. If God, in his own time, granteth me to write something further about matters connected with Painting I will do so in the hope that this Art may not rest upon use and wont alone, but that in time it may be taught on true and orderly principles and may be understood to the praise of God and the use and pleasure of all lovers of Art."

EUCLID OF ALEXANDRIA

(c. 300 B.C.)

Our knowledge of the life of Euclid is meagre and indirect. Even in ancient times there was no account of his life available. It is now strongly believed that he had been a mathematician of note in Athens for some time before his arrival in Alexandria, where, under his direct tutelage and influence, there arose a powerful school of Greek mathematics. In allusions to him in ancient writings, he is rarely mentioned by name, being referred to simply as the author of the *Elements*. Proclus (412—485 A.D.) the great historian on whom we rely for almost all our information concerning the ancient Greek mathematicians, was himself forced to employ inference in arriving at his conclusions that Euclid was younger than the pupils of Plato and older than Archimedes, and therefore that he lived in the time of the first Ptolemy, i.e., c. 300 B.C. We learn something of his character from Pappus (c. 300 A.D.) who, contrasting the attitude of Apollonius and Euclid towards their predecessors, pointedly mentions Euclid's fairness in acknowledging the achievements of others and his kindness to anyone who could in the least degree advance the development of mathematics. Both commentators have been amply supported in their appraisal of Euclid's character and personality by the evidence of Euclid's own writing and collateral works. Euclid is thus known to us not only as the first of the great mathematicians of the Alexandrian school, but also as a kindly teacher, honorable and fair minded, with no trace of acquisitiveness regarding either money or reputation.

Using the method of definitions, axioms, postulates, and propositions in logical sequence, Euclid organized the geometrical knowledge extant in his time in thirteen books. The entire treatise was known as the *Elements*. Here he presented a judicious selection of both old and recent works, sometimes rearranging the original order of theorems, and in such cases adding new proofs where the old proofs had become invalid by reason of the rearrangement. In addition to Pythagorean geometry he included the Eudoxian theory of proportion and the method of exhaustions. He dealt with both commensurable and incommensurable quantities. Although specific contributions original with Euclid are difficult to trace, it is generally agreed that he is the originator of the "Euclidean algorithm" for finding the greatest common measure of two given numbers, and of the proof of the infinity of primes. Euclid was the first writer on mathematics to include the concept of parallel lines among his postulates.

While the *Elements* is generally conceded to be Euclid's masterpiece, other works in mathematics, astronomy, mechanics, music and optics have been attributed to him. Surviving (though in incomplete form) are the *Data* containing problems in geometry apparently intended for those who had completed the study of the *Elements,* the *De Divisionibus,* containing problems in the division of areas, the *Optics,* in two forms, one of which is most probably Euclid's own, and the *Phaenomena,* on the geometry of the sphere.

Through countless editions, translations, commentaries and revisions, Euclid's *Elements* remained for more than two thousand years a most important means whereby students received an introduction to the study of mathematics. During the period of some two hundred years just passed, the methodology displayed by Euclid so insistently and so successfully in his *Elements,* has proved itself again and again to be a powerful inspiration in the development of new mathematical systems. However far the subject matter of a modern system may be removed from the substance of the *Elements,* its structure nevertheless, rests on a basis of axiomatic method taught by Euclid.

ELEMENTS

From *The Thirteen Books of Euclid's Elements*

by Sir Thomas L. Heath

BOOK I

Postulate 5.

Καὶ ἐὰν εἰς δύρ εὐθείας εὐθεῖα ἐμπίπτουσα τὰς ἐντὸς καὶ ἐπὶ τὰ αὐτὰ μέρη γωνίας· δύο ὀρθῶν ἐλάσσονας ποιῇ, ἐκβαλλομένας τὰς δύο εὐθείας ἐπ' ἄπειρον συμπίπτειν, ἐφ' ἃ μέρη εἰσὶν αἱ τῶν δύο ὀρθῶν ἐλάσσονες.

That, if a straight line falling on two straight lines make the interior angles on the same side less than two right angles, the two straight lines, if produced indefinitely, meet on that side on which are the angles less than the two right angles.

Although Aristotle gives a clear idea of what he understood by a *postulate,* he does not give any instances from geometry; still less has he any allusion recalling the particular postulates found in Euclid. We naturally infer that the formulation of these postulates was Euclid's own work. There is a more positive indication of the originality of Postulate 5, since in the passage (*Anal. prior,* II. 16, 65 a 4) quoted above in the note on the definition of parallels he alludes to some *petitio principii* involved in the theory of parallels current in his time. This reproach was removed by Euclid when he laid down this epoch-making Postulate. When we consider the countless successive attempts made through more than twenty centuries to prove the Postulate, many of them by geometers of ability, we cannot but admire the genius of the man who concluded that such a hypothesis, which he found necessary to the validity of his whole system of geometry, was really indemonstrable.

From the very beginning, as we know from Proclus, the Postulate was attacked as such, and attempts were made to prove it as a theorem or to get rid of it by adopting some other definition of parallels; while in modern times the literature of the subject is enormous. Riccardi (*Saggio di una bibliografia Euclidea,* Part IV., Bologna, 1890) has twenty quarto pages of titles of monographs relating to Post. 5 between the dates 1607 and 1887. Max Simon (*Ueber die Entwicklung der Elementar-geometrie im XIX. Jahrhundert,* 1906) notes that he has seen three new attempts, as late as 1891 (a century after Gauss laid the foundation of non-Euclidean geometry), to prove the theory of parallels independently of the Postulate. Max Simon himself (pp. 53—61) gives a large number of references to books or articles on the subject and refers to the copious information, as to contents as well as names, contained in Schotten's *Inhalt und Methode des planimetrischen Unterrichts,* II. pp. 183—332.

Alternatives for Postulate 5.

It may be convenient to collect here a few of the more noteworthy substitutes which have from time to time been formally suggested or tacitly assumed.

(1) *Through a given point only one parallel can be drawn to a given straight line* or, *Two straight lines*

which intersect one another cannot both be parallel to one and the same straight line.

This is commonly known as "Playfair's Axiom," but it was of course not a new discovery. It is distinctly stated in Proclus' note to Eucl. I. 31.

(1 *a*) *If a straight line intersect one of two parallels, it will intersect the other also* (Proclus).

(1 *b*) *Straight lines parallel to the same straight line are parallel to one another.*

The forms (1 *a*) and (1 *b*) are exactly equivalent to (1).

(2) *There exist straight lines everywhere equidistant from one another* (Posidonius and Geminus); with which may be compared Proclus' tacit assumption that *Parallels remain, throughout their length, at a finite distance from one another.*

(3) *There exists a triangle in which the sum of the three angles is equal to two right angles* (Legendre).

(4) *Given any figure, there exists a figure similar to it of any size we please* (Wallis, Carnot, Laplace).

Saccheri points out that it is not necessary to assume so much, and that it is enough to postulate that *there exist two unequal triangles with equal angles.*

(5) *Through any point within an angle less than two-thirds of a right angle a straight line can always be drawn which meets both sides of the angle* (Legendre).

With this may be compared the similar axiom of Lorenz (*Grundriss der reinen und angewandten Mathematik*, 1791): *Every straight line through a point within an angle must meet one of the sides of the angle.*

(6) *Given any three points not in a straight line, there exists a circle passing through them* (Legendre, W. Bolyai).

(7) "*If I could prove that a rectilineal triangle is possible the content of which is greater than any given area, I am in a position to prove perfectly rigorously the whole of geometry*" (Gauss, in a letter to W. Bolyai, 1799).

Cf. the proposition of Legendre numbered IV. above, and the axiom of Worpitzky: *There exists no triangle in which every angle is as small as we please.*

(8) *If in a quadrilateral three angles are right angles, the fourth angle is a right angle also* (Clairaut, 1741).

(9) *If two straight lines are parallel, they are figures opposite to (or the reflex of) one another with respect to the middle points of all their transversal segments* (Veronese, *Elementi*, 1904).

Or, *Two parallel straight lines intercept, on every transversal which passes through the middle point of a segment included between them, another segment the middle point of which is the middle point of the first* (Ingrami, *Elementi*, 1904).

Veronese and Ingrami deduce immediately Playfair's Axiom.

BOOK VII

Proposition i.

Two unequal numbers being set out, and the less being continually subtracted in turn from the greater, if the number which is left never measures the one before it until an unit is left, the original numbers will be prime to one another.

For, the less of two unequal numbers *AB*, *CD* being continually subtracted from the greater, let the number which is left never measure the one before it until an unit is left;

I say that *AB*, *CD* are prime to one another, that is, that an unit alone measures *AB*, *CD*.

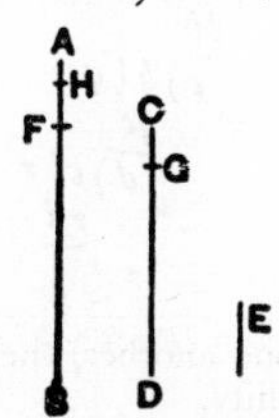

For, if *AB*, *CD* are not prime to one another, some number will measure them.

Let a number measure them, and let it be *E*; let *CD*, measuring *BF*, leave *FA* less than itself,

let *AF*, measuring *DG*, leave *GC* less than itself, and let *GC*, measuring *FH*, leave an unit *HA*.

Since, then, E measures CD, and CD measures BF, therefore E also measures BF.

But it also measures the whole BA; therefore it will also measure the remainder AF.

But AF measures DG; therefore E also measures DG.

But it also measures the whole DC. therefore it will also measure the remainder CG.

But CG measures FH; therefore E also measures FH.

But it also measures the whole FA; therefore it will also measure the remainder, the unit AH, though it is a number: which is impossible.

Therefore no number will measure the numbers AB, CD; therefore AB, CD are prime to one another.

[VII. Def. 12]

Q. E. D.

It is proper to remark here that the representation in Books VII. to IX. of numbers by straight lines is adopted by Heiberg from the MSS. The method of those editors who substitute *points* for lines is open to objection because it practically necessitates, in many cases, the use of specific numbers, which is contrary to Euclid's manner.

"Let CD, measuring BF, leave FA less than itself." This is a neat abbreviation for saying, measure along BA successive lengths equal to CD until a point F is reached such that the length FA remaining is less than CD; in other words, let BF be the largest exact multiple of CD contained in BA.

Euclid's method in this proposition is an application to the particular case of prime numbers of the method of finding the greatest common measure of two numbers not prime to one another, which we shall find in the next proposition. With our notation, the method may be shown thus. Supposing the two numbers to be a, b, we have, say,

$$\begin{array}{llll} b)\,a\,(p & & & \\ \underline{pb} & & & \\ \quad c)\,b\,(q & & & \\ \qquad \underline{qc} & & & \\ \qquad\quad d)\,c\,(r & & & \\ \qquad\qquad \underline{rd} & & & \\ \qquad\qquad\; 1 & & & \end{array}$$

If now a, b are not prime to one another, they must have a common measure e, where e is some integer, not unity.

And since e measures a, b, it measures $a - pb$, i.e. c.

Again, since e measures b, c, it measures $b - qc$, i.e. d, and lastly, since e measures c, d, it measures $c - rd$, i.e. 1: which is impossible.

Therefore there is no integer, except unity, that measures a, b, which are accordingly prime to one another.

Observe that Euclid assumes as an axiom that, if a, b are both divisible by c, so is $a - pb$. In the next proposition he assumes as an axiom that c will in the case supposed divide $a + pb$.

PROPOSITION 2.

Given two numbers not prime to one another, to find their greatest common measure.

Let *AB, CD* be the two given numbers not prime to one another.

Thus it is required to find the greatest common measure of *AB, CD*.

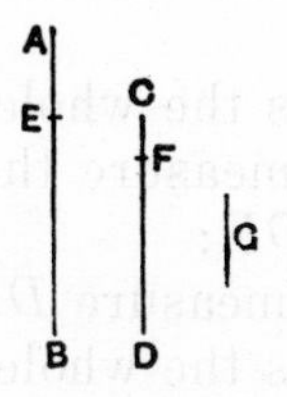

If now *CD* measures *AB*—and it also measures itself —*CD* is a common measure of *CD, AB*.

And it is manifest that it is also the greatest; for no greater number than *CD* will measure *CD*.

But, if *CD* does not measure *AB*, then, the less of the numbers *AB, CD* being continually subtracted from the greater, some number will be left which will measure the one before it.

For an unit will not be left; otherwise *AB, CD* will be prime to one another [VII. 1], which is contrary to the hypothesis.

Therefore some number will be left which will measure the one before it.

Now let *CD*, measuring *BE*, leave *EA* less than itself, let *EA*, measuring *DF*, leave *FC* less than itself, and let *CF* measure *AE*.

Since then, *CF* measures *AE*, and *AE* measures *DF*, therefore *CF* will also measure *DF*.

But it also measures itself;
therefore it will also measure the whole *CD*.

But *CD* measures *BE*;
therefore *CF* also measures *BE*.

But it also measures *EA*;
therefore it will also measure the whole *BA*.

But it also measures *CD*;

therefore CF measures AB, CD.

Therefore CF is a common measure of AB, CD.

I say next that it is also the greatest.

For, if CF is not the greatest common measure of AB, CD, some number which is greater than CF will measure the numbers AB, CD.

Let such a number measure them, and let it be G.

Now, since G measures CD, while CD measures BE, G also measures BE.

But it also measures the whole BA;
therefore it will also measure the remainder AE.

But AE measures DF;
therefore G will also measure DF.

But it also measures the whole DC;
therefore it will also measure the remainder CF, that is, the greater will measure the less: which is impossible.

Therefore no number which is greater than CF will measure the numbers AB, CD;

therefore CF is the greatest common measure of AB, CD.

PORISM. From this it is manifest that, if a number measure two numbers, it will also measure their greatest common measure.

Q. E. D.

Here we have the exact method of finding the greatest common measure given in the text-books of algebra, including the *reductio ad absurdum* proof that the number arrived at is not only a common measure but the *greatest* common measure. The process of finding the greatest common measure is simply shown thus:

$$\begin{array}{l} b)\,a\,(p \\ \quad\underline{pb} \\ \quad\; c)\,b\,(q \\ \qquad\;\underline{qc} \\ \qquad\; d)\,c\,(r \\ \qquad\quad\;\underline{rd} \end{array}$$

We shall arrive, says Euclid, at some number, say d, which measures the one before it, i.e. such that $c = rd$. Otherwise the process would go on until we arrived at unity. This is impossible because in that case a, b would be prime to one another, which is contrary to the hypothesis.

Next, like the text-books of algebra, he goes on to show that d will be *some* common measure of a, b. For d measures c;
therefore it measures $qc + d$, that is, b,
and hence it measures $pb + c$, that is, a.

Lastly, he proves that d is the *greatest* common measure of a, b as follows.

Suppose that e is a common measure greater than d.

Then e, measuring a, b, must measure $a - pb$, or c.

Similarly e must measure $b - qc$, that is, d: which is impossible, since e is by hypothesis greater than d.

Therefore etc.

Euclid's proposition is thus *identical* with the algebraical proposition as generally given, e.g. in Todhunter's algebra, except that of course Euclid's numbers are integers.

PROPOSITION 29.

Any prime number is prime to any number which it does not measure.

Let A be a prime number, and let it not measure B; I say that B, A are prime to one another.

For, if B, A are not prime to one another, some number will measure them.

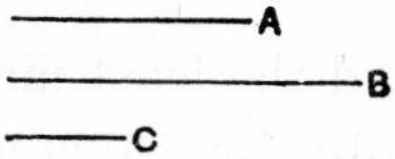

Let C measure them.

Since C measures B, and A does not measure B, therefore C is not the same with A.

Now, since C measures B, A, therefore it also measures A which is prime, though it is not the same with it: which is impossible.

Therefore no number will measure B, A.

Therefore A, B are prime to one another.

Q. E. D.

If a is prime and does not measure b, then a, b are prime to one another. The proof is self-evident.

PROPOSITION 30.

If two numbers by multiplying one another make some number, and any prime number measure the product, it also measure one of the original numbers.

For let the two numbers A, B by multiplying one another make C, and let any prime number D measure C; I say that D measures one of the numbers A, B.

For let it not measure A.

Now D is prime;

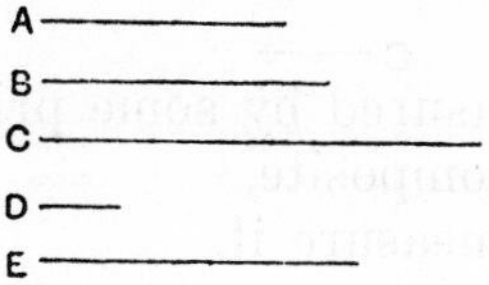

therefore A, D are prime to one another. [VII. 29]

And, as many times as D measures C, so many units let there be in E.

Since then D measures C according to the units in E, therefore D by multiplying E has made C.

[VII. Def. 15]

Further, A by multiplying B has also made C; therefore the product of D, E is equal to the product of A, B.

Therefore, as D is to A, so is B to E. [VII. 19]

But D, A are prime to one another, primes are also least,

[VII. 21]

and the least measure the numbers which have the same ratio the same number of times, the greater the greater and the less the less, that is, the antecedent the antecedent and the consequent the consequent;

[VII. 20]

therefore D measures B.

Similarly we can also show that, if D do not measure B, it will measure A.

Therefore D measures one of the numbers A, B.

Q. E. D.

If c, a prime number, measure ab, c will measure either a or b.
Suppose c does not measure a.
Therefore c, a are prime to one another. [VII. 29]
Suppose $ab = mc$.
Therefore $c : a = b : m$. [VII. 19]
Hence [VII. 20, 21] c measures b.
Similarly, if c does not measure b, it measures a.
Therefore it measures one or other of the two numbers a, b.

PROPOSITION 31.

Any composite number is measured by some prime number.

Let A be a composite number;

A

B

C

I say that A is measured by some prime number.

For, since A is composite, some number will measure it.

Let a number measure it, and let it be B.

Now, if B is prime, what was enjoined will have been done.

But if it is composite, some number will measure it.

Let a number measure it, and let it be C.

Then, since C measures B,
and B measures A
therefore C also measures A.

And, if C is prime, what was enjoined will have been done.

But if it is composite, some number will measure it.

Thus, if the investigation be continued in this way, some prime number will be found which will measure the number before it, which will also measure A.

For, if it is not found, an infinite series of numbers will measure the number A, each of which is less than the other: which is impossible in numbers.

Therefore some prime number will be found which will measure the one before it, which will also measure A.

Therefore any composite number is measured by some prime number.

BOOK IX

Proposition 20.

Prime numbers are more than any assigned multitude of prime numbers.

Let A, B, C be the assigned prime numbers;
I say that there are more prime numbers than A, B, C.

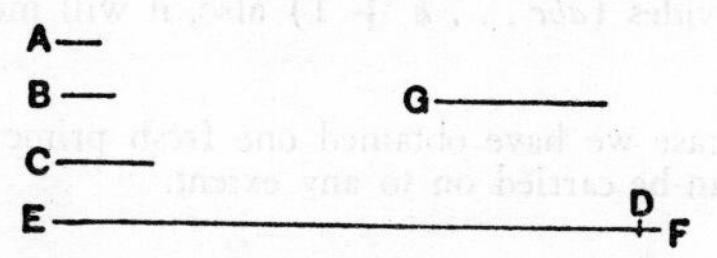

For let the least number measured by A, B, C be taken, and let it be DE;
let the unit DF be added to DE.

Then EF is either prime or not.

First, let it be prime;

then the prime numbers A, B, C, EF have been found which are more than A, B, C.

Next, let EF not be prime; therefore it is measured by some prime number. [VII. 31]

Let it be measured by the prime number G.

I say that G is not the same with any of the numbers A, B, C.

For, if possible, let it be so.

Now A, B, C measure DE; therefore G also will measure DE.

But it also measures EF.

Therefore G, being a number, will measure the remainder, the unit DF: which is absurd.

Therefore G is not the same with any one of the numbers A, B, C.

And by hypothesis it is prime.

Therefore the prime numbers A, B, C, G have been found which are more than the assigned multitude of A, B, C.

Q. E. D.

We have here the important proposition that *the number of prime numbers is infinite*.

The proof will be seen to be the same as that given in our algebraical text-books. Let $a, b, c, \ldots k$ be any prime numbers.

Take the product $abc \ldots k$ and add unity.

Then $(abc \ldots k + 1)$ is either a prime number or not a prime number.

(1) If it *is*, we have added another prime number to those given.

(2) If it is *not*, it must be measured by some prime number [VII. 31], say p.

Now p cannot be identical with any of the prime numbers $a, b, c, \ldots k$.

For, if it is, it will divide $abc \ldots k$.

Therefore, since it divides $(abc \ldots k + 1)$ also, it will measure the difference, or unity: which is impossible.

Therefore in any case we have obtained one fresh prime number.

And the process can be carried on to any extent.

GOTTLOB FREGE

(1848-1925)

Gottlob Frege was born in Wismar, Germany in 1848. Educated at the Universities of Jena and Gottingen, he received his first appointment at Jena as *Privatdozent* in 1871. He became a professor of mathematics there in 1879. During a long career at Jena, Frege published several highly significant works, the most important of which are: *Begriffsschrift* (1879), *Grundlagen der Arithmetik* (1884), *Function und Begriff* (1891), *Begriff und Gegenstand* (1892), *Sinn und Bedeutung* (1892), *Grundgesetze I* (1893), *II* (1903). His efforts were directed toward establishing the principle that mathematics is based on the general laws of logic. Indeed, he went so far as to take the position that mathematics is so intimately bound up with logic that no separation of the two can be effected. In the implementation of this thesis, Frege pioneered in the construction of a logical symbolism and in the development of symbolical methods of logical analysis. Due in a large measure to the difficulty of grasping his symbolism as well as to the novelty of the ideas contained in them, his works were met with a vast silence. Frege openly expressed his disappointment in seeking mention of his writings in the technical journals again and again but finding none whatever. The silence was broken eventually by Bertrand Russell. However, despite the great extent to which Russell found Frege's views in agreement with his own, he nevertheless found it possible to derive from Frege's system, a paradox about the class of all classes which are not members of themselves. Frege replied to Russell's criticism, but he failed to convince himself completely of the adequacy of his reply, and feeling that he had not removed the logical flaw from his work, he wrote nothing in the field of foundations of arithmetic from that time on. Later logicians, on the other hand, provided satisfactory replies to Russell's criticism and also to the objections which had been raised by Wittgenstein and others to the Frege-Russell definitions. A new evaluation of Frege's work ensued, in which the rich significance of his fundamental ideas was recognized. Frege's work proved to be both instructive and inspirational.

The present tendency is to regard Frege as the greatest logician of the nineteenth century, for although approximately a third of his life fell in the twentieth century, his major contributions to logic and mathematics appeared in the nineteenth. In 1948, *Sinn und Bedeutung* was translated into Italian and into English; another English translation of the same work appeared in 1949. *Grundlagen der Arithmetik* was translated into English in 1950 and there have been reprints of this translation since then. Controversies about Frege's work, where they exist, turn not upon the soundness or the value of his ideas but upon the suitability of the technical terms which have been selected (or invented) by translators in their striving to achieve accuracy in their presentation of Frege's meaning. The first to define number in purely logical terms, Frege presented his definition of a number in his *Grundlagen der Arithmetik,* a work in which he made a deliberate effort to use a minimum of symbolism and the simplest possible language.

●

THE FOUNDATIONS OF ARITHMETIC

Translated by J. L. Austin

To obtain the concept of Number, we must fix the sense of a numerical identity.

§62. How, then, are numbers to be given to us, if we cannot have any ideas or intuitions of them? Since it is only in the context of a proposition that words have any meaning, our problem becomes this: To define the sense of a proposition in which a number word occurs. That, obviously, leaves us still a very wide choice. But we have already settled that number words are to be understood as standing for self-subsistent objects. And that is enough to give us a class of propositions which must have a sense, namely those which express our recognition of a number as the same again. If we are to use the symbol a to signify an object, we must have a criterion for deciding in all cases whether b is the same as a, even if it is not always in our power to apply this criterion. In our present case, we have to define the sense of the proposition

"the number which belongs to the concept F is the same as that which belongs to the concept G";

that is to say, we must reproduce the content of this

proposition in other terms, avoiding the use of the expression

"the Number which belongs to the concept *F*".

In doing this, we shall be giving a general criterion for the identity of numbers. When we have thus acquired a means of arriving at a determinate number and of recognizing it again as the same, we can assign it a number word as its proper name.

§ 63. HUME[1] long ago mentioned such a means: "When two numbers are so combined as that the one has always an unit answering to every unit of the other, we pronounce them equal." This opinion, that numerical equality or identity must be defined in terms of one-one correlation, seems in recent years to have gained widespread acceptance among mathematicians.[2] But it raises at once certain logical doubts and difficulties, which ought not to be passed over without examination.

It is not only among numbers that the relationship of identity is found. From which it seems to follow that we ought not to define it specially for the case of numbers. We should expect the concept of identity to have been fixed first, and that then, from it together with the concept of Number, it must be possible to deduce when Numbers are identical with one another, without there being need for this purpose of a special definition of numerical identity as well.

As against this, it must be noted that for us the concept of Number has not yet been fixed, but is only due to be determined in the light of our definition of numerical identity. Our aim is to construct the content of a judgement which can be taken as an identity such that each side of it is a number. We are therefore proposing not to define identity specially for this case, but to use the concept of identity, taken as already known, as a means for arriving at that which is to be regarded as being identical. Admittedly, this seems to be a very odd

---

[1] Baumann, op. cit., Vol. II, p. 565 *Treatise,* Bk. I, Part iii, Sect. 1.

[2] Cf. E. Schroder, op. cit., pp. 7-8; E. Kossak, *Die Elemente der Arithmetik, Programm des Friedrichs-Werder'schen Gymnasiums,* Berlin 1872, p. 16; G. Cantor, *Grundlagen einer allgemeinen Mannichfaltigkeitslehre,* Leipzig 1883.

kind of definition, to which logicians have not yet paid enough attention; but that it is not altogether unheard of, may be shown by a few examples.

§ 64. The judgement "line *a* is parallel to line *b*", or, using symbols,

$$a\ /\ /\ b,$$

can be taken as an identity. If we do this, we obtain the concept of direction, and say: "the direction of line *a* is identical with the direction of line *b*". Thus we replace the symbol / / by the more generic symbol =, through removing what is specific in the content of the former and dividing it between *a* and *b*. We carve up the content in a way different from the original way, and this yields us a new concept. Often, of course, we conceive of the matter the other way round, and many authorities define parallel lines as lines whose directions are identical. The proposition that "straight lines parallel to the same straight line are parallel to one another" can then be very conveniently proved by invoking the analogous proposition about things identical with the same thing. Only the trouble is, that this is to reverse the true order of things. For surely everything geometrical must be given originally in intuition. But now I ask whether anyone has an intuition of the direction of a straight line. Of a straight line, certainly; but do we distinguish in our intuition between this straight line and something else, its direction? That is hardly plausible. The concept of direction is only discovered at all as a result of a process of intellectual activity which takes its start from the intuition. On the other hand, we do have an idea of parallel straight lines. Our convenient proof is only made possible by surreptitiously assuming, in our use of the word "direction", what was to be proved; for if it were false that "straight lines parallel to the same straight line are parallel to one another", then we could not transform $a\ /\ /\ b$ into an identity.

We can obtain in a similar way from the parallelism of planes a concept corresponding to that of direction in the case of straight lines; I have seen the name "orientation"† used for this. From geometrical similarity is derived the concept of shape, so that instead of "the two triangles are similar" we say "the two triangles are of identical shape" or "the shape of the one is identical with that of the other". It is possible to derive yet another concept in this way, to which no name has yet been given, from the collineation of geometrical forms.

§ 65. Now in order to get, for example, from parallelism[1] to the concept of direction, let us try the following definition:

The proposition

"line *a* is parallel to line *b*"

is to mean the same as

"the direction of line *a* is identical with the direction of line *b*".

This definition departs to some extent from normal practice, in that it serves ostensibly to adapt the relation of identity, taken as already known, to a special case, whereas in reality it is designed to introduce the expression "the direction of line *a*", which only comes into it incidentally. It is this that gives rise to a second doubt—are we not liable, through using such methods, to become involved in conflict with the well-known laws of identity? Let us see what these are. As analytic truths they should be capable of being derived from the concept itself alone. Now LEIBNIZ's[2] definition is as follows:

"Things are the same as each other, of which one can be substituted for the other without loss of truth".*

This I propose to adopt as my own definition of identity. Whether we use "the same", as LEIBNIZ does, or "identical", is not of any importance. "The same" may indeed be thought to refer to complete agreement in all respects, "identical"** only to agreement in this respect or that;

† [*Stellung*]

[1] I have chosen to discuss here the case of parallelism, because I can express myself less clumsily and make myself more easily understood. The argument can readily be transferred in essentials to apply to the case of numerical identity.

[2] *Non inelegans specimen demonstrandi in abstractis* (Erdmann edn., p. 94).

* [*Eadem sunt, quorum unum potest substitui alteri salva veritate.*]

** [Still more "equal" or "similar", which the German *gleich* can also mean.]

but we can adopt a form of expression such that this distinction vanishes. For example, instead of "the segments are identical in length", we can say "the length of the segments is identical" or "the same", and instead of "the surfaces are identical in colour", "the colour of the surfaces is identical". And this is the way in which the word has been used in the examples above. Now, it is actually the case that in universal substitutability all the laws of identity are contained.

In order, therefore, to justify our proposed definition of the direction of a line, we should have to show that it is possible, if line *a* is parallel to line *b*, to substitute

"the direction of *b*"

everywhere for

"the direction of *a*".

This task is made simpler by the fact that we are being taken initially to know of nothing that can be asserted about the direction of a line except the one thing, that it coincides with the direction of some other line. We should thus have to show only that substitution was possible in an identity of this one type, or in judgement-contents containing such identities as constituent elements.[1] The meaning of any other type of assertion about directions would have first of all to be defined, and in defining it we can make it a rule always to see that it must remain possible to substitute for the direction of any line the direction of any line parallel to it.

§ 66. But there is still a third doubt which may make us suspicious of our proposed definition. In the proposition "the direction of *a* is identical with the direction of *b*" the direction of *a* plays the part of an object[2], and our

---

[1] In a hypothetical judgement, for example, an identity of directions might occur as antecedent or consequent.

[2] This is shown by the definite article. A concept is for me that which can be predicate of a singular judgement-content, an object that which can be subject of the same. If in the proposition

"the direction of the axis of the telescope is identical with the direction of the Earth's axis"

we take the direction of the axis of the telescope as subject, then the predicate is "identical with the direction of the Earth's axis". This is a concept. But the direction of the Earth's axis is only an element in the predicate; it, since it can also be made the subject, is an object.

definition affords us a means of recognizing this object as the same again, in case it should happen to crop up in some other guise, say as the direction of b. But this means does not provide for all cases. It will not, for instance, decide for us whether England is the same as the direction of the Earth's axis—if I may be forgiven an example which looks nonsensical. Naturally no one is going to confuse England with the direction of the Earth's axis; but that is no thanks to our definition of direction. That says nothing as to whether the proposition

"the direction of a is identical with q"

should be affirmed or denied, except for the one case where q is given in the form of "the direction of b". What we lack is the concept of direction; for if we had that, then we could lay it down that, if q is not a direction, our proposition is to be denied, while if it is a direction, our original definition will decide whether it is to be denied or affirmed. So the temptation is to give as our definition:

q is a direction, if there is a line b whose direction is q.

But then we have obviously come round in a circle. For in order to make use of this definition, we should have to know already in every case whether the proposition

"q is identical with the direction of b"

was to be affirmed or denied.

§67. If we were to try saying: q is a direction if it is introduced by means of the definition set out above, then we should be treating the way in which the object q is introduced as a property of q, which it is not. The definition of an object does not, as such, really assert anything about the object, but only lays down the meaning of a symbol. After this has been done, the definition transforms itself into a judgement, which does assert about the object; but now it no longer introduces the object, it is exactly on a level with other assertions made about it. If, moreover, we were to adopt this way out, we should have to be presupposing that an object can only be given in one single way; for otherwise it would not follow, from the fact that q *was* not introduced by means of our definition, that it *could* not have been introduced by means of it. All identities would then amount simply to this, that whatever is given to us in the same way is to be reckoned as the same. This, however, is a principle so obvious and so sterile as not to be worth stating. We could not, in fact, draw from it any conclusion which was not the same as one of our premisses. Why is it, after all, that we are able to make use of identities with such significant results in such divers fields? Surely it is rather because we are able to recognize something as the same again even although it is given in a different way.

§68. Seeing that we cannot by these methods obtain any concept of direction with sharp limits to its application, nor therefore, for the same reasons, any satisfactory concept of Number either, let us try another way. If line a is parallel to line b, then the extension of the concept "line parallel to line a" is identical with the extension of the concept "line parallel to line b"; and conversely, if the extensions of the two concepts just named are identical, then a is parallel to b. Let us try, therefore, the following type of definition:

the direction of line a is the extension of the concept "parallel to line a";

the shape of triangle t is the extension of the concept "similar to triangle t".

To apply this to our own case of Number, we must substitute for lines or triangles concepts, and for parallelism or similarity the possibility of correlating one to one the objects which fall under the one concept with those which fall under the other. For brevity, I shall, when this condition is satisfied, speak of the concept F being *equal** to the concept G; but I must ask that this

* [*Gleichzahlig*—an invented word, literally "identinumerate" or "tautarithmic"; but these are too clumsy for constant use. Other translators have used "equinumerous"; "equinumerate" would be better. Later writers have used "similar" in this connexion (but as a predicate of "class" not of "concept").]

word be treated as an arbitrarily selected symbol, whose meaning is to be gathered, not from its etymology, but from what is here laid down.

My definition is therefore as follows:

> the Number which belongs to the concept F is the extension[1] of the concept "equal to the concept F".

§ 69. That this definition is correct will perhaps be hardly evident at first. For do we not think of the extensions of concepts as something quite different from numbers? How we do think of them emerges clearly from the basic assertions we make about them. These are as follows:

1. that they are identical,
2. that one is wider than the other.

But now the proposition:

> the extension of the concept "equal to the concept F" is identical with the extension of the concept "equal to the concept G"

is true if and only if the proposition

> "the same number belongs to the concept F as to the concept G"

is also true. So that here there is complete agreement.

Certainly we do not say that one number is wider than another, in the sense in which the extension of one concept is wider than that of another; but then it is also quite impossible for a case to occur where

> the extension of the concept "equal to the concept F"

would be wider than

> the extension of the concept "equal to the concept G".

For on the contrary, when all concepts equal to G are also equal to F, then conversely also all concepts equal

---

[1] I believe that for "extension of the concept" we could write simply "concept". But this would be open to the two objections:

1. that this contradicts my earlier statement that the individual numbers are objects, as is indicated by the use of the definite article in expressions like "the number two" and by the impossibility of speaking of ones, twos, etc. in the plural, as also by the fact that the number constitutes only an element in the predicate of a statement of number;

2. that concepts can have identical extensions without themselves coinciding.

I am, as it happens, convinced that both these objections can be met; but to do this would take us too far afield for present purposes. I assume that it is known what the extension of a concept is.

to F are equal to G. "Wider" as used here must not, of course, be confused with "greater" as used of numbers.

Another type of case is, I admit, conceivable, where the extension of the concept "equal to the concept F" might be wider or less wide than the extension of some other concept, which then could not, on our definition, be a Number; and it is not usual to speak of a Number as wider or less wide than the extension of a concept; but neither is there anything to prevent us speaking in this way, if such a case should ever occur.

Our definition completed and its worth proved.

§70. Definitions show their worth by proving fruitful. Those that could just as well be omitted and leave no link missing in the chain of our proofs should be rejected as completely worthless.

Let us try, therefore, whether we can derive from our definition of the Number which belongs to the concept F any of the well-known properties of numbers. We shall confine ourselves here to the simplest.

For this it is necessary to give a rather more precise account still of the term "equality". "Equal" we defined in terms of one-one correlation, and what must now be laid down is how this latter expression is to be understood, since it might easily be supposed that it had something to do with intuition.

We will consider the following example. If a waiter wishes to be certain of laying exactly as many knives on a table as plates, he has no need to count either of them; all he has to do is to lay immediately to the right of every plate a knife, taking care that every knife on the table lies immediately to the right of a plate. Plates and knives are thus correlated one to one, and that by the identical spatial relationship. Now if in the proposition

"a lies immediately to the right of A"

we conceive first one and then another object inserted in place of a and again of A, then that part of the content which remains unaltered throughout this process constitutes the essence of the relation. What we need is a generalization of this.

If from a judgement-content which deals with an object *a* and an object *b* we subtract *a* and *b*, we obtain as remainder a relation-concept which is, accordingly, incomplete at two points. If from the proposition

"the Earth is more massive than the Moon"

we subtract "the Earth", we obtain the concept "more massive than the Moon". If, alternatively, we subtract the object, "the Moon", we get the concept "less massive than the Earth". But if we subtract them both at once, then we are left with a relation-concept, which taken by itself has no [assertible] sense any more than a simple concept has: it has always to be completed in order to make up a judgement-content. It can however be completed in different ways: instead of Earth and Moon I can put, for example, Sun and Earth, and this *eo ipso* effects the subtraction.

Each individual pair of correlated objects stands to the relation-concept much as an individual object stands to the concept under which it falls—we might call them the subject of the relation-concept. Only here the subject is a composite one. Occasionally, where the relation in question is convertible, this fact achieves verbal recognition, as in the proposition "Peleus and Thetis were the parents of Achilles."[1] But not always. For example, it would scarcely be possible to put the proposition "the Earth is bigger than the Moon" into other words so as to make "the Earth and the Moon" appear as a composite subject; the "and" must always indicate that the two things are being put in some way on a level. However, this does not affect the issue.

The doctrine of relation-concepts is thus, like that of simple concepts, a part of pure logic. What is of concern to logic is not the special content of any particular relation, but only the logical form. And whatever can be asserted of this, is true analytically and known a priori. This is as true of relation-concepts as of other concepts.

---

[1] This type of case should not be confused with another, in which the "and" joins the subjects in appearance only, but in reality joins two propositions.

Just as

"*a* falls under the concept *F*"

is the general form of a judgement-content which deals with an object *a*, so we can take

"*a* stands in the relation ϕ to *b*"

as the general form of a judgement-content which deals with an object *a* and an object *b*.

§ 71. If now every object which falls under the concept *F* stands in the relation ϕ to an object falling under the concept *G*, and if to every object which falls under *G* there stands in the relation ϕ an object falling under *F*, then the objects falling under *F* and under *G* are correlated with each other by the relation ϕ.

It may still be asked, what is the meaning of the expression

> "every object which falls under *F* stands in the relation ϕ to an object falling under *G*"

in the case where no object at all falls under *F*. I understand this expression as follows:
the two propositions

"*a* falls under *F*"

and

"*a* does not stand in the relation ϕ to any object falling under *G*"

cannot, whatever be signified by *a*, both be true together; so that either the first proposition is false, or the second is, or both are. From this it can be seen that the proposition "every object which falls under *F* stands in the relation ϕ to an object falling under *G*" is, in the case where there is no object falling under *F*, true; for in that case the first proposition

"*a* falls under *F*"

is always false, whatever *a* may be.

In the same way the proposition

> "to every object which falls under *G* there stands in the relation ϕ an object falling under *F*"

means that the two propositions

"a falls under G"

and

"no object falling under F stands to a in the relation ϕ"

cannot, whatever a may be, both be true together.

§72. We have thus seen when the objects falling under the concepts F and G are correlated with each other by the relation ϕ. But now in our case, this correlation has to be one-one. By this I understand that the two following propositions both hold good:

1. If d stands in the relation ϕ to a, and if d stands in the relation ϕ to e, then generally, whatever d, a and e may be, a is the same as e.
2. If d stands in the relation ϕ to a, and if b stands in the relation ϕ to a, then generally, whatever d, b and a may be, d is the same as b.

This reduces one-one correlation to purely logical relationships, and enables us to give the following definition:

the expression

"the concept F is equal to the concept G"

is to mean the same as the expression

"there exists a relation ϕ which correlates one to one the objects falling under the concept F with the objects falling under the concept G".

We now repeat our original definition:

the Number which belongs to the concept F is the extension of the concept "equal to the concept F"

and add further:

the expression

"n is a Number"

is to mean the same as the expression

"there exists a concept such that n is the Number which belongs to it".

Thus the concept of Number receives its definition, apparently, indeed, in terms of itself, but actually without any fallacy, since "the Number which belongs to the concept *F*" has already been defined.

§73. Our next aim must be to show that the Number which belongs to the concept *F* is identical with the Number which belongs to the concept *G* if the concept *F* is equal to the concept *G*. This sounds, of course, like a tautology. But it is not; the meaning of the word "equal" is not to be inferred from its etymology, but taken to be as I defined it above.

On our definition [of "the Number which belongs to the concept *F*"], what has to be shown is that the extension of the concept "equal to the concept *F*" is the same as the extension of the concept "equal to the concept *G*", if the concept *F* is equal to the concept *G*. In other words: it is to be proved that, for *F* equal to *G*, the following two propositions hold good universally:

> if the concept *H* is equal to the concept *F*,
> then it is also equal to the concept *G*;

and

> if the concept *H* is equal to the concept *G*,
> then it is also equal to the concept *F*.

The first proposition amounts to this, that there exists a relation which correlates one to one the objects falling under the concept *H* with those falling under the concept *G*, if there exists a relation ϕ which correlates one to one the objects falling under the concept *F* with those falling under the concept *G* and if there exists also a relation ψ which correlates one to one the objects falling under the concept *H* with those falling under the concept *F*. The following arrangement of letters will make this easier to grasp:

$$H \; \psi \; F \; \phi \; G.$$

Such a relation can in fact be given: it is to be found in the judgement-content

> "there exists an object to which c stands in the relation ψ and which stands to b in the relation ϕ",

if we subtract from it c and b—take them, that is, as the terms of the relation. It can be shown that this relation is one-one, and that it correlates the objects falling under the concept H with those falling under the concept G.

A similar proof can be given of the second proposition also.[1] And with that, I hope, enough has been indicated of my methods to show that our proofs are not dependent at any point on borrowings from intuition, and that our definitions can be used to some purpose.

§74. We can now pass on to the definitions of the individual numbers.

Since nothing falls under the concept "not identical with itself", I define nought as follows:

> 0 is the Number which belongs to the concept "not identical with itself".

Some may find it shocking that I should speak of a concept in this connexion. They will object, very likely, that it contains a contradiction and is reminiscent of our old friends the square circle and wooden iron. Now I believe that these old friends are not so black as they are painted. To be of any use is, I admit, the last thing we should expect of them; but at the same time, they cannot do any harm, if only we do not assume that there is anything which falls under them—and to that we are not committed by merely using them. That a concept contains a contradiction is not always obvious without investigation; but to investigate it we must first possess it and, in logic, treat it just like any other. All that can be demanded of a concept from the point of view of logic and with an eye to rigour of proof is only that the limits to its application should be sharp, that we should be able to decide definitely about every object whether it falls under that concept or not. But this demand is completely satisfied by concepts which, like "not identical with it-

[1] And likewise of the converse: If the number which belongs to the concept F is the same as that which belongs to the concept G, then the concept F is equal to the concept G.

self", contain a contradiction; for of every object we know that it does not fall under any such concept.[1]

On my use of the word "concept",

"a falls under the concept F"

is the general form of a judgement-content which deals with an object a and permits of the insertion for a of anything whatever. And in this sense

"a falls under the concept 'not identical with itself'"

has the same meaning as

"a is not identical with itself"

or

"a is not identical with a".

I could have used for the definition of nought any other concept under which no object falls. But I have made a point of choosing one which can be proved to be such on purely logical grounds; and for this purpose "not identical with itself" is the most convenient that offers, taking for the definition of "identical" the one from LEIBNIZ given above [(§ 65)], which is in purely logical terms.

§ 75. Now it must be possible to prove, by means of what has already been laid down, that every concept under which no object falls is equal to every other concept under which no object falls, and to them alone; from which it follows that 0 is the Number which belongs to any such concept, and that no object falls under any concept if the number which belongs to that concept is 0.

If we assume that no object falls under either the concept F or the concept G, then in order to prove them equal we have to find a relation ϕ which satisfies the following conditions:

---

[1] The definition of an object in terms of a concept under which it falls is a very different matter. For example, the expression "the largest proper fraction" has no content, since the definite article claims to refer to a definite object. On the other hand, the concept "fraction smaller than 1 and such that no fraction smaller than one exceeds it in magnitude" is quite unexceptionable: in order, indeed, to prove that there exists no such fraction, we must make use of just this concept, despite its containing a contradiction. If, however, we wished to use this concept for defining an object falling under it, it would, of course, be necessary first to show two distinct things:

1. that some object falls under this concept;
2. that only one object falls under it.

Now since the first of these propositions, not to mention the second, is false, it follows that the expression "the largest proper fraction" is senseless.

every object which falls under F stands in the relation ϕ to an object which falls under G; and to every object which falls under G there stands in the relation ϕ an object falling under F.

In view of what has been said above [(§71)] on the meaning of these expressions, it follows, on our assumption [that no object falls under either concept], that these conditions are satisfied by every relation whatsoever, and therefore among others by identity, which is moreover a one-one relation; for it meets both the requirements laid down [in §72] above.

If, to take the other case, some object, say a, does fall under G, but still none falls under F, then the two propositions

"a falls under G"

and

"no object falling under F stands to a in the relation ϕ"

are both true together for every relation ϕ; for the first is made true by our first assumption and the second by our second assumption. If, that is, there exists no object falling under F, then a fortiori there exists no object falling under F which stands to a in any relation whatsoever. There exists, therefore, no relation by which the objects falling under F can be correlated with those falling under G so as to satisfy our definition [of equality], and accordingly the concepts F and G are unequal.

§76. I now propose to define the relation in which every two adjacent members of the series of natural numbers stand to each other. The proposition:

"there exists a concept F, and an object falling under it x, such that the Number which belongs to the concept F is n and the Number which belongs to the concept 'falling under F but not identical with x' is m"

is to mean the same as

"n follows in the series of natural numbers directly after m".

I avoid the expression "*n* is *the* Number following next after *m*", because the use of the definite article cannot be justified until we have first proved two propositions. For the same reason I do not yet say at this point "$n = m + 1$," for to use the symbol = is likewise to designate $(m + 1)$ an object.

§77. Now in order to arrive at the number 1, we have first of all to show that there is something which follows in the series of natural numbers directly after 0.

Let us consider the concept—or, if you prefer it, the predicate—"identical with 0". Under this falls the number 0. But under the concept "identical with 0 but not identical with 0", on the other hand, no object falls, so that 0 is the Number which belongs to this concept. We have, therefore, a concept "identical with 0" and an object falling under it 0, of which the following propositions hold true:

> the Number which belongs to the concept "identical with 0" is identical with the Number which belongs to the concept "identical with 0";
>
> the Number which belongs to the concept "identical with 0 but not identical with 0" is 0.

Therefore, on our definition [(§76], the Number which belongs to the concept "identical with 0" follows in the series of natural numbers directly after 0.

Now if we give the following definition:

> 1 is the Number which belongs to the concept "identical with 0",

we can then put the preceding conclusion thus:

> 1 follows in the series of natural numbers directly after 0.

It is perhaps worth pointing out that our definition of the number 1 does not presuppose, for its objective legitimacy, any matter of observed fact.[1] It is easy to get confused over this, seeing that certain subjective conditions must be satisfied if we are to be able to arrive at the definition, and that sense experiences are what

[1] Non-general proposition.

prompt us to frame it.[2] All this, however, may be perfectly correct, without the propositions so arrived at ceasing to be a priori. One such condition is, for example, that blood of the right quality must circulate in the brain in sufficient volume—at least so far as we know; but the truth of our last proposition does not depend on this; it still holds, even if the circulation stops; and even if all rational beings were to take to hibernating and fall asleep simultaneously, our proposition would not be, say, cancelled for the duration, but would remain quite unaffected. For a proposition to be true is just not the same thing as for it to be thought.

§ 78. I proceed to give here a list of several propositions to be proved by means of our definitions. The reader will easily see for himself in outline how this can be done.

1. If a follows in the series of natural numbers directly after 0, then a is $= 1$.
2. If 1 is the Number which belongs to a concept, then there exists an object which falls under that concept.
3. If 1 is the Number which belongs to a concept F; then, if the object x falls under the concept F and if y falls under the concept F, x is $= y$; that is, x is the same as y.
4. If an object falls under the concept F, and if it can be inferred generally from the propositions that x falls under the concept F and that y falls under the concept F that x is $= y$, then 1 is the Number which belongs to the concept F.
5. The relation of m to n which is established by the proposition:

   "n follows in the series of natural numbers directly after m"

   is a one-one relation.
6. Every Number except 0 follows in the series of natural numbers directly after a Number.

[2] Cf. B. Erdmann, *Die Axiome der Geometrie,* p. 164.

CARL FRIEDRICH GAUSS

(1777—1855)

Carl Friedrich Gauss (originally Johann Carl Friedrich Gauss), astronomer, physicist, and greatest mathematician of his time, was born in Brunswick, Germany, on April 23, 1777. He was the son of Gerhard Gauss, a day laborer and small contractor who was himself the son of a peasant. His mother, of sturdy stock, lived to the age of ninety-seven. Gerhard Gauss had the usual parental desire to have his sons join him in his trade, but he was thwarted in this by the extremely early and startling evidences of Carl's unique genius. Speaking of the experiences of his youth, Gauss used to say that he could reckon almost before he had learned to talk. When he was scarcely three years old, as he watched his father at work on the computation of weekly wages and the like, one day, the talented child corrected an error in one of his father's accounts. When he was ten years old, he was familiar with the binomial theorem and the theory of infinite series. At his first school in Brunswick, Gauss attracted the attention of a gifted young mathematical assistant, Bartels, under whose sympathetic and understanding tutelage he made phenomenal strides in mathematics. When Gauss had reached the age of fourteen, Bartels arranged an audience for him with Charles William Ferdinand, the reigning Duke of Brunswick. The Duke, impressed by Gauss's personality and potentialities, agreed to sponsor his education and in 1792 Gauss was sent to the Collegium Carolinum (at first against his father's wishes). In 1795 he enrolled in the University of Gottingen, where he came under the influence of Kastner. His three years at Gottingen were extraordinarily productive of original work. Gauss stated in his diary that so many new ideas came crowding into his mind before he was twenty, that he could record only a fraction of them. By 1796 mathematics had become his favorite field of study. "Mathematics," he would say, "is the queen of the sciences, and arithmetic is the queen of mathematics." By 1798 most of the work for his famous *Disquisitiones Arithmeticae* (published 1801) had been done. Gauss spent that year at the University of Helmstadt where he had access to a fine library and where he met the professor of mathematics, Johann F. Pfaff, who was to be his lifelong friend. He received his doctor's degree at Helmstadt in 1799 and soon thereafter added investigations in astronomy, geodesy and physics to his mathematical researches. In 1807, while he was still a private teacher in Brunswick, the fame of his work brought him an offer of a professorial chair in the St. Petersberg Academy. However, he was immediately offered a double appointment at home, as the first director of the new Gottingen Observatory and professor of mathematics at the university. Accepting the offer at Gottingen, Gauss's life thereafter was dedicated to observations, study, writing and teaching. The teaching phase of his work, unfortunately, was not always the happiest. "This winter," Gauss wrote to his friend, Bessel, "I am giving two courses of lectures to three students, of which one is only moderately prepared, the other less than moderately, and the third lacks both preparation and ability. Such are the onera of a mathematical profession."* Nevertheless, Gauss was exceedingly generous in his expression of appreciation of mathematical ability wherever it genuinely existed, and among the distinguished mathematicians who were his pupils, we find great names such as Dirichlet and Riemann.

Gauss remained a man of simple tastes throughout his life. It is said that he never wore any of the numerous decorations that were granted to him. He was fortunate in the enjoyment of good health, and despite the strain of night observations, he rarely required a physician. Gauss's later years continued to be marked by his exceptional mental vigor and originality. His interest in languages was undiminished. At the age of sixty he studied and mastered the Russian language. At the age of seventy he added a new proof to those he had already composed for the fundamental theorem of algebra. He remained active until a few months before his death on February 23, 1855.

Combining an abundant inventiveness and a zeal for perfection of form, Gauss enriched and influenced almost every field of pure and applied mathematics. His motto, "Pauca sed matura," applied to all his writings. Fundamental theorems in many branches of analysis were introduced in *Disquisitiones Arithmeticae* (1801) and in his *Superficies Curvas* (1827). The theory of numbers as a separate, systematic branch of mathematics dates from the publication of his *Disquisitiones*. His *Theoria Motus* (1809) was a landmark in the application of mathematics to celestial mechanics. Every work Gauss produced was an event in the history of science.

ON THE CONGRUENCE OF NUMBERS

Translated from the Latin by Ralph G. Archibald

From *Disquisitiones Arithmeticae* (1801)

First Section

Concerning Congruence of Numbers in General

Congruent Numbers, Moduli, Residues, and Non-residues

1

If a number a divides the difference of the numbers b and c, b and c are said to be *congruent with respect to* a;

* R. E. Moritz, *Memorabilia Mathematica* No. 974.

but if not, *incongruent*. We call a the *modulus*. In the former case, each of the numbers b and c is called a *residue* of the other, but in the latter case, a *non-residue*.

These notions apply to all integral numbers both positive and negative,[1] but not to fractions. For example, —9 and +16 are congruent with respect to the modulus 5; —7 is a residue of +15 with respect to the modulus 11, but a non-residue with respect to the modulus 3. Now, since every number divides zero, every number must be regarded as congruent to itself with respect to all moduli.

2

If k denotes an indeterminate integral number, all residues of a given number a with respect to the modulus m are contained in the formula $a + km$. The easier of the propositions which we shall give can be readily demonstrated from this standpoint; but anyone will just as easily perceive their truth at sight.

We shall denote in future the congruence of two numbers by this sign, $\equiv$, and adjoin the modulus in parentheses when necessary. For example, $-16 \equiv 9 \pmod 5$, $-7 \equiv 15 \pmod{11}$.[1]

3

THEOREM.—*If there be given the m consecutive integral numbers*

$$a, a + 1, a + 2, \ldots, a + m - 1,$$

and another integral number A, then some one of the former will be congruent to this number A with respect to the modulus m; and, in fact, there will be only one such number.

If, for instance, $\dfrac{a-A}{m}$ is an integer, we shall have

[1] Obviously, the modulus is always to be taken *absolutely*,—that is, without any sign.

[1] We have adopted this sign on account of the great analogy which exists between an equality and a congruence. For the same reason Legendre, in memoirs which will later be frequently quoted, retained the sign of equality itself for a congruence. We hesitated to follow this notation lest it introduce an ambiguity.

$a \equiv A$; but if it is fractional, let k be the integer immediately greater (or, when it is negative, immediately *smaller* if no regard is paid to sign). Then $A + km$ will fall between a and $a + m$, and will therefore be the number desired. Now, it is evident that all the quotients $\frac{a - A}{m}$, $\frac{a + 1 - A}{m}$, $\frac{a + 2 - A}{m}$, etc., are situated between $k - 1$ and $k + 1$. Therefore not more than one can be integral.

Least Residues

4

Every number, then, will have a residue not only in the sequence $0, 1, 2, \ldots, m - 1$, but also in the sequence $0, -1, -2, \ldots, -(m - 1)$. We shall call these *least residues.* Now, it is evident that, unless 0 is a residue, there will always be two: one *positive,* the other *negative.* If they are of different magnitudes, one of them will be less than $\frac{m}{2}$; but if they are of the same magnitude, each will equal $\frac{m}{2}$ when no regard is paid to sign. From this it is evident that any number has a residue not exceeding half the modulus. This residue is called the *absolute minimum.*

For example, with respect to the modulus 5, —13 has the positive least residue 2, which at the same time is the absolute minimum, and has —3 as the negative least residue. With respect to the modulus 7, +5 is its own positive least residue, —2 is the negative least residue and at the same time the absolute minimum.

Elementary Propositions Concerning Congruences

5

From the notions just established we may derive the following obvious properties of congruent numbers.

The numbers which are congruent with respect to a composite modulus, will certainly be congruent with respect to any one of its divisors.

If several numbers are congruent to the same number with respect to the same modulus, they will be congruent among themselves (with respect to the same modulus).

The same identity of moduli is to be understood in what follows.

Congruent numbers have the same least residues, incongruent numbers different least residues.

6

If the numbers A, B, C, etc. and the numbers a, b, c, etc. are congruent each to each with respect to any modulus, that is, if

$$A \equiv a,\ B \equiv b,\ etc.,$$

then we shall have

$$A + B + C + etc. \equiv a + b + c + etc.$$

If $A \equiv a$ and $B \equiv b$, we shall have $A - B \equiv a - b$.

7

If $A \equiv a$, we shall also have $kA \equiv ka$.

If k is a positive number, this is merely a particular case of the proposition of the preceding article when we place $A = B = C$ etc. and $a = b = c$ etc. If k is negative, $-k$ will be positive. Then $-kA \equiv -ka$, and consequently $kA \equiv ka$.

If $A \equiv a$ and $B \equiv b$, we shall have $AB \equiv ab$. For, $AB \equiv Ab \equiv ba$.

8

If the numbers A, B, C, etc. and the numbers a, b, c, etc. are congruent each to each, that is, if $A \equiv a$, $B \equiv b$, etc., the products of the numbers of each set will be congruent; that is, ABC etc. $\equiv abc$ etc.

From the preceding article, $AB \equiv ab$, and for the same reason $ABC = abc$; in a like manner we can consider as many factors as desired.

If we take all the numbers A, B, C, etc. equal, and also the corresponding numbers a, b, c, etc., we obtain this theorem:

If $A \equiv a$ and if k is a positive integer, we shall have $A^k \equiv a^k$.

9

Let X be a function of the indeterminate x, of the form

$$Ax^a + Bx^b + Cx^c + \text{etc.},$$

where A, B, C, etc., denote any integral numbers, and a, b, c, etc., non-negative integral numbers. If, now, to the indeterminate x there be assigned values which are congruent with respect to any stated modulus, the resulting values of the function X will then be congruent.

Let f and g be two congruent values of x. Then by the preceding articles $f^a \equiv g^a$ and $Af^a = Ag^a$; in the same way $Bf^b \equiv Bg^b$, etc. Hence

$Af^a + Bf^b + Cf^c + \text{etc.} \equiv Ag^a + Bg^b + Cg^c + \text{etc.}$ Q.E.D.

It is easily seen, too, how this theorem can be extended to functions of several indeterminates.

10

If, therefore, all consecutive integral numbers are substituted for x, and if the values of the function X are reduced to least residues, these residues will constitute a sequence in which the same terms repeat after an interval of m terms (m denoting the modulus); or, in other words, this sequence will be formed by a *period of m* terms repeated indefinitely. Let, for example, $X = x^3 - 8x + 6$ and $m = 5$. Then for $x = 0, 1, 2, 3$, etc., the values of X give the positive least residues, 1, 4, 3, 4, 3, 1, 4, etc., where the first five, namely, 1, 4, 3, 4, 3, are repeated without end. And furthermore, if the sequence is continued backwards, that is, if negative values are assigned to x, the same period occurs in the inverse order. It is therefore evident that terms different from those constituting the period cannot occur in the sequence.

11

In this example, then, X can be neither $\equiv 0$ nor $\equiv 2$ (mod 5), and can still less be $=0$ or $=2$. Whence it follows that the equations $x^3 - 8x + 6 = 0$ and $x^3 - 8x + 4 = 0$ cannot be solved in integral numbers, and therefore, as we know, cannot be solved in rational numbers. It is obviously true in general that, if it is impossible to satisfy the congruence $X \equiv 0$ with respect to some particular modulus, then the equation $X = 0$ has no rational root when X is a function of the unknown x, of the form

$$x^n + Ax^{n-1} + \cdot Bx^{n-} + \text{etc.} + N,$$

where A, B, C, etc. are integers and n is a positive integer. (It is well known that all algebraic equations can be brought to this form.) This criterion, though presented here in a natural manner, will be treated at greater length in Section VIII. From this brief indication, some idea, no doubt, can be formed regarding the utility of these researches.

●

THEORIA MOTUS

THEORY OF THE MOTION OF THE HEAVENLY BODIES MOVING ABOUT THE SUN IN CONIC SECTIONS.

Translated by CHARLES HENRY DAVIS

PREFACE

To determine the orbit of a heavenly body, without any hypothetical assumption, from observations not embracing a great period of time, and not allowing a selec-

tion with a view to the application of special methods, was almost wholly neglected up to the beginning of the present century; or, at least, not treated by any one in a manner worthy of its importance; since it assuredly commended itself to mathematicians by its difficulty and elegance, even if its great utility in practice were not apparent. An opinion had universally prevailed that a complete determination from observations embracing a short interval of time was impossible,—an ill-founded opinion,—for it is now clearly shown that the orbit of a heavenly body may be determined quite nearly from good observations embracing only a few days; and this without any hypothetical assumption.

Some ideas occurred to me in the month of September of the year 1801, engaged at the time on a very different subject, which seemed to point to the solution of the great problem of which I have spoken. Under such circumstances we not unfrequently, for fear of being too much led away by an attractive investigation, suffer the associations of ideas, which, more attentively considered, might have proved most fruitful in results, to be lost from neglect. And the same fate might have befallen these conceptions had they not happily occurred at the most propitious moment for their preservation and encouragement that could have been selected. For just about this time the report of the new planet, discovered on the first day of January of that year with the telescope at Palermo, was the subject of universal conversation; and soon afterwards the observations made by that distinguished astronomer Piazzi from the above date to the eleventh of February were published. Nowhere in the annals of astronomy do we meet with so great an opportunity, and a greater one could hardly be imagined, for showing most strikingly, the value of this problem, than in this crisis and urgent necessity, when all hope of discovering in the heavens this planetary atom, among innumerable small stars after the lapse of nearly a year, rested solely upon a sufficiently approximate knowledge of its orbit to be based upon these very few observations.

Could I ever have found a more seasonable opportunity to test the practical value of my conceptions, than now in employing them for the determination of the orbit of the planet Ceres, which during these forty-one days had described a geocentric arc of only three degrees, and after the lapse of a year must be looked for in a region of the heavens very remote from that in which it was last seen? This first application of the method was made in the month of October, 1801, and the first clear night, when the planet was sought for* as directed by the numbers deduced from it, restored the fugitive to observation. Three other new planets, subsequently discovered, furnished new opportunities for examining and verifying the efficiency and generality of the method.

Several astronomers wished me to publish the methods employed in these calculations immediately after the second discovery of Ceres; but many things—other occupations, the desire of treating the subject more fully at some subsequent period, and, especially, the hope that a further prosecution of this investigation would raise various parts of the solution to a greater degree of generality, simplicity, and elegance,—prevented my complying at the time with these friendly solicitations. I was not disappointed in this expectation, and have no cause to regret the delay. For, the methods first employed have undergone so many and such great changes, that scarcely any trace of resemblance remains between the method in which the orbit of Ceres was first computed, and the form given in this work. Although it would be foreign to my purpose, to narrate in detail all the steps by which these investigations have been gradually perfected, still, in several instances, particularly when the problem was one of more importance than usual, I have thought that the earlier methods ought not to be wholly suppressed. But in this work, besides the solutions of the principal problems, I have given many things which, during the long time I have been engaged upon the motions of the heavenly bodies in conic sections, struck me as worthy

* By de ZACH, December 7, 1801.

of attention, either on account of their analytical elegance, or more especially on account of their practical utility. But in every case I have devoted greater care both to the subjects and methods which are peculiar to myself, touching lightly and so far only as the connection seemed to require, on those previously known.

FIRST BOOK.

General Relations Between Those Quantities by Which the Motions of Heavenly Bodies About the Sun Are Defined.

FIRST SECTION

Relations pertaining simply to position in the orbit.

1.

In this work we shall consider the motions of the heavenly bodies so far only as they are controlled by the attractive force of the sun. All the secondary planets are therefore excluded from our plan, the perturbations which the primary planets exert upon each other are excluded, as is also all motion of rotation. We regard the moving bodies themselves as mathematical points, and we assume that all motions are performed in obedience to the following laws, which are to be received as the basis of all discussion in this work.

I. The motion of every heavenly body takes place in the same fixed plane in which the centre of the sun is situated.

II. The path described by a body is a conic section having its focus in the centre of the sun.

III. The motion in this path is such that the areas of the spaces described about the sun in different intervals of time are proportional to those intervals. Accordingly, if the times and spaces are expressed in numbers, any space whatever divided by the time in which it is described gives a constant quotient.

IV. For different bodies moving about the sun, the squares of these quotients are in the compound ratio of the parameters of their orbits, and of the sum of the masses of the sun and the moving bodies.

Denoting, therefore, the parameter of the orbit in which the body moves by $2p$, the mass of this body by μ (the mass of the sun being put $= 1$), the area it describes about the sun in the time t by $\frac{1}{2}g$, then $\frac{g}{t\sqrt{p}\sqrt{(1+\mu)}}$ will be a constant for all heavenly bodies. Since then it is of no importance which body we use for determining this number, we will derive it from the motion of the earth, the mean distance of which from the sun we shall adopt for the unit of distance; the mean solar day will always be our unit of time. Denoting, moreover, by π the ratio of the circumference of the circle to the diameter, the area of the entire ellipse described by the earth will evidently be $\pi\sqrt{p}$, which must therefore be put $= \frac{1}{2}g$, if by t is understood the sidereal year; whence, our constant becomes $= \frac{2\pi}{t\sqrt{(1+\mu)}}$. In order to ascertain the numerical value of this constant, hereafter to be denoted by k, we will put, according to the latest determination, the sidereal year or $t = 365.2563835$, the mass of the earth, or $\mu = \frac{1}{354710} = 0.0000028192$, whence results

$\log 2\pi$	0.7981798684
Compl. $\log t$	7.4374021852
Compl. $\log \sqrt{(1+\mu)}$ . . .	9.9999993878
$\log k$	8.2355814414
$k =$	0.01720209895.

2.

The laws above stated differ from those discovered by our own KEPLER in no other respect than this, that they are given in a form applicable to all kinds of conic sections, and that the action of moving body on the sun, on which depends the factor $\sqrt{(1 + \mu)}$, is taken into account. If we regard these laws as phenomena derived from innumerable and indubitable observations, geometry shows what action ought in consequence to be exerted upon bodies moving about the sun, in order that these phenomena may be continually produced. In this way it is found that the action of the sun upon the bodies moving about it is exerted just as if an attractive force, the intensity of which is reciprocally proportional to the square of the distance, should urge the bodies towards the centre of the sun. If now, on the other hand, we set out with the assumption of such an attractive force, the phenomena are deduced from it as necessary consequences. It is sufficient here merely to have recited these laws, the connection of which with the principle of gravitation it will be the less necessary to dwell upon in this place, since several authors subsequently to the eminent NEWTON have treated this subject, and among them the illustrious LA PLACE, in that most perfect work the Mecanique Celeste, in such a manner as to leave nothing further to be desired.

3.

Inquiries into the motions of the heavenly bodies, so far as they take place in conic sections, by no means demand a complete theory of this class of curves; but a single general equation rather, on which all others can be based, will answer our purpose. And it appears to be particularly advantageous to select that one to which, while investigating the curve described according to the law of attraction, we are conducted as a characteristic equation. If we determine any place of a body in its orbit by the distances x, y, from two right lines drawn in the plane of the orbit intersecting each other at right angles in the centre of the sun, that is, in one of the foci of the curve, and further, if we denote the distance of the body from the sun by r (always positive), we shall have between r, x, y, the linear equation $r + \alpha x + \beta y = \gamma$, in which α, β, γ represent constant quantities, γ being from the nature of the case always positive. By changing the position of the right lines to which x, y, are referred, this position being essentially arbitrary, provided only the lines continue to intersect each other at right angles, the form of the equation and also the value of γ will not be changed, but the values of α and β will vary, and it is plain that the position may be so determined that β shall become $= 0$, and α, at least, not negative. In this way by putting for α, γ, respectively e, p, our equation takes the form $r + ex = p$. The right line to which the distances y are referred in this case, is called the *line of apsides*, p is the *semi-parameter*, e the *eccentricity;* finally the conic section is distinguished by the name of *ellipse, parabola,* or *hyperbola,* according as e is less than unity, equal to unity, or greater than unity.

It is readily perceived that the position of the line of apsides would be fully determined by the conditions mentioned, with the exception of the single case where both α and β were $= 0$; in which case r is always $= p$, whatever the right lines to which x, y, are referred. Accordingly, since we have $e = 0$, the curve (which will be a circle) is according to our definition to be assigned to the class of ellipses, but it has this peculiarity, that the position of the apsides remains wholly arbitrary, if indeed we choose to extend that idea to such a case.

4.

Instead of the distance x let us introduce the angle v, contained between the line of apsides and a straight line drawn from the sun to the place of the body (*the radius vector*), and this angle may commence at that part of the line of apsides at which the distances x are positive, and may be supposed to increase in the direction of the motion of the body. In this way we have $x = r \cos v$, and thus our formula becomes $r = \dfrac{p}{1 + e \cos v}$, from which immediately result the following conclusions:—

I. For $v = 0$, the value of the radius vector r becomes a minimum, that is, $= \frac{p}{1 + e}$: this point is called the perihelion.

II. For opposite values of v, there are corresponding equal values of r; consequently the line of apsides divides the conic section into two equal parts.

III. In the *ellipse*, v increases continuously from $v = 0$, until it attains its maximum value, $\frac{p}{1 - e}$, in *aphelion*, corresponding to $v = 180°$; after aphelion, it decreases in the same manner as it had increased, until it reaches the perihelion, corresponding to $v = 360°$. That portion of the line of apsides terminated at one extremity by the perihelion and at the other by the aphelion is called the *major axis;* hence the semi-axis major, called also the *mean distance*, $= \frac{p}{1 - ee}$; the distance of the middle point of the axis (*the centre of the ellipse*) from the focus will be $\frac{ep}{1 - ee} = ea$, denoting by a the semi-axis major.

IV. On the other hand, the aphelion in its proper sense is wanting in the parabola, but r is increased indefinitely as v approaches $+ 180°$, or $- 180°$. For $v = \pm 180°$ the value of r becomes infinite, which shows that the curve is not cut by the line of apsides at a point opposite the perihelion. Wherefore, we cannot, with strict propriety of language, speak of the major axis or of the centre of the curve; but by an extension of the formulas found in the ellipse, according to the established usage of analysis, an infinite value is assigned to the major axis, and the centre of the curve is placed at an infinite distance from the focus.

V. In the hyperbola, lastly, v is confined within still narrower limits, in fact between $v = -(180° - \psi)$, and

$v = +\ (180° - \psi)$, denoting by ψ the angle of which the cosine $= \frac{1}{e}$. For whilst v approaches these limits, r increases to infinity; if, in fact, one of these two limits should be taken for v, the value of r would result infinite, which shows that the hyperbola is not cut at all by a right line inclined to the line of apsides above or below by an angle $180° - \psi$. For the values thus excluded, that is to say, from $180° - \psi$ to $180° + \psi$, our formula assigns to r a negative value. The right line inclined by such an angle to the line of apsides does not indeed cut the hyperbola, but if produced reversely, meets the other branch of the hyperbola, which, as is known, is wholly separated from the first branch and is convex towards that focus, in which the sun is situated. But in our investigation, which, as we have already said, rests upon the assumption that r is taken positive, we shall pay no regard to that other branch of the hyperbola in which no heavenly body could move, except one on which the sun should, according to the same laws, exert not an attractive but a repulsive force. Accordingly, the aphelion does not exist, properly speaking, in the hyperbola also; that point of the reverse branch which lies in the line of apsides, and which corresponds to the values $v = 180°$, $r = -\frac{p}{e-1}$, might be considered as analogous to the aphelion. If now, we choose after the manner of the ellipse to call the value of the expression $\frac{p}{1-ee}$, even here where it becomes negative, the semi-axis major of the hyperbola, then this quantity indicates the distance of the point just mentioned from the perihelion, and at the same time the position opposite to that which occurs in the ellipse. In the same way $\frac{ep}{1-ee}$, that is, the distance from the focus to the middle point between these two points (the centre of the hyperbola), here obtains a negative value on account of its opposite direction.

5.

We call the angle v the *true anomaly* of the moving body, which, in the parabola is confined within the limits $-180°$ and $+180°$, in the hyperbola between $-(180° - \psi)$ and $+(180° - \psi)$, but which in the ellipse runs through the whole circle in periods constantly renewed. Hitherto, the greater number of astronomers have been accustomed to count the true anomaly in the ellipse not from the perihelion but from the aphelion, contrary to the analogy of the parabola and hyperbola, where, as the aphelion is wanting, it is necessary to begin from the perihelion: we have the less hesitation in restoring the analogy among all classes of conic sections, that the most recent French astronomers have by their example led the way.

It is frequently expedient to change a little the form of the expression $r = \frac{p}{1 + e \cos v}$; the following forms will be especially observed:—

$$r = \frac{p}{1 + e - 2e \sin^2 \frac{1}{2} v} = \frac{p}{1 - e + 2e \cos^2 \frac{1}{2} v}$$

$$r = \frac{p}{(1 + e) \cos^2 \frac{1}{2} v + (1 - e) \sin^2 \frac{1}{2} v}.$$

Accordingly, we have in the parabola

$$r = \frac{p}{2 \cos^2 \frac{1}{2} v};$$

in the hyperbola the following expression is particularly convenient,

$$r = \frac{p \cos \psi}{2 \cos \frac{1}{2}(v + \psi) \cos \frac{1}{2}(v - \psi)}$$

THE FOUNDATIONS OF MATHEMATICS

translated by G. Waldo Dunnington.

The subject of mathematics includes all extensive magnitudes (those in which parts can be conceived); intensive magnitudes (all non-extensive magnitudes) insofar as they are dependent on the extensives. To the former class of magnitudes belong: space or geometrical magnitudes which include lines, surfaces, solids, and angles; to the latter: velocity, density, rigidity, pitch and timbre of tones, intensity of tones and of light, probability, etc.

A magnitude in itself cannot become the subject of a scientific investigation; mathematics considers magnitudes only in reference to each other. The relationship of magnitudes to each other which they have only insofar as they are magnitudes, is called an arithmetical relationship. In geometrical magnitudes there occurs a relation in respect to position and this is called a geometric relationship. It is clear that geometric magnitudes can also have arithmetical relationships to each other.

Mathematics really teaches general truths which concern the relations of magnitudes and the purpose of it is to present magnitudes which have known relationships to known magnitudes or to magnitudes known to these, i.e., to make a presentation of them possible. But now we can have a presentation of a magnitude in a twofold manner, either by direct perception (a direct presentation), or by comparison with others, by direct perception of given magnitudes (indirect presentation). Accordingly the duty of the mathematician is either really to present the magnitude sought or to indicate the way one proceeds from the presentation of a magnitude directly given to the presentation of the magnitude sought (arithmetical presentation). This latter occurs by means of numbers, which show how many times one must repeatedly present the directly given magnitude* to get a presentation of the magnitude sought. That magnitude one calls unity and the process measuring.

These various relations of magnitudes and the various modes of presenting magnitudes are the foundations of both major disciplines of mathematics. Arithmetic regards magnitudes in arithmetical relations and presents them arithmetically; geometry regards magnitudes in geometric relations and presents them geometrically. To present geometrically magnitudes which have arithmetical relations, which was so customary among the ancients, is no longer the custom at present, otherwise one would have to regard this as a part of geometry. On the contrary, one applies the arithmetical mode of presentation most frequently to magnitudes in geometrical relationships, e.g., in trigonometry, also in the theory of curves, which are regarded as geometric disciplines. That moderns have thus preferred the arithmetical presentation rather than the geometrical, does not occur without reason, especially since our method of counting (the base ten) is so much easier than that of the ancients.

Since a great difference can occur among the arithmetical relations of magnitudes to each other, the parts of the arithmetical sciences are of a very different nature. Most important is the circumstance of whether in this relationship the concept of the infinite must be presupposed or not; the first case belongs to the calculation of the infinite, or higher mathematics, the latter to common or lower mathematics.

---

1. What is the essential condition that a combination of concepts may be thought of as referring to a *quantity?*

2. Everything becomes much simpler if one at first turns from infinite divisibility and merely considers discrete quantities. As, e.g., in biquadratic residues the points as objects, the passages from one to another, i.e.,

* Occasionally, also, how many times one must conceive a part of the same as repeated, which then gives the idea of the broken number (fraction).

relationships, as quantities, where the meaning of $a + bi - c - di$ is at once clear.

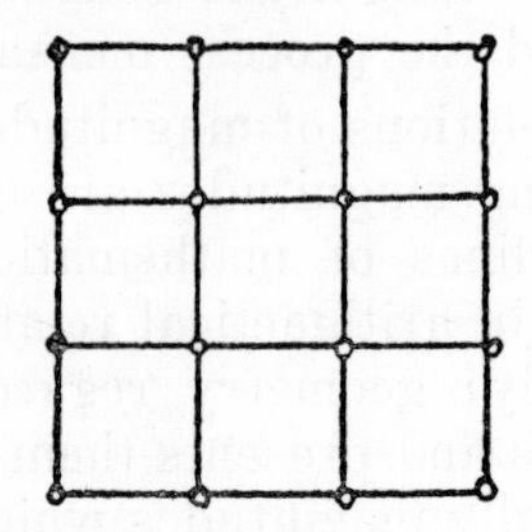

3. Mathematics is thus in the most general sense the science of relationships. Relationship predicates two things and is then called simple relationship, etc.

4. Points in a line are the general presentation of things, where each thing has a relationship of inequality only to two.

If a point can have a relationship to more than two things, then the representation of that is the condition of points in a plane, which are connected by lines. However, if an investigation is to be possible here, then it can concern only those points which are in a mutual relationship to three, and where there is a relationship between the relationships.

●

GENERAL INVESTIGATIONS OF CURVED SURFACES OF 1825 AND 1827

translated by JAMES C. MOREHEAD and ADAM M. HILTEBEITEL

GAUSS'S ABSTRACT OF THE DISQUISITIONES GENERALES CIRCA SUPERFICIES CURVAS, PRESENTED TO THE ROYAL SOCIETY OF GOTTINGEN.

Gottingische gelehrte Anzeigen. No. 177. Pages 1761-1768. 1827. November 5.

On the 8th of October, Hofrath Gauss presented to the Royal Society a paper:

Disquisitiones generales circa superficies curvas.

Although geometers have given much attention to general investigations of curved surfaces and their results cover a significant portion of the domain of higher geometry, this subject is still so far from being exhausted, that it can well be said that, up to this time, but a small portion of an exceedingly fruitful field has been cultivated. Through the solution of the problem, to find all representations of a given surface upon another in which the smallest elements remain unchanged, the author sought some years ago to give a new phase to this study. The purpose of the present discussion is further to open up other new points of view and to develop some of the new truths which thus become accessible. We shall here give an account of those things which can be made intelligible in a few words. But we wish to remark at the outset that the new theorems as well as the presentations of new ideas, if the greatest generality is to be attained, are still partly in need of some limitations or closer determinations, which must be omitted here.

In researches in which an infinity of directions of straight lines in space is concerned, it is advantageous to represent these directions by means of those points upon a fixed sphere, which are the end points of the radii drawn parallel to the lines. The centre and the radius of this *auxiliary sphere* are here quite arbitrary. The radius may be taken equal to unity. This procedure agrees fundamentally with that which is constantly employed in astronomy, where all directions are referred to a fictitious celestial sphere of infinite radius. Spherical trigonometry and certain other theorems, to which the author has added a new one of frequent application, then serve for the solution of the problems which the comparison of the various directions involved can present.

If we represent the direction of the normal at each point of the curved surface by the corresponding point of the sphere, determined as above indicated, namely, in this way, to every point on the surface, let a point on the sphere correspond; then, generally speaking, to every line on the curved surface will correspond a line on the sphere, and to every part of the former surface will correspond a part of the latter. The less this part differs from a plane, the smaller will be the corresponding part on the sphere. It is, therefore, a very natural idea to use as the measure of the total curvature, which is to be assigned to a part of the curved surface, the area of the corresponding part of the sphere. For this reason the author calls this area the *integral curvature* of the corresponding part of the curved surface. Besides the magnitude of the part, there is also at the same time its *position* to be considered. And this position may be in the two parts similar or inverse, quite independently of the relation of their magnitudes. The two cases can be distinguished by the positive or negative sign of the total curvature. This distinction has, however, a definite meaning only when the figures are regarded as upon definite sides of the two surfaces. The author regards the figure in the case of the sphere on the outside, and in the case of the curved surface on that side upon which we consider the normals erected. It follows then that the positive sign is taken in the case of convexo-convex or concavo-concave surfaces (which are not essentially different), and the negative in the case of concavo-convex surfaces. If the part of the curved surface in question consists of parts of these different sorts, still closer definition is necessary, which must be omitted here.

The comparison of the areas of two corresponding parts of the curved surface and of the sphere leads now (in the same manner as, *e. g.*, from the comparison of volume and mass springs the idea of density) to a new idea. The author designates as *measure of curvature* at a point of the curved surface the value of the fraction whose denominator is the area of the infinitely small part of the curved surface at this point and whose numerator is the area of the corresponding part of the surface of the auxiliary sphere, or the integral curvature of that element. It is clear that, according to the idea of the author, integral curvature and measure of curvature in the case of curved surfaces are analogous to what, in the case of curved lines, are called respectively amplitude and curvature simply. He hesitates to apply to curved surfaces the latter expressions, which have been accepted more from custom than on account of fitness. Moreover, less depends upon the choice of words than upon this, that their introduction shall be justified by pregnant theorems.

The solution of the problem, to find the measure of curvature at any point of a curved surface, appears in different forms according to the manner in which the nature of the curved surface is given. When the points in space, in general, are distinguished by three rectangular coordinates, the simplest method is to express one coordinate as a function of the other two. In this way we obtain the simplest expression for the measure of curvature. But, at the same time, there arises a remarkable relation between this measure of curvature and the curvatures of the curves formed by the intersections of the curved surface with planes normal to it. EULER, as is well known, first showed that two of these cutting planes which intersect each other at right angles have this property, that in one is found the greatest and in the other the smallest radius of curvature; or, more correctly, that in them the two extreme curvatures are found. It will follow then from the above mentioned expression for the measure of curvature that this will be equal to a fraction whose numerator is unity and whose denominator is the product of the extreme radii of curvature. The expression for the measure of curvature will be less simple, if the nature of the curved surface is determined by an equation in x, y, z. And it will become still more complex, if the nature of the curved surface is given so that x, y, z are expressed in the form of functions of two new variables p, q. In this last case the expression involves fifteen elements, namely, the partial differential coefficients of the first and second orders of x, y, z with respect to p and q. But it is less important in itself than for the reason that it facilitates the transition to another expression, which must be classed with the most remarkable theorems of this study. If the nature of the curved surface be expressed by this method, the general expression for any linear element upon it, or for $\sqrt{(dx^2 + dy^2 + dz^2)}$, has the form $\sqrt{(E\,dp^2 + 2\,F\,dp\,.\,dq + G\,dq^2)}$, where E, F, G are again functions of p and q. The new expression for the measure of curvature mentioned above contains merely these magnitudes and their partial differential coefficients of the first and second order. Therefore we notice that, in order to determine the measure of curvature, it is necessary to know only the general expression for a linear element; the expressions for the coordinates x, y, z are not required. A direct result from this is the remarkable theorem: If a curved surface, or a part of it, can be developed upon another surface, the measure of curvature at every point remains unchanged after the development. In particular, it follows from this further: Upon a curved surface that can be developed upon a plane, the measure of curvature is everywhere equal to zero. From this we derive at once the characteristic equation of surfaces developable upon a plane, namely,

$$\frac{\partial^2 z}{\partial x^2} \cdot \frac{\partial^2 z}{\partial y^2} - \left(\frac{\partial^2 z}{\partial x\,.\,\partial y}\right)^2 = 0,$$

when z is regarded as a function of x and y. This equation has been known for some time, but according to the author's judgment it has not been established previously with the necessary rigor.

These theorems lead to the consideration of the theory of curved surfaces from a new point of view, where a wide and still wholly uncultivated field is open to investigation. If we consider surfaces not as boundaries of bodies, but as bodies of which one dimension vanishes, and if at the same time we conceive them as flexible but not extensible, we see that two essentially different relations must be distinguished, namely, on the one hand, those that presuppose a definite form of the surface in space; on the other hand, those that are independent of the various forms which the surface may assume. This discussion is concerned with the latter. In accordance with what has been said, the measure of curvature belongs to this case. But it is easily seen that the consideration of figures constructed upon the surface, their angles, their areas and their integral curvatures, the joining of the points by means of shortest lines, and the like, also belong to this case. All such investigations must start from this, that the very nature of the curved surface is given by means of the expression of any linear element in the form $\sqrt{(E\ dp^2 + 2\ F\ dp\ .\ dq + G\ dq^2)}$. The author has embodied in the present treatise a portion of his investigations in this field, made several years ago, while he limits himself to such as are not too remote for an introduction, and may, to some extent, be generally helpful in many further investigations. In our abstract, we must limit ourselves still more, and be content with citing only a few of them as types. The following theorems may serve for this purpose.

If upon a curved surface a system of infinitely many shortest lines of equal lengths be drawn from one initial point, then will the line going through the end points of these shortest lines cut each of them at right angles. If at every point of an arbitrary line on a curved surface shortest lines of equal lengths be drawn at right angles to this line, then will all these shortest lines be perpendicular also to the line which joins their other end points. Both these theorems, of which the latter can be regarded as a generalization of the former, will be demonstrated both analytically and by simple geometrical considerations. *The excess of the sum of the angles of a triangle formed by shortest lines over two right angles is equal to the total curvature of the triangle.* It will be assumed here that that angle (57° 17′ 45″) to which an arc equal to the radius of the sphere corresponds will be taken as the unit for the angles, and that for the unit of total curvature will be taken a part of the spherical surface, the area of which is a square whose side is equal to the radius of the sphere. Evidently we can express this important theorem thus also: the excess over two right angles of the angles of a triangle formed by shortest lines is to eight right angles as the part of the surface of the auxiliary sphere, which corresponds to it as its integral curvature, is to the whole surface of the sphere. In general, the excess over $2n - 4$ right angles of the angles of a polygon of n sides, if these are shortest lines, will be equal to the integral curvature of the polygon.

The general investigations developed in this treatise will, in the conclusion, be applied to the theory of triangles of shortest lines, of which we shall introduce only a couple of important theorems. If a, b, c be the sides of such a triangle (they will be regarded as magnitudes of the first order); A, B, C the angles opposite; α, β, γ the measures of curvature at the angular points; σ the area of the triangle, then, to magnitudes of the fourth order, $\frac{1}{3}(\alpha + \beta + \gamma)\sigma$ is the excess of the sum $A + B + C$ over two right angles. Further, with the same degree of exactness, the angles of a plane rectilinear triangle whose sides are a, b, c, are respectively

$$A - \tfrac{1}{12}(2\alpha + \beta + \gamma)\sigma$$
$$B - \tfrac{1}{12}(\alpha + 2\beta + \gamma)\sigma$$
$$C - \tfrac{1}{12}(\alpha + \beta + 2\gamma)\sigma.$$

We see immediately that this last theorem is a generalization of the familiar theorem first established by LEGENDRE. By means of this theorem we obtain the angles of a plane triangle, correct to magnitudes of the fourth order, if we diminish each angle of the corresponding spherical triangle by one-third of the spherical excess. In the case of non-spherical surfaces, we must apply unequal reductions to the angles, and this inequality, generally speaking, is a magnitude of the third order. However, even if the whole surface differs only a little from the spherical form, it will still involve also a factor denoting the degree of the deviation from the spherical form. It is unquestionably important for the higher geodesy that we be able to calculate the inequalities of those reductions and thereby obtain the thorough conviction that, for all measurable triangles on the surface of the earth, they are to be regarded as quite insensible. So it is, for example, in the case of the greatest triangle of the triangulation carried out by the author. The greatest side of this triangle is almost fifteen geographical* miles, and the excess of the sum of its three angles over two right angles amounts almost to fifteen seconds. The three reductions of the angles of the plane triangle are 4″.95113, 4″.95104, 4″.95131. Besides, the author also developed the missing terms of the fourth order in the above expressions. Those for the sphere possess a very simple form. However, in the case of measurable triangles upon the earth's surface, they are quite insensible. And in the example here introduced they would have diminished the first reduction by only two units in the fifth decimal place and increased the third by the same amount.

* This German geographical mile is four minutes of arc at the equator, namely, 7.42 kilometers, and is equal to about 4.6 English statute miles. [Translators.]

HIPPOCRATES OF CHIOS

(Fifth Century B.C.)

Hippocrates of Chios, author of the first systematic treatise in geometry, was a Greek merchant and mathematician whose historically important activities fell in the third quarter of the fifth century B.C. He is not to be confused with his namesake and younger contemporary, Hippocrates of Cos, ancient Greek physician called the "Father of Medicine," who flourished in the fourth quarter of the century. Hippocrates of Chios is credited with taking a large part in breaking the secrecy surrounding the mathematics of the Pythagoreans. The circumstances under which Hippocrates of Chios lost his fortune and then perforce resorted to teaching geometry for his livelihood is variously told by ancient writers. Aristotle held him up as an example of a person who may possess considerable capacity in one respect and at the same time be completely inept in others. Hippocrates of Chios, Aristotle said, though skilled in geometry, appeared in other respects to have been weak and stupid, since through his simplicity he had been defrauded of a large sum of money by the collectors of customs in Byzantium. Johannes Philoponus believed that Hippocrates had lost everything to pirates at sea, that he went to Athens to prosecute them, that inordinately protracted legal procedures prolonged his stay there, and that during this time he frequented the schools of the philosophers, becoming extraordinarily skillful in geometry. Referring to Hippocrates as "one of the Pythagoreans," Iamblichus stated that on account of the misfortune of having lost his property, he was permitted by the Pythagoreans to make money by teaching geometry. This was the means, Iamblichus believed, by which the secrets of the Pythagorean science of geometry were made known and the way opened for the advancement of mathematics.

Thus engaged in teaching geometry, Hippocrates of Chios composed a text book called *Elements,* for those desirous of studying the subject systematically. It was the first treatise of its kind ever written. Fragments of this earliest Greek geometry in our possession have been obtained from extracts of the history of geometry written by Eudemus of Rhodes, a pupil of Aristotle. Although the actual work by Eudemus is lost, many parts of it are well known to us through quotations from it by later writers. Eudemus's account clearly shows that Hippocrates of Chios was a great originator of mathematics as well as a capable systematizer. He is credited with the discovery of methods of proof which soon became well established methods of procedures in Greek geometry. Hippocrates was the inventor of the method of "reduction," whereby a problem is solved by showing its dependence upon a subsidiary problem, the solution of the original problem following immediately upon the solution of the subsidiary problem. In the *Elements* written by Hippocrates, this frequently took the form of *reductio ad absurdum.* Ignoring the restriction to the use of the straight line and the circle in the construction of his geometrical figures, Hippocrates solved the Delian problem (required by the oracle of Delos: to construct a cube whose volume is twice that of a given cube) to the subsidiary problem of inserting two mean proportionals between a given line segment and another twice as long. Above all else, Hippocrates of Chios achieved his greatest fame for his highly significant studies and discoveries in the squaring of a lune, the crescent shaped plane figure bounded by the arcs of two intersecting circles, and for the numerous geometrical theorems he invented and proved.

•

THE ELEMENTS OF HIPPOCRATES

From *Greek Geometry from Thales to Euclid*

by George J. Allman

Simplicius has preserved in his *Commentary on the Physics of Aristotle* a pretty full and partly literal extract from the *History of Geometry* of Eudemus, which contains an account of the work of Hippocrates.

SQUARING A LUNE.

'Let a semicircle $\alpha\beta\gamma$ be described on the straight line $\alpha\beta$; bisect $\alpha\beta$ in δ; from the point δ draw a perpendicular $\delta\gamma$ to $\alpha\beta$, and join $\alpha\gamma$; this will be the side of the square inscribed in the circle of which $\alpha\beta\gamma$ is the semicircle. On $\alpha\gamma$ describe the semicircle $\alpha\epsilon\gamma$. Now since the square on $\alpha\beta$ is equal to double the square on $\alpha\gamma$ (and since the squares on the diameters are to each other as the respective circles or semicircles), the semicircle $\alpha\gamma\beta$ is double the semicircle $\alpha\epsilon\gamma$. The quadrant $\alpha\gamma\delta$ is, therefore, equal to the semicircle $\alpha\epsilon\gamma$. Take away the common segment lying between the circumference $\alpha\gamma$ and the side of the square; then the remaining lune $\alpha\epsilon\gamma$ will be equal

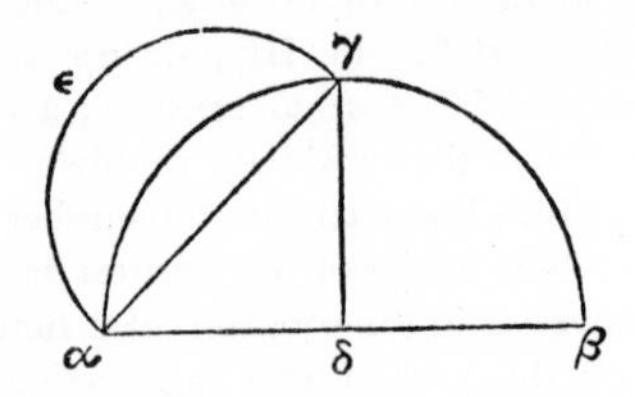

to the triangle $\alpha\gamma\delta$; but this triangle is equal to a square.

'Eudemus,[39] however, tells us in his *History of Geometry,* that Hippocrates demonstrated the quadrature of the lune, not merely the lune on the side of the square, but generally, if one might say so: if, namely, the exterior arc of the lune be equal to a semicircle, or greater or less than it. I shall now put down literally[40] what Eudemus relates, adding only a short explanation by referring to Euclid's Elements, on account of the summary manner of Eudemus, who, according to archaic custom, gives concise proofs.

'In the second book of his *History of Geometry,* Eudemus says:—

"The squaring of lunes seeming to relate to an uncommon class of figures was, on account of their relation to the circle, first treated of by Hippocrates, and was rightly viewed in that connection. We may, therefore, more fully touch upon and discuss them. He started with and laid down as the first thing useful for them, that similar segments of circles have the same ratio as the squares on their bases. This he proved by showing that circles have the same ratio as the squares on their diameters. Now, as circles are to each other, so are also similar segments; but similar segments are those which contain the same part of their respective circles, as a semicircle to a semicircle, the third part of a circle to the third part of another circle. For which reason, also,

[39] Bretsch., *Geom. vor. Eukl.,* p. 109.

[40] Simplicius did not adhere to his intention, or else some transcriber has added to the text.

similar segments contain equal angles. The latter are in all semicircles right, in larger segments less than right angles, and so much less as the segments are larger than semicircles; and in smaller segments they are larger than right angles, and so much larger as the segments are smaller than semicircles. Having first shown this, he described a lune which had a semicircle for boundary, by circumscribing a semicircle about a right-angled isosceles triangle, and describing on the hypotenuse a segment of a circle similar to those cut off by the sides. The segment over the hypotenuse then being equal to the sum of those on the two other sides, if the common part of the triangle which lies over the segment on the base be added to both, the lune will be equal to the triangle.

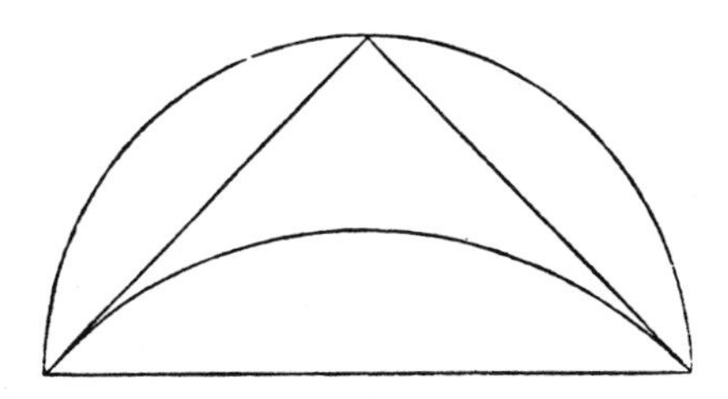

Since the lune, then, has been shown to be equal to a triangle, it can be squared. Thus, then, Hippocrates, by taking for the exterior arc of the lune that of a semicircle, readily squares the lune.

"Hippocrates next proceeds to square a lune whose exterior arc is greater than a semicircle. In order to do so, he constructs a trapezium[42] having three sides equal to each other, and the fourth—the greater of the two parallel sides—such that the square on it is equal to three times that on any other side; he circumscribes a circle about the trapezium, and on its greatest side describes a segment of a circle similar to those cut off from the circle by the three equal sides.[43] By drawing a diag-

[42] Trapezia, like this, cut off from an isosceles triangle by a line parallel to the base, occur in the Papyrus Rhind.

[43] Then follows a proof, which I have omitted, that the circle can be circumscribed about the trapezium. This proof is obviously supplied by Simplicius, as is indicated by the change of person . . . as well as by the reference to Euclid, I. 9.

onal of the trapezium, it will be manifest that the section in question is greater than a semicircle, for the square on this straight line subtending two equal sides of the

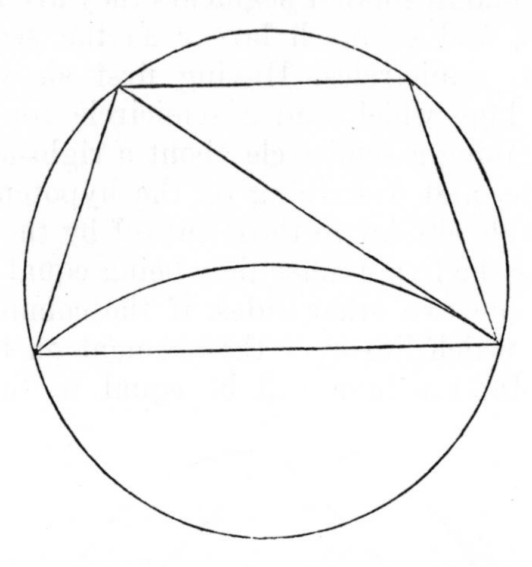

trapezium must be greater than twice the square on either of them, or than double the square on the third equal side: the square on the greatest side of the trapezium, which is equal to three times the square on any one of the other sides, is therefore less than the square on the diagonal and the square on the third equal side. Consequently, the angle subtended by the greatest side of the trapezium is acute, and the segment which contains it is, therefore, greater than a semicircle: but this is the exterior boundary of the lune.

"Further, Hippocrates shows that a lune with an exterior arc less than a semicircle can be squared, and gives the following construction for the description of such a lune:[45]—

"Let $\alpha\beta$ be the diameter of a circle whose centre is κ; let $\gamma\delta$ cut $\beta\kappa$ in the point of bisection γ, and at right angles; through β draw the straight line $\beta\zeta\epsilon$, so that the

[45] Bretschneider, p. 114, notices the archaic manner in which lines and points are denoted in this investigation— . . .
and infers from it that Eudemus is quoting the very words of Hippocrates. I have found this observation useful in aiding me to separate the additions of Simplicius from the work of Eudemus.

part of it, $\zeta\epsilon$, intercepted between the line $\gamma\delta$ and the circle shall be such that two squares on it shall be equal to three squares on the radius $\beta\kappa$; join $\kappa\zeta$, and produce it to meet the straight line drawn through ϵ parallel to $\beta\kappa$, and let them meet at η; join $\kappa\epsilon$, $\beta\eta$ (these lines will be equal); describe then a circle round the trapezium $\beta\kappa\epsilon\eta$; also, circumscribe a circle about the triangle $\epsilon\zeta\eta$. Let the centres of these circles be λ and μ respectively.

"Now, the segments of the latter circle on $\epsilon\zeta$ and $\zeta\eta$ are similar to each other, and to each of the segments of the former circle on the equal straight lines $\epsilon\kappa$, $\kappa\beta$, $\beta\eta$; and, since twice the square on $\epsilon\zeta$ is equal to three times the square on $\kappa\beta$, the sum of the two segments on $\epsilon\zeta$, and $\zeta\eta$ is equal to the sum of the three segments on $\epsilon\kappa$, $\kappa\beta$, $\beta\eta$; to each of these equals add the figure bounded by the

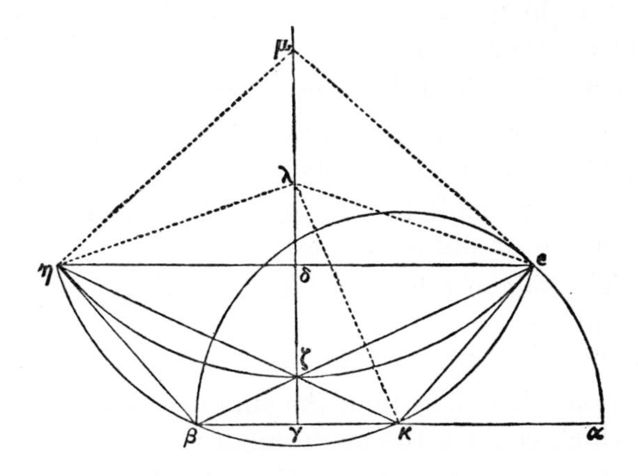

straight lines $\epsilon\kappa$, $\kappa\beta$, $\beta\eta$, and the arc $\eta\zeta\epsilon$, and we shall have the lune whose exterior arc is $\epsilon\kappa\beta\eta$ equal to the rectilineal figure composed of the three triangles $\zeta\beta\eta$, $\zeta\beta\kappa$, $\zeta\kappa\epsilon$.[48]

"That the exterior arc of this lune is smaller than a

[48] A pentagon with a re-entrant angle is considered here: but observe—1°, that it is not called a pentagon, that term being then restricted to the regular pentagon; and, 2°, that it is described as a rectilineal figure composed of three triangles.

semicircle, Hippocrates proves, by showing that the angle $\epsilon\kappa\eta$ lying within the exterior arc of the segment is obtuse, which he does thus: Since the square on $\epsilon\zeta$ is once and a-half the square on the radius $\beta\kappa$ or $\kappa\epsilon$, and since, on account of the similarity of triangles $\beta\kappa\epsilon$ and $\beta\zeta\kappa$, the square on $\kappa\epsilon$ is greater than twice the square on $\kappa\zeta$, it follows that the square on $\epsilon\zeta$ is greater than the squares on $\epsilon\kappa$ and $\kappa\zeta$ together. The angle $\epsilon\kappa\eta$ is therefore obtuse, and consequently the segment in which it lies is less than a semicircle."

If we examine this oldest fragment of Greek geometry, we see, in the first place, that there is in it a definition of similar segments of circles; they are defined to be those which contain the same quotum of their respective circles, as for instance, a semicircle is similar to a semicircle, the third part of one circle is similar to the third part of another circle.

Next we find the following theorems:—

(*a*). Similar segments contain equal angles;

(*b*). These in all semicircles are right; segments which are larger or smaller than semicircles contain, respectively, acute or obtuse angles;

(*c*). The side of a hexagon inscribed in a circle is equal to the radius;

(*d*). In any triangle the square on a side opposite to an acute angle is less than the sum of the squares on the sides which contain the acute angle;

(*e*). In an obtuse-angled triangle the square on the side subtending the obtuse angle is greater than the sum of the squares on the sides containing it;

(*f*). In an isosceles triangle whose vertical angle is double the angle of an equilateral triangle, the square on the base is equal to three times the square on one of the equal sides;

(*g*). In equiangular triangles the sides about the equal angles are proportional;

(*h*). Circles are to each other as the squares on their diameters;

(*i*). Similar segments of circles are to each other as the squares on their bases.

Lastly, we observe that the solution of the following problems is required:—

(*a*). Construct a square which shall be equal to a given rectilineal figure;

(*b*). Find a line the square on which shall be equal to three times the square on a given line;

(*c*). Find a line such that twice the square on it shall be equal to three times the square on a given line;

(*d*). Being given two straight lines, construct a trapezium such that one of the parallel sides shall be equal to the greater of the two given lines, and each of the three remaining sides equal to the less;

(*e*). About the trapezium so constructed describe a circle;

(*f*). Describe a circle about a given triangle;

(*g*). From the extremity of the diameter of a semicircle draw a chord such that the part of it intercepted between the circle and a straight line drawn at right angles to the diameter at the distance of one half the radius shall be equal to a given straight line;

(*h*). Describe on a given straight line a segment of a circle which shall be similar to a given one.

HSIA-HOU YANG

(Sixth Century)

Hsia-hou Yang, one of the three greatest Chinese mathematicians of the sixth century, was the author of one of the most practical of the older Chinese mathematical works, the *Hsia-hou Yang Suan-ching* ("Arithmetical Classic of Hsia-hou Yang"). This treatise became one of the standard texts on the required list for the examination of civil servants during the T'ang Dynasty (618—906). Internal evidences in his writings indicate that Hsia-hou Yang wrote and taught his arithmetic in the middle or late sixth century. The *Hsia-hou Yang Suan-ching* was based on previous Chinese mathematical classics, primarily upon Chang Tsang's *K'iu-ch'ang Suan-shu* ("Arithmetical Rules in Nine Sections") of the second century B. C., and upon the *Sun-Tsu Suan-ching* ("Arithmetic of Sun-Tsu") of the third century A. D. Divided into numerous small items, it was embodied in the great fifteenth century Chinese encyclopaedia, *Yung-lo Ta-tien.* In the eighteenth century, the learned Tai Chen of Peking collated the various entries in the *Yung-lo Ta-tien* which had been taken from the *Hsia-hou Yang Suan-ching.* Making use of the index of the encyclopaedia from which it was possible to reconstruct the arrangement of the original material, he painstakingly reconstituted and edited Hsia-hou Yang's famous work. Tai Chen's edition, the source of our modern version, was published in 1776 with the encouragement and financial support of the Emperor Khien-Lung who honored the publication by writing a preface to it.

The original work is said to have been concisely put in a total of twelve thousand words on thirty-six double pages. Hsia-hou Yang laid great stress on usefulness, and accordingly he included only the material needed in the solution of commercial problems or in the business of government. No rules were given. Occasionally some explanation was briefly stated, but in the main, each problem was accompanied merely by the answer. The problems were varied. Some were on mensuration, others were concerned with taxes, with the computation of commissions, and even with questions regarding the division of loot and food by army officers among the soldiers. The problems were such as required no more than elementary calculations involving fractions, square and cube roots, and percentage.

ARITHMETICAL CLASSIC OF HSIA-HOU YANG

by Pere Louis Vanhee, S.J.

In the first section the five operations of addition, subtraction, multiplication, division, and square and cube roots are given. The work on division is subdivided into (1) "ordinary division"; (2) "division by ten, hundred, and so on," especially intended for work in mensuration; (3) "division by simplification" (*yo ch'u*). The last problem in the section is as follows:

"There are 1843 *k'o,* 8 *t'ow,* 3 *ho* of coarse rice. A contract requires that this be exchanged for refined rice at the rate of 1 *k'o,* 4 *t'ow* for 3 *k'o.* How much refined rice must be given?" The answer is 860 *k'o,* 534 *ho.* The solution is given as follows: "Multiply the given number by 1 *k'o,* 4 *t'ow* and divide by 3 *k'o* and you will obtain the result."[1]

Fractions are also mentioned, special names being given to the four most common ones, as follows:

1/2 is called *chung p'an* (even part);
1/3 is called *shaw p'an* (small part);
2/3 is called *thai p'an* (large part);
1/4 is called *joh p'an* (weak part).

In the second section there are twenty-eight applied problems relating to taxes, commissions, and such questions as concern the division by army officers of loot and food (silk, rice, wine, soy sauce, vinegar, and the like) among their soldiers.

The third section contains forty-two problems each beginning with the word "now," which is here taken as substantially equivalent to the word "if." Five of these problems, translated as literally as possible, are as follows:

Ex. 1. Now for 1 pound of gold one gets 1200 pieces of silk. How many can you get for 1 ounce? Answer: For

[1] 1 *k'o* = 10 *t'ow* = 100 *ho.* The *k'o* may be roughly translated as a bushel.

1 ounce you get exactly 75 pieces. Solution: Take the given number of pieces, have it divided by 16 ounces, and you will obtain the answer.[2]

Ex. 2. Now you have 192 ounces of silk. How many *choo* have you? Answer: Four thousand six hundred eight.[3]

Ex. 15. Now 2000 packages of cash must be carried to the town at the rate of 10 cash per bundle. How much will be given to the mandarin and how much to the carrier? Answer: 1980 packages and 198-2/101 cash to the mandarin; 19 packages and 801-98/101 to the carrier. Solution: Take the total number as the dividend, and 1 package plus 10 cash as the divisor.[1]

Ex. 24. Out of 3485 ounces of silk how many pieces of satin can be made, 5 ounces being required for each piece? Answer: 697. Solution: Multiply the number of ounces by 2 and go back by one row. Dividing by 5 will also give the answer.[2]

Ex. 42. Now they build a wall, high 3 rods, broad 5 feet at the upper part and 15 feet at the lower part; the length 100 rods. For a 2-foot square a man works 1 day. How many days are required? Answer: 75,000. Solution: Take half the sum of the upper and lower breadths, have it multiplied by the height and length; the product will

---

[2] The Chinese pound was, from early times, divided into 16 ounces or *taels*.

[3] The result (4608) is written in words instead of in numeral characters. The zero was not in use in the sixth century; but this did not, of course, prevent the use of the ordinary Chinese numerals of that period. The answer shows that the ounce was at that time divided into 24 *choo*.

At the beginning of most of the early Chinese books on arithmetic there is the following statement from Sun-tzi's *Suan-king*, a work referred to in Smith's *History of Mathematics*, vol. I, p. 141: "Weight begins with one grain of millet; ten grains make one *ts'en;* ten *ts'en* make one *choo;* 24 *choo* make one ounce (*tael*); 16 ounces make one pound; 30 pounds make one *kiun;* 4 *kiun* make 1 stone."

[1] A package or string of cash contains 1000 farthings. The two results reduce to periodic fractions. There is no reason given for the division of 2,000,000 by 1010.

[2] This is an early use of our rule for dividing by 5. The expression about going back one row seems to refer to the use of counters. So far as known, the *suan-pan*, in its present form, was not yet invented.

be the dividend. As the divisor you will use the square of the given 2 feet.[3]

Hsia-hou Yang also uses percentage. He shows considerable ability in finding various areas and volumes. His work is evidently a good type of practical textbook of the time, a fact that is shown by its popularity and the high esteem in which it has always been held. Yuan Yuan[4], for example, in his well-known biographical work, speaks of it as "an easy text, intended for daily use."

---

[3] 1 rod = 10 feet = 100 inches. The amount made by one man in a day is evidently intended to be the volume of a rectangular solid of base 2 ft. square and of height 1 rod; that is, 40 cubic feet. The divisor, therefore, is 40.

[4] See Smith, *loc. cit.*, vol. I, p. 535. Yuan Yuan was born in 1764 and died in 1849.

MOHAMMED BEN MUSA AL-KHOWARIZMI

(c. 825)

Mohammed ben Musa al-Khowarizmi (also, Abu Abdallah Muhammed ibn Musa al-Khwarizmi), son of Moses, the Khowarezmite, was born in the city of Khowarezm (modern Khiva). He was one of the greatest of the scientists who were encouraged by the Caliph Al-Mamun to gather at his court at Baghdad in the early ninth century and to participate in the work of his newly organized *Bayt al-hikma* (House of Wisdom). Al-Mamun constructed two astronomical observatories for his new academy and he made strenuous efforts to obtain extant scientific works for it. In his eagerness to collect scientific manuscripts, he went so far as to send a mission to the Byzantine Emperor Leon for the purpose of securing Greek works. The writings collected by Al-Mamun were immediately translated into Arabic by the scholars of his academy. It was in this scholarly atmosphere of the *Bayt al-hikma* that al-Khowarizmi worked and reached the peak of his activities as an astronomer, mathematician and geographer. He gained fame early through his abridgment (known as the less *Sind-hind*) of al-Fazan's Arabic translation (the greater *Sind-hind*) of the first Hindu astronomical tables to be brought to the Arabian court. Al-Khowarizmi's less *Sind-hind,* a popular work from the first, was followed by an enlarged version containing observations made by al-Khowarizmi himself, and including some material possibly based on Ptolemy. The fact that the enlarged work remained in use for centuries after his death is a small part of the evidence of al-Khowarizmi's influence on the scholars who followed him. Arabian and European writers continued to explain al-Khowarizmi's works for hundreds of years. His trigonometric tables, revised and enlarged by Meslama al-Majriti (about 1000 A.D.) were translated into Latin by Adelhard of Bath (about 1126).

Exceptional historical interest attaches to two of his mathematical works, one on arithmetic, the other on algebra. The treatise on arithmetic which had taught the methods of Hindu computation to the Arabs served a like purpose for the European scholars. A Latin translation of this work entitled *Algoritmi de numero Indorum* appeared about 1120. The Latinized version of his name in the opening words *Dixit Algoritmi* (Algorithm says) made his name synonymous with the art of computation, giving rise to the term *augrim* in Chaucer's *A Treatise on the Astrolabe,* and to the modern word algorism (or algorithm). The works of Alexander de Villa Dei (c. 1220) and of John Halifax (Sacrobosco), drawing upon al-Khowarizmi's arithmetic, spread the knowledge of the Hindu system in Europe. Sacrobosco's *Algorismus vulgaris,* written about 1250, was widely used as late as the sixteenth century.

Al-Khowarizmi's algebra *Al-jabr w'al-mugabala* contained the first systematic treatment of the subject. The very name of the branch of mathematics to which the treatise is devoted "algebra" is derived from the title of this work. In the complete absence of axiomatic foundations and of proofs depending upon them, and in the analytical presentation of its solutions, al-Khowarizmi's algebra evidences the author's marked preference for Hindu over Greek methods. Nevertheless, the content shows a blending of Eastern and Greek achievements. Through the persistent reappearance in subsequent algebra texts of certain features of his work, such as the particular equations used, or the numerical problems cited, or the order in which the equations or problems are discussed, al-Khowarizmi's influence upon writers in the field of algebra can be traced directly or indirectly for more than seven hundred years after his death.

●

THE ALGEBRA OF MOHAMMED BEN MUSA

Translated from the Arabic, with explanatory notes

by FREDERIC ROSEN

THE AUTHOR'S PREFACE.

IN THE NAME OF GOD, GRACIOUS AND MERCIFUL!

This work was written by MOHAMMED BEN MUSA, of KHOWAREZM. He commences it thus:

Praised be God for his bounty towards those who deserve it by their virtuous acts: in performing which, as by him prescribed to his adoring creatures, we express our thanks, and render ourselves worthy of the continuance (of his mercy), and preserve ourselves from change: acknowledging his might, bending before his power, and revering his greatness!

MOHAMMED BEN MUSA'S
COMPENDIUM
ON CALCULATING BY
COMPLETION AND REDUCTION.

When I considered what people generally want in calculating, I found that it always is a number.

I also observed that every number is composed of units, and that any number may be divided into units.

I observed that the numbers which are required in calculating by Completion and Reduction are of three kinds, namely, roots, squares, and simple numbers relative to neither root nor square.

A root is any quantity which is to be multiplied by itself, consisting of units, or numbers ascending, or fractions descending.*

A square is the whole amount of the root multiplied by itself.

A simple number is any number which may be pronounced without reference to root or square.

A number belonging to one of these three classes may be equal to a number of another class; you may say, for instance, "squares are equal to roots," or "squares are equal to numbers," or "roots are equal to numbers."†

Of the case in which *squares are equal to roots,* this is an example. "A square is equal to five roots of the same;"‡ the root of the square is five, and the square is twenty-five, which is equal to five times its root.

So you say, "one third of the square is equal to four roots;"§ then the whole square is equal to twelve roots; that is a hundred and forty-four; and its root is twelve.

Or you say, "five squares are equal to ten roots;"|| then one square is equal to two roots; the root of the square is two, and its square is four.

---

* By the word root, is meant the simple power of the unknown quantity.

† $cx^2=bx$ $\quad cx^2=a$ $\quad bx=a$

‡ $x^2=5x$ $\quad \therefore x=5$

§ $\frac{x^2}{3}=4x$ $\quad \therefore x^2=12x$ $\quad \therefore x=12$

|| $5x^2=10x$ $\quad \therefore x^2=2x$ $\quad \therefore x=2$

In this manner, whether the squares be many or few, (*i. e.* multiplied or divided by any number), they are reduced to a single square; and the same is done with the roots, which are their equivalents; that is to say, they are reduced in the same proportion as the squares.

As to the case in which *squares are equal to numbers;* for instance, you say, " a square is equal to nine;"* then this is a square, and its root is three. Or "five squares are equal to eighty;"† then one square is equal to one-fifth of eighty, which is sixteen. Or "the half of the square is equal to eighteen;"‡ then the square is thirty-six, and its root is six.

Thus, all squares, multiples, and sub-multiples of them, are reduced to a single square. If there be only part of a square, you add thereto, until there is a whole square; you do the same with the equivalent in numbers.

As to the case in which *roots are equal to numbers;* for instance, "one root equals three in number;"§ then the root is three, and its square nine. Or "four roots are equal to twenty;"|| then one root is equal to five, and the square to be formed of it is twenty-five. Or "half the root is equal to ten;"¶ then the whole root is equal to twenty, and the square which is formed of it is four hundred.

---

* $x^2=9 \qquad x=3$

† $5x^2=80 \therefore x^2=\frac{80}{5}=16$

‡ $\frac{x^2}{2}=18 \therefore x^2=36 \therefore x=6$

§ $x=3$

|| $4x=20 \qquad \therefore x=5$

¶ $\frac{x}{2}=10 \qquad \therefore x=20$

I found that these three kinds; namely, roots, squares, and numbers, may be combined together, and thus three compound species arise;* that is, "squares and roots equal to numbers;" "squares and numbers equal to roots;" "roots and numbers equal to squares."

Roots and Squares are equal to Numbers;† for instance, "one square, and ten roots of the same, amount to thirty-nine dirhems;" that is to say, what must be the square which, when increased by ten of its own roots, amounts to thirty-nine? The solution is this: you halve the number‡ of the roots, which in the present instance yields five. This you multiply by itself; the product is twenty-five. Add this to thirty-nine; the sum is sixty-four. Now take the root of this, which is eight, and subtract from it half the number of the roots, which is five; the remainder is three. This is the root of the square which you sought for; the square itself is nine.

* The three cases considered are,

$$\text{1st. } cx^2 + bx = a$$
$$\text{2d. } cx^2 + a = bx$$
$$\text{3d. } cx^2 = bx + a$$

† 1st case: $cx^2 + bx = a$

Example $x^2 + 10x = 39$

$$x = \sqrt{\left[\left(\tfrac{10}{2}\right)^2 + 39\right]} - \tfrac{10}{2}$$
$$= \sqrt{64} - 5$$
$$= 8 - 5 = 3$$

‡ *i. e.* the coefficient.

The solution is the same when two squares or three, or more or less be specified;* you reduce them to one single square, and in the same proportion you reduce also the roots and simple numbers which are connected therewith.

For instance, "two squares and ten roots are equal to forty-eight dirhems;"† that is to say, what must be the amount of two squares which, when summed up and added to ten times the root of one of them, make up a sum of forty-eight dirhems? You must at first reduce the two squares to one; and you know that one square of the two is the moiety of both. Then reduce every thing mentioned in the statement to its half, and it will be the same as if the question had been, a square and five roots of the same are equal to twenty-four dirhems; or, what must be the amount of a square which, when added to five times its root, is equal to twenty-four dirhems? Now halve the number of the roots; the moiety is two and a half. Multiply that by itself; the product is six and a quarter. Add this to twenty-four; the sum is thirty dirhems and a quarter. Take the root of this; it is five and a half. Subtract from this the moiety of the number of the roots, that is two and a half; the remainder is three.

---

* $cx^2+bx=a$ is to be reduced to the form $x^2+\frac{b}{c}x=\frac{a}{c}$

† $$2x^2+10x=48$$
$$x^2+5x=24$$
$$x=\sqrt{[(\tfrac{5}{2})^2+24]}-\tfrac{5}{2}$$
$$=\sqrt{[6\tfrac{1}{4}+24]}-2\tfrac{1}{2}$$
$$=5\tfrac{1}{2}-2\tfrac{1}{2}=3$$

This is the root of the square, and the square itself is nine.

The proceeding will be the same if the instance be, "half of a square and five roots are equal to twenty-eight dirhems;"* that is to say, what must be the amount of a square, the moiety of which, when added to the equivalent of five of its roots, is equal to twenty-eight dirhems? Your first business must be to complete your square, so that it amounts to one whole square. This you effect by doubling it. Therefore double it, and double also that which is added to it, as well as what is equal to it. Then you have a square and ten roots, equal to fifty-six dirhems. Now halve the roots; the moiety is five. Multiply this by itself; the product is twenty-five. Add this to fifty-six; the sum is eighty-one. Extract the root of this; it is nine. Subtract from this the moiety of the number of roots, which is five; the remainder is four. This is the root of the square which you sought for; the square is sixteen, and half the square eight.

Proceed in this manner, whenever you meet with squares and roots that are equal to simple numbers: for it will always answer.

---

* $\frac{x^2}{2}+5x=28$

$x^2+10x=56$

$x=\sqrt{[(\frac{10}{2})^2+56]}-\frac{10}{2}$

$=\sqrt{25+56}-5$

$=\sqrt{81}-5$

$=9-5=4$

*Squares and Numbers are equal to Roots;** for instance, "a square and twenty-one in numbers are equal to ten roots of the same square." That is to say, what must be the amount of a square, which, when twenty-one dirhems are added to it, becomes equal to the equivalent of ten roots of that square? Solution: Halve the number of the roots; the moiety is five. Multiply this by itself; the product is twenty-five. Subtract from this the twenty-one which are connected with the square; the remainder is four. Extract its root; it is two. Subtract this from the moiety of the roots, which is five; the remainder is three. This is the root of the square which you required, and the square is nine. Or you may add the root to the moiety of the roots; the sum is seven; this is the root of the square which you sought for, and the square itself is forty-nine.

When you meet with an instance which refers you to this case, try its solution by addition, and if that do not serve, then subtraction certainly will. For in this case both addition and subtraction may be employed, which will not answer in any other of the three cases in which

---

* 2d case. $cx^2+a=bx$

Example. $x^2+21=10x$

$$x=\frac{10}{2}\pm\sqrt{[(\tfrac{10}{2})^2-21]}$$
$$=5\pm\sqrt{25-21}$$
$$=5\pm\sqrt{4}$$
$$=5\pm2$$

the number of the roots must be halved. And know, that, when in a question belonging to this case you have halved the number of the roots and multiplied the moiety by itself, if the product be less than the number of dirhems connected with the square, then the instance is impossible;* but if the product be equal to the dirhems by themselves, then the root of the square is equal to the moiety of the roots alone, without either addition or subtraction.

In every instance where you have two squares, or more or less, reduce them to one entire square,† as I have explained under the first case.

Roots and Numbers are equal to Squares;‡ for instance, "three roots and four of simple numbers are equal to a square." Solution: Halve the roots; the moiety is one and a half. Multiply this by itself; the product is two and a quarter. Add this to the four; the sum is six and a quarter. Extract its root; it is two and a half. Add this to the moiety of the roots, which was one and a half; the sum is four. This is the root of the square, and the square is sixteen.

---

* If in an equation, of the form $x^2+a=bx$, $(\frac{b}{2})^2 \angle a$, the case supposed in the equation cannot happen. If $(\frac{b}{2})^2=a$, then $x=\frac{b}{2}$

† $cx^2+a=bx$ is to be reduced to $x^2+\frac{a}{c}=\frac{b}{c}x$

‡ 3d case $cx^2=bx+a$

Example $x^2=3x+4$

$$
\begin{aligned}
x^2 &= \sqrt{[(\tfrac{3}{2})^2+4]}+\tfrac{3}{2} \\
&= \sqrt{(1\tfrac{1}{4})^2+4}+1\tfrac{1}{2} \\
&= \sqrt{2\tfrac{1}{4}+4}+1\tfrac{1}{2} \\
&= \sqrt{6\tfrac{1}{4}}+1\tfrac{1}{2} \\
&= 2\tfrac{1}{2}+1\tfrac{1}{2}=4
\end{aligned}
$$

Whenever you meet with a multiple or sub-multiple of a square, reduce it to one entire square.

OF THE SIX PROBLEMS.

First Problem.

I have divided ten into two portions; I have multiplied the one of the two portions by the other; after this I have multiplied the one of the two by itself, and the product of the multiplication by itself is four times as much as that of one of the portions by the other.*

Computation: Suppose one of the portions to be thing, and the other ten minus thing: you multiply thing by ten minus thing; it is ten things minus a square. Then multiply it by four, because the instance states "four times as much." The result will be four times the product of one of the parts multiplied by the other. This is forty things minus four squares. After this you multiply thing by thing, that is to say, one of the portions by itself. This is a square, which is equal to forty things minus four squares. Reduce it now by the four squares, and add them to the one square. Then the equation is: forty things are equal to five squares; and one square will be equal to eight roots, that is, sixty-four; the root of this is eight, and this is one of the two portions, namely, that which is to be multiplied by itself. The remainder from the ten is two, and that is the other portion. Thus the question leads you to one of the six cases, namely, that of "squares equal to roots." Remark this.

Second Problem.

I have divided ten into two portions: I have multiplied each of the parts by itself, and afterwards ten by itself:

---

* $x^2 = 4x(10-x) = 40x - 4x^2$

$5x^2 = 40x$

$x^2 = 8x$

$x = 8;\ (10-x) = 2$

the product of ten by itself is equal to one of the two parts multiplied by itself, and afterwards by two and seven-ninths; or equal to the other multiplied by itself, and afterwards by six and one-fourth.*

Computation: Suppose one of the parts to be thing, and the other ten minus thing. You multiply thing by itself, it is a square; then by two and seven-ninths, this makes it two squares and seven-ninths of a square. You afterwards multiply ten by ten; it is a hundred, which much be equal to two squares and seven-ninths of a square. Reduce it to one square, through division by nine twenty-fifths;* this being its fifth and four-fifths of its fifth, take now also the fifth and four-fifths of the fifth of a hundred; this is thirty-six, which is equal to one square. Take its root, it is six. This is one of the two portions; and accordingly the other is four. This question leads you, therefore, to one of the six cases, namely, "squares equal to numbers."

VARIOUS QUESTIONS.

In the same manner, if the question be: "A square, multiply its root by four of its roots, and the product

---

* $10^2 = x^2 \times 2\frac{7}{9}$

$100 = x^2 \times \frac{25}{9}$

$\frac{9}{25} \times 100 = x^2$

$36 = x^2$

$6 = x$

* $\frac{9}{25} = \frac{1}{5} \times \frac{4}{5} + \frac{1}{5}$

will be three times the square, with a surplus of fifty dirhems."* Computation: You multiply the root by four roots, it is four squares, which are equal to three squares and fifty dirhems. Remove three squares from the four; there remains one square, equal to fifty dirhems. One root of fifty, multiplied by four roots of the same, gives two hundred, which is equal to three times the square, and a residue of fifty dirhems.

If the instance be: "A square, which when added to twenty dirhems, is equal to twelve of its roots,"† then the solution is this: You say, one square and twenty dirhems are equal to twelve roots. Halve the roots and multiply them by themselves; this gives thirty-six. Subtract from this the twenty dirhems, extract the root from the remainder, and subtract it from the moiety of the roots, which is six. The remainder is the root of the square: it is two dirhems, and the square is four.

If the instance be: "To find a square, of which if one-third be added to three dirhems, and the sum be subtracted from the square, the remainder multiplied by

---

* $4x^2 = 3x^2 + 50$

$x^2 = 50$

† $x^2 + 20 = 12x$

$x = 6 \pm \sqrt{36 - 20} = 6 \pm 4 = 10 \text{ or } 2$

itself restores the square;"* then the computation is this: If you subtract one-third and three dirhems from the square, there remain two-thirds of it less three dirhems. This is the root. Multiply therefore two-thirds of thing less three dirhems by itself. You say two-thirds by two-thirds is four ninths of a square; and less two-thirds by three dirhems is two roots: and again, two-thirds by three dirhems is two roots; and less three dirhems by less three dirhems is nine dirhems. You have, therefore, four-ninths of a square and nine dirhems less four roots, which are equal to one root. Add the four roots to the one root, then you have five roots, which are equal to four-ninths of a square and nine dirhems. Complete now your square; that is, multiply the four-ninths of a square by two and a fourth, which gives one square; multiply likewise the nine dirhems by two and a quarter; this gives twenty and a quarter; finally, multiply the five roots by two and a quarter; this gives eleven roots and a quarter. You have, therefore, a square and twenty dirhems and a quarter, equal to eleven roots and a quarter. Reduce this according to what I taught you about halving the roots.

---

* $\left[x-\left(\frac{x}{3}+3\right)\right]^2=x$

or $\left[\frac{2x}{3}-3\right]^2=x$

$\frac{4x^2}{9}+9=5x$

$x^2+20\frac{1}{4}=11\frac{1}{4}x$

$x=9$, or $2\frac{1}{4}$

In any circle, the product of its diameter, multiplied by three and one-seventh, will be equal to the periphery. This is the rule generally followed in practical life, though it is not quite exact. The geometricians have two other methods. One of them is, that you multiply the diameter by itself; then by ten, and hereafter take the root of the product; the root will be the periphery. The other method is used by the astronomers among them: it is this, that you multiply the diameter by sixty-two thousand eight hundred and thirty-two and then divide the product by twenty thousand; the quotient is the periphery. Both methods come very nearly to the same effect.*

If you divide the periphery by three and one-seventh, the quotient is the diameter.

The area of any circle will be found by multiplying the moiety of the circumference by the moiety of the diameter; since, in every polygon of equal sides and angles, such as triangles, quadrangles, pentagons, and so on, the area is found by multiplying the moiety of the circumference by the moiety of the diameter of the middle circle that may be drawn through it.

If you multiply the diameter of any circle by itself, and subtract from the product one-seventh and half one-seventh of the same, then the remainder is equal to the area of the circle. This comes very nearly to the same result with the method given above.†

---

* The three formulas are,

$$\text{1st, } 3\tfrac{1}{7}d = p \quad \text{i.e. } 3.1428\,d$$

$$\text{2d, } \sqrt{10d^2} = p \quad \text{i.e. } 3.16227\,d$$

$$\text{3d, } \frac{d \times 62832}{20000} = p \quad \text{i.e. } 3.1416\,d$$

† The area of a circle whose diameter is d is $\pi\frac{d^2}{4} = \frac{22}{7 \times 4}d^2 = \left(1 - \frac{1}{7} - \frac{1}{2 \times 7}\right)d^2$.

Every part of a circle may be compared to a bow. It must be either exactly equal to half the circumference, or less or greater than it. This may be ascertained by the arrow of the bow. When this becomes equal to the moiety of the chord, then the arc is exactly the moiety of the circumference: is it shorter than the moiety of the chord, then the bow is less than half the circumference; is the arrow longer than half the chord, then the bow comprises more than half the circumference.

If some one says: "There is a triangular piece of land, two of its sides having ten yards each, and the basis twelve; what must be the length of one side of a quadrate situated within such a triangle?" the solution is this. At first you ascertain the height of the triangle, by multiplying the moiety of the basis, (which is six) by itself, and subtracting the product, which is thirty-six, from one of the two short sides multiplied by itself, which is one hundred; the remainder is sixty-four: take the root from this; it is eight. This is the height of the triangle. Its area is, therefore, forty-eight yards: such being the product of the height multiplied by the moiety of the basis, which is six. Now we assume that one side of the quadrate inquired for is thing. We multiply it by itself; thus it becomes a square, which we keep in mind. We know that there must remain two triangles on the two sides of the quadrate, and one above it. The two triangles on both sides of it are equal to each other: both having the same height and being rectangular. You find their area by multiplying thing by six less half a thing, which gives six things less half a square. This is the area of both the triangles on the two sides of the quadrate together. The area of the upper triangle will be found by multiplying eight less thing, which is the height, by half one thing. The product is four things less half a square. This altogether is equal to the area of the quadrate plus that of the three triangles: or, ten things are equal to forty-eight, which is the area of the great triangle. One thing from this is four yards and four-fifths of a yard; and this is the length of any side of the quadrate. Here is the figure:

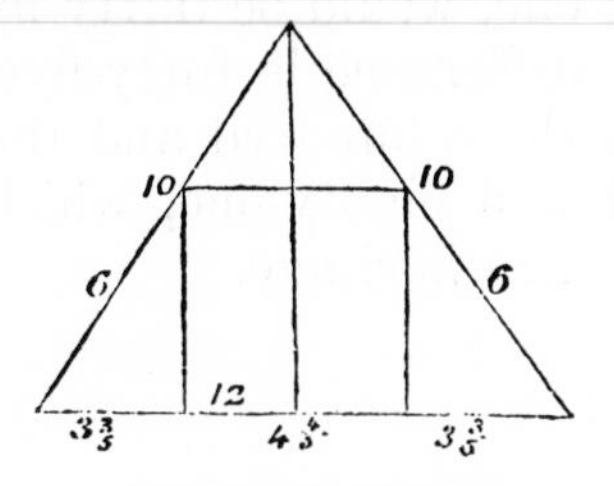

ON LEGACIES.

If he leaves two sons and a daughter,† and bequeaths to some one as much as would be the share of a third son, if he had one; then you must consider, what would be the share of each son, in case he had three. Assume this to be seven, and for the entire heritage take a number, one-fifth of which may be divided into sevenths, and one-seventh of which may be divided into fifths. Such a number is thirty-five. Add to it two-sevenths of the same, namely, ten. This gives forty-five. Herefrom the legatee receives ten, each son fourteen, and the daughter seven.

If he leaves a mother, three sons, and a daughter, and bequeaths to some one as much as the share of one of his sons less the amount of the share of a second daughter, in case he had one; then you distribute the heritage into such a number of parts as may be divided among

† A son is entitled to receive twice as much as a daughter. Were there three sons and one daughter, each son would receive 2/7ths of the residue. Let x be the stranger's legacy.

$$\therefore \tfrac{2}{7}[1-x]=x \quad \therefore x=\tfrac{2}{9}, \text{ and } 1-x=\tfrac{7}{9}$$

Each Son's share. . . . $=\tfrac{2}{5}[1-x]=\tfrac{2}{5}\times\tfrac{7}{9}=\tfrac{14}{45}$

The Daughter's share $=\tfrac{1}{5}[1-x]$ . . . . . . $=\tfrac{7}{45}$

The Stranger's legacy $=\tfrac{2}{9}$ . . . . $=\tfrac{10}{45}$

the actual heirs, and also among the same, if a second daughter were added to them.* Such a number is three hundred and thirty-six. The share of the second daughter, if there were one, would be thirty-five, and that of a son eighty; their difference is forty-five, and this is the legacy. Add to it three hundred and thirty-six, the sum is three hundred and eighty-one, which is the number of parts of the entire heritage.

---

* Let x be the stranger's legacy; $1-x$ is the residue.

A widow's share of the residue is $\frac{1}{6}$th: there remains $\frac{5}{6}[1-x]$, to be distributed among the children.

Since there are 3 sons, and 1 daughter, a son's share is .... $\frac{2}{7} \times \frac{5}{6}[1-x]$

Were there 3 sons and 2 daughters, a daughter's share would be ...... $\frac{1}{8} \times \frac{5}{6}[1-x]$

The difference $= \frac{9}{56} \times \frac{5}{6}[1-x]$

$\therefore x = \frac{45}{336}[1-x]$ $\quad\quad \therefore x = \frac{45}{381}$

$1-x = \frac{336}{381}$; the widow's share $= \frac{56}{381}$

the daughter's share $= \frac{40}{381}$

GOTTFRIED WILHELM v. LEIBNIZ

(1646—1716)

The universal genius of Gottfried von Leibniz was early in evidence and his extraordinary power marked all of his varied activities in law, diplomacy, philosophy, theology, mathematics and science. Leibniz was born on June 21, 1646 at Leipzig. He was the only son of his father's third wife. His father died when Gottfried was only six years old. Before he was twelve years of age, Leibniz was fluent in Latin and he had begun the study of Greek. Permission to use his father's law library was then granted to him and he entered upon preparatory studies for a career at law. At fifteen he was enrolled in the university at Leipzig, where he studied law, philosophy and mathematics. At the age of seventeen, he wrote his *De Principiis Individuis.* At twenty he experienced the sharp turns of fortune that shaped the course of his eventful and turbulent life. Refused a law degree at Leipzig in 1666 because of his youth, it was said, he went to Altdorf where, in the same year, he was not only granted a degree but also given an offer of a professorship at that university. At the age of twenty-one, Leibniz had already joined the ranks of serious writers on philosophy, mathematics and jurisprudence. Refusing the position at Altdorf, he accompanied the Baron v. Boyneburg to Frankfort. There, as the Baron's protege and friend, he entered upon a political career in the service of the Elector of Mainz. Two of his political writings, *Thoughts on Public Safety* and *Consilium Aegyptiacum,* intended to benefit the German States, brought him an appointment as an aide to a diplomatic mission to Paris on behalf of the Elector. Strongly attracted to the society of the leading scientists and mathematicians in Paris, Leibniz renewed his mathematical studies at this time, and attacked the current problems in mathematics and science with characteristic gusto. By 1673 he had published articles on logic, natural philosophy, mathematics, mechanics, and optics, as well as on theology, law and politics, making some original contributions in each of these fields. Improving on Pascal's calculating machine he devised one which performed the four fundamental operations and also extracted roots. Nevertheless, a professorship at Paris and the academic life which he now sought, were denied to him, and in 1676 Leibniz entered the service of the Duke of Hanover. He returned to Germany from Paris by a route which enabled him to visit London and Amsterdam and afforded him an opportunity of meeting with the great mathematicians and scientists of England and Holland.

Leibniz remained in the service of the Brunswick family for forty years to the day of his death. His duties as librarian of the great Hanover library did not preclude his continuing political and scientific activities. Under his aegis the *Akademie der Wissenschaften* was established in Berlin. His genealogical researches in Italy and elsewhere in Europe established the Hanoverian claim of succession to the throne of Great Britain. He planned to write an encyclopaedia. An enormous mass of his writings found after his death attested to his preparatory efforts. Unfortunately these writings were in a disorganized state and some were no more than fragments of projected articles. Leibniz's heirs released his entire literary remains to the Hanover National Library for a nominal sum. In addition to this large literary legacy, Leibniz also left a fairly large amount of money, most of which was found cached in a chest in his home.

It was Leibniz's lot to be involved almost continually in one controversy or another. The most widely publicized of these was his dispute with Newton over priority in the discovery of the calculus, but every field in which he wrote offered some feature of controversy. His death in 1716 interrupted his famous disputative correspondence with Samuel Clarke. During the period immediately after his death, Leibniz was known principally as a philosopher. In the modern view, his contributions to mathematics take on a larger significance. Broad applications of the science of symbolism to philosophy, to the art of invention, and to other fields of learning, continued to interest him throughout his life. His first thoughts on the concept of a symbolic logic appeared in his *De Arte combinatoria* (1666), and he returned to his fundamental idea again and again, clarifying, emending and implementing it. Two fragments found among his papers contain Leibniz's introduction to symbolic logic. They clearly establish him as one of the founders of the science.

●

TWO FRAGMENTS FROM LEIBNIZ

(Translated from the Latin of Gehrhardt's text, *Die Philosophischen Schriften von G. W. Leibniz, Band VII,* "*Scientia Generalis. Characteristica,*" XIX and XX.)

From *A Survey of Symbolic Logic*

by Clarence I. Lewis

These two fragments represent the final form of Leibniz's "universal calculus": their date is not definitely known, but almost certainly they were written after 1685.

Of the two, XX is in all respects superior, as the reader will see, but XIX also is included because it contains the operation of "subtraction" which is dropped in XX. Leibniz's comprehension of the fact that + and — (or, in the more usual notation, "multiplication" and "division") are not simple inverses in this calculus, and his appreciation of the complexity thus introduced, is the chief point of interest in XIX. The distinction of "subtraction" (in intension) and negation, is also worthy of note. It will be observed that, in both these fragments, $A + B$ (or $A \oplus B$) may be interpreted in two ways: (1) As "both A and B" in intension; (2) as "either A or B", the class made up of the two classes A and B, in extension. The "logical" illustrations mostly follow the first interpretation, but in XX (see esp. *scholium to defs.* 3, 4, 5, *and* 6) there are examples of the application to logical classes in extension. The illustration of the propositions by the relations of line-segments also exhibits the application to relations of extension. Attention is specifically called to the parallelism between relations of intension and relations of extension in the remark appended to prop. 15, in XX. The *scholium to axioms* 1 *and* 2, in XX, is of particular interest as an illustration of the way in which Leibniz anticipates later logistic developments.

The Latin of the text is rather careless, and constructions are sometimes obscure. Gehrhardt notes (p. 232) that the manuscript contains numerous interlineations and is difficult to read in many places.

XIX

Non inelegans specimen demonstrandi in abstractis[1]

Def. 1. Two terms are the *same* (*eadem*) if one can be substituted for the other without altering the truth of any statement (*salva veritate*). If we have A and B, and

[1] This title appears in the manuscript, but Leibniz has afterward crossed it out. Although pretentious, it expresses admirably the intention of the fragment, as well as of the next.

A enters into some true proposition, and the substitution of B for A wherever it appears, results in a new proposition which is likewise true, and if this can be done for every such proposition, then A and B are said to be the *same;* and conversely, if A and B are the same, they can be substituted for one another as I have said. Terms which are the same are also called *coincident* (*coincidentia*); A and A are, of course, said to be the same, but if A and B are the same, they are called *coincident.*

Def. 2. Terms which are not the same, that is, terms which cannot always be substituted for one another, are *different* (*diversa*). *Corollary.* Whence also, whatever terms are not different are the same.

Charact. 1.[2] $A = B$ signifies that A and B are the *same,* or *coincident.*

Charact. 2.[3] $A \neq B$, or $B \neq A$, signifies that A and B are *different.*

Def. 3. If a plurality of terms taken together coincide with one, then any one of the plurality is said to *be in* (*inesse*) or to *be contained in* (*contineri*) that one with which they coincide, and that one is called the *container.* And conversely, if any term be contained in another, then it will be one of a plurality which taken together coincide with that other. For example, if A and B taken together coincide with L, then A, or B, will be called the *inexistent* (*inexistens*) or the *contained;* and L will be called the *container.* However, it can happen that the container and the contained coincide, as for example, if (A and B) $= L$, and A and L coincide, for in that case B will contain nothing which is different from A. . . .[4]

Scholium. Not every inexistent thing is a part, nor is every container a whole—e. g., an inscribed square and a diameter are both in a circle, and the square, to be sure, is a certain part of the circle, but the diameter is not a

---

[2] We write $A = B$ where the text has $A \infty B$.

[3] We write $A \neq B$ where the text has A non ∞B.

[4] Lacuna in the text, followed by "significet A, significabit Nihil"

part of it. We must, then, add something for the accurate explanation of the concept of whole and part, but this is not the place for it. And not only can those things which are not parts be contained in, but also they can be subtracted (or "abstracted", *detrahi*); e. g., the center can be subtracted from a circle so that all points except the center shall be in the remainder; for this remainder is the locus of all points within the circle whose distance from the circumference is less than the radius, and the difference of this locus from the circle is a point, namely the center. Similarly the locus of all points which are moved, in a sphere in which two distinct points on a diameter remain unmoved, is as if you should subtract from the sphere the axis or diameter passing through the two unmoved points.

On the same supposition [that A and B together coincide with L], A and B taken together are called *constituents* (*constituentia*), and L is called *that which is constituted* (*constitutum*).

Charact. 3. $A + B = L$ signifies that A *is in* or *is contained in* L.

Scholium. Although A and B may have something in common, so that the two taken together are greater than L itself, nevertheless what we have here stated, or now state, will still hold. It will be well to make this clear by an example: Let L denote the straight line RX, and A denote a part of it, say the line RS, and B denote another part, say the line XY. Let either of these parts, RS or

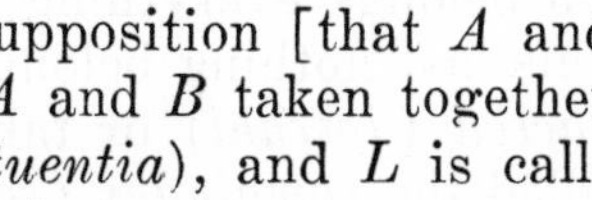

$$\begin{matrix} R & Y & S & X \\ \bullet\!\!-\!\!-\!\!- & \bullet\!\!-\!\!-\!\!- & \bullet\!\!-\!\!-\!\!- & \bullet \end{matrix}$$

XY, be greater than half the whole line, RX; then certainly it cannot be said that $A + B$ equals L, or $RS + XY$ *equals* RX. For inasmuch as YS is a common part of RS and XY, $RS + XY$ will be equal to $RX + SY$. And yet it can truly be said that the lines RS and XY together *coincide* with the line RS.[5]

[5] Italics ours.

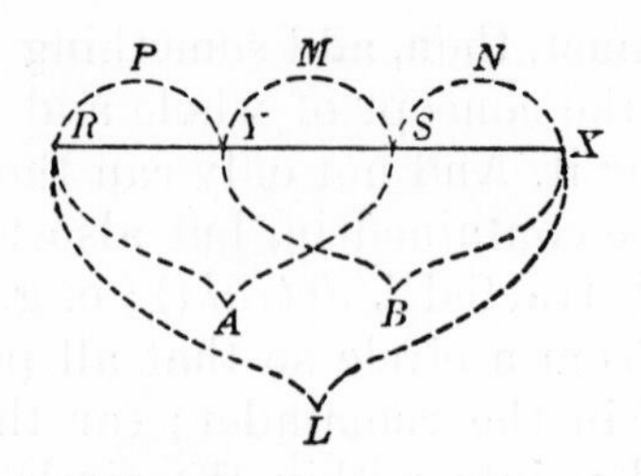

Def. 4. If some term M is in A and also in B, it is said to be common to them, and they are said to be *communicating* (*communicantia*).[6] But if they have nothing in common, as A and N (the lines RS and XS, for example), they are said to be *non-communicating* (*incommunicantia*).

Def. 5. If A is in L in such wise that there is another term, N, in which belongs everything in L except what is in A, and of this last nothing belongs in N, then A is said to be *subtracted* (*detrahi*) or taken away (*removeri*), and N is called the *remainder* (*residuum*).

Charact. 4. $L - A = N$ signifies that L is the container from which if A be *subtracted* the *remainder* is N.

Def. 6. If some one term is supposed to coincide with a plurality of terms which are added (*positis*) or subtracted (*remotis*), then the plurality of terms are called the *constituents,* and the one term is called the thing constituted.[7]

Scholium. Thus all terms which are in anything are constituents, but the reverse does not hold; for example, $L - A = N$, in which case L is not in A.

Def. 7. Constitution (that is, addition or subtraction) is either tacit or expressed,—N or $- M$ the tacit constitution of M itself, as A or $- A$ in which N is. The expressed constitution of N is obvious.[8]

Def. 8. *Compensation* is the operation of adding and

[6] The text here has "communicatia", clearly a misprint.

[7] Leibniz's idea seems to be that if $A + N = L$ then L is "constituted" by A and N, and also if $L - A = N$ then L and A "constitute" N. But it may mean that if $L - A = N$, then A and N "constitute" L.

[8] This translation is literal: the meaning is obscure, but see the diagram above.

subtracting the same thing in the same expression, both the addition and the subtraction being expressed [as $A + M — M$]. *Destruction* is the operation of dropping something on account of compensation, so that it is no longer expressed, and for $M — M$ putting Nothing.

Axiom 1. If a term be added to itself, nothing new is constituted or $A + A = A$.

Scholium. With numbers, to be sure, 2 + 2 makes 4, or two coins added to two coins make four coins, but in that case the two added are not identical with the former two; if they were, nothing new would arise, and it would be as if we should attempt in jest to make six eggs out of three by first counting 3 eggs, then taking away one and counting the remaining 2, and then taking away one more and counting the remaining 1.

Axiom 2. If the same thing be added and subtracted, then however it enter into the constitution of another term, the result coincides with Nothing. Or A (however many times it is added in constituting any expression) — A (however many times it is subtracted from that same expression) = Nothing.

Scholium. Hence $A — A$ or $(A + A —) — A$ or A $(A + A)$, etc. = Nothing. For by axiom 1, the expression in each case reduces to $A — A$.

Postulate 1. Any plurality of terms whatever can be added to constitute a single term; as for example, if we have A and B, we can write $A + B$, and call this L.

Post. 2. Any term, A, can be subtracted from that in which it is, namely $A + B$ or L, if the remainder be given as B, which added to A constitutes the container L—that is, on this supposition [that $A + B = L$] the remainder $L — A$ can be found.

Scholium. In accordance with this postulate, we shall give, later on, a method for finding the difference between two terms, one of which, A, is contained in the other, L, even though the remainder, which together with A constitutes L, should not be given—that is, a method for finding $L — A$, or $A + B — A$, although A and L only are given, and B is not.

Theorem 1

Terms which are the same with a third, are the same with each other.

If $A = B$ and $B = C$, then $A = C$. For if in the proposition $A = B$ (true by hyp.) C be substituted for B (which can be done by def. 1, since, by hyp., $B = C$), the result is $A = C$. Q.E.D.

Theorem 2

If one of two terms which are the same be different from a third term, then the other of the two will be different from it also.

If $A = B$ and $B \neq C$, then $A \neq C$. For if in the proposition $B \neq C$ (true by hyp.) A be substituted for B (which can be done by def. 1, since, by hyp., $A = B$), the result is $A \neq C$. Q.E.D.

[Theorem in the margin of the manuscript.]

Here might be inserted the following theorem: *Whatever is in one of two coincident terms, is in the other also.*

If A is in B and $B = C$, then also A is in C. For in the proposition A is in B (true by hyp.) let C be substituted for B.

Theorem 3

If terms which coincide be added to the same term, the results will coincide.

If $A = B$, then $A + C = B + C$. For if in the proposition $A + C = A + C$ (true *per se*) you substitute B for A in one place (which can be done by def. 1, since $A = B$), it gives $A + C = B + C$. Q.E.D.

Corollary. *If terms which coincide be added to terms which coincide, the results will coincide.* If $A = B$ and $L = M$, then $A + L = B + M$. For (by the present theorem) since $L = M$, $A + L = A + M$, and in this assertion putting B for A in one place (since by hyp. $A = B$) gives $A + L = B + M$. Q.E.D.

Theorem 4

A container of the container is a container of the contained; or if that in which something is, be itself in a third thing, then that which is in it will be in that same third thing—that is, if A is in B and B is in C, then also A is in C.

For A is in B (by hyp.), hence (by def. 3 or charact. 3) there is some term, which we may call L, such that $A + L = B$. Similarly, since B is in C (by hyp.), $B + M = C$, and in this assertion putting $A + L$ for B (since we show that these coincide) we have $A + L + M = C$. But putting N for $L + M$ (by post. 1) we have $A + N = C$. Hence (by def. 3) A is in C. Q.E.D.

Theorem 5

Whatever contains terms individually contains also that which is constituted of them.

If A is in C and B is in C, then $A + B$ (constituted of A and B, def. 4) is in C. For since A is in C, there will be some term M such that $A + M = C$ (by def. 3). Similarly, since B is in C, $B + N = C$. Putting these together (by the corollary to th. 3), we have $A + M + B + N = C + C$. But $C + C = C$ (by ax. 1), hence $A + M + B + N = C$. And therefore (by def. 3) $A + B$ is in C. Q.E.D.[9]

Theorem 6

Whatever is constituted of terms which are contained, is in that which is constituted of the containers.

If A is in M and B is in N, then $A + B$ is in $M + N$. For A is in M (by hyp.) and M is in $M + N$ (by def. 3), hence A is in $M + N$ (by th. 4). Similarly, B is in N (by hyp.) and N is in $M + N$ (by def. 3), hence B is in $M + N$ (by th. 4). But if A is in $M + N$ and B is in $M + N$, then also (by th. 5) $A + B$ is in $M + N$. Q.E.D.

Theorem 7

If any term be added to that in which it is, then nothing new is constituted; or if B is in A, then $A + B = A$.

[9] In the margin of the manuscript at this point Leibniz has an untranslatable note, the sense of which is to remind him that he must insert illustrations of these propositions in common language.

For if B is in A, then [for some C] $B + C = A$ (def. 3). Hence (by th. 3) $A + B = B + C + B = B + C$ (by ax. 1) $= A$ (by the above). Q.E.D.

Converse of the Preceding Theorem

If by the addition of any term to another nothing new is constituted, then the term added is in the other.

If $A + B = A$, then B is in A; for B is in $A + B$ (def. 3), and $A + B = A$ (by hyp.). Hence B is in A (by the principle which is inserted between ths. 2 and 3). Q.E.D.

Theorem 8

If terms which coincide be subtracted from terms which coincide, the remainders will coincide.

If $A = L$ and $B = M$, then $A - B = L - M$. For $A - B = A - B$ (true *per se*), and the substitution, on one or the other side, of L for A and M for B, gives $A - B = L - M$. Q.E.D.

[Note in the margin of the manuscript.] In dealing with concepts, *subtraction* (*detractio*) is one thing, negation another. For example, "non-rational man" is absurd or impossible. But we may say; An ape is a man except that it is not rational. [They are] men except in those respects in which man differs from the beasts, as in the case of Grotius's Jumbo[10] (*Homines nisi qua bestiis differt homo, ut in Jambo Grotii*). "Man" — "rational" is something different from "non-rational man". For "man" — "rational" = "brute". But "non-rational man" is impossible. "Man" — "animal" — "rational" is Nothing. Thus subtractions can give Nothing or simple non-existence—even less than nothing—but negations can give the impossible.[11]

[10] Apparently an allusion to some description of an ape by Grotius.

[11] This is not an unnecessary and hair-splitting distinction, but on the contrary, perhaps the best evidence of Leibniz's accurate comprehension of the logical calculus which appears in the manuscripts. It has been generally misjudged by the commentators, because the commentators have not understood the logic of intension. The distinction of the merely non-existent and the impossible (self-contradictory or absurd) is absolutely essential to any calculus of relations in intension. And this distinction of subtraction (or in the more usual notation, division) from negation, is equally necessary. It is by the confusion of these two that the calculuses of Lambert and Castillon break down.

XX

Def. 1. Terms which can be substituted for one another wherever we please without altering the truth of any statement (*salva veritate*), are the *same* (*eadem*) or *coincident* (*coincidentia*). For example, "triangle" and "trilateral", for in every proposition demonstrated by Euclid concerning "triangle", "trilateral" can be substituted without loss of truth.

$A = B$[12] signifies that A and B are the same, or as we say of the straight line XY and the straight line YX, $XY = YX$, or the shortest path of a [point] moving from X to Y coincides with that from Y to X.

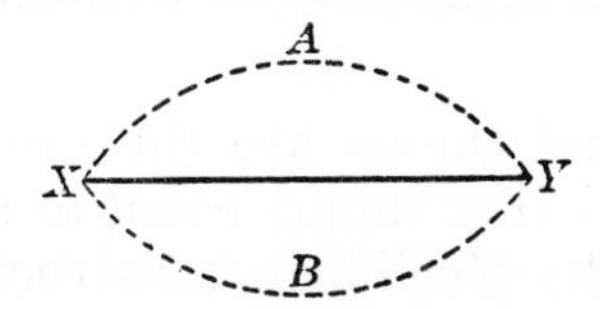

Def. 2. Terms which are not the same, that is, terms which cannot always be substituted for one another, are *different* (*diversa*). Such are "circle" and "triangle", or "square" (supposed perfect, as it always is in Geometry) and "equilateral quadrangle", for we can predicate this last of a rhombus, of which "square" cannot be predicated.

$A \neq B$[13] *signifies* that A and B are different, as for example, the straight lines XY and RS.

R *Y* *S* *X*

Prop. 1. *If $A = B$, then also $B = A$. If anything be the same with another, then that other will be the same with it.* For since $A = B$ (by hyp.), it follows (by def. 1) that in the statement $A = B$ (true by hyp.) B can be substituted for A and A for B; hence we have $B = A$.

---

[12] $A = B$ for $A \infty B$, as before.

[13] $A \neq B$ for A non ∞B, as before.

Prop. 2. *If $A \neq B$, then also $B \neq A$. If any term be different from another, then that other will be different from it.* Otherwise we should have $B = A$, and in consequence (by the preceding prop.) $A = B$, which is contrary to hypothesis.

Prop. 3. *If $A = B$ and $B = C$, then $A = C$. Terms which coincide with a third term coincide with each other.* For if in the statement $A = B$ (true by hyp.) C be substituted for B (by def. 1, since $A = B$), the resulting proposition will be true.

Coroll. If $A = B$ and $B = C$ and $C = D$, then $A = D$; and so on. For $A = B = C$, hence $A = C$ (by the above prop.). Again, $A = C = D$; hence (by the above prop.) $A = D$.

Thus since equal things are the same in magnitude, the consequence is that things equal to a third are equal to each other. The Euclidean construction of an equilateral triangle makes each side equal to the base, whence it results that they are equal to each other. If anything be moved in a circle, it is sufficient to show that the paths of any two successive periods, or returns to the same point, coincide, from which it is concluded that the paths of any two periods whatever coincide.

Prop. 4. *If $A = B$ and $B \neq C$, then $A \neq C$. If of two things which are the same with each other, one differ from a third, then the other also will differ from that third.* For if in the proposition $B \neq C$ (true by hyp.) A be substituted for B, we have (by def. 1, since $A = B$) the true proposition $A \neq C$.

Def. 3. *A is in L*, or *L contains A*, is the same as to say that L can be made to coincide with a plurality of terms, taken together, of which A is one.

Def. 4. Moreover, all those terms such that whatever is in them is in L, are together called *components* (*componentia*) with respect to the L thus *composed* or constituted.

$B \oplus N = L$ *signifies* that B is in L; and that B and N

together compose or constitute L.[14] The same thing holds for a larger number of terms.

Def. 5. I call terms one of which is in the other *subalternates* (*subalternantia*), as A and B if either A is in B or B is in A.

Def. 6. Terms neither of which is in the other [I call] *disparate* (*disparata*).

Axiom 1. $B \oplus N = N \oplus B$, or transposition here alters nothing.

Post. 2. Any plurality of terms, as A and B, can be added to compose a single term, $A \oplus B$ or L.

Axiom 2. $A \oplus A = A$. If nothing new be added, then nothing new results, or repetition here alters nothing. (For 4 coins and 4 other coins are 8 coins, but not 4 coins and the same 4 coins already counted).

Prop. 5. *If A is in B and $A = C$, then C is in B. That which coincides with the inexistent, is inexistent.* For in the proposition, A is in B (true by hyp.), the substitution of C for A (by def. 1 of coincident terms, since, by hyp., $A = C$) gives, C is in B.

Prop. 6. *If C is in B and $A = B$, then C is in A. Whatever is in one of two coincident terms, is in the other also.* For in the proposition, C is in B, the substitution of A for C (since $A = C$) gives, A is in B. (This is the converse of the preceding.)

Prop. 7. *A is in A. Any term whatever is contained in itself.* For A is in $A \oplus A$ (by def. of "inexistent", that is, by def. 3) and $A \oplus A = A$ (by ax. 2). Therefore (by prop. 6), A is in A.

Prop. 8. *If $A = B$, then A is in B. Of terms which coincide, the one is in the other.* This is obvious from the preceding. For (by the preceding) A is in A—that is (by hyp.), in B.

Prop. 9. *If $A = B$, then $A \oplus C = B \oplus C$. If terms which coincide be added to the same term, the results will coincide.* For if in the proposition, $A \oplus C = A \oplus C$ (true

[14] In this fragment, as distinguished from XIX, the logical or "real" sum is represented by $\oplus$. Leibniz has carelessly omitted the circle in many places, but we write $\oplus$ wherever this relation is intended.

per se), for A in one place be substituted B which coincides with it (by def. 1), we have $A \oplus C = B \oplus C$.

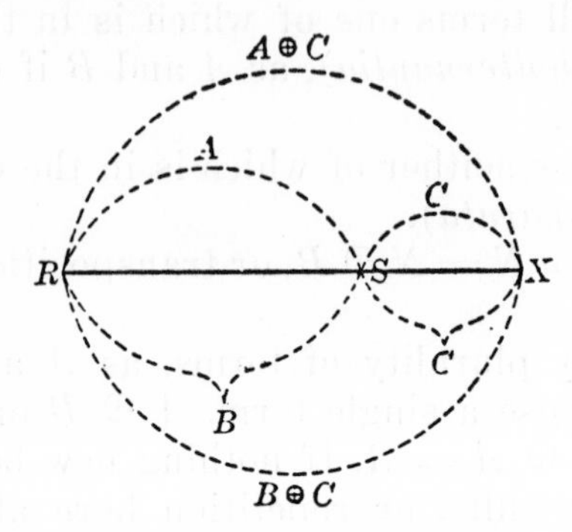

A "triangle" B "trilateral"	coincide

$A \oplus C$ "equilateral triangle" $B \oplus C$ "equilateral trilateral"	coincide

Scholium. This proposition cannot be converted—much less, the two which follow.

Prop. 10. *If* $A = L$ *and* $B = M$, *then* $A \oplus B = L \oplus M$. *If terms which coincide be added to terms which coincide, the results will coincide.* For since $B = M$, $A \oplus B = A \oplus M$ (by the preceding), and putting L for the second A (since, by hyp., $A = L$) we have $A \oplus B = L \oplus M$.

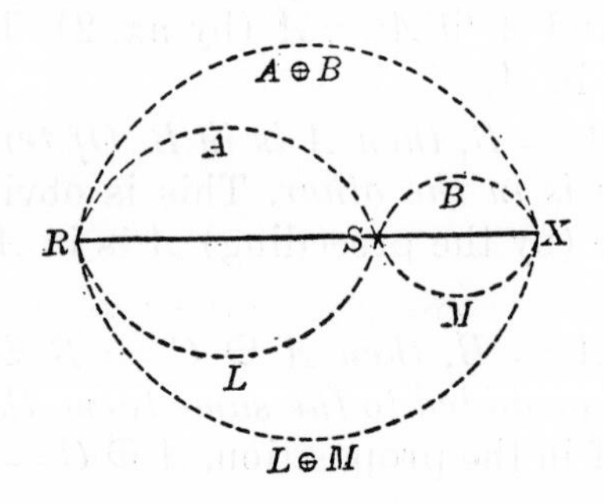

A "triangle", and L "trilateral" coincide. B "regular" coincides with M "most capacious of equally-many-sided figures with equal perimeters". "Regular triangle" coincides with "most capacious of trilaterals making equal peripheries out of three sides".

Scholium. This proposition cannot be converted, for if $A \oplus B = L \oplus M$ and $A = L$, still it does not follow that that $B = M$,—and much less can the following be converted.

Prop. 11. *If* $A = L$ *and* $B = M$ *and* $C = N$, *then* $A \oplus B \oplus C = L \oplus M \oplus N$. And so on. *If there be any number of terms under consideration, and an equal number of them coincide with an equal number of others, term for term, then that which is composed of the former coincides with that which is composed of the latter.* For (by the preceding, since $A = L$ and $B = M$) we have $A \oplus B = L \oplus M$. Hence, since $C = N$, we have (again by the preceding) $A \oplus B \oplus C = L \oplus M \oplus N$.

Prop. 12. *If* B *is in* L, *then* $A \oplus B$ *will be in* $A \oplus L$. *If the same term be added to what is contained and to what contains it, the former result is contained in the latter.* For $L = B \oplus N$ (by def. of "inexistent"), and $A \oplus B$ is in $B \oplus N \oplus A$ (by the same), that is, $A \oplus B$ is in $L \oplus A$.

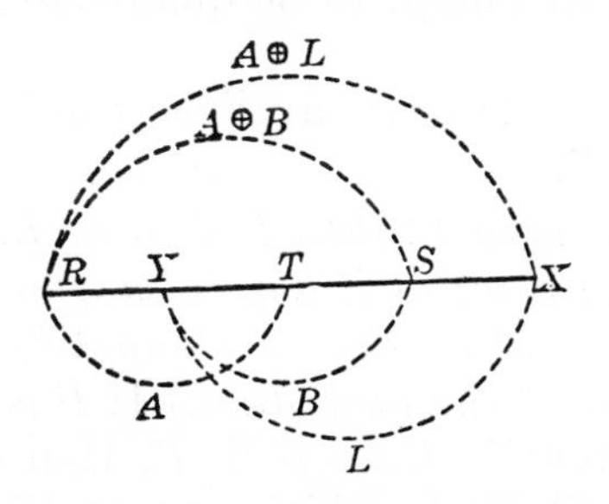

B "equilateral", L "regular", A "quadrilateral". "Equilateral" is in or is attribute of "regular". Hence "equilateral quadrilateral" is in "regular quadrilateral" or "perfect square". YS is in RX. Hence $RT \oplus YS$, or RS, is in $RT \oplus RX$, or in RX.

Scholium. This proposition cannot be converted; for if $A \oplus B$ is in $A \oplus L$, it does not follow that B is in L.

Prop. 13. *If* $L \oplus B = L$, *then* B *is in* L. *If the addition of any term to another does not alter that other, then the term added is in the other.* For B is in $L \oplus B$ (by def. of "inexistent") and $L \oplus B = L$ (by hyp.), hence (by prop. 6) B is in L.

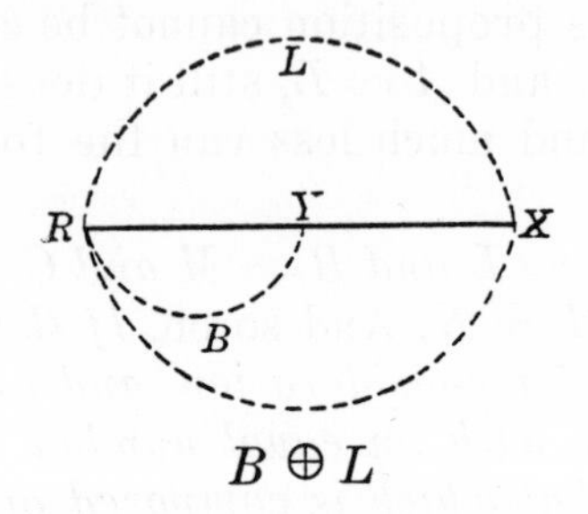

$RY \oplus RX = RX$. Hence RY is in RX.
RY is in RX. Hence $RY \oplus RX = RX$.
Let L be "parallelogram" (every side of which is parallel to some side),[15] B be "quadrilateral".
"Quadrilateral parallelogram" is in the same as "parallelogram".
Therefore to be quadrilateral is in [the intension of] "parallelogram".
Reversing the reasoning, to be quadrilateral is in "parallelogram".
Therefore, "quadrilateral parallelogram" is the same as "parallelogram".

Prop. 14. *If B is in L, then $L \oplus B = L$. Subalternates compose nothing new; or if any term which is in another be added to it, it will produce nothing different from that other.* (*Converse of the preceding.*) If B is in L, then (by def. of "inexistent") $L = B \oplus P$. Hence (by prop. 9) $L \oplus B = B \oplus P \quad \oplus B$, which (by ax. 2) is $= B \oplus P$, which (by hyp.) is $= L$.

Prop. 15. *If A is in B and B is in C, then also A is in C. What is contained in the contained, is contained in the container.* For A is in B (by hyp.), hence $A \oplus L = B$ (by def. of "inexistent"). Similarly, since B is in C, $B \oplus M = C$, and putting $A \oplus L$ for B in this statement (since

[15] Leibniz uses "parallelogram" in its current meaning, though his language may suggest a wider use.

we have shown that these coincide), we have $A \oplus L \oplus M = C$. Therefore (by def. of "inexistent") A is in C.

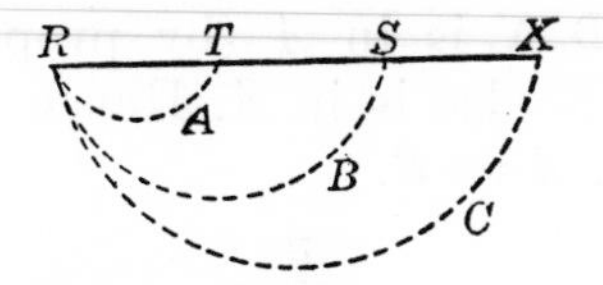

RT is in *RS*, and *RS* in *RX*.

Hence *RT* is in *RX*.

A "quadrilateral", *B* "parallelogram", *C* "rectangle".

To be quadrilateral is in [the intension of] "parallelogram", and to be parallelogram is in "rectangle" (that is, a figure every angle of which is a right angle). If instead of concepts *per se*, we consider individual things comprehended by the concept, and put *A* for "rectangle", *B* for "parallelogram", *C* for "quadrilateral", the relations of these can be inverted. For all rectangles are comprehended in the number of the parallelograms, and all parallelograms in the number of the quadrilaterals. Hence also, all rectangles are contained amongst (*in*) the quadrilaterals. In the same way, all men are contained amongst (*in*) all the animals, and all animals amongst all the material substances, hence all men are contained amongst the material substances. And conversely, the concept of material substance is in the concept of animal, and the concept of animal is in the concept of man. For to be man contains [or implies] being animal.

Scholium. This proposition cannot be converted, and much less can the following.

Coroll. If $A \oplus N$ is in *B*, *N* also is in *B*. For N is in $A \oplus N$ (by def. of "inexistent").

Prop. 16. *If A is in B and B is in C and C is in D, then also A is in D.* And so on. *That which is contained in what is contained by the contained, is in the container.* For if *A* is in *B* and *B* is in *C*, *A* also is in *C* (by the preceding). Whence if *C* is in *D*, then also (again by the preceding) *A* is in *D*.

Prop. 17. *If A is in B and B is in A, then A = B. Terms which contain each other coincide.* For if A is in B, then $A \oplus N = B$ (by def. of "inexistent"). But B is in A (by hyp.), hence $A \oplus N$ is in A (by prop. 5). Hence (by coroll. prop. 15) N also is in A. Hence (by prop. 14) $A = A \oplus N$, that is, $A = B$.

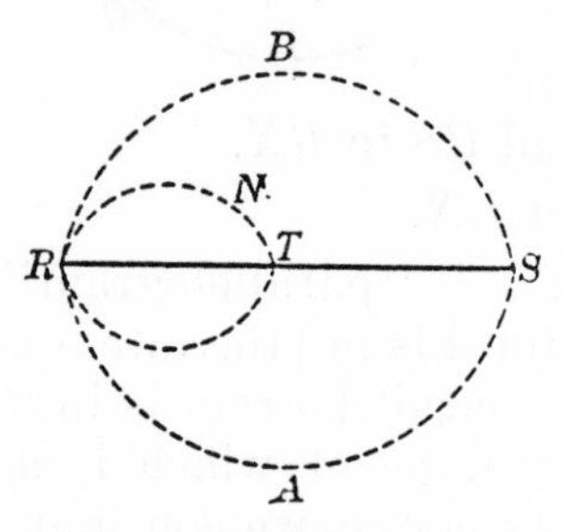

$RT, N; RS, A; SR \oplus RT, B$.

To be trilateral is in [the intension of] "triangle", and to be triangle is in "trilateral". Hence "triangle" and "trilateral" coincide. Similarly, to be omniscient is to be omnipotent.

Prop. 18. *If A is in L and B is in L, then also $A \oplus B$ is in L. What is composed of two, each contained in a third, is itself contained in that third.* For since A is in L (by hyp.), it can be seen that $A \oplus M = L$ (by def. of "inexistent"). Similarly, since B is in L, it can be seen that $B \oplus N = L$. Putting these together, we have (by prop. 10) $A \oplus M \oplus B \oplus N = L \oplus L$. Hence (by ax. 2)[16] $A \oplus M \oplus B \oplus N = L$. Hence (by def. of "inexistent") $A \oplus B$ is in L.

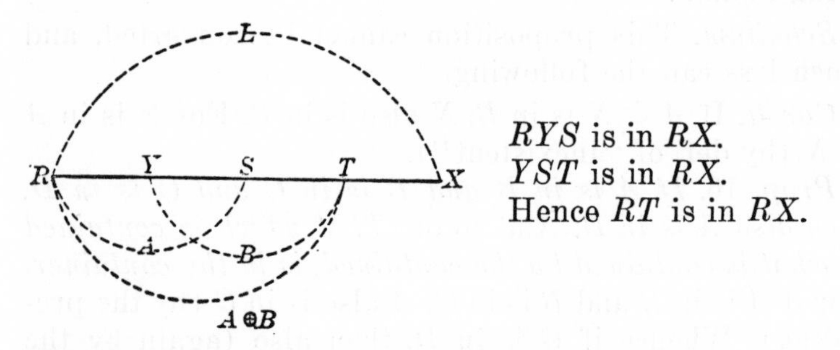

[16] The number of the axiom is given in the text as 5, a misprint.

A "equiangular", B "equilateral", $A \oplus B$ "equiangular equilateral" or "regular", L "square". "Equiangular" is in [the intension of] "square", and "equilateral" is in "square". Hence "regular" is in "square".

Scholium to defs. 3, 4, 5, *and* 6. We say that the concept of the genus *is in* the concept of the species; the individuals of the species amongst (*in*) the individuals of the genus; a part in the whole; and indeed the ultimate and indivisible in the continuous, as a point is in a line, although a point is not a part of the line. Likewise the concept of the attribute or predicate is in the concept of the subject. And in general this conception is of the widest application. We also speak of that which is in something as contained in that in which it is. We are not here concerned with the notion of "contained" in general—with the manner in which those things which are "in" are related to one another and to that which contains them. Thus our demonstrations cover also those things which compose something in the distributive sense, as all the species together compose the genus. Hence all the inexistent things which suffice to constitute a container, or in which are all things which are in the container, are said to compose that container; as for example, $A \oplus B$ are said to *compose* L, if A, B, and L denote the straight lines RS, YX, and RX, for $RS \oplus YX = RX$. And such parts which complete the whole, I am accustomed to call "cointegrants", especially if they have no common part; if they have a common part, they are called "co-members", as RS and RX. Whence it is clear that the same thing can be composed in many different ways if the things of which it is composed are themselves composite. Indeed if the resolution could finally be carried to infinity, the variations of composition would be infinite. Thus all synthesis and analysis depends upon the principles here laid down. And if those things which are contained are homogeneous with that in which they are contained, they are called parts and the container is called the whole. If two parts, however chosen, are such that a third can be found having a part of one and a part of the other in common, then that which is composed of them is continuous. Which illustrates by what small and simple additions one concept arises from another. And I call by the name "subalternates" those things one of which is in the other, as the species in the genus, the straight line RS in the straight line RX; "disparates" where the opposite is the case, as the straight lines RS and YX, two species of the same genus, perfect metal and imperfect metal—and particularly, members of the different divisions of the same whole, which (members) have something in common, as for example, if you divide "metal" into "perfect" and "imperfect", and again into "soluble in *aqua fortis*" and "insoluble", it is clear that "metal which is insoluble in *aqua fortis*" and "perfect metal" are two disparate things, and there is metal which is perfect, or is always capable of being fulminated in a cupel,[24] and yet is soluble in *aqua fortis*, as silver, and on the other hand, there is imperfect metal which is insoluble in *aqua fortis*, as tin.

Scholium to axioms 1 *and* 2. Since the ideal form of the general [or ideal form in general, *speciosa generalis*] is nothing but the representation of combinations by means of symbols, and their manipulation, and the discoverable laws of combination are various,[25] it results from this that various modes of computation arise. In this place, however, we have nothing to do with the theory of the variations which consist simply in changes of order [i. e., the theory of permutations], and AB [more consistently, $A \oplus B$] is for us the same as BA [or $B \oplus A$]. And also we here take no account of repetition—that is AA [more consistently, $A \oplus A$] is for us the same as A. Thus wherever these laws just mentioned can be used, the present calculus can be applied. It is obvious that it can also be used in the composition of absolute concepts, where neither laws of order nor of repetition

[24] The text here has " . . . fulminabile persistens in capella": the correction is obvious.

[25] " . . . variaeque sint combinandi leges excogitabiles, . . . " "Excogitabiles", "discoverable by imagination or invention", is here significant of Leibniz's theory of the relation between the "universal calculus" and the progress of science.

obtain; thus to say "warm and light" is the same as to say "light and warm", and to say "warm fire" or "white milk", after the fashion of the poets, is pleonasm; white milk is nothing different from milk, and rational man—that is, rational animal which is rational—is nothing different from rational animal. The same thing is true when certain given things are said to be contained in (*inexistere*) certain things. For the real addition of the same is a useless repetition. When two and two are said to make four, the latter two must be different from the former. If they were the same, nothing new would arise, and it would be as if one should in jest attempt to make six eggs out of three by first counting 3 eggs, then taking away one and counting the remaining 2, and then taking away one more and counting the remaining 1. But in the calculus of numbers and magnitudes, A or B or any other symbol does not signify a certain object but anything you please with that number of congruent parts, for any two feet whatever are denoted by 2; if foot is the unit or measure, then $2 \oplus 2$ makes the new thing 4, and 3 times 3 the new thing 9, for it is presupposed that the things added are always different (although of the same magnitude); but the opposite is the case with certain things, as with lines. Suppose we describe by a moving [point] the straight line, $RY \oplus YX = RYX$ or $P \oplus B = L$, going from R to X. If we suppose this same [point] then to return from X to Y and stop there, although it does indeed describe YX or B a second time, it produces nothing different than if it had described YX once. Thus $L \oplus B$ is the same as L—that is, $P \oplus B \oplus B$ or $RY \oplus YX \oplus XY$ is the same as $RY \oplus YX$. This caution is of much importance in making judgments, by means of the magnitude and motion of those things which generate[26] or describe, concerning the magnitude of those things which are generated or described. For care must be taken either that

[26] Reading "generant" for "generantur"—a correction which is not absolutely necessary, since a motion which generates a line is also itself generated; but, as the context shows, "generare" and "describere" are here synonymous.

one [step in the process] shall not choose the track of another as its own—that is, one part of the describing operation follow in the path of another—or else [if this should happen] this [reduplication] must be subtracted so that the same thing shall not be taken too many times. It is clear also from this that "components", according to the concept which we here use, can compose by their magnitudes a *magnitude* greater than the magnitude of the *thing* which they compose.[27] Whence the composition of things differs widely from the composition of magnitudes. For example, if there are two parts, A or RS and B or RX, of the whole line L or RX, and each of these is greater than half of RX itself—if, for example, RX is 5 feet and RS 4 feet and YX 3 feet—obviously the magnitudes of the parts compose a magnitude of 7 feet, which is greater than that of the whole; and yet the lines RS and YX themselves compose nothing different from RX,—that is, $RS \oplus YX = RX$. Accordingly I here denote this real addition by $\oplus$, as the addition of magnitudes is denoted by $+$. And finally, although it is of much importance, when it is a question of the actual generation of things, what their order is (for the foundations are laid before the house is built), still in the mental construction of things the result is the same whichever ingredient we consider first (although one order may be more convenient than another), hence the order does not here alter the thing developed. This matter is to be considered in its own time and proper place. For the present, however, $RY \oplus YS \oplus SX$ is the same as $YS \oplus RY \oplus SX$.

[27] Italics ours.

LI YEH

(c. 1178—c. 1265)

Li Yeh, one of China's greatest mathematicians, was born in Luan-ch'eng in Northern China at a time of prolonged strife between the northern kingdom and the Sung monarchy in the south. He undoubtedly received an excellent education, for we learn that he passed a government examination for civil servants and that having served the Ch'in government in various capacities as a civil officer, he rose to the position of governor of Ch'in Chou. When the province was seized by the Mongol invaders, Li Yeh escaped by fleeing in disguise. Collecting as many books as he could, he retired to a life of seclusion, study and poverty. During the period of the ascendancy of Kublai Khan, Li Yeh was summoned by the conqueror and questioned concerning governmental service, but he assumed no duties under the Khan's government at that time. We hear that for many years he taught ever increasing numbers of pupils in a Mongolian territory. In 1264, Li Yeh declined Kublai's offer of an office on the grounds of his advanced age and infirmity. However, he could not refuse the subsequent insistent offer of a chair in the Han-lin academy. His tenure was brief. After only a few months, Li Yeh resigned and the following year he died at the age of eighty-seven.

Li Yeh was the author of hundreds of manuscripts. The chief mathematical works among them were his *Tse-yuan Hai-ching* ("Sea Mirror of the Circle-measurement") written (1248) in twelve books and his *I-ku Yen-tuan* (1257), a treatise on algebra. Li Yeh presented an algebraic treatment of problems in mensuration, trigonometry and other topics. His general method, *t'ien-yuen-shu* ("the method of the celestial element"), came to be known as *tengen jutsu* in Japanese works. The appearance of a circle for zero in the works of Li Yeh and his contemporaries in China is believed to be due to mathematical treatises brought to China from foreign lands to the west, by numerous visitors, such as the Venetians, Nicolo and Maffeo Polo and Nicolo's famous son, Marco Polo, who came to China during that period. Employing a place value arrangement of the terms of an equation, Li Yeh solved the equation with the aid of computing rods, red and black for positive and negative quantities. This procedure survived for centuries in both China and Japan. A new notation for negative numbers was introduced by Li Yeh. Replacing the use of red ink to represent positive numbers and black ink for negative numbers, he employed only a diagonal stroke over the representation of the number, or a part of it, to show that it was negative. Li Yeh was also known by his familiar name, Jin-king and by his *nom de plume,* Li Ching Chai.

THE ALGEBRAIC WORKS OF LI YEH

From *The Development of Mathematics in China and Japan*

by YOSHIO MIKAMI

Li Yeh proceeds in the twelve books or chapters of the "Sea-Mirror" to establish his rules. In the opening of the treatise he gives a diagram which is as shown in the figure.

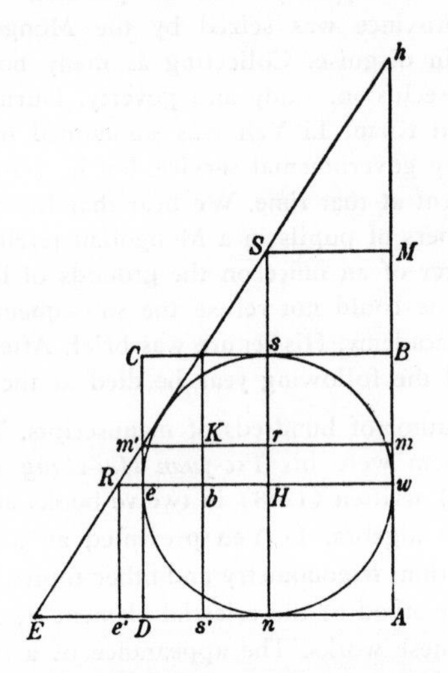

In the first book or chapter Li Yeh describes the relations of the various parts in this figure, and the 2nd and further books are devoted to the consideration of various rules of calculation in relation to these quantities. The treatment is done in the algebraical way.

The same author's subsequent composition, the *I-ku Yen-tuan,* was also devoted to algebraical treatment. The ways of representing algebraical expressions are however different in these two works.

We have already remarked upon Ch'in Chiu-shao's employment of the term *t'ien-yuen,* which means celestial element. This same term was also employed by Li Yeh. Ch'in referred to the celestial element in his treatment of indeterminate problems, as we have said; he did not however employ the term in connection with his manipulation of numerical equations, with which he has become so prominent in history. It was in this latter connection that Li Yeh used the term celestial element.

In the algebraical process of Li Yeh's celestial element in his *I-ku Yen-tuan* unity is employed as the representative of an unknown number. This was certainly done with the aid of a calculating piece. But in writing in his work Li uses the ideogram *yuen* or element written by the side of it to distinguish it from other terms in an expression, which are arranged in a vertical column. The absolute term comes under the linear term and it is marked by the ideogram *tai,* perhaps implying the meaning that it is in the place of the *tai-chi* or extreme limit or great extreme. The square of the celestial element is arranged immediately above the element; next above comes the cube; and so on upwards. Thus the equation

$$x^3 + 15x^2 + 66x - 360 = 0$$

would be written as given annexed.

The square and further terms are not expressly indicated, but these are designated by the relative positions to the great extreme or the absolute term. In practice the two ideograms *yuen* and *tai* are not necessary; one of them may be advantageously omitted.

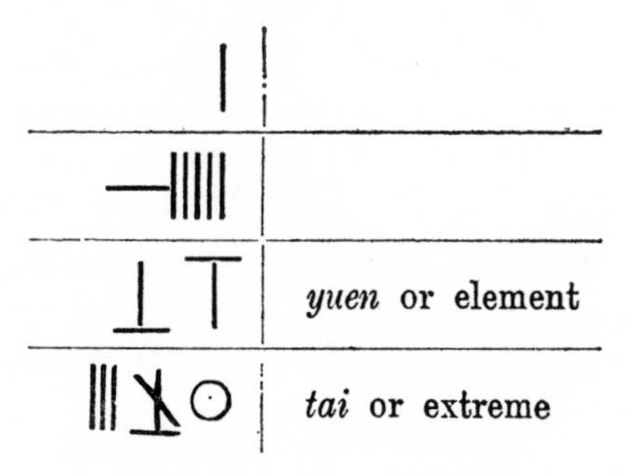

Li Yeh's way of arranging equations as found in the

"Sea-Mirror" is utterly different from that of Ch'in, who had followed the development of the root-extraction process of old times. It is utterly unknown however to us as to what reason or reasons had induced our author to adopt such an arrangement. But in the *I-ku Yen-tuan* Li Yeh changes his arrangement in the same way as Ch'in has done, bringing the absolute term uppermost and other terms successively below it. And this way was destined to prevail thenceforth.

The Chinese had been accustomed long before to use red and black calculating pieces to distinguish positive and negative numbers, and the equations were ultimately to be arranged with these pieces. But it is not convenient to use two different colours in writing and especially in the case of printing. Thus there soon arose the usage of distinguishing numbers of different signs, when representing them in writing, by referring to a specially designed symbol. Such a symbol is met with in both works of Li Yeh. If we are not sure whether he was the first Chinese who used the symbol, yet his works are perhaps the oldest writings wherein it was made use of, that are transmitted to our time. This symbol consists of a diagonal stroke drawn through the right-hand figure. Thus

𝍠〇𝍦𝍩𝍣̸, 𝍨̸, 𝍠〇𝍡̸〇〇

stand respectively for — 10724, — 9 and — 10200.

LIU HUI

(Third Century)

Liu Hui (also, Lew Hway), a celebrated Chinese scholar and mathematician, lived in the Kingdom of Wei in North China during the period of the Three Kingdoms in the third century A. D. He is known to us through his commentaries on Chang Tsang's "Arithmetical Rules in Nine Sections". The commentaries, written in 263, in the reign of Ch'en-lui-Wang of the Wei Kingdom, survive to this day. Antedating by a thousand years the development in China of the algebra of the celestial element, Liu Hui's work contains remarkable results achieved through his construction of rules which were effective as formulas for the solution of the problems proposed. In the commentaries, Liu Hui attempted the quadrature of the circle by the method of successively doubling the number of sides of an inscribed polygon. Starting with a regular hexagon inscribed in a circle of unit radius, he proceeded to the calculation of the length of a side of a polygon of 192 sides, and, in this work, developed the value 157:50 for the ratio (π) of the circumference of the circle to its diameter. Liu Hui noted, moreover, that this ratio was somewhat smaller than the actual value.

Liu Hui included some problems of his own in his commentaries on the ancient classic. A supplement consisting of problems in practical trigonometry with their solutions, was originally appended to the last book of the old "Nine Sections". This group of problems appeared later as a separate work under the title *Chung-ch'a,* which refers to the use of stiles of different lengths for taking observations and to the repeated applications of the right triangle relations in the resulting figure. During the T'ang (618-906) the title *Chung-ch'a* was changed to *Hai-tao Suan-ching* (sometimes also, *Hai-tao Suan-shu*), "Sea-Island Arithmetic Classic", the new title having been taken from the first problem of the *Chung-ch'a* dealing with the measure of an island lying at a distance from the observer. Liu Hui's treatise was one of the nine Chinese works specified as approved mathematical studies in the Japanese university established in 701 by the Emperor Monbu. We are indebted to many scholars for the survival of the work. An edition of it was issued (1775) by the illustrious scholar Tai Cheng, imperial librarian and mathematician, who drew the various parts of the work from the great encyclopaedia *Yung-lo Tai-tien* of the Yung-lo period (1403-1424).

SEA-ISLAND ARITHMETIC CLASSIC

From *The Development of Mathematics in China and Japan*

by Yoshio Mikami

The first problem in the "Sea-island Arithmetical Classic" is this:

"There is a sea island that is to be measured. Two rods that are both 30 feet (a) high are erected at the distance of 1000 paces (b) from each other, making the rod in the rear to come in the same straight line with the island and the other rod. When a man walks 123 paces (c) back from the nearer rod, the top of the island is just visible through the end of that rod, if he tries to see with his eye brought on the ground. The summit of the island peak is also seen co-straight with the end of the hind rod, when seen bringing the eye in contact with the ground from a point 127 paces (d) back from that rod. It is required to know the height and the distance of the island."

The rule given for the solution of this problem runs:

"Rule. With the height of the rods multiply the distance of the rods, and take (the product) as the dividend; and carry the division taking the difference (of the distances walked back from the rods) as the divisor; add to the quotient the rod's height, when we obtain the height of the island.

"To find the distance of the island from the nearer rod, multiply with the distance walked back from that rod the distance between the two rods, and divide the product by the difference of the distances walked back from the rods, when the quotient gives the distance required."

This rule is equivalent to the formulae,

$$(\text{height}) = a + \frac{ab}{d-c}; \qquad (\text{distance}) = \frac{cb}{d-c}.$$

It is not known how Liu Hui got at these expressions, but it appears not improbable that they were deduced from the two proportions,

$$\frac{x}{x+c}=\frac{a}{c}, \quad \text{and} \quad \frac{x+b}{x+b+d}=\frac{a}{d},$$

or what are equivalent to them.

The term *chung-ch'a* seems to indicate an agreement with our view. The term was originally intended to mean double or repeated applications of the consideration as met with in the chapter on the right triangle in the "Nine Sections", i. e., the double application of proportions.

The second of Liu Hui's problems is as follows:

"There grows on a hill a pine-tree, whose height is not known. Two rods, each 20 feet high (a), are so erected in the plain below at the mutual distance of 50 paces (b), that they come in a straight line with the tree. The top of the tree and the end of the front rod make a sraight line with a point on the ground 7 paces and 4 feet (c) behind the rod, and at this point the base of the tree measures 2·8 feet (e) on the top of the rod. The top of the tree again makes a straight line with the end of the hind rod and a point on the ground 8 paces and 5 feet (d) behind the rod. It is required to know the height of the pine-tree and the distance of the hill from the (front) rod."

The rule that is intended to solve this problem leads to the formulae,

$$(\text{height})=\frac{eb}{d-c}+e; \qquad (\text{distance})=\frac{bc}{d-c}.$$

The third problem is:

"One sees to the south a square town of unknown size. He erects two rods 60 feet (a) apart from east to west, which are joined with a string at the eye's height, and let the eastern rod be costraight with the S. E. corner and the N. E. corner of the town. He gets 5 paces (b) to the north of the eastern rod, and observes the N. W. corner of the town through a point of the string at 22·6½ feet (c) from the east end. Again getting back to

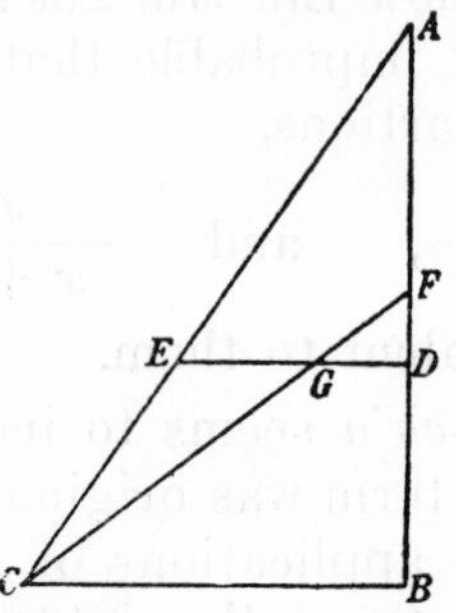

the north 13 paces and 2 feet (d) from the rod, the observer sees the N. W. corner of the town just costraight with the western rod. What are then one side of the town and the distance of the town from the rod?"

This problem is the same as asking for the lengths (see the figure) $CB = x$ and $BD = y$ in terms of $DE = a$, $DF = b$, $DG = c$, $DA = d$. [In the figure B is a right angle and DE is drawn parallel to BC.]

The formulae in the answer are given in forms equivalent to

$$x = \frac{(d-b)\,c}{\dfrac{cd}{a} - b}, \qquad y = \frac{\left(d - \dfrac{cd}{a}\right) b}{\dfrac{cd}{a} - b}.$$

Liu Hui gives in his "Arithmetical Classic" six further similar problems, together with the rules for their solutions.

Liu Hui's studies of these complicated problems appear to tell that he was acquainted with some way of algebraical manipulations. When we moreover reflect on the contents of some parts of the "Nine Sections", we cannot but ascribe the birth of algebra to Chinese mathematicians in a comparatively early part of their history, much earlier than the time of the appearance of Ch'in Chiu-shao and Li Yeh in the 13th century, when, as is generally believed, the Chinese algebra was born. We put therefore a stress on Liu Hui's considerations of these complicated problems, that had taken place in the 3rd century, a whole millennium previous to the dawning of the algebra of the celestial element.

THE MAYA CIVILIZATION

The Maya civilization, one of the greatest of the pre-Hispanic American cultures, reached the height of its development during its Great or Classical Period, from the 4th to the 9th centuries A. D. Extending over a large area in Central America it roughly spanned the present British Honduras, the provinces of Mexico situated on the Yucatan Peninsula, the Republic of Guatemala, and the western portions of Honduras and El Salvador. The Maya people lived in settled communities. The great majority of them engaged in agriculture and hunting. Dominating the scattered settlements in which they lived were the urban religious and ceremonial centers. The religion of the Maya greatly influenced all their activities. It was at the basis of the evolution of their architecture and their sculpture. It was the inspiration for the invention of their writing, their mathematics and their extraordinary calendar system. Evidences of their skill in precise stone work have been found in pyramidal structures, which were used as platforms for temples or for observation posts. With the debris of centuries removed from some of the numerous mounds marking the sites of the ancient cities, stone pyramids have been found buried one beneath another, the innermost one serving as the tomb of a priest or other person of great dignity. Elaborate ornamentation on stone or on stucco facings shows a distinctive artistic development. Judging by the size of the pyramids (a pyramid in the ancient Maya city of Tikal, in the Department of Peten, Guatemala, rises to 229 feet) great numbers of people were employed in their construction. Many more were undoubtedly attracted to the cities during the religious festivals. At times, religious rites involved the gruesome spectacle of human sacrifices, but in later years great progress was made toward the abandonment of this practice. The Maya people were very advanced in ceramic arts. They had textiles and they wore personal ornaments of carved jade, bone, shell and pyrite.

When the stabilizing forces which had unified the distant Maya cities weakened, the peace which they had maintained was replaced by war, pestilence and famine. To stem the ensuing decline, an alliance of three of the city-states, Uxmal, Chichen-Itza and Mayapan, in the League of Mayapan, was formed (1004), and under the "New Empire" religion, science and art flourished once more. However, in the succeeding centuries, the Maya were conquered by invaders from Mexico, first by the Toltecs and then by the Aztecs. In the mutual interchange of cultural influences between conqueror and conquered, the Maya feathered serpent god was accepted by the Aztecs and its representation became a prominent motif in Aztec art. It is believed, too, that the Aztecs took over the Maya calendar. Archaeological research has revealed that, long before the arrival of the Spaniards in Yucatan, there was a sudden abandonment by the Maya of one great city after another. The direct cause of the desertion has not yet been clearly established.

We possess little in the way of a documented history of the Maya. The slim sum total of such a history consists of reports by Spanish priests, a small number of native writings, and hieroglyphic inscriptions carved on the stone facades of buildings and upon shaftlike stone monuments known as "stelae". In his *Relacion de las cosas de Yucatan,* Bishop Diego de Landa tells of the burning of certain Maya books, written on long strips of bark or parchment, folded like a screen. Three of these books have survived and are now known as the "codices". They contain explanations and records of ceremonial rites, prophecies, and historical events, written in hieroglyphs. The "Books of Chilan (or Chilam) Balam" are also an important source of information. They were written with the encouragement of the Spaniards, by Maya writers in the Maya language, but in Spanish script. The paucity of documented history despite the possession by the Maya of a written language is due to the general destruction in the 16th century by the Spaniards, and by the natives who had been converted, of all articles which might serve to keep the old Maya traditions alive.

While much remains to be done in the decipherment of Maya inscriptions, the parts dealing with their numerical system and calendar are well understood. The Maya system of numeration employed place values and it was the first in which systematic use was made of a symbol for zero. Maya mathematicians were skillful in computation. Their knowledge of astronomy combined with their arithmetic, enabled them to construct a complex calendrical system. The extremely accurate method of reckoning time, yielded by the Maya system is all the more astonishing when it is remembered that it was fully developed and widely used as early as the 4th century A. D.

MAYA NUMERATION

From *The Numeration, Calendar Systems and Astronomical Knowledge of the Mayas*

by Chas. P. Bowditch

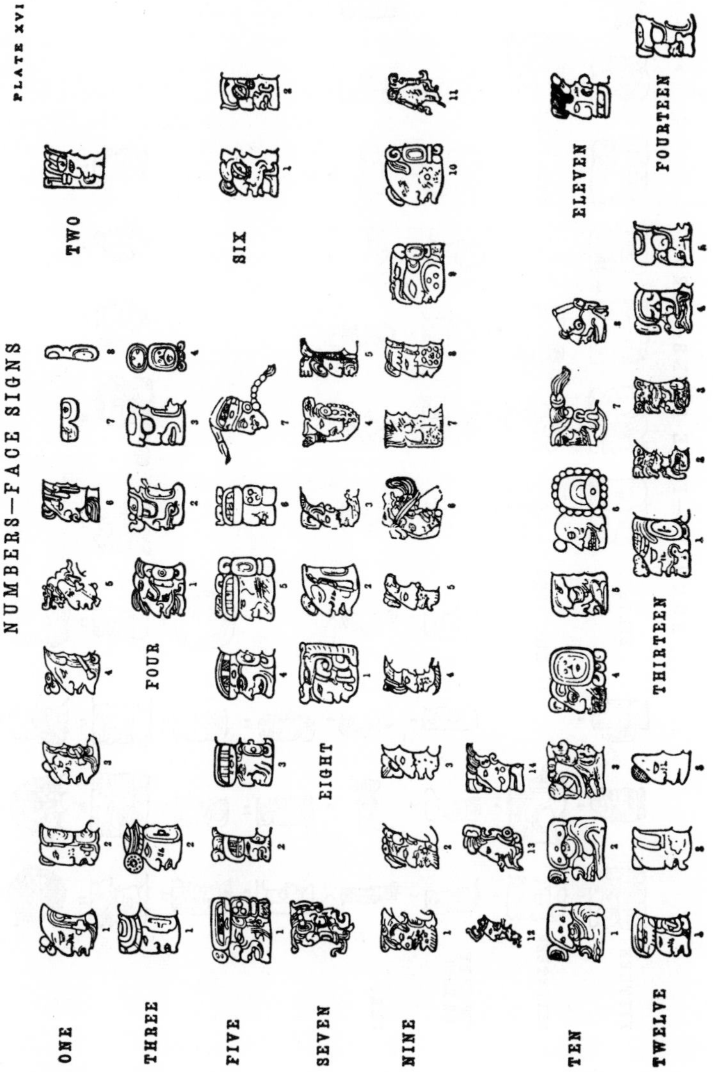

PLATE XVI

NUMBERS—FACE SIGNS

ONE

TWO

THREE

FOUR

FIVE

SIX

SEVEN

EIGHT

NINE

TEN

ELEVEN

TWELVE

THIRTEEN

FOURTEEN

From *The Numeration, Calendar Systems and Astronomical Knowledge of the Mayas*

by Chas. P. Bowditch

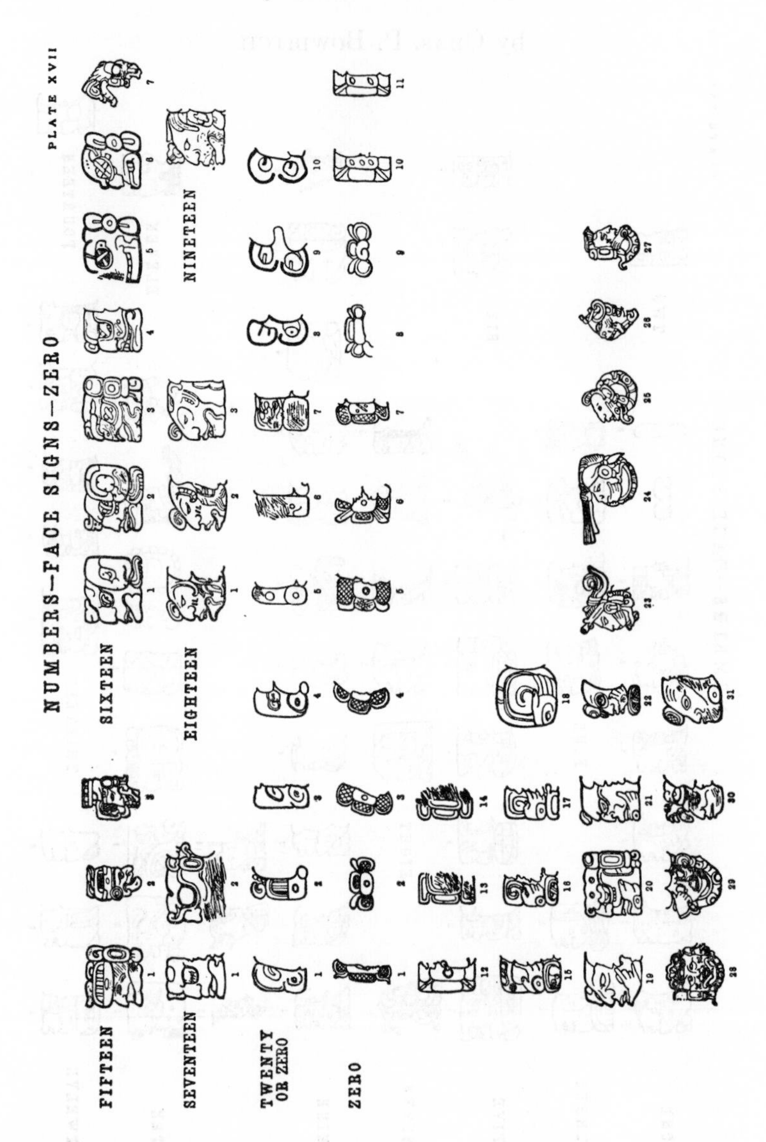

CHARACTERISTICS OF HEAD-VARIANT NUMERALS 0 TO 19, INCLUSIVE

Forms	Characteristics
Head for 0........	Clasped hand across lower part of face.
Head for 1........	Forehead ornament composed of *more than one part.*
Head for 2........	Oval in upper part of head. (?)
Head for 3........	Banded headdress or fillet
Head for 4........	Bulging eye with square iris, snaglike front tooth, curling fang from back of mouth.
Head for 5........	Normal form of tun sign as headdress.
Head for 6........	"Hatchet eye."
Head for 7........	Large scroll passing under eye and curling up in front of forehead.
Head for 8........	Forehead ornament composed of *one part.*
Head for 9........	Dots on lower cheek or around mouth and in some cases beard.
Head for 10........	Fleshless lower jaw and in some cases other death's head characteristics, truncated nose, etc.
Head for 11........	Undetermined.
Head for 12........	Undetermined; type of head known, however.
Head for 13........	(*a*) Long pendulous nose, bulging eye, and curling fang from back of mouth. (*b*) Head for 3 with fleshless lower jaw of head for 10.
Head for 14........	Head for 4 with fleshless lower jaw of head for 10.
Head for 15........	Head for 5 with fleshless lower jaw of head for 10.
Head for 16........	Head for 6 with fleshless lower jaw of head for 10.
Head for 17........	Head for 7 with fleshless lower jaw of head for 10.
Head for 18........	Head for 8 with fleshless lower jaw of head for 10.
Head for 19........	Head for 9 with fleshless lower jaw of head for 10.

TABLE X. From *An Introduction to the Study of Maya Hieroglyphs*

by SYLVANUS G. MORLEY

From *The Numeration, Calendar Systems and Astronomical Knowledge of the Mayas*

by Chas. P. Bowditch

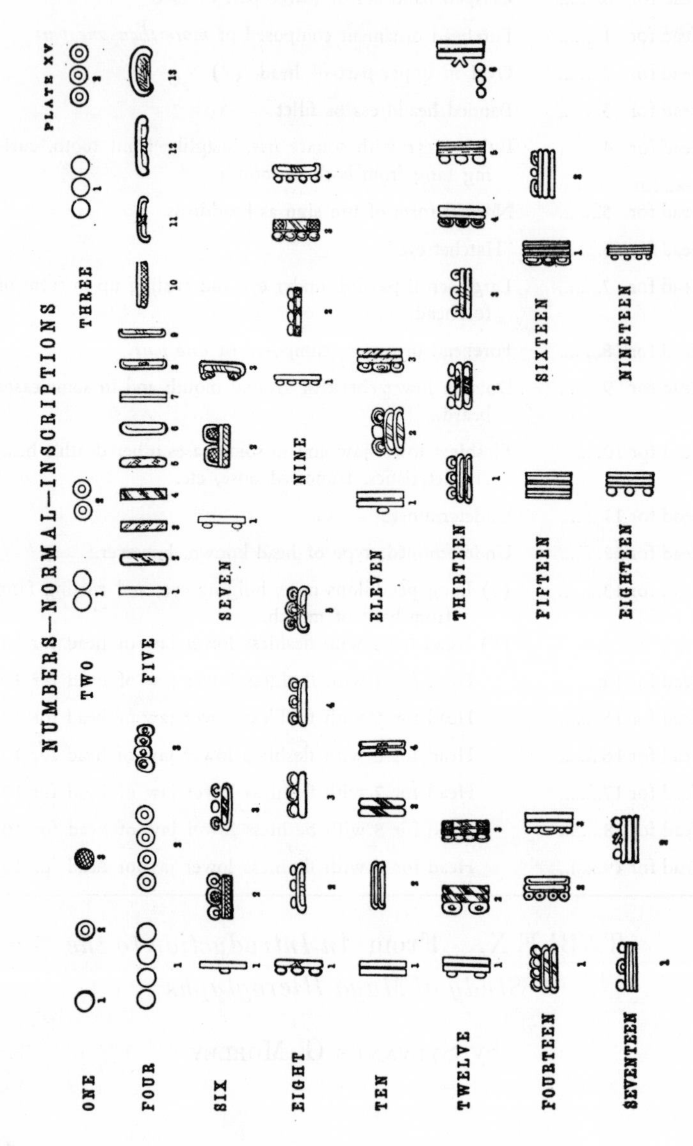

MAYA CALENDAR

From *The Ancient Maya*

by SYLVANUS GRISWOLD MORLEY

Since arithmetic and the calendar play such an important part in the Maya inscriptions, a brief description of Maya arithmetic and the Maya calendar is necessary to their better understanding.

TZOLKIN OR SACRED YEAR OF 260 DAYS

In all probability the only part of their highly elaborate calendar and chronology with which the common folk, the corn farmers, the hewers of wood and drawers of water, were familiar was the sacred year of 260 days, the *tzolkin* or "count of days." This time-period was the most fundamental fact of their religion, since it determined for everybody the very pattern of his or her ceremonial life. The ancient Maya, man or woman, regarded his or her birthday not as the position in the tropical year, that is the month-day, upon which he was born, as we do, but the day of the *tzolkin,* or 260-day sacred year upon which he was born. The god of the particular day of this 260-day period upon which a man was born was his patron saint, his guardian deity, his celestial godfather, so to speak. Doubtless the god of the month in which he was born was also closer to him than the other eighteen month-gods, but his own particular *tzolkin* god was his strongest protector, his closest ally among the Heavenly Ones. Indeed, we have seen that among the Cakchiquels of the highlands of Guatemala a man took his given name from the day of the *tzolkin* upon which he happened to have been born, as Oxlahuh Tzii (Maya 13 Oc) for example.

The 260 days of the sacred year were formed by prefixing the numbers 1 to 13 inclusive to the twenty Maya day-glyphs, the names of which are given below, begin-

FIG. 18.—Glyphs for the twenty Maya days: (*a*) Imix; (*b*) Ik; (*c*) Akbal; (*d*) Kan; (*e*) Chicchan; (*f*) Cimi; (*g*) Manik; (*h*) Lamat; (*i*) Muluc; (*j*) Oc; (*k*) Chuen; (*l*) Eb; (*m*) Ben; (*n*) Ix; (*o*) Men; (*p*) Cib; (*q*) Caban; (*r*) Eznab; (*s*) Cauac; (*t*) Ahau.

ning with Ik, one of the Old Empire year bearers, and their corresponding hieroglyphs in Figure 18.

Ik	Manik	Eb	Caban
Akbal	Lamat	Ben	Eznab
Kan	Muluc	Ix	Cauac
Chicchan	Oc	Men	Ahau
Cimi	Chuen	Cib	Imix

The Maya calendar, however, had no day named Ik, Akbal, or Kan alone, that is no day-name without an accompanying number, but, instead, each one of the twenty day-names in the list above, as already noted, had a number from 1 to 13 inclusive prefixed to it, thus —1 Ik, 2 Akbal, 3 Kan, and so on. Not until every one of these thirteen numbers had been attached in turn to every one of the twenty day-names given above was a *tzolkin* complete.

If we commence with the number 1, for example, and prefix it to the first name in the list, Ik, viz. 1 Ik, and proceed without interruption to prefix the numbers from 1 to 13 inclusive in succession to each of these twenty names, the fourteenth name, Men, will have the number 1 again; the fifteenth name, Cib, the number 2 again; and so on until the first name, Ik in the second round of the twenty day-names comes back again with the number next in order, or 8. It follows, therefore, since 13 and 20 have no common factor, that, before any given number can be prefixed a second time to any given name, 259 days thereafter will have had to elapse, the 261st day having the same designation "1 Ik" as the first day, that is, one complete round of 260 differently named days—the *tzolkin* or "count of days." This is probably the oldest part of the Maya calendar, and certainly it was by far the most important to the masses, determining for each individual not only his birthday but also the ceremonial pattern of his life.

In order to give any day in the Maya calendar its complete description, however, it was further necessary to add to the days of the *tzolkin,* or 260-day ceremonial

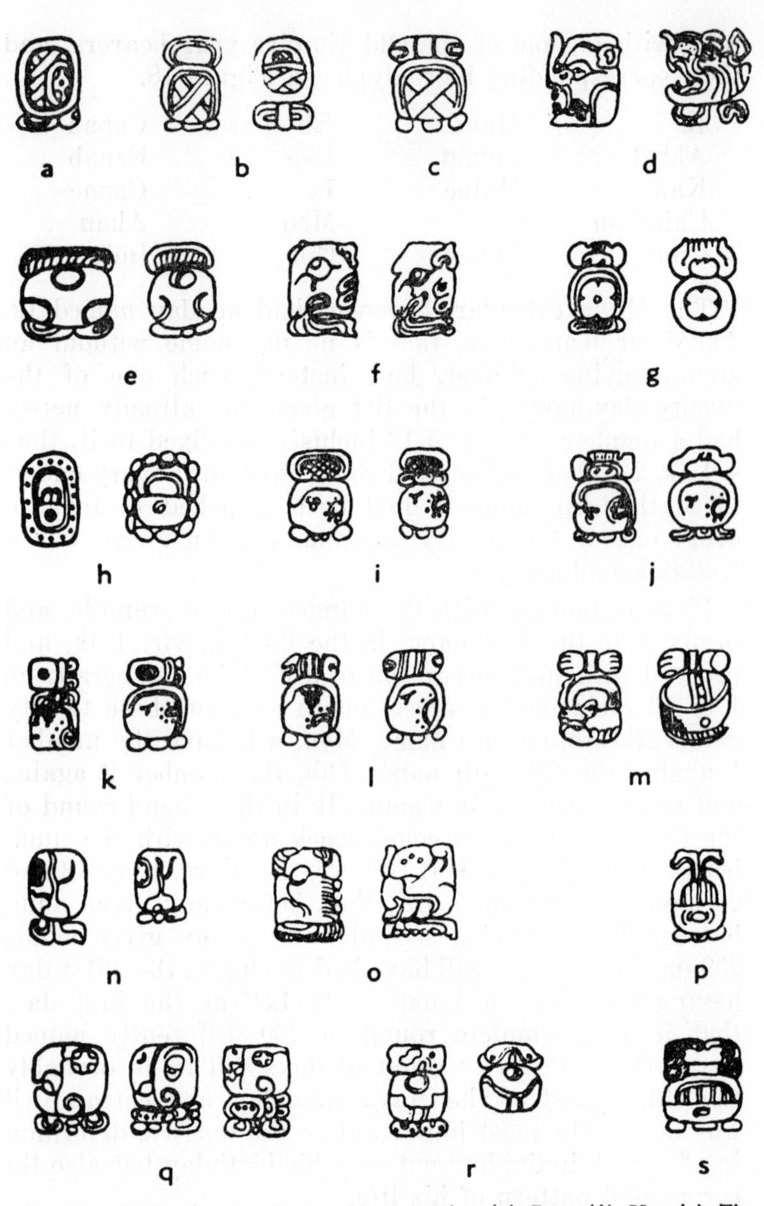

FIG. 19.—Glyphs for the nineteen Maya months: (*a*) Pop; (*b*) Uo; (*c*) Zip; (*d*) Zotz; (*e*) Tzec; (*f*) Xul; (*g*) Yaxkin; (*h*) Mol; (*i*) Chen; (*j*) Yax; (*k*) Zac; (*l*) Ceh; (*m*) Mac; (*n*) Kankin; (*o*) Muan; (*p*) Pax; (*q*) Kayab; (*r*) Cumhu; (*s*) Uayeb.

year, the corresponding month-position in the *haab* or 365-day calendar year which each occupied, as for example, I Imix 4 Uayeb, 2 Ik o Pop, 3 Akbal 1 Pop, 4 Kan 2 Pop, et cetera.

CALENDAR YEAR OF 365 DAYS

The Maya calendar year, or *haab,* was composed of 19 months—18 months of 20 days each, and 1 closing month of 5 days, making a total of 365 month-positions in the calendar year. These 19 divisions are given below and their corresponding hieroglyphs are shown in Figure 19.

Pop	Tzec	Chen	Mac	Kayab
Uo	Xul	Yax	Kankin	Cumhu
Zip	Yaxkin	Zac	Muan	Uayeb
Zotz	Mol	Ceh	Pax	

In order to show clearly how the 260 days of the *tzolkin* were combined with the 365 positions of the *haab* or calendar year, let us represent them graphically as two cogwheels (Fig. 20), the smaller wheel, *A,* having 260 cogs, each named for one of the 260 days of the *tzolkin*, and the larger wheel, *B,* having 365 cogs, each intercog space being named for one of the 365 positions of the *haab* or calendar year.

Before we can enmesh these two wheels we must know two further facts about the Maya calendar. First, the Maya New Year's Day, or the first day of their first month, was written 0 (zero) Pop, Pop being the first month of the year (see above); and the first position in that month was written 0 rather than 1, as we would write it. This follows from the fact that the Maya regarded time as a series of elapsed periods, and a month position 1 Pop indicated to them the second day of Pop rather than the first day. This latter method is the way we number the hours of the day. For example, when we say one o'clock, in reality the first hour after noon is gone and we are about to start the second hour. So it was with the ancient Maya when they wrote 1 Pop; the first day, 0 Pop, had already passed and the second day (written 1 Pop) was about to commence. It follows from

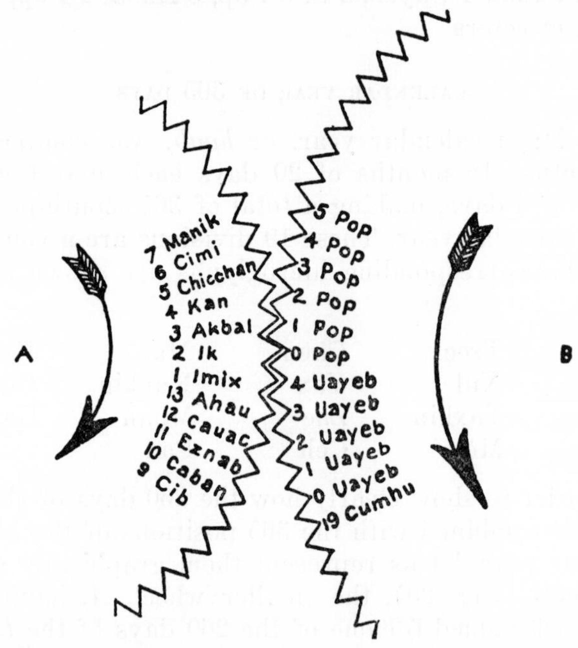

FIG. 20.—Diagram showing the enmeshing of the 365-day calendar year (B) with the 260-day sacred year (A).

the foregoing that although the Maya months were each 20 days in length, except the last which had but 5 days, their month-positions were numbered from 0 to 19 inclusive, and in the case of the last month from 0 to 4 inclusive, and *not* as we would have numbered them from 1 to 20 inclusive and 1 to 5 inclusive in the case of the last month. This makes the first day of the Maya year 0 Pop, and not 1 Pop as we would write it.

The second fact we must know before combining the *tzolkin* with the *haab* is that only 52 of the 260 differently named days of the former could ever occupy the first position of the *haab,* or indeed, the first position of any one of its 19 divisions. These 52 days are those in which the names Ik, Manik, Eb, and Caban appear (at the tops of the four columns earlier), and since each one of these names had the number 1 to 13 inclusive prefixed to it in turn, it results that only 52, or 4 x 13, of the 260 different days of the *tzolkin* could begin the Maya calendar year or any one of its 19 divisions. These 52 possible Maya New Year's Days, or year-bearers as they have been called, fell, during the Old Empire, upon the following days:

1 Ik	1 Manik	1 Eb	1 Caban	1 Ik
2 Manik	2 Eb	2 Caban	2 Ik	2 Manik
3 Eb	3 Caban	3 Ik	3 Manik	etc., etc.
4 Caban	4 Ik	4 Manik	4 Eb	
5 Ik	5 Manik	5 Eb	5 Caban	
6 Manik	6 Eb	6 Caban	6 Ik	
7 Eb	7 Caban	7 Ik	7 Manik	
8 Caban	8 Ik	8 Manik	8 Eb	
9 Ik	9 Manik	9 Eb	9 Caban	
10 Manik	10 Eb	10 Caban	10 Ik	
11 Eb	11 Caban	11 Ik	11 Manik	
12 Caban	12 Ik	12 Manik	12 Eb	
13 Ik	13 Manik	13 Eb	13 Caban	

It should be observed, however, that at the time of the Spanish Conquest, the days with which the Maya New Year began had shifted forward two positions, and that instead of beginning with days named Ik, Manik, Eb, or Caban, they began with days named Kan, Muluc, Ix, or Cauac (listed earlier).

CALENDAR ROUND

We are now in position to bring together, or enmesh, the two wheels in Figure 20, *A* representing the *tzolkin* and *B* the *haab* or calendar year. Let us do this in such a way that the cog of Wheel *A*, named after the day "2 Ik" of the *tzolkin*, will fit into the intercog-space on Wheel *B* corresponding to the Maya New Year's Day or position "0 Pop," giving the complete designation of this particular day as "2 Ik 0 Pop."

Now let us revolve both wheels, *A* to the right like the hands of a clock, and *B* to the left, counterclockwise. Our problem is to find out how many complete revolutions each wheel will have to make before the cog named "2 Ik" on Wheel *A* will return to the intercog-space named "0 Pop" on Wheel *B*.

This problem is an old arithmetical friend of grammar school days—the least common multiple. We must first ascertain the least common multiple of 260 and 365, during which process we shall also have ascertained how many complete revolutions the two wheels in Figure 20 will have to make before any one of the 260 different cogs of Wheel *A* will return to the same intercog-space of Wheel *B* from which it started, in a complete number of revolutions of each wheel.

Both 260 and 365 are divisible by 5, the first giving a quotient of 52, the second one of 73, but there is no further common factor, so the least common multiple of 260 and 365 is $5 \times 52 \times 73 = 18{,}980$; therefore our first wheel, *A*, will make 73 complete revolutions, while the second wheel, *B*, will make 52 complete revolutions before cog "2 Ik" of Wheel *A* will return to intercog-space "0 Pop" of Wheel *B* in a complete number of revolutions of each.

Translating this problem of arithmetic back into terms of the Maya calendar, we may say that before any given day of the *tzolkin* could return to any given position of the *haab*, 73 *tzolkins* or 52 *haab*, or 18,980 days would have had to have elapsed. This is true since $73 \times 260 = 52 \times 365 = 18{,}980$ days.

In other words, once every 52 *haab* or calendar years of 365 days each, any given day, for example, "2 Ik," coincided with the first position of the year, "0 Pop," and this combination, or any other combination possible, recurred thereafter at intervals of 52 years each, throughout time. Thus any Maya who lived more than 52 years began to see New Year's Days of exactly the same name or, in fact, any other given days repeat themselves.

We do not know the ancient Maya name, or even the hieroglyph for this period of $52 \times 365 = 18{,}980$ days, important as it must have been, but modern students of the Maya calendar have called it the Calendar Round, because in this period of time the 260 days of the *tzolkin* will have occupied all of the 365 positions in the *haab* possible for them to occupy before the sequence will have begun to repeat itself, that is, one complete round of the 18,980 possible dates or 1 Calendar Round.

Not one of the peoples of Middle America who probably borrowed their respective calendars from the Maya, such as the Aztecs, the Mixtec, and the Zapotec for example, ever devised or made use of any time period higher than this 18,980-day period (52 years of 365 days). The Aztecs, for example, conceived time as an endless succession of these 52 × 365 day-periods to which they gave the name *xiuhmolpilli,* meaning in their language "year bundle," that is to say, the complete round of the years.

The Aztec had two special glyphs for this period, arising directly from their beliefs concerning it. The first was a knot (Fig. 21, *a*) indicating thereby that the bundle of 52 years had been tied up, finished, or completed at the end of this period, and the second was the fire-drill and stick for kindling the Sacred Fire (Fig. 21, *b*). The Aztec believed that the world would come to an end only at the close of one of these 52-year periods; and on the last night of the *xiuhmolpilli,* we are told, the population of Tenochtitlan (Mexico City) withdrew to the hills surrounding the city to await the coming of dawn. When the sun rose on that morning, there was general rejoicing, the Sacred Fire was rekindled, the houses were cleaned and set in order and the business of life was resumed as usual. The gods had given mankind another 52-year lease of life.

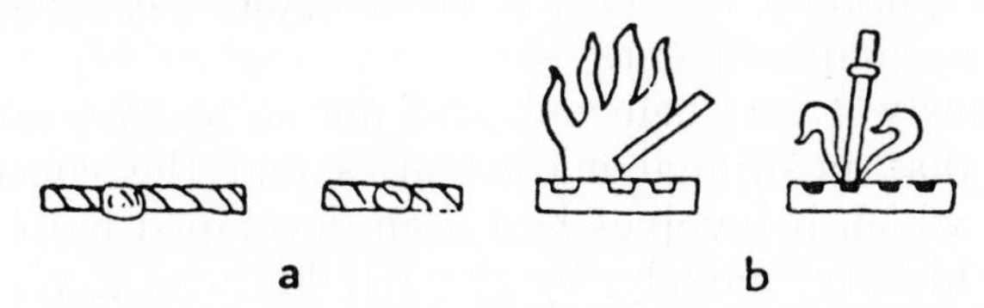

FIG. 21.—Aztec glyphs for the *xiuhmolpilli* or 52-year period, (*a*) two examples of the knot; (*b*) two examples of the stick and drill for kindling the sacred fire.

Neither the Maya name nor the corresponding glyph for this highly important time period is known, although it was almost certainly a Maya conception originally, being the basis of their calendar system.

The Maya, like the Aztec, also conceived time as an endless succession of these 18,980 different possible combinations of the 260 days (the *tzolkin*) and the 365 different positions of the calendar year (*haab*); but at a very early date, probably as early as the fourth century before the beginning of the Christian Era, they perceived that even the first few multiples only of this period—37,960, 56,940, 75,920, 94,900, 113,880, etc.—would involve them immediately in complex numbers, which became increasingly difficult to handle as time went on.

●

MAYA ARITHMETIC

In order to escape such rapidly mounting calendric chaos, the ancient Maya priests devised a simple numerical system which even today, more than two thousand years later, stands as one of the most brilliant achievements of the human mind.

Some time during the fourth or third centuries before Christ, the Maya priests *for the first time in the history of the human race devised a system of numeration by position, involving the conception and use of the mathematical quantity of zero,* a tremendous abstract intellectual accomplishment.

Formerly it was believed, and not so many years ago either, that positional mathematics and the conception of zero which it involves had been developed but once in human history, namely, by the Hindus who devised the decimal notation with its accompanying numerical symbols about the eighth century of the Christian Era. From India this decimal numerical system passed to Arabia, hence the term Arabic numerals, and was carried from Arabia by the Arabs into Egypt. From northern Africa the Moors introduced it into Spain, and it did not come into general use among our own ancestors of western Europe until the fifteenth century—about seven hundred years after its invention in southern central Asia.

We now know, however, that the ancient Maya had developed their own system of positional mathematics, based upon 20 as its unit of progression instead of 10, that is, vigesimal instead of decimal, at least a thousand years earlier than its invention in the Old World by the Hindus and nearly two thousand years before positional mathematics came into general use among our own ancestors of western Europe.

But for a single break in the third order of units to make the third order approximate the length of the solar year as nearly as possible, the Maya vigesimal system is almost as simple as our own decimal system.

The unit of the Maya calendar was the day or *kin.* The second order of units, consisting of 20 *kins,* was called the *uinal.* In a perfect vigesimal system of numeration, the third term should be 400, that is, 20 × 20 × 1, but at this point, *in counting time only,* the Maya introduced a single variation, in order to make the period of their third order agree in length with their calendar year as nearly as possible. The third order of the Maya vigesimal system, the *tun,* therefore, was composed of 18 (instead of 20) *uinals,* or 360 (instead of 400) *kins;* 360 days or *kins* being a much closer approximation to the length of the 365-day calendar year than 400 days.

Above the third order, however, the unit of progression used to form all the higher numbers is uniformly 20, as will be seen below, where the names and numerical values of the nine known different orders of time periods are given:

20 *kins*	= 1 *uinal* or 20 days
18 *uinals*	= 1 *tun* or 360 days
20 *tuns*	= 1 *katun* or 7,200 days
20 *katuns*	= 1 *baktun** or 144,000 days
20 *baktuns*	= 1 *pictun* or 2,880,000 days
20 *pictuns*	= 1 *calabtun* or 57,600,000 days
20 *calabtuns*	= 1 *kinchiltun* or 1,152,000,000 days
20 *kinchiltuns*	= 1 *alautun* or 23,040,000,000 days

The break in the third order of units mentioned above, 360 instead of 400, the latter of which is the correct value of the third term in a strictly vigesimal system, however, was used only *in counting time;* in counting everything else the Maya followed the vigesimal progression consistently—1, 20, 400 (instead of 360), 8,000 (instead of 7,200), 160,000 (instead of 144,000), 3,200,000 (instead of 2,880,000), and so on.

TWO FORMS FOR EACH MAYA GLYPH

Practically speaking every Maya hieroglyph occurs in two forms in the inscriptions—(1) what has been called the normal or regular form and (2) a head-variant, the latter being the head of a deity, man, animal, bird, serpent, or even some mythological creature who lived only in the minds of his creators; and very, very rarely (only seven examples known), there is a third form where the glyph is the full figure of a deity, man, animal, bird, or serpent.

The glyphs for the foregoing nine time periods are given in Figure 22, normal forms at the left, head-variants at the right. In the cases of the last three periods, corresponding head-variants have not been identified as yet.

Like ourselves, the ancient Maya made use of two different notations in writing their numbers: (1) bar-and-dot numerals which may be compared to our own

* The period of the fifth order, the *baktun,* was originally called the "cycle" by modern investigators. The ancient name for this period, however, was probably *baktun* as given above.

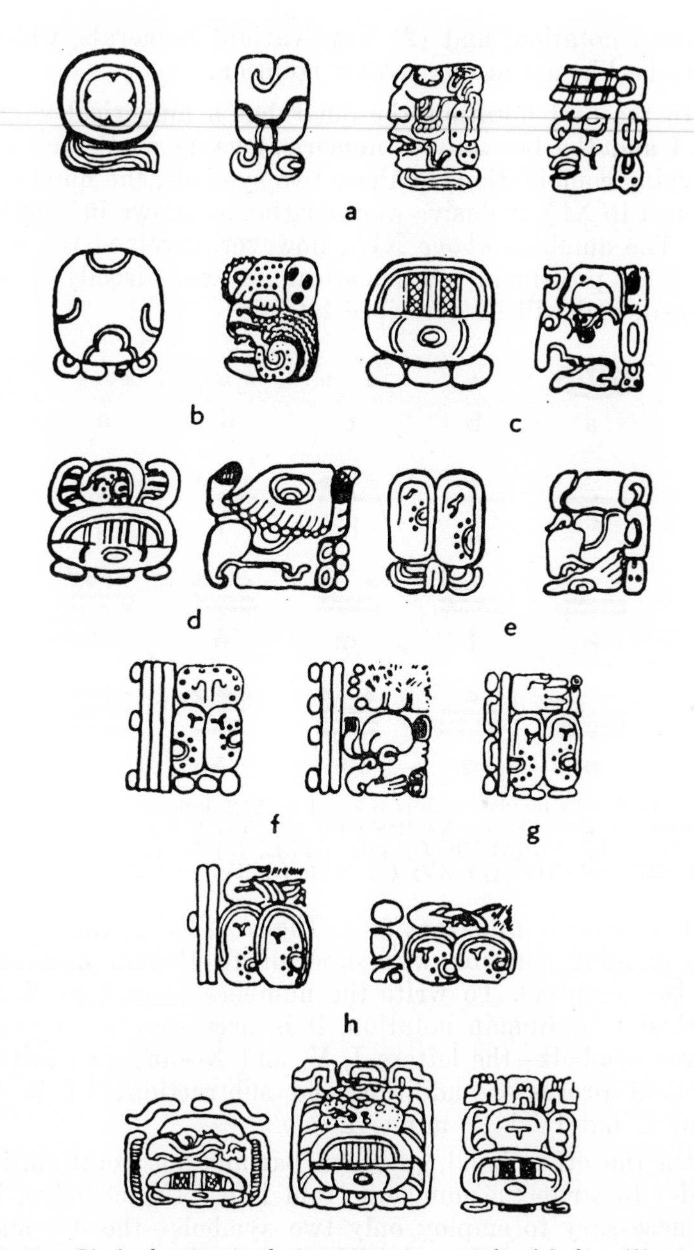

FIG. 22.—Glyphs for the nine known Maya time-periods: (*a*) *kin;* (*b*) *uinal;* (*c*) *tun;* (*d*) *katun;* (*e*) *baktun;* (*f*) *pictun;* (*g*) *calabtun;* (*h*) *kinchiltun;* (*i*) *alautun* or Initial Series introducing-glyph.

Roman notation, and (2) head-variant numerals, which may be likened to our Arabic notation.

In the first notation, the dot • has a numerical value of I and the bar ▬ a numerical value of V, and by varying combinations of these two symbols, the numbers from I to XIX inclusive were written as shown in Figure 23. The numbers *above* XIX, however, involved the use of their positional mathematical system, already mentioned, and will be described later.

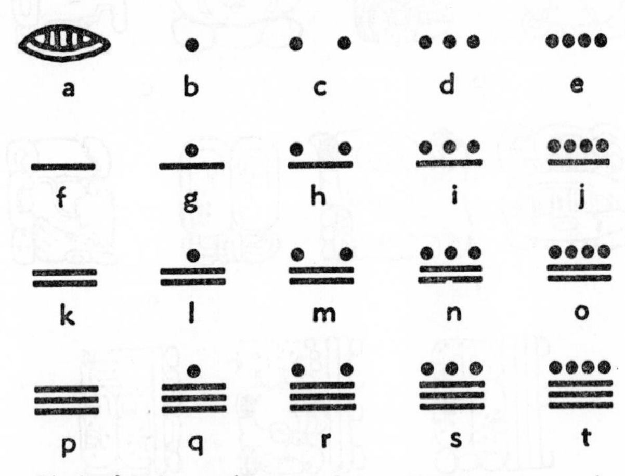

FIG. 23.—Glyphs for the numbers o and I to XIX inclusive, in bar-and-dot notation, the Maya "Roman Notation": (*a*) zero; (*b*) I; (*c*) II; (*d*) III; (*e*) IV; (*f*) V; (*g*) VI; (*h*) VII; (*i*) VIII; (*j*) IX; (*k*) X; (*l*) XI; (*m*) XII; (*n*) XIII; (*o*) XIV; (*p*) XV; (*q*) XVI; (*r*) XVII; (*s*) XVIII; (*t*) XIX.

It is readily apparent from Figure 23 that the Maya bar-and-dot notation was superior to Roman notation in two respects. To write the numbers from I to XIX inclusive in Roman notation, it is necessary to employ three symbols—the letters I, V, and X—and two arithmetical processes—addition and subtraction: VI is V plus I, but IV is V minus I.

On the other hand, in Maya bar-and-dot notation, in order to write the numbers from I to XIX inclusive, it is necessary to employ only two symbols—the dot and the bar—and only one arithmetical process, namely addition. In other words, Maya bar-and-dot notation used not only one symbol less to write the numbers from I to XIX inclusive than Roman notation requires, but also one arithmetical process less.

The second notation employed by the ancient Maya in writing their numbers made use of different types of human heads to represent the numbers from 1 to 13, inclusive, and zero. The Maya head-notation is comparable to our own Arabic notation, wherein there are ten different symbols representing zero and the first nine numbers—0, 1, 2, 3, 4, 5, 6, 7, 8, and 9. These fourteen Maya head-variant numerals are nothing more nor less than the heads of the patron deities of the first fourteen numbers described in the preceding chapter.

It will be remembered that in forming the days of the *tzolkin,* 13 numbers from 1 to 13 inclusive were prefixed to the glyphs for the twenty days in succession. There is evidence that the ancient Maya regarded the first thirteen numbers and zero as *the primary numbers,* since each one of them has a special head to represent it, that is each of those numbers has its own patron deity.[2]

The head-variant for 10 is the death's head, or skull, and in forming the head-variants for the numbers from 14 to 19 inclusive, the fleshless lower jaw of the death's head was the part used to represent the value of 10 in these composite heads for these six higher numbers. Thus if the fleshless lower jaw is applied to the lower part of the head for 6, which is characterized by a pair of crossed sticks in the large eye socket, the resulting head will be that for 16; that is, 10 + 6. Or again, if this same fleshless lower jaw is applied to the lower part of the head for 9, which is characterized by a circle of dots on the lower cheek, the resulting head will be that for 19; or 10 + 9; further, by applying the fleshless lower jaw to the heads for 4, 5, 7, and 8, the heads for 14, 15, 17, and 18, respectively, are also obtained.

It is not improbable that the 13 heads representing the 13 numbers from 1 to 13 inclusive are those of the *Oxla-*

[2] The head-variant for the number 11 has not yet been surely identified.

huntiku or Thirteen Gods of the Upper World as opposed to the *Bolontiku* or Nine Gods of the Lower World, and that each one of the former was associated with one of these thirteen numbers, being its especial patron.

MAYA VIGESIMAL SYSTEM OF MATHEMATICS

In order to write the numbers *above* the first order of units, (those above 19), the ancient Maya made use of their positional system of numeration. In our own decimal system, the positions to the *left* of the decimal point *increase by tens from right to left*—units, tens, hundreds, thousands, etc. In the Maya positional system, however, the values of the positions *increase by twenties from bottom to top, with the single exception of the third position which, in counting time alone, is only* 18 *instead of* 20 *times the second,* an irregularity already mentioned.

To illustrate this, let us see how the Maya would have written various numbers of days above 20, selected at random. Take for example, the number 20 itself. This is 1 complete unit of the second order and no units of the first order, and thus involves two symbols, a symbol for zero in the first or lowest position to show that no units of the first order are involved in the number, and one unit of the second order.

One of the commonest symbols for zero in the Maya hieroglyphic writing was the conventionalized shell (the lower or first symbol in Fig. 24, *a*), and by placing a shell  in the first or lowest position to denote 0 units of the first order and a dot • in the second position to denote 1 unit of the second order, the number 20 was written (Fig. 24, *a*).

The number 37 was written as shown in Figure 24, *b,* that is, 17 units of the first order and 1 unit of the second order; the number 300 as shown in Figure 24, *c,* that is, 0 units of the first order and 15 units of the second order. The number 360, the third order of units, was written as shown in Figure 24, *d,* that is, 0 units of the first order, 0 units of the second order, and 1 unit of the third order of days.

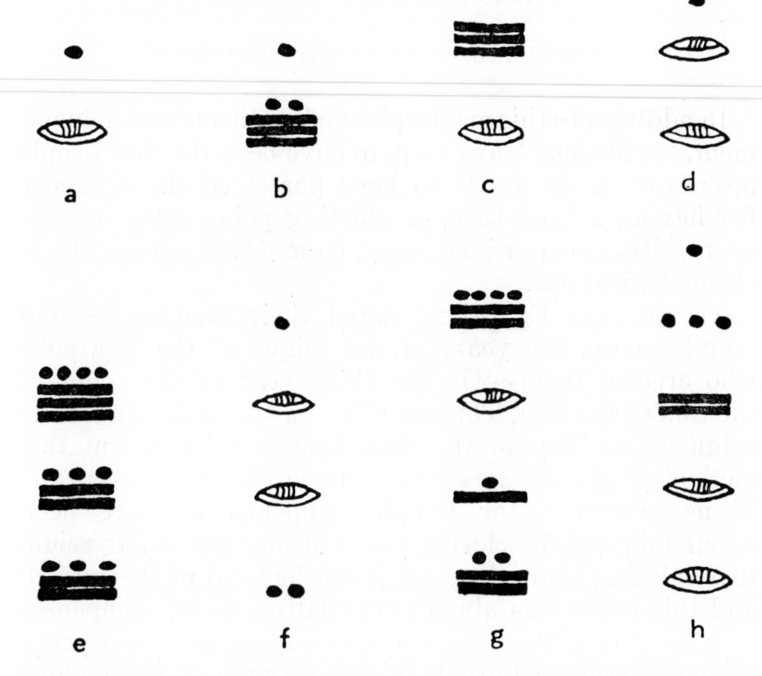

FIG. 24.—Examples of Maya numbers above XIX in bar-and-dot notation: (*a*) 20; (*b*) 37; (*c*) 300; (*d*) 360; (*e*) 7,113; (*f*) 7,202; (*g*) 100,932; (*h*) 169,200.

The number 7,113 was written as shown in Figure 24, *e*, that is, 13 units of the first order, 13 units of the second order, and 19 units of the third order. The number 7,202, involving four orders of time units, is shown in Figure 24, *f*, or 2 units of the first order, 0 units of the second order, 0 units of the third order, and 1 unit of the fourth order. The number 100,932 is shown in Figure 24, *g*, or 12 units of the first order, 6 units of the second order, 0 units of the third order, and 14 units of the fourth order. Finally the number 169,200, involving five orders of time units, is shown in Figure 24, *h*, or 0 units of the first order, 0 units of the second order, 10 units of the third order, 3 units of the fourth order, and 1 unit of the fifth order.

MAYA CHRONOLOGY

STARTING POINT OF THE SYSTEM

In addition to this masterpiece of mathematical achievement, the ancient Maya seem to have been the first people anywhere in the world to have perceived the necessity for having a fixed base, or starting point, some definite event, either real or imaginary, from which to count their chronological era.

The ancient Egyptians dated their monuments and temples from the years of the reigns of the Pharaohs who erected them—"In the third year of the reign of the Son of the Sun, Thutmose"; "In the fifth year of the reign of the Son of the Sun, Rameses," etc. But this method of dating was relatively crude and inaccurate. If no monument or temple happened to have been erected during the closing years of any particular reign, these closing years dropped from the total of the record, and this error was always cumulative, never compensative, so that in the course of the several thousand years of the Pharaonic Period, this one source of error alone amounted to several centuries.

Even until fairly recent times the custom of dating from the years of the reigns of successive sovereigns was a general practice throughout Europe.

Most peoples, however, sooner or later have realized the necessity of having a fixed starting point from which all their chronological records could be counted; but the indications are that the ancient Maya were the first of all peoples to reach this important and, chronologically speaking, basic concept.

The specific events, selected by different peoples of the world at different times for the starting points of their respective chronologies, may be classified into two general groups: (1) those starting from specific historical events, and (2) those starting from obviously hypothetical, that is to say assumed, events.

The most familiar chronology of the first group is our

own Christian Era, the starting point of which is the birth of Christ, our years being reckoned as B.C. (Before Christ) or A.D. (Anno Domini—"In the Year of Our Lord"), according as they precede or follow this event.

The Greeks reckoned time by four-year periods called Olympiads from the earliest Olympic Festival of which the winner's name was known, namely, from the games held in 776 B.C., the winner of which was a certain Coroebus. The Romans took as their starting point the supposed foundation of Rome by Romulus and Remus in 753 B.C., counting their years from this event.

The Babylonian chronological epoch was called the "Era of Nabonassar," and dated from the beginning of that king's reign in 747 B.C. The death of Alexander the Great in 325 B.C. ushered in the "Era of Alexander." With the occupation of Babylon in 311 B.C. by Seleucus Nicator began the so-called "Era of the Seleucidae." The conquest of Spain by Augustus Caesar in 38 B.C. marked the beginning of a chronology which endured for more than fourteen centuries in the Iberian Peninsula. The Mohammedans selected as the starting point of their chronology the Flight of the Prophet Mohammed from Mecca in A.D. 622, events being described in Mohammedan chronology as having occurred so many years after the Hegira or Flight. Indeed, this last chronology has persisted in Turkey down to within the past two decades, only having been partially abolished by Kemal Pasha.

It will be noted that every one of the foregoing chronological systems has for its starting point some actual historical event, the occurrence, if not the date, of which is indubitable. There are, however, other chronologies, those belonging to the second group mentioned above, that begin with an event the very nature of which renders the date of its starting point necessarily hypothetical. Here should be included those chronologies which reckon time from a supposititious date of the creation of the world.

For example, the "Era of Constantinople," the chronological system used in the Greek Church, commences with the Creation, which is reckoned as having taken place in 5509 B.C. The Jews consider the same event as having taken place in 3761 B.C. and begin their era at that time. Perhaps the most familiar example of a chronology belonging to this second group is that of the old family Bible, which fixes the creation of man, that is the birth of Adam, as having occurred in 4004 B.C. Archbishop Usher is responsible for this chronology, having naively fixed the date of Adam's birth by adding the years of the generations beginning with Adam and ending with Joseph, the father of Christ as given in the Bible (the Book of Genesis and the Gospel according to St. Matthew), reaching a total of 4,004 years.

While we do not know the nature of the event with which the ancient Maya began their chronology, it is practically certain that it was hypothetical rather than historical.

This is true because the zero date of the Maya chronological era, "4 Ahau 8 Cumhu," precedes their earliest contemporary records . . . i.e., for more than 3,400 years after the beginning of their time count—that is, during the first 8 *baktuns* and nearly through the ninth *baktun*—there is not a single contemporary date; of the Maya Era the first record occurs in 8.14.3.1.12. This can mean only one thing, namely, that the starting point of Maya chronology was selected as such a very long time (probably nearly 3,000 years) *after* it was actually current time; and further, that this long blank period, devoid of contemporaneous records of any kind, probably is to be interpreted simply as a priestly approximation of past time as a whole, rather than regarded as a chronological era that had been in use for more than three thousand years before its first records appear.

It was suggested earlier that the actual inauguration of the Maya calendar probably took place in 7.0.0.0.0, or 7.6.0.0.0 of the Maya Era—either 2,760 or 2,878 years after its zero date. In view of this fact and in view of the absence of all contemporary records dating from the first three thousand four hundred years of the Maya Era, we are forced to conclude that the astronomer-priests who devised Maya chronology selected for its starting point a date 7 *baktuns* (2,760 years) earlier than the date of its actual inauguration. Therefore it seems much more likely that Maya chronology began with some hypothetical event, rather than with an actual historical occurrence. Possibly it may have commenced with a supposititious event like the creation of the world, from which the chronologies used in the Greek and Jewish Churches, as well as in the old family Bible, are reckoned. Perhaps it may even have been counted from the supposed date of the birth of their gods, in which indefinite and remote past we must leave this question as yet undetermined.

THE INITIAL SERIES, OR LONG COUNT

The Initial Series method of dating was first so named by A. P. Maudslay, the English archaeologist and explorer. When it occurs, this time count is usually found at the beginning of the inscription; hence the name "Initial Series," which Maudslay gave to it.

Ernst Forstemann, the German archaeologist, first worked out the details of the Initial Series count as they are presented in the codices, in 1887. J. T. Goodman, the American archaeologist, though better known as the man who gave Mark Twain his first literary job as cub reporter on the *Virginia City Enterprise* of Virginia City, Nevada, first deciphered this time count in the inscriptions on the monuments in 1890, basing his work on Maudslay's magnificent reproductions of Maya sculptures. Goodman's discoveries, made quite without knowledge of Forstemann's slightly earlier investigations, are in perfect agreement with the latter's findings and prove beyond all possibility of doubt that the ancient Maya Initial Series time count is now as clearly understood as our own Gregorian calendar.

A brief description of a typical Initial Series follows: At the beginning stands a large glyph, usually four times as large as the other glyphs in the inscription, which has been called the introducing-glyph because it "introduces" the Initial Series time count (Fig. 25). The only part of this large initial glyph which varies in the different inscriptions (except for minor differences in style) is the central element, of which there are nineteen different forms, one for each of the nineteen divisions or months of the Maya calendar year, already described. These variable central elements, in all probability, as suggested in the preceding chapter, are the name-glyphs of the deities who presided over the nineteen divisions or months of the year. The form recorded in any given introducing-glyph is probably that of the name-glyph of the specific deity who was patron of the month in which the corresponding Initial Series terminal date fell.

Maya inscriptions are to be read from left to right and top to bottom in pairs of columns so that the two columns of smaller glyphs immediately below the large introducing-glyph in Figure 25 are to be read from left to right and top to bottom.

The first five glyphs in these two columns, following this order of reading, are the number of baktuns, katuns, tuns, uinals, and kins involved in writing this particular date, that is, the periods of 144,000, 7,200, 360, 20, and 1 days, respectively, that have elapsed from the starting point of Maya chronology—the date 4 Ahau 8 Cumhu, described above but not actually recorded—down to the date reached by this particular Initial Series number.

Although the unit of the Maya Initial Series is the day, while that of our own Christian chronology is the year, the two systems are not unlike in their respective methods of record. For example, when we write the date Monday, December 31, A.D. 1945, we mean that 1 period of one thousand years, 9 periods of one hundred years, 4 periods of ten years and 5 periods of one year have elapsed since the birth of Christ, the starting point of our own chronology, called "Anno Domini," (abbreviated to A.D.) meaning "In the Year of Our Lord," to reach a day Monday, which was the 31st day of the month of December.

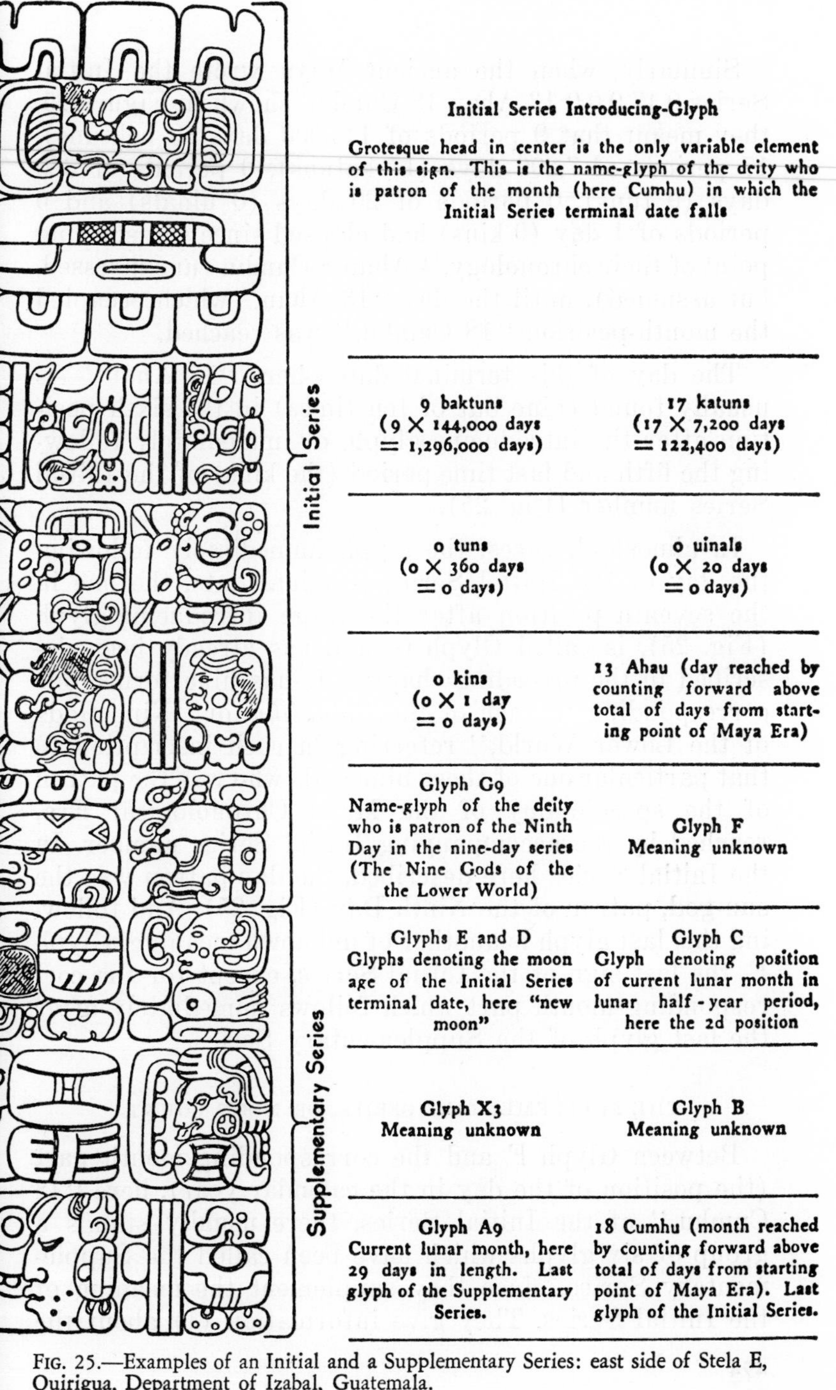

Initial Series
Supplementary Series
Initial Series Introducing-Glyph
Grotesque head in center is the only variable element of this sign. This is the name-glyph of the deity who is patron of the month (here Cumhu) in which the Initial Series terminal date falls
9 baktuns (9 × 144,000 days = 1,296,000 days)
17 katuns (17 × 7,200 days = 122,400 days)
0 tuns (0 × 360 days = 0 days)
0 uinals (0 × 20 days = 0 days)
0 kins (0 × 1 day = 0 days)
13 Ahau (day reached by counting forward above total of days from starting point of Maya Era)
Glyph G9
Name-glyph of the deity who is patron of the Ninth Day in the nine-day series (The Nine Gods of the Lower World)
Glyph F
Meaning unknown
Glyphs E and D
Glyphs denoting the moon age of the Initial Series terminal date, here "new moon"
Glyph C
Glyph denoting position of current lunar month in lunar half-year period, here the 2d position
Glyph X3
Meaning unknown
Glyph B
Meaning unknown
Glyph A9
Current lunar month, here 29 days in length. Last glyph of the Supplementary Series.
18 Cumhu (month reached by counting forward above total of days from starting point of Maya Era). Last glyph of the Initial Series.

FIG. 25.—Examples of an Initial and a Supplementary Series: east side of Stela E, Quirigua, Department of Izabal, Guatemala.

Similarly, when the ancient Maya wrote the Initial Series 9.17.0.0.0 13 Ahau 18 Cumhu, shown in Figure 25, they meant that 9 periods of 144,000 days (9 baktuns), 17 periods of 7,200 days (17 katuns), 0 periods of 360 days (0 tuns), 0 periods of 20 days (0 uinals) and 0 periods of 1 day (0 kins) had elapsed since the starting point of their chronology, 4 Ahau 8 Cumhu (unexpressed, but assumed), until the day "13 Ahau" which occupied the month-position "18 Cumhu," was reached.

The day of this terminal date—here "13 Ahau"—is usually found (nine out of ten times) in the sixth position after the introducing-glyph, or immediately following the fifth and last time period (the kins) of the Initial Series number (Fig. 25).

In almost all cases, the glyph immediately following the day of the Initial Series terminal date, the one in the seventh position after the large introducing-glyph (Fig. 25), is called Glyph G, and has already been described in the preceding chapter. It has nine forms, one corresponding to each of the *Bolontiku,* or "Nine Gods of the Lower World," referring in each inscription to that particular one of these nine gods who was the patron of the specific day of the Maya Chronological Era, reached by the accompanying Initial Series number. In the Initial Series here described, the day-patron was the sun-god, patron of the Ninth Day (Fig. 25). And following this last glyph is another of unknown meaning, Glyph F, the last sign of the Initial Series, except for the corresponding month part which follows immediately after the last glyph of the Supplementary Series.

THE SUPPLEMENTARY SERIES, OR MOON COUNT

Between Glyph F and the corresponding month part (the position of the day in the calendar year), here "18 Cumhu," of the Initial Series, there usually stands a group of six glyphs which have been called the Supplementary Series, since they supplement the meaning of the Initial Series. They give information (1) about the moon on the date recorded by the accompanying Initial Series, that is the age of the moon, probably counted from new moon; (2) the length of the particular lunar month in which the Initial Series date fell, that is, whether it was composed of 29 or 30 days, here 29 days; (3) the number of the particular lunation in the lunar half-year period, here 2; and a few other as yet undetermined points. Finally, following the last glyph of the Supplementary Series is the month-glyph of the Initial Series terminal date, in the text illustrated here, "18 Cumhu" (Fig. 25).

And thus by means of their simple, yet highly efficient, vigesimal numerical system, as expressed in their amazingly accurate Initial Series or Long Count, the ancient Maya were able to fix any given date in their chronology with such a high degree of precision that it could not recur, fulfilling all the prescribed conditions, until after a lapse of 374,440 years—a truly colossal achievement for any chronological system, whether ancient or modern.

METRODORUS

(c. 500 A.D.)

Metrodorus, a Greek grammarian and mathematician, is credited with the compilation of the mathematical portion of the Greek Anthology. He is said by some to have lived as early as the third century A. D., but it is more likely that he flourished during the reigns of the Emperor Anastasius I (491—518 A.D.) and of his successor, the Emperor Justin (518—527 A.D.).

The modern version of the Greek Anthology is based on a tenth century manuscript found in the library of the Elector Palatine at Heidelberg, in 1606. The manuscript, known from the place of its discovery as the Palatine ms., consisted of fifteen books of short poems or epigrams, organized according to subject matter. After enthusiastic and unusually extended study, it was translated, edited and published in thirteen volumes (1794—1814). Selections found in previous anthologies, but not included in the Palatine ms. were added to the Anthology as a sixteenth book. The Palatine ms. and the Planudean ms. (Florence 1494) which it replaced in popularity, were both based on previous Greek anthologies. Of these, the *Garland* of Meleagar of Gadara (1st century B.C.), was the first to be compiled. Meleagar's *Garland* was greatly admired in his time and the basic value of the Greek Anthology today rests in a large measure upon the material taken from his collection. In the *Garland,* Meleagar added some epigrams of his own to selections from the works of contemporary poets and earlier writers, going as far back as 700 B.C. Similar anthologies were compiled in the first century A.D. and later. In the sixth century the format was changed from an alphabetical order according to the initial letter of the first word of the selection, to an arrangement according to subject matter. As each of the great collections added some selections written subsequently to those already compiled, the ninth and tenth century manuscripts of the Greek anthologies contained representative extracts of the most highly valued writings composed over a span of about seventeen hundred years.

Book XIV of the Greek Anthology is devoted to mathematical problems, riddles and oracles. The problems are written in epigrammatic form and on the basis of their style, they are believed to have been written by Metrodorus. Although Metrodorus may have added some problems of his own, he is generally credited, not with devising the problems, but with collecting them. Judging by their content, many of the problems may have originated in the fifth century B.C. or earlier. There are simple problems of the type found in the Rhind Papyrus (17th century B.C.). Problem 49 is illustrative of the application of the rule given by Thymaridas, an early Pythagorean (6th century B.C.). The rule, known as the "flower" or "bloom" of Thymaridas, was used to solve simultaneous equations when the number of unknowns was the same as the number of equations. Problems 12 and 50 are reminiscent of references by Plato (428—347 B.C.) to the use of bowls made of the same or of different metals as aids in the education of Egyptian children (*Laws* VII, 819). Problems are included which lead to types of determinate and indeterminate equations dealt with by Diophantus (c. 250 A.D.). Problem 126 is the famous source of our information concerning the details of the life of Diophantus.

●

THE GREEK ANTHOLOGY

translated by William R. Paton.

BOOK XIV

6.—Problem

"Best of clocks, how much of the day is past?" There remain twice two-thirds of what is gone.

Solution: 5-1/7 hours are past and 6-6/7 remain.

7.—Problem

I am a brazen lion; my spouts are my two eyes, my mouth, and the flat of my right foot. My right eye fills a jar in two days, my left eye in three, and my foot in four. My mouth is capable of filling it in six hours; tell me how long all four together will take to fill it.

Solution: The scholia propose several, two of which, by not counting fractions, reach the result of four hours; but the strict sum is 3-33/37 hours.

11.—Problem

I desire my two sons to receive the thousand staters of which I am possessed, but let the fifth part of the legitimate one's share exceed by ten the fourth part of what falls to the illegitimate one.

Solution: 577-7/9 and 422-2/9.

12.—Problem

Croesus the king dedicated six bowls weighing six minae,[2] each one drachm heavier than the other.

Solution: The weight of the first is 97½ drachm, and so on.

48.—Problem

The Graces were carrying baskets of apples, and in each was the same number. The nine Muses met them and asked them for apples, and they gave the same number to each Muse, and the nine and three had each of them the same number. Tell me how many they gave and how they all had the same number.

Solution: The three Graces had three baskets with four apples in each, *i.e.* twelve in all, and they each gave three to the Muses. Any multiple of twelve does equally well.

49.—Problem

Make me a crown weighing sixty minae, mixing gold and brass, and with them tin and much-wrought iron. Let the gold and bronze together form two-thirds, the gold and tin together three-fourths, and the gold and iron three-fifths. Tell me how much gold you must put in, how much brass, how much tin, and how much iron, so as to make the whole crown weigh sixty minae.

Solution: Gold 30-1/2, brass 9-1/2, tin 14-1/2, iron 5-1/2.

50.—Problem

Throw me in, silversmith, besides the bowl itself, the third of its weight, and the fourth, and the twelfth; and casting them into the furnace stir them, and mixing them all up take out, please, the mass, and let it weigh one mina.

[2] One mina = 100 drachms.

Solution: The bowl weighs 3/5 of a mina, or 60 drachmae.

51.—PROBLEM

A. I HAVE what the second has and the third of what the third has. *B*. I have what the third has and the third of what the first has. *C*. And I have ten minae and the third of what the second has.

Solution: *A* has 45 minae, *B* has 37-1/2, and *C* has 22-1/2.

116

MOTHER, why dost thou pursue me with blows on account of the walnuts? Pretty girls divided them all among themselves. For Melission took two-sevenths of them from me, and Titane took the twelfth. Playful Astyoche and Philinna have the sixth and third. Thetis seized and carried off twenty, and Thisbe twelve, and look there at Glauce smiling sweetly with eleven in her hand. This one nut is all that is left to me.

Solution: There were 336 (96 + 28 + 56 + 112 + 20 + 12 + 11 + 1).

117

A. WHERE are thy apples gone, my child? *B*. Ino has two-sixths and Semele one-eighth, and Autonoe went off with one-fourth, while Agave snatched from my bosom and carried away a fifth. For thee ten apples are left, but I, yes I swear it by dear Cypris, have only this one.

Solution: There were 120 (40 + 15 + 30 + 24 + 11).

118

MYRTO once picked apples and divided them among her friends; she gave the fifth part to Chrysis, the fourth to Hero, the nineteenth to Psamathe, and the tenth to Cleopatra, but she presented the twentieth part to Parthenope and gave only twelve to Evadne. Of the whole number a hundred and twenty fell to herself.

Solution: 380 (76 + 95 + 20 + 38 + 19 + 12 + 120).

119

Ino and Semele once divided apples among twelve girl friends who begged for them. Semele gave them each an even number and her sister an odd number, but the latter had more apples. Ino gave to three of her friends three-sevenths, and to two of them one-fifth of the whole number. Astynome took eleven away from her and left her only two apples to take to the sisters. Semele gave two quarters of the apples to four girls, and to the fifth one sixth part, to Eurychore she made a gift of four; she remained herself rejoicing in the possession of the four other apples.

Solution: Ino distributed 35 (15 + 7 + 11 + 2) and Semele 24 (12 + 4 + 4 + 4).

120

The walnut-tree was loaded with many nuts, but now someone has suddenly stripped it. But what does he say? "Parthenopea had from me the fifth part of the nuts, to Philinna fell the eighth part, Aganippe had the fourth, and Orithyia rejoices in the seventh, while Eurynome plucked the sixth part of the nuts. The three Graces divided a hundred and six, and the Muses got nine times nine from me. The remaining seven you will find still attached to the farthest branches."

Solution: There were 1680 nuts.

121

From Cadiz to the city of the seven hills the sixth of the road is to the banks of Baetis, loud with the lowing of herds, and hence a fifth to the Phocian soil of Pylades —the land is Vaccaean, its name derived from the abundance of cows. Thence to the precipitous Pyrenees is one-eighth and the twelfth part of one-tenth. Between the Pyrenees and the lofty Alps lies one-fourth of the road. Now begins Italy and straight after one-twelfth appears the amber of the Po. O blessed am I who have accomplished two thousand and five hundred stades journeying from thence! For the Palace on the Tarpeian rock is my journey's object.

Solution: The total distance is 15,000 stades (say 1,500 miles); from Cadiz to the Guadalquivir, *i.e.* to its upper waters, 2,500, thence to the Vaccaei (south of the Ebro) 3,000, thence to the Pyrenees 2,000, thence to the Alps 3,750, thence to the Po 1,250, thence to Rome 2,500.

123

TAKE, my son, the fifth part of my inheritance, and thou, wife, receive the twelfth; and ye four sons of my departed son and my two brothers, and thou my grieving mother, take each an eleventh part of the property. But ye, my cousins, receive twelve talents, and let my friend Eubulus have five talents. To my most faithful servants I give their freedom and these recompenses in payment of their service. Let them receive as follows. Let Onesimus have twenty-five minae and Davus twenty minae, Syrus fifty, Synete ten and Tibius eight, and I give seven minae to the son of Syrus, Synetus. Spend thirty talents on adorning my tomb and sacrifice to Infernal Zeus. From two talents let the expense be met of my funeral pyre, the funeral cakes, and grave-clothes, and from two let my corpse receive a gift.[1]

Solution: The whole sum is 660 talents (132 + 55 + 420 + 12 + 5 + 2 + 34).

124

THE sun, the moon, and the planets of the revolving zodiac spun such a nativity for thee; for a sixth part of thy life to remain an orphan with thy dear mother, for an eighth part to perform forced labour for thy enemies. For a third part the gods shall grant thee home-coming, and likewise a wife and a late-born son by her. Then thy son and wife shall perish by the spears of the Scythians, and then having shed tears for them thou shalt reach the end of thy life in twenty-seven years.

Solution: He lived 72 years (12 + 9 + 24 + 27).

[1] Probably precious ointment.

126

This tomb holds Diophantus. Ah, how great a marvel! the tomb tells scientifically the measure of his life. God granted him to be a boy for the sixth part of his life, and adding a twelfth part to this, he clothed his cheeks with down; He lit him the light of wedlock after a seventh part, and five years after his marriage He granted him a son. Alas! late-born wretched child; after attaining the measure of half his father's life, chill Fate took him. After consoling his grief by this science of numbers for four years he ended his life.

Solution: He was a boy for 14 years, a youth for 7, at 33 he married, at 38 he had a son born to him who died at the age of 42. The father survived him for 4 years, dying at the age of 84.

129

A traveller, ploughing with his ship the broad gulf of the Adriatic, said to the captain, "How much sea have we still to traverse?" And he answered him, "Voyager, between Cretan Ram's Head and Sicilian Peloris are six thousand stades, and twice two-fifths of the distance we have traversed remains till the Sicilian strait."

Solution: They had travelled 3,333⅓ stades and had still 2,666-2/3 to travel.

130

Of the four spouts one filled the whole tank in a day, the second in two days, the third in three days, and the fourth in four days. What time will all four take to fill it?

Answer: 12/25 of a day.

131

Open me and I, a spout with abundant flow, will fill the present cistern in four hours; the one on my right requires four more hours to fill it, and the third twice as much. But if you bid them both join me in pouring forth a stream of water, we will fill it in a small part of the day.

Answer: In 2-2/11 hours.

132

This is Polyphemus the brazen Cyclops, and as if on him someone made an eye, a mouth, and a hand, connecting them with pipes. He looks quite as if he were dripping water and seems also to be spouting it from his mouth. None of the spouts are irregular; that from his hand when running will fill the cistern in three days only, that from his eye in one day, and his mouth in two-fifths of a day. Who will tell me the time it takes when all three are running?

Answer: 6/23 of a day.

133

What a fine stream do these two river-gods and beautiful Bacchus pour into the bowl. The current of the streams of all is not the same. Nile flowing alone will fill it up in a day, so much water does he spout from his paps, and the thyrsus of Bacchus, sending forth wine, will fill it in three days, and thy horn, Achelous, in two days. Now run all together and you will fill it in a few hours.

Answer: 6/11 of a day.

134

O woman, how hast thou forgotten Poverty? But she presses hard on thee, goading thee ever by force to labour. Thou didst use to spin a mina's weight of wool in a day, but thy eldest daughter spun a mina and one-third of thread, while thy younger daughter contributed a half-mina's weight. Now thou providest them all with supper, weighing out one mina only of wool.

Answer: The mother in a day 6/17, the daughters respectively 8/17 and 3/17.

135

We three Loves stand here pouring out water for the bath, sending streams into the fair-flowing tank. I on the right, from my long-winged feet, fill it full in the sixth part of a day; I on the left, from my jar, fill it in four hours; and I in the middle, from my bow, in just half a day. Tell me in what a short time we should fill it, pouring water from wings, bow, and jar all at once.

Answer: 1/11 of a day.

136

BRICK-MAKERS, I am in a great hurry to erect this house. To-day is cloudless, and I do not require many more bricks, but I have all I want but three hundred. Thou alone in one day couldst make as many, but thy son left off working when he had finished two hundred, and thy son-in-law when he had made two hundred and fifty. Working all together, in how many hours can you make these?

Answer: 2/5 of a day.

137

LET fall a tear as you pass by; for we are those guests of Antiochus whom his house slew when it fell, and God gave us in equal shares this place for a banquet and a tomb. Four of us from Tegea lie here, twelve from Messene, five from Argos, and half of the banqueters were from Sparta, and Antiochus himself. A fifth of the fifth part of those who perished were from Athens, and do thou, Corinth, weep for Hylas alone.

Solution: There were 50 guests.

138

NICARETE, playing with five companions of her own age, gave a third of the nuts she had to Cleis, the quarter to Sappho, and the fifth to Aristodice, the twentieth and again the twelfth to Theano, and the twenty-fourth to Philinnis. Fifty nuts were left for Nicarete herself.

Solution: She had 1,200 nuts (400 + 300 + 240 + 160 +50 + 50).

139

DIODORUS, great glory of dial-makers, tell me the hour since when the golden wheels of the sun leapt up from the east to the pole. Four times three-fifths of the distance he has traversed remain until he sinks to the western sea.

Answer: 3 hours and 9/17 had passed, 8 hours and 8/17 remained.

140

Blessed Zeus, are these deeds pleasing in thy sight that the Thessalian women[1] do in play? The eye of the moon is blighted by mortals; I saw it myself. The night still wanted till morning twice two-sixths and twice one-seventh of what was past.

Solution: 6-6/41 of the night had gone by and 5-35/41 remained.

141

Tell me the transits of the fixed stars and planets when my wife gave birth to a child yesterday. It was day, and till the sun set in the western sea it wanted six times two-sevenths of the time since dawn.

Answer: It was 4-8/19 hours from sunrise.

142

Arise, work-women, it is past dawn; a fifth part of three-eighths of what remains is gone by.

Answer: 36/43 of an hour had gone by.

143

The father perished in the shoals of the Syrtis, and this, the eldest of the brothers, came back from that voyage with five talents. To me he gave twice two-thirds of his share, on our mother he bestowed two-eighths of my share, nor did he sin against divine justice.

Solution: The elder brother had 1-5/7 talents, the younger 2-2/7, the mother 1 talent.

[1] Witches.

144

A. How heavy is the base I stand on together with myself! *B.* And my base together with myself weighs the same number of talents. *A.* But I alone weigh twice as much as your base. *B.* And I alone weigh three times the weight of yours.

Answer: From these data not the actual weights but the proportions alone can be determined. The statue *A* was a third part heavier than *B,* and *B* only weighed ¾ of the statue *A.* The base of *B* weighed thrice as much as the base of *A.*

145

A. GIVE me ten minas and I become three times as much as you. *B.* And if I get the same from you I am five times as much as you.

Answer: $A = 15\text{-}5/7$, $B = 18\text{-}4/7$.

146

A. GIVE me two minas and I become twice as much as you. *B.* And if I got the same from you I am four times as much as you.

Answer: $A = 3\text{-}5/7$, $B = 4\text{-}6/7$.

147.—*Answer of Homer to Hesiod when he asked the Number of the Greeks who took part in the War against Troy*

THERE were seven hearths of fierce fire, and in each were fifty spits and fifty joints on them. About each joint were nine hundred Achaeans.

Answer: 315,000.

MOSCOW PAPYRUS

(c. 1850 B.C.)

The Moscow Mathematical Papyrus, an ancient mathematical document, was discovered early in the 1890's in the Necropolis of Dra Abu'l Negga in Egypt. Shortly after the find, it was purchased by W. Golenishchev, a professor of Egyptian philology in the Egyptian University at Cairo. In 1912, after Professor Golenishchev's death, his entire collection including this papyrus, was acquired by the Moscow Museum of Fine Arts. Here it became the subject of intensive study by the curator of the Egyptological division and his associates. The painstaking efforts of these scholars and of other dedicated scientists drawn into the work by the world wide interest in the papyrus, met with enormous difficulties. Numerous scribal errors and the loss of some fragments of the papyrus complicated the impediments normally inherent in the decipherment of an ancient language. After many years of work, the text was translated and accompanied by a detailed discussion of its contents.

The papyrus, which belongs to the latter part of the Middle Kingdom (2700—1670), is long and narrow, about eight centimeters in height. The text is in hieratic writing, underneath which the remnants of an earlier writing may be discerned. The Moscow Papyrus may be representative of a development in the method of writing, since the present writing is horizontal, reading from right to left, while the earlier partly erased writing is horizontal in some places and vertical in others. The textual material of the papyrus consists of twenty-five mathematical problems and their solutions, written in thirty-eight columns of varying length. The columns are well separated except in one instance where they run together. At the end of the last problem, a second long piece of papyrus is attached. Apart from some signs of an old writing remaining after an obviously incomplete erasure of a previous work, the attached papyrus is blank, offering mute evidence of the scribe's unfulfilled intention of writing a much larger work.

The problem types and methods of solution contained in the Moscow Papyrus are substantially the same as those of the Rhind and other Egyptian mathematical papyri. However, the Moscow Papyrus exhibits some advance in the geometrical problems of which it contains four. As in the Rhind, the solutions of the geometrical problems are basically arithmetical, offering no trace of a proof in the Euclidean sense. An analysis of the mathematical background needed for the formulation of the solutions has shown that the problems presented in the Moscow Papyrus required greater knowledge and ingenuity than those of any other Egyptian mathematical works that have come down to us. In particular, problem 14 of the Moscow Papyrus, where the volume of the frustum of a square pyramid is found, represents the high point of ancient Egyptian mathematics.

FOUR GEOMETRICAL PROBLEMS FROM THE MOSCOW MATHEMATICAL PAPYRUS

By Battiscombe Gunn and T. Eric Peet

With Plates

Problem No. 6.

(Transcription, Pl. xxxv.)

Example[1] *of calculating*[2] *an enclosure.*

If you are told: An enclosure of a set *and* 2 arurae, *the breadth having* ¾ *of the length:*

You are to treat ¾ *so as to find* 1; *the result is* 1⅓. [*You are to take*] *this* [12] *which is in a set and* 2 arurae 1⅓ <*times*>; *result* 16. *You are to calculate its square root; result* 4—*for the length, and the breadth has* ¾ *of it, namely* 3.

The correct procedure:

	4			
	12	3	\1	4
			\2	8

Notes on the Text.

Line 1. The word for the subject of the calculation is damaged both here and in line 2. The sign preceding (the latter clear in both cases) will be , the word being shown by the following in line 2 to be feminine. suits the damaged signs perfectly in both places—judging by the photograph—and seems to be the only word that does so. The word is used of many kinds of rectangular enclosed spaces, *cf.* not only the meanings "room," "house," but also *ꜥt nt ḫt*, "enclosure of trees," *i.e.*, "orchard[3]."

Lines 2, 4. . On the reading and meaning see the commentary.

Line 3. Before is a small gap, but it is unlikely that any signs are lost. For *ḫpr·ḫr m X*, cf. *Berlin Pap.* 6619 and the references *Journal*, xii, 125.

Line 4. The scribe has certainly omitted before .

Lines 4, 5. The fragment now mounted at the beginnings of these lines is undoubtedly out of place. The restorations in the transcription, Pl. xxxv, suit the gaps and the sense.

Line 6. The hieratic sign for "8" at the end is quite abnormal (as are a number of this scribe's numerals), but the reading is certain.

---

[1] To avoid confusion the numbers of the lines, given in the plates of transcriptions and referred to in the Notes on the Text, are omitted in the translations.

[2] Literally, "making" (*irt*). This verb is used of a number of various operations in the mathematical texts; in these four problems we find it meaning to "work out" the volume or area of a figure; to "take" a number so many times (multiplication) or "take" a fraction of a number; to "treat" a number so as to find another (division); to "extract" a square root.

[3] *Cf.* Brugsch, *Worterb.*, Suppl., 185-86.

PROBLEM Nº 6.

1
2
3
4
5
6

PROBLEM Nº 7.

1
2
3
4
5
6

Moscow Mathematical Papyrus. Problems 6, 7
Plate XXXV.

PROBLEM № 17.

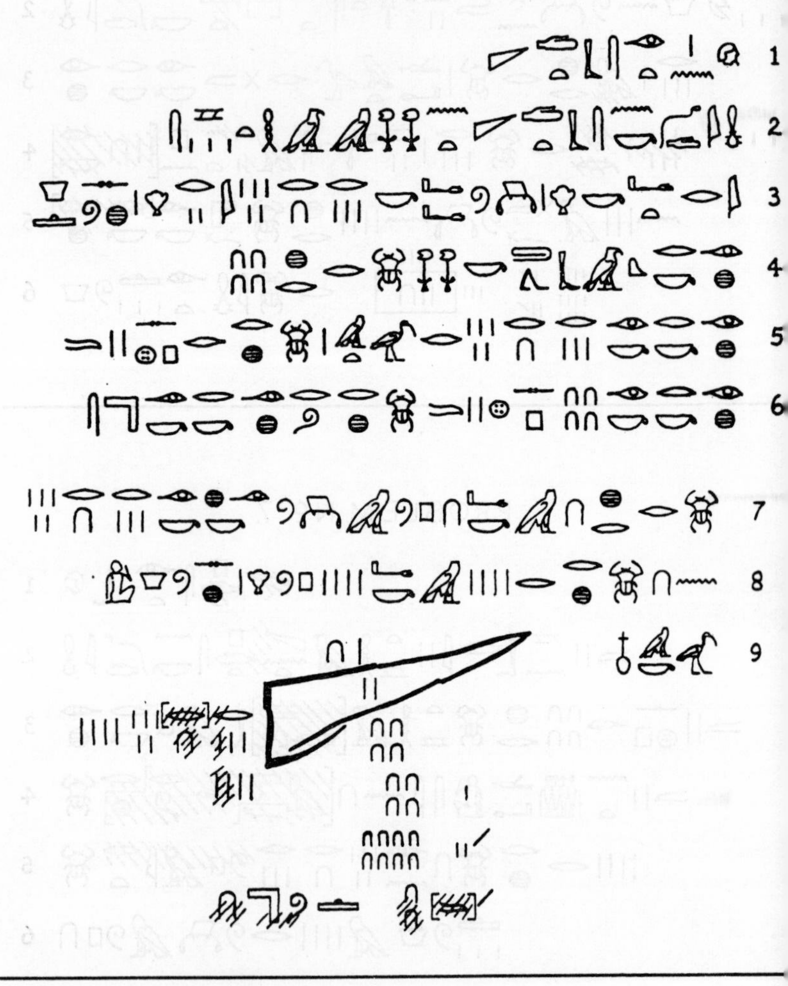

Moscow Mathematical Papyrus. Problem 17
Plates XXXV, XXXVI.

PROBLEM No 14.

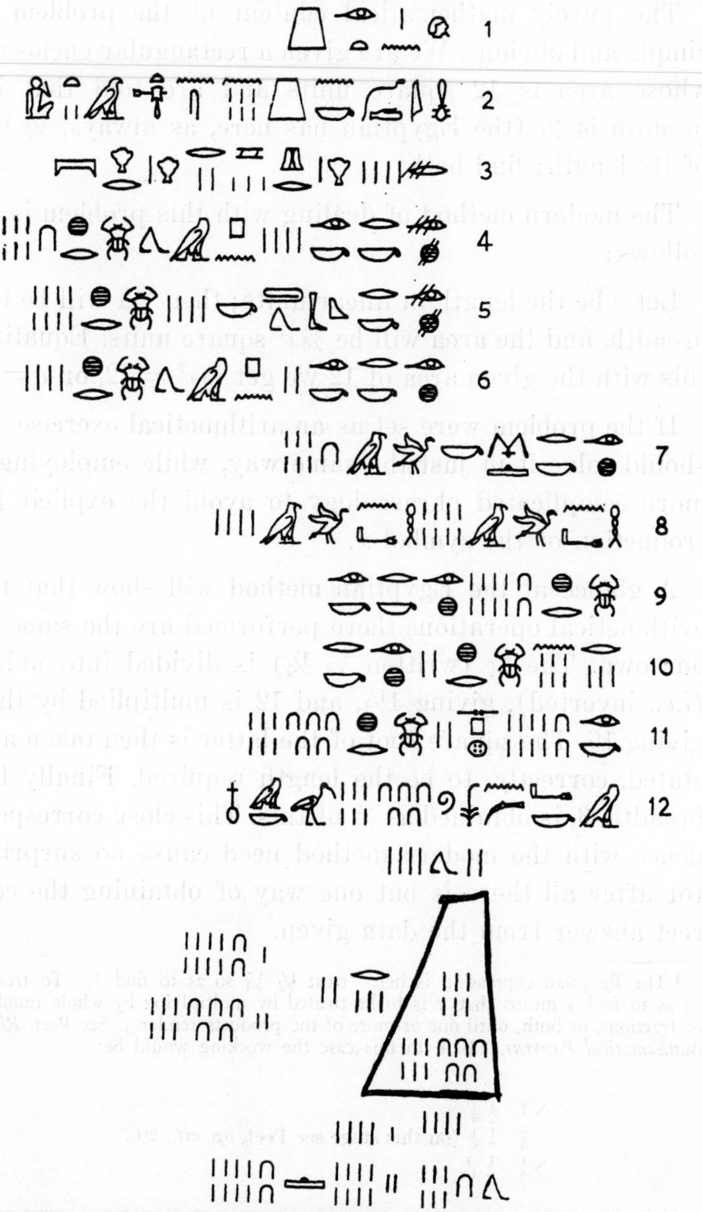

1

2

3

4

5

6

7

8

9

10

11

12

Moscow Mathematical Papyrus. Problem 14
Plate XXXVI.

COMMENTARY.

The purely mathematical content of the problem is simple and obvious. We are given a rectangular enclosure whose area is 12 square units and are told that its breadth is $\frac{3}{4}$ (the Egyptian has here, as always, $\frac{1}{2}$ $\frac{1}{4}$) of its length; find both.

The modern method of dealing with this problem is as follows:

Let x be the length in linear units; then $\frac{3}{4}x$ will be the breadth, and the area will be $\frac{3}{4}x^2$ square units. Equating this with the given area of 12 we get $\frac{3}{4}x^2 = 12$, or $x = 4$.

If the problem were set as an arithmetical exercise we should solve it in just the same way, while employing a more complicated phraseology to avoid the explicit introduction of the symbol x.

A glance at the Egyptian method will show that the arithmetical operations there performed are the same as our own. The $\frac{3}{4}$ (written $\frac{1}{2}$ $\frac{1}{4}$) is divided into unity[1] (*i.e.*, inverted), giving $1\frac{1}{3}$, and 12 is multiplied by this, giving 16. The square root of the latter is then taken and stated, correctly, to be the length required. Finally the breadth, 3, is obtained as $\frac{3}{4}$ of this. This close correspondence with the modern method need cause no surprise, for after all there is but one way of obtaining the correct answer from the data given.

---

[1] The Egyptian expression is here "treat $\frac{1}{2}$ $\frac{1}{4}$ so as to find 1." To treat x so as to find y means that x is to be treated by multiplying by whole numbers or fractions, or both, until one or more of the products render y. See Peet, *Rhind Mathematical Papyrus*, 13-14. In this case the working would be:

\ 1	$\frac{1}{2}$ $\frac{1}{4}$	
$\frac{2}{3}$	$\frac{1}{3}$ $\frac{1}{6}$	(on this stage see Peet, *op. cit.*, 20).
\ $\frac{1}{3}$	$\frac{1}{6}$ $\frac{1}{12}$	

Since $\frac{1}{2}$, $\frac{1}{4}$, 1/6 and 1/12 together render 1, the answer is 1 and 1/3.

At the same time it is obvious that the mental process involved in the Egyptian method is not the same as that involved in ours. This is hardly the place in which to discuss the psychological meaning of the use of the unknown x in mathematics, but it is at least clear that this, whether used explicitly in an algebraical solution or implicitly in some purely "arithmetical" one, gives to the modern method an abstract character entirely foreign to Egyptian mathematics. Once we have named our two sides x and $\frac{3}{4}x$ and multiplied them together to get the area—a concrete enough process this—we are in the realm of pure and abstract mathematics until we have found the value of x, namely 4, when we look back to the beginning to see what x was and so formulate our answer.

The Egyptian method, if we understand it rightly, is much more concrete than this. As usual, the solution shown gives only the operations to be performed. In the following paragraph we attempt to reconstruct the reasoned Egyptian solution of this problem, those parts which are found in the text being printed in italics:

"A rectangle having breadth ¾ of the length will have ¾ the area of a square on the length, since, one side of any rectangle being constant, the area varies directly as the length of the adjacent sides. The length of our enclosure will therefore be equal to the side of a square whose area shall have the same proportion to the area of the enclosure that the length of the latter has to its breadth. The breadth being ¾ of the length, *you must divide* ¾ *into* 1 to find the proportion of length to breadth; *the result is* 1⅓. *The area of our enclosure, namely* 12, *is* therefore *to be multiplied by* 1⅓; *result* 16, which is the area of the square sought. To find the length of a side of this square, *you are to calculate the square root*[1] *of* 16; *result* 4; *this is the length of the enclosure*[2]. *The breadth of the enclosure is* 3/4 *of it* (the length), *namely* 3.''

The figure, with indications of length, breadth and area, and the multiplication of 4 by 3 which accompanies it[3], constitute the proof, introduced here, as occasionally elsewhere, by *irt mi hpr*[4].

So much for the mathematical aspect of the problem. We have now to examine the square and linear measures employed.

The area of the enclosure is given in lines 2 and 4 as [hieroglyph]. No word written with [hieroglyph] is known to us elsewhere as a measure[5]. The hieratic sign rendered by us [hieroglyph] is a short horizontal stroke, perhaps meant to be slightly curved in line 2, and straight (but inclining upwards to the right as do all "horizontal" strokes in this script) in line 4[6]; this sign is identical with that used, with numerals under it, as here, in Middle Kingdom papyri and in the Rhind Papyrus for the *setat* (*arura*), a unit of area containing a square *khet*, the *khet* being a linear measure of 100 cubits; this sign is represented by [hieroglyph], [hieroglyph] and the like in hieroglyphic. Now the group [hieroglyph] is clearly an equivalent of the "12" which is to be restored in line 4, for we there read "[you are to take] this [12] which is in [hieroglyph], $1\frac{1}{3}$ ⟨times⟩; result 16." Whatever doubt may exist otherwise as to the exactitude of our restoration here, there can be none as to the "12," since the missing number, multiplied by $1\frac{1}{3}$, gives 16. The simplest interpretation of this difficult group would therefore seem to be that the [hieroglyph] stands, as elsewhere, for "2 *arurae*," and is preceded by a word [hieroglyph], otherwise unknown, representing a unit of square measure equal to 10 *arurae*. The principal objection to this view is that it is impossible to understand why the usual term for a unit equal to 10 *arurae*, namely the "thousand-of-land," is not used here, as it is elsewhere in this very papyrus[7]. That in both cases the word [hieroglyph] has no determinative and is not followed by the numeral "1"[8] could be put down to the ignorance of the scribe; the whole book abounds in errors both of orthography and in the forms of signs.

---

[1] The word for "square root" is written, here as elsewhere, with the sign [hieroglyph], which represents either a "corner" or more probably a "right-angle." The underlying idea is perhaps that a right-angle with equal arms, say of 3 in length, [hieroglyph]3, is the root of, in the sense of giving the *data* for, a square of 9. It is written [hieroglyph] in this MS, [hieroglyph] in *Berlin Pap.* 6619 and [hieroglyph] in *Kahun Papyri*, 8.40. If it is a masculine word it is probably to be read *tm*; cf. Schäfer in *Zeitschr. f. äg. Spr.*, XL, 96, title *ḥri-(ni)-tm*.

[2] The reckoner might equally well have elected to find the breadth first, it being the side of a square whose area is $\frac{3}{4}$ (Egyptian $\frac{1}{2}$ $\frac{1}{4}$) of the given enclosure, *i.e.*, 9 square units. The resulting 3 would actually have been found more simply than the length, for the division of unity by $\frac{3}{4}$ would have been avoided. This would, however, have had to be performed in the end in order to obtain the length 4 from the breadth 3.

[3] Once (4 is) 4; twice (4 is) 8; (once and twice = 3 times, 4 and 8 = 12).

[4] See Peet, *Rhind Math. Pap.*, 23, and Gunn in *Journal*, XII, 126.

[5] A word [hieroglyph] occurs in Gardiner, *Admonitions*, 14.4 (p. 90), and is tentatively translated by him "ground." It is certainly not used there as a measure.

[6] The apparent turn downwards at the right-hand end in line 4 is probably a deception of the photograph, though it is impossible to be quite certain.

[7] "2 thousands-of-land" is written [hieroglyph] in Problem No. 7 and [hieroglyph] in No. 17 (see below).

[8] The omission of the numeral seems to be without parallel. The Egyptian for "1 cubit 3 palms," for instance, is [hieroglyph], never [hieroglyph].

Problem No. 7.

(Transcription, Pl. xxxv.)

Example of calculating a triangle.

If you are told: A triangle of 2 *thousands-of-land, the "bank" of* 2½:

You are to double the area; result 40 (arurae). *Take* (*it*) 2½ *times; result* [100. *Take its square root, namely*] 10. *Evoke* 1 *from* 2½; *what results is 2/5*[7]. *Apply this to* 10; *result* 4. *It is* 10 (khet) *in length by* 4 (khet) *in breadth.*

Notes on the Text.

Lines 1, 2. The determinative of *śpdt*, "triangle," here, as in Problem No. 17 and the damaged Problem No. 4, has a shape quite different from that of the sign with which the same word is written in the Rhind Papyrus. In the latter the sign is the symmetrical upright *point* (thorn?)[1], with apex at top, with which all forms and derivatives of *śpd* (primarily meaning "to be sharp") are normally written in hieroglyphic and hieratic. In the Moscow Papyrus, on the other hand, it is a different sign, a scalene *triangle*, with vertical "base" and the apex high up on the right[2]. Thus the word *śpdt*, "the pointed," in its special meaning of "triangle" here receives a new determinative, a triangle.

Line 3. The restoration of the determinatives of *ḳꜣb* is based on the writings in Cols. 33 (Problem 17, line 4) and 27 (Problem 14, line 5).

Line 4. The restoration would just fill the gap. The tail of the [hieroglyph] is visible. The trace after [hieroglyph] suits [hieroglyph] (as in No. 17, line 6) and not [hieroglyph]. For the imperative *ir* in place of the more normal *ir·ḫr·k ir·k*, for which there is here no room, *cf.* lines, 3, 5 of this problem. Between [hieroglyph] and ∩ there is not room for more than [hieroglyph], though one might expect [hieroglyph] as in the last problem.

Line 5. For *ḫprt im pw* cf. Peet, *op. cit.*, 14, bottom.

Commentary.

Here is a problem in regard to which there can fortunately be no possible doubt. A triangle of given area is such that (to use our terms) its perpendicular height is 2½ times the base[3]; find both.

The measures employed are well known. The unit of area is the "thousand-of-land," expressed here, as in the Kahun Papyri and often in the Rhind Papyrus, by a

---

[7] Written 1/3 1/15.

[1] Certainly a concrete object. Influenced by the derivative *spdt*, "triangle," Moller (*op. cit.*, No. 567) and Gardiner doubtfully (*Grammar*, p. 522) have classed the sign with "Geometrical Figures."

[2] The triangles in the figures annexed to Problems 17 (see below) and 4 have the same form; see also the commentary below. The figures in Pl. xxxvi are facsimiles from the photographs.

[3] The Egyptian expression "the bank of 2½" is dealt with below.

simple "1" for each "thousand"; it was so called because it was regarded as made up of a thousand strips each 100 cubits (or one *khet*) long by 1 cubit broad[4]. It was equal to 10 *arurae* (or square *khet*), and thousands-of-land and decuple multiples of the *arurae* were used interchangeably in calculations, as we see from the odd-looking operation: twice 2 are 40[5]. The linear measure, although expressed merely by numerals, is obviously the *khet*.

We have seen in the preceding problem that, given the area of a rectangle and the proportions of its length and breadth, these latter dimensions can be ascertained. The Egyptian knew further that the area of a rectangle is double that of a triangle of the same "length" and breadth[6]." Therefore a problem of this kind can be solved by doubling the given area of the triangle and then operating as in the preceding problem.

You are, then, *to double the area; result* 40 (arurae)[7]. We now proceed as in Problem 6, with the difference that there we were told that the breadth was ¾ of the length, while here we are told that the length is 2½ times the breadth.

A given square will have 2½ times the area of a rectangle whose length is equal to a side of that square and is also 2½ times as long as the adjacent sides. To find, then, the area of a square having its side equal to the length of our rectangle, *you are to take* the area of the latter 2½ *times; result* 100. Of this 100 (*arurae*) you must now *take the square root, namely* 10, to find the side of the square, equal to the length of our rectangle. You must now find the breadth of the latter; to do this, *evoke* 1 *from* multiples or fractions of 2½, for the number or numbers which effect this will give us the number which has the same relation to 1 that 1 has to 2½. We

[4] See Griffith in *Proc. Soc. Bibl. Arch.*, 1892, 415.

[5] Similarly *Rhind Pap.*, No. 52: "you are to multiply 20 (*arurae*) 5 times; result 10 (thousands-of-land)."

[6] See Peet, *op. cit.*, 91 foll.; Gunn in *Journal*, xii, 133.

[7] The italicized words actually occur in the Egyptian text.

find that the fraction ⅓ of 2½ gives 2/3 1/6 (*i.e.*, 5/6), and that 1/15 of 2½ gives 1/6; since 5/6 and 1/6 are equal to 1, *what results as* the answer *is* ⅓ + 1/15, or 2/5 ; *i.e.*, 2/5 is to 1 as 1 is to 2½. Now, as the length of our rectangle has been found to be 10, *apply* (the fraction 2/5) *to* 10, that is, take 2/5 of 10, to find the breadth; *result* 4. But we know that the rectangle thus obtained has the dimensions of the sought triangle; therefore the latter *is* 10 (*khet*) *in length by* 4 (*khet*) *in breadth.*

We might expect the solution to be followed, as in the preceding problem and in the very similar No. 17, by a figure and some sort of proof; but our scribe has not provided these.

Problem No. 17.

(Transcription, Pls. xxxv, xxxvi.)

Example of calculating a triangle.

If you are told: A triangle of 2 *thousand* (*s-of-land*) *in its area, and what you put on the length, you must put* 2/5 *thereof*[2] *on the breadth*:

You are to double the 2 *thousands; result* 40 (arurae). *You are to treat* 2/5 *so as to find* 1; *result,* 2-1/2 *times. You are to take* 40 2½ *times; result* 100. *You are to calculate its square root; result* 10. *See, it is* 10 (khet) *in length. You are to take* 2/5 *of* 10; *result* 4. *See, it is* 4 (khet) *on the breadth.*

You will find (*it*) *right.*

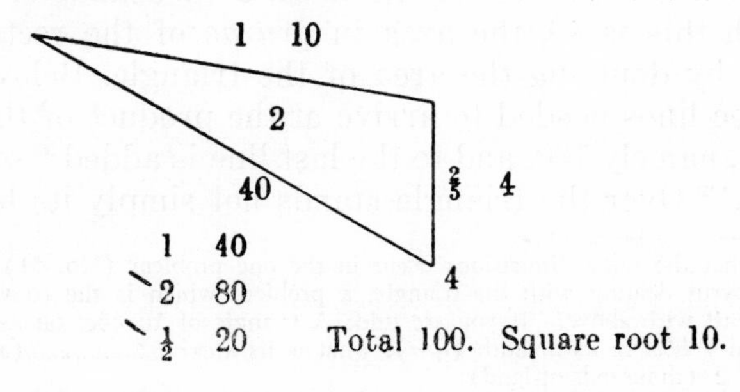

[2] Here and below, 2/5 is a translation of the "1/3 1/15" of the original.

Notes on the Text.

Lines 1, 2. The writing [hieroglyphs] **(elsewhere in this book** [hieroglyphs]**) is interesting as showing the early reduction of *p* to *b* in this root, a change already known for the late period from** [hieroglyphs] **> ⲥⲟⲃⲧⲉ and** [hieroglyphs] **[> *šbdt*] > Σῶθις; *cf.* Sethe in *Zeitschr. f. äg. Spr.*, L, 80.**

Lines 2, 4. The hieratic sign for [hieroglyphs] **is quite abnormally formed, but the reading is not in doubt.**

Line 3. [hieroglyphs] **is an interesting example of the Prospective Relative Form.**

Line 7. [hieroglyphs] a bungle of [hieroglyphs].

Line 8. The abnormal determination of a dimension-word by [hieroglyph] occurs elsewhere in this book; *cf.* p. 178, note 4 below.

Line 9. This sentence frequently follows the solution of a problem in this book (*cf.* No. 14 below); it occurs also in *Berlin Pap.* 6619 (*Zeitschr. f. äg. Spr.*, XXXVIII, Pl. 4), No. 3.

Figure. In the original the triangle is carelessly drawn, with no regard to the proportions, as in the transcription. Three of the numerals to the left (in the original) of the triangle are damaged, but traces remain of all of them, and of the reading there is no doubt.

Commentary.

In its nature and in the measures used[1], this problem is similar to that of No. 7; the only difference is that here we are told that the breadth is 2/5 of the length, whereas in No. 7 we were told that the length was 2½ times the breadth, statements which amount to the same thing, but which necessitate a variation in the Egyptian method of solution. As in No. 7, the given area of 2 thousands-of-land is doubled, giving 40 *arurae,* the equivalent of 4 thousands-of-land. The problem is now precisely similar to No. 6, and is worked out in the same way.

There follows a figure accompanied by some of the detailed working, not, as in No. 6, by the proof. In the triangle is a 2, indicating its area, 2 thousands-of-land. Beneath this is 40, the area in *arurae* of the rectangle formed by doubling the area of the triangle. Below are the three lines needed to arrive at the product of this 40 and 2½, namely 100, and to the last line is added "square root 10."[2] Over the triangle stands not simply its length

[1] Note that the same dimensions occur in the one problem (No. 51) in the Rhind Papyrus dealing with the triangle, a problem which is the converse of the two dealt with above: "If you are told: A triangle of 10 *khet* on its length (*mrit*) and 4 *khet* in its breadth (*tp-r*), what is its area? ....(answer) its area is 2 (thousands-of-land)."

[2] The lower part of this line is broken away; but the general dimensions of the papyrus show that there was no room for any further working-out.

10 (*khet*) just found, but a 10 immediately preceded by a 1. It may be that the 1 marks the 10 as the object of multiplication in the following computation:

1	10
2/5	4

for to the left (in the original) of the "breadth" is 2/5 4, standing for 2/5 of 10 = 4; but in such cases 1 as multiplier is always written in hieratic with a dot[3] instead of the usual stroke. Under the figures 2/5 4 stood the numeral 4; this is the measure in *khet* of the breadth, found by the above computation. As its correct place against the breadth was already filled up by the "2/5 4," the writer placed it as close as possible below.

The way in which the ratio of breadth to length of the triangle is stated in this problem is not without interest. In Problem 7 we saw that the ratio of length to breadth was expressed by the idiom "*ideb* of 2½." For the contrary ratio, however, namely breadth as fraction of length, there appears to be no technical term.

For our knowledge of the Middle Kingdom geometry of the triangle we now have four documents: *Rhind Pap.*, No. 51, *Moscow Pap.*, Nos. 7 and 17, discussed above, and No. 4, unpublished and incomplete, but of the same nature as *Rhind Pap.*, No. 51[3]. On these the following general remarks may be made:

1. They make it certain that the Egyptians of the period knew of the properties of the isosceles triangle which we should express by the following equations (a = area, h = height, b = base):

$$a = h \cdot \frac{b}{2};\quad h = \sqrt{2a \cdot \frac{h}{b}};\quad b = \frac{b}{h}\sqrt{2a \cdot \frac{h}{b}}.$$

2. There is nothing to show that these calculations were restricted to isosceles triangles. In the formation of the

[3] Rendered, however, in our plates of transcription as a short stroke.

[3] The obscure and faulty *Rhind Pap.*, No. 53 is disregarded here. In *Rhind Pap.*, No. 52 the translation, Peet, *op. cit.*, 94-5, Gunn in *Journal*, xii, 133, . . . "truncated triangle" correctly renders the idea conveyed by the Egyptian word, but obscures the fact that we have to do, from our standpoint, not with any sort of triangle but with a symmetrical trapezoid.

problems the general word *spdt,* "triangle," is used, and the solutions, both in the terms used and the methods employed, apply equally well to any sort of triangle. The figure attached to the Rhind problem is, it is true, isosceles; but that attached to *Moscow Pap.*, No. 17, is definitely scalene[4], as is the determinative of the word *spdt* in *Moscow Pap.*, Nos. 4, 7, 17. In the absence of any evidence to the contrary, we may take it as quite probable that the calculations summarized in the preceding paragraph were known to be valid for all triangles.

Problem No. 14.

(Transcription, Pl. xxxvi.)

Example of calculating a truncated pyramid.

If you are told: *A truncated pyramid of* 6 *for the vertical height by* 4 *on the base by* 2 *on the top*:

You are to square this 4; *result* 16. *You are to double* 4; *result* 8. *You are to square this* 2; *result* 4. *You are to add the* 16 *and the* 8 *and the* 4; *result* 28. *You are to take* ⅓ *of* 6; *result* 2. *You are to take* 28 *twice; result* 56. *See, it is of* 56.

You will find (*it*) *right.*

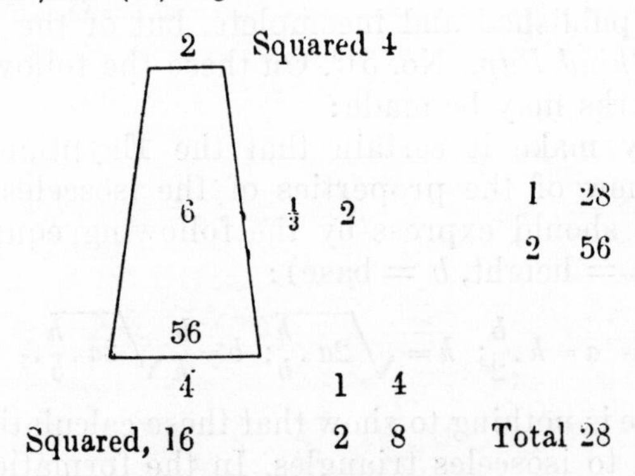

Notes on the Text.

The text is well preserved and presents no difficulties.

Figure. The solid is of course represented, as in the

[4] That of No. 4 is damaged, but as far as it goes it resembles that of No. 17.

hieratic ideogram (see line 1), as a simple trapezoid, and in the original is roughly drawn without regard to the proportions, as in the transcription.

Commentary.

The problem is to determine the volume of what we call a truncated pyramid, or frustum of a pyramid, the *data* being the vertical height (*stwti*) and the respective lengths of the sides of the two squares which bound the solid below and above.

If we call the height h and the sides of the lower and upper squares a and b respectively, the working may be represented as follows:

Square a, result 16. Multiply a by b, result 8. Square b, result 4. Add these results, total 28.

Take one-third of h, result 2. Multiply 28 by this, result 56, which is the volume sought.

Expressing these operations by a general formula, we have.

$$V = (a^2 + ab + b^2)\frac{h}{3},$$

which is exactly the formula used to-day to determine the volume of such solids.

The figure, and the numbers which accompany it, are quite straightforward. In the centre of the figure stands its height, 6. Below is the side a, namely 4, "squared, 16." Similarly above we have the side b, namely 2, "squared, 4." On the left (in the original), opposite the 6 inside the figure, we read ⅓ 2, indicating that one-third of the height 6 is 2. Below on the left (in the original) is the multiplication of a and b, that is 4 multiplied by 2, and this is followed by the total, 28, of the 16, the 8 and the 4. Above this is the final step, the multiplication of 28 by 2, giving 56. This number, which is that of the required volume, is then inserted in the figure, near the base.

R. NEHEMIAH

(c. 150 A.D.)

R. Nehemiah, a Hebrew rabbi, scholar and teacher, who lived in Palestine during the second century of the Common Era, was the author of the Mishnat ha-Middot, the earliest Hebrew treatise on geometry known to us. Nehemiah was one of the *Tannaim,* that is, one of the spiritual and intellectual leaders of Palestine of the first and second centuries, whose teachings, when compiled and codified, were to become the basis of a very extensive future rabbinical literature. A pupil of the famous R. Akiba, and a contemporary of Meir and Judah b. Ilai, Nehemiah belonged to the "Fourth Generation" of *Tannaim,* a group of scholars and teachers who were the source of religious and civil authority in Palestine from about 140 to 165. Nehemiah's maxims together with his explanations and supplementary notes, further enriched and elucidated by succeeding writers, constitute the foundation of the *Tosefta,* the rabbinical interpretation of Biblical law, as it has come down to us. The substance of his teachings, and the method of full and detailed presentation preferred by him, reveal Nehemiah as a zealous and untiring force in advancing the study and understanding of the Bible-verse. Nehemiah was also a mathematician. In this capacity, he was concerned with the determination of the calendar and with the study of the measures of the Ark and of the Tabernacle.

The old *Tannaitic* treatise, the *Mishnat ha-Middot,* became known in modern times through the translation and publication of two manuscripts. The first manuscript, Cod. Hebr. 36, in the Munich Library, containing five chapters dealing with the elements of plane and solid geometry appeared in a German translation in 1862. The other, MS. Heb. c. 18 of the Bodleian Library, more recently found, is a fragment consisting of two leaves which contain part of the first, second and fifth chapters already known and, in addition, the beginning of a sixth chapter, hitherto unknown. The fragment, on vellum and in Syr. Rabb. characters (sixth chapter), contains explanations of the size and the construction of the Tabernacle. The two manuscripts together have made it clear that the first five chapters of the *Mishnat ha-Middot* form a brief treatise on geometry which was introductory to a work elucidating the details of the construction and the measurements of the Tabernacle. The geometrical principles presented in the *Mishnat ha-Middot* were known for the most part to the mathematicians of Nehemiah's day. His own contributions were introduced in the manner of the ancient authors, by the words, "Nehemiah says." There is considerable evidence in the *Mishnat ha-Middot,* of Nehemiah's knowledge of Greek mathematics on the one hand, and on the other, of the influence of the old Hebrew work on Persian-Hindu-Arabic mathematics.

MISHNAT HA MIDDOT

Translation and Notes by SOLOMON GANDZ

Chapter I.

§1. There are four ways to grasp the area, namely: the quadrilateral, the trilateral[3], the circle, and the bow-figure[4–5]. The rule is as follows: the second figure is the half of the first one, and the fourth is the half of the third one[6]. All the rest of the figures are closely connected with them, respectively as the hook with the ring.

§2. The quadrilateral has three aspects[9]: the side, the thread[11] and the roof[12]. Which is the side? That holds

---

[3] Not "quadrangle" and "triangle;" see Grandz, The origin of Angle Geometry, p. 473ff. Isis v. 12.

[4] I. e.: segment.

[5] Euclid, Elements, I, deff. 15-29 (cf. also Hero, Opera Omnia, IV, p. 180), speaks of five forms of figures in such an order that the boundary lines are increasing in number from one to *n* lines, to wit: 1. the circle, 2. the semicircle, 3. the trilateral, 4. the quadrilateral, and 5. the multilateral. Our treatise brings only four figures, and in the converse order. It is interesting to note that Ganesa (c. 1520 A. D.), the Hindu commentator to the Lilavati of Bhascara (c. 1150 A. D.), has the same order and number as the Mishnat ha-Middot. He says: "Plane figure is four-fold: triangle, quadrangle, circle and bow;" see Colebrooke, p. 58, note. Although Ganesa lived as late as *c.* 1520, he must have followed some old tradition and source common to Hindu mathematics and Mishnat ha-Middot; see Gandz, The Origin of Angle Geometry, p. 477.

[6] So he understands here under "bow-figure" the semicircle, while in the following—I, 5; V, 4 seq.—any segment is meant. Dr. Neugebauer calls the attention to the fact that in Babylonian mathematics, too, no distinction is made between semicircle and segment.

[9] Literally "face," then "view," "viewpoint." The meaning is: it can be considered, investigated from three viewpoints; there are three elements to be examined in the quadrilateral.

[11] Khawt, = "thread, cord, rope," then "line." The word "line" comes from the Latin *linea*; this comes from *linum* "linen, rope;" see Tropfke, IV, 2nd ed., p. 38. The word is commonly used for "diagonal" and "diameter" in this treatise; see I, 3, 4; II, 3, 8; III, 4; V, 1, 2, 3, 7. The Chinese use a word denoting "rope" for the diagonal; see Cantor, I, 4th ed., pp. 679-80. The same is the case with the Hindus; see Colebrooke, p. 59, note 2; Smith, History of Mathematics, I, p. 98. On the use of the same term for diagonal and diameter see hereafter, note 16. Cf. also Gandz, Die Harpendonapten, p. 272f.

[12] "Roof," "surface," "area;" compare these words with the Arabic *sath,* originally "flat roof;" see the writer's article "Origin of the term Root" in The American Mathematical Monthly, vol. 33, p. 263, note 2. This Arabic *sath,* that is a translation of the Hebrew *gag,* was later retranslated by the Hebrew *shetah,* and used by Savasorda and Israeli, &c.

fast the walls of the roof[13]; for it is written[14]: *Foursquare shall be the altar*[15]. And the thread (diagonal) which is? That cuts[16] through from one angle to the other angle, *from*[17] *one corner to the other corner*. And that is the greatest [straight line] in the length of the roof[18]. And the roof itself is the area.

§ 3. And the trilateral has four aspects: the side-pair[20], the basis, the pillar, and the roof. Which is the side-pair? These are the two straight lines to the right and

---

[13] The quadrilateral is imagined as the flat roof of a building, and its sides as holding fast the walls of the building.

[14] Exodus, XXVII, 1.

[15] The reason for the quotation of this verse is not quite clear. The author apparently understands under m'ruvet a square; see hereafter, note 18, and above, note 5a. He cites this verse the altar shall be a square and thinks also of the continuation in v. 7: And the staves shall be upon the two sides of the altar, where the word tzeleh is used for the side of the square altar. This way of quoting only one part of a verse, or one verse of a section and thinking also of the following parts or verses is usual in the Midrashim. They rely upon it that the reader will look up the whole verse or section.

[16] The line that cuts the figure running from one corner to the other corner. It is worth while to note that the ancient Greek terminology had no special term for the diagonal, but called it a "line stretched from one corner to the other corner." The Sophists created the term meaning "diameter," using it promiscuously for the diagonal and the diameter of the circle. Hero introduced the term which stands for "diagonal." I refer to Hebrew-Aramaic *zalaf* = "the dropping, dripping of the rain", and remark that strings of the rain-drops usually come diagonally. This is corroborated by the Arabic *qutr* = "dropping rain, diagonal." The height is the falling stone, or plummet, because it falls perpendicularly. The diagonal is the string of the raindrops falling diagonally; see note 26a hereafter.

[17] Exodus, XXVI, 28; XXXVI, 33. The fact is that these verses refer to the two corners of one side and not to the opposite corners of the diagonal. These verses, as many of the following passages of the Scriptures, seem to be adduced only to show that the terms or similar words occur also in the bible. It is in the style of the old Mishnah to connect the law with the bible in any way. Cf. Zunz, Gesammelte Schriften, III, p. 243, who says concerning the Baraitha di Semuel: "Bei einzelnen Satzen werden, gleichsam um dem Gedachtnisse des Lesers zu Hilfe zu kommen, Bibelstellen angefugt."

[18] The author thinks only of the square or rectangle where both diagonals are equal and the longest lines. In the rhombus this is not the case. Cf. also notes 5a and 30.

[20] Comp. Schapira, p. 15, note 1. It is clear that the isosceles is here meant, having two equal sides or legs. In the Rhind Mathematical Papyrus, too, the figures show that only isosceles were taken into consideration; see Gandz, Origin of Angle-Geometry, p. 470; Cantor, I[4], p. 111; Chace, A. B., The Rhind Math. Pap., p. 36. Peet, pp. 91-92, brings a full discussion of the subject without reaching a decision. But Struve, pp. 147-152, convincingly proves the isosceles character of the triangles. Struve's conclusion was adopted by Neugebauer and corroborated by a Babylonian parallel; see QS. B 1, p. 416. Much later the scalene was considered; hence the name scalene = "limping." The normal triangle was that with two even legs.

left side; for it is written[24]: *For thou shalt spread abroad to the right and the left.* And the basis? That is upon which the two sides are established; for it is written[25]: *Upon which the house is established.* And the pillar? That is the common thread running down[26a] to the basis from between the two sides. And it is in the corner[27], *for the corners of the tabernacle.* And the roof itself is the area.

§ 4. The circle has three aspects: the circumference, the thread and the roof. Which is the circumference? That is the rope surrounding the circle; for it is written[29]: *And a rope of thirty cubits encompassed it round about.* And the thread? That is the straight-line from brim to brim; for it is written[31]: *From brim to brim.* And the roof itself is the area.

§ 5. And the bow figure[32] has four aspects: the bow, the

---

[24] Isaiah, 54, 3.

[25] Judges, 16, 26, 29. The Hebrew thought of the triangle as of an erected isosceles representing the tent with two equal pillars established upon the base; hence the name keveh = "basis", and tzeleh = "wall, side." "To the Egyptian mind," however, "triangles mostly lie flat on the ground;" cf. Chace, R. M. P., p. 37, note 1, quoting Gunn, and Struve, Quellen u. Studien, A. 1, p. 154. Therefore the Egyptian terms *tp r* = "mouth" for the base, and *mryt* = "rim, edge," "border" for the side or rather for the height; see Struve, p. 154 seq.; Neugebauer, QS, B. 1, p. 416, note 14, and notes 20, 37 of this chapter.

[26a] Yerekh = Arabic *warad* = Assyrian *aradu*, or *waradu* = "to come down, fall down." Hence the Assyrian term *urdu, urdam,* meaning "the coming down" for the arrow of the segment and for the height; see Neugebauer, QS, B. 1, p. 82 Archiv f. Orientforschung 7, p. 91 nr. 3 (1931). The Egyptian term for height is also *pr m ws* = "what comes out, or falls down from the window;" see Struve, QS, A. 1, p. 136; Neugebauer, QS, B. 1, p. 436, note 72. The Greek term for the perpendicular is equivalent to = "let fall, let down." Al-Khowarizmi, in his geometry, calls the foot point of the perpendicular: "The point where the stone falls down." They all think of the "plumb-line" or "plummet", that falls perpendicularly. The diagonal is the *ziliptu* = *qutr,* "the falling raindrops; see above, note 16.

[27] Add: "For it is written." The verse is in Exodus, 26, 23.

[29] I Kings, 7, 23.

[31] I Kings, 7, 23: "And he made the molten sea of ten cubits from brim to brim." The circle is thought of as lying flat on the ground; see further V, 1, 3. Like the molten sea and the Egyptian triangles, see above note 25, it has a brim. See also Heath, Euclid I, p. 184, citing Proclus' quotation from the oracles: "the centre from which all (lines extending) as far as the *rim* are equal."

[32] Literally: "the bow-like, arched, vaulted."

chord[32a], the arrow[33] and the roof. Which is the bow? That is a portion of the circle; for it is written[35]: *Like the appearance of the bow that is in the cloud.* The chord? That is which holds fast [36] the mouth [37] of the bow; for it is written[38]: *The bent bow.* And the arrow? That is the straight line from the middle of the bow to the middle of the chord[40]; for it is written[41]: *They fix their arrows upon the chord.* And the roof itself is the area.

§ 6. How does one measure the area in numbers[42]? You

[32a] Or "string.;" see also II, 4, and V, 5-7. The Hindus have for the "chord" the term *jya,* or *jiva,* which came to be the origin of our *sinus.* In the geometry of al-Khowarizmi, we have still the term *watar* corresponding to the Hebrew *yeter.* Later on the Arabs transliterated the Hindu *jiva* as *jiba,* which was mistaken for the Arabic word *jaib,* "bosom, fold," and then translated, first by Gerhard of Cremona (c. 1150), as *sinus.* This origin of the term *sinus* was first discovered by Munk in Journal Asiatique, 1863, p. 478, note. The most elaborate report on the subject and its literature is given by Tropfke, Geschichte der Elementar-Mathematik, V², pp. 31-33. Cf. also Braunmuhl, Geschichte der Trigonometrie, I, p. 49. Ruska, in Zeitschrift fur Mathematik und Physik, 1895, Literarisch-Historischer Teil, p. 127, says: "Es scheint, dass der ganze Wortkomplex Bogen, Sehne, Pfeil aus der indischen Trigonometrie herruhrt." Here, however, we find this terminology in the Hebrew geometry of c. 150 A. D.

[33] It is quite natural that the primitive mind borrowed his terminology for the segment from the hunter's bow. (The hunter's bow is also believed by some scholars to have suggested the first musical instrument, the stringed instrument; see L. Thorndike, History of Civilization, p. 24 and cf. also Wreszinski, W., Atlas zur altagyptischen Kulturgeschichte, plates No. 80, 81, representing Egyptian artisans of the 15th century B. C. in the procedure of making bows; ib. also the main literature for the history of the bow.) The same terminology was also used in the Talmudic sources see Babli Erubin 55a (cf. also Tosefta IV, 3; ed. Zuckermandel, VI, 1; Yer. V, 1).

[35] Ezekiel, I, 28.

[36] Compare above, § 2 "the side that holds fast the walls of the roof," and note 13.

[37] The Egyptians called the base of an isosceles triangle and of an isosceles trapezium *tpr* = "the mouth;" see Peet, Rhind Mathematical Papyrus, p. 91, Struve, p. 152, and Neugebauer, QS, B. 1, p. 416, 419; the Hindus named the upper side of a quadrangle *mukha,* or *vadana,* = "opening, mouth;" see Colebrooke, p. 72, note 4, and p. 307, § 36, quoted by Cantor, I⁴, p. 647, and above note 25.

[38] Isaiah 21, 15. There is no mention of the chord here. The meaning is perhaps, that the bow is bent by the chord that holds fast the two ends.

[40] The arrow is the height of the segment. We may say that M. ha M. here teaches to construct a perpendicular by drawing a straight line from the middle of the arc to the middle of the chord, which is essentially like Euclid, Elements I, 12 (see Heath, I, p. 271). Only, that Euclid also proves it.

[41] Psalms, II, 2. This verse could have been used for all the three terms. The beginning reads: "For, lo, the wicked bend the bow."

[42] The meaning is: How do you compute the area when the numbers of the sides are given?

figure one upon one[43] that is the area[44], and it is one cubit upon one cubit. Thus, if a roof[45] has equal sides and angles you count them from each side, [and if it has one cubit to each side then the whole roof is one]. And if the plane[47] has two [cubits] from each side and the angles are equal, the area contains four times the measure of the unit, which is one cubit upon one cubit. And if it has three from each side, then [the area] is nine times the measure of the unit, and so is four upon four and five upon five. From now on go ahead and figure according to this measure[49] upwards[50].

§ 7. Those[51] less than a unit you divide as follows: One cubit[52] into two threads, cutting each other in the middle, [running] from the right side to the left side and also from the top to the bottom. The roof is thus divided into four sections and you find half a cubit upon half a cubit

---

43 See Gandz, "Terminology of Multiplication," p. 261, notes 74-77.

44 I. e. the unit of the area.

45 Surface or plane; see note 12 above.

47 **טבלא = tabula = τάβλα = "board, tablet;" it is here used for surface and plane like the term "roof." Usually the tablet was square, טבלא מרובעת ; see Mishna Erubin, IV, 8; V, 1.**

49 Or "method."

50 This somewhat elaborate definition of the unit of the area is very important. It is lacking in Euclid; see Gutmann's note to Hibbur ha Meshiha, p. 22, § 42. Its first appearance is here, from where al-Khowarizmi took it; § 1 of his geometry.

51 § 7 gives the geometric demonstration for the rule of the fractions. The same demonstration is also found in the Hibbur ha Meshiha, § 43, p. 23 for the integers, I. e., to prove that the double side gives four times the square of the unit, etc. In § 8 the arithmetical form of the rule is given and an arithmetical demonstration by the change of the position in the decimal order. Then comes in § 9 the general rule corresponding to the multiplication of fractions, and finally II, 1 gives the general rule for getting the area of rectangles by multiplying length into breadth. Contrary to his habit, the author of the Mishnat-ha-Middot gives here demonstrations and proofs in order to bring home the very important idea and right conception of the areal content. The error in those times was widespread that the same perimeter gives the same area, and plain people could not understand how the square of the double side can give more than the double of the area; see the interesting examples quoted by Cantor I[4], pp. 172-73, and confer also the wonderful passage in Plato's "Dialogi," ed. Hermann, III (Lipsiae 1851), pp. 333 to 339; Engl. translation by B. Jowett, II, 3rd ed., pp. 41-46. There Socrates proves to Menon's boy that the double square does not develop from the double line, as the boy originally thought and answered, but from the diagonal of the first square. The proof is by drawing and demonstration like here.—See also Gandz, Terms relating to Area, p. 85.

52 Is to be bisected.

[for each side] and the area itself is the fourth part of a cubit, which is the fourth of a square cubit. So is a third upon a third, and a fifth upon fifth, with equal and unequal [sides]. From now on go ahead and figure with fractions according to this measure[56] downwards.

§8. They already said[57]: Half upon half is a fourth [part], and so is a third upon a third a ninth [part]. With these and their similars, with equal and unequal [sides]. . . . You figure as follows: Ten upon ten are amounting to a hundred. The half of ten is five. Five times five are twenty and five, and this is the fourth of 100. And the position of the 10 is in the 1, and the position of the 100 in the 10, and of the 1000 in the 100. From now on go ahead and figure with the fractions according to the measure of the units[61]. But with the units it is[62] increasing and with the fractions it is decreasing.

§9. The rule is as follows: Half upon a half is the half of the half. And a third upon a third is the third of the third. So is the half upon a third the half of the third. And so is a fourth upon a third the fourth of the third. With these and their similars with equal and unequal [sides].

Chapter II.

§1. If someone wants to measure quadrilateral fields, with equal or unequal sides, let him multiply length upon breadth, and the result[3] from both is the area.

§2. If a trilateral, with equal or unequal sides, let him multiply the pillar[4] in the half of the basis, and the result from both is the area. But there are many other methods for that[6].

---

56 Or "method," see note 49.

57 I. e. it is an old tradition, or rule.

61 Integers.

62 The product and the square content.

3 Literally: oleh = to go up, "climb, ascend, reach:" cf. the Latin *resilio* "to spring back, rebound," from which the term "result" comes, and the Arabic *fama balagha* "to reach, amount."

4 Literally: ha-omed = "the upright standing."

6 For the finding of the area of the triangle; This may allude to the methods set forth in chapter IV.

§3. How is it with the circle? Let him multiply the thread[7] into itself, and throw away[8] from it one seventh and the half of a seventh; the rest is the area. For instance: The thread is 7 long[9], its multiplication [into itself] is 49; a seventh and half a seventh [of it] is $10\frac{1}{2}$; the area is thus $38\frac{1}{2}$[10].

§4. How is it with the bow [figure][11]? Let him add the arrow to the chord, [take] both together and multiply them into the half of the arrow and put them aside[12]; and again let him take the half of the chord, multiply it into itself and divide it upon 14 and the result let him add to

---

[7] The diameter; see chap. I, notes 11, 16.

[8] This is the usual term for subtraction.

[9] Literally: "extended to seven;" the length of diameter is usually given as seven, that the circumference $\left(c. = \frac{22}{7} d\right)$ might give a whole number (22): see V, 3.

[10] The formula given here for the area of the circle is $A = d^2 - \frac{1}{7} d^2 - \frac{1}{14} d^2 = \frac{11}{14} d^2$. This is based, of course, upon the formula $A = \frac{1}{2}$ *circumference* multiplied by the radius, or $\frac{c}{2} . \frac{d}{2}$, and upon the computation of $\pi = 3 + \frac{1}{7}$. We have then $\pi r^2 = \frac{22}{7} . \frac{d^2}{4} = \frac{11}{14} d^2$. The same formula is given Hero, IV, p. 387, in the name of Archimedes as follows: eleven squares erected upon the diameter are equal to fourteen areas of the circle, $11 d^2 = 14 A$; $A = \frac{11}{14} d^2$; see also ib. III, p. 65, and IV, p. 182-83. In Hero, ib. IV, p. 332, Euclid is quoted to have given the area of the circle as $d^2 - \frac{1}{7} d^2 - \frac{1}{14} d^2$, exactly like the Mishnat ha Middot. Hero, ib., uses also ἐκβάλλω "to throw away" the seventh and fourteenth part of d^2 and the usual numbers are $d = 7$, $c = 22$. As a matter of fact, however, Euclid in his Elements, or other writings known to us, never gives the computation of the area of the circle, nor of other areas or volumes; — The formula $A = d^2 - \frac{1}{7} d^2 - \frac{1}{14} d^2$ is also in Hibbur ha Meshiha, §96, p. 61; in the geometry of al-Khowarizmi, §4 *in fine*, and of al-Karkhi (c. 1020), Kafi fil Hisab, II, p. 23.

[11] The segment.

[12] As one addend.

the one[13] standing [aside]; the resulting [sum] is the area[14]. But there are other methods in that[15].

§ 5. If one wants to measure a square solid[16] in numbers, with equal or unequal sides, having length, breadth and thickness, six faces[18], "each one had six wings"[19], let him multiply length into breadth into depth[20], and the result from all three is the volume[20a] of the solid, and that is also the body.

§ 6. If it was circular[23], or trilateral[24], or of any number of sides, provided that its depth was straight and fair[26],

---

13 Addend.

14 If we call the chord c, the arrow h, and F the area, then the formula is $F = (c + h)\frac{h}{2} + \frac{1}{14}\left(\frac{c}{2}\right)^2$. For the semicircle the formula is accurate. $c + h = 3r$; hence the formula is $\frac{3r^2}{2} + \frac{1}{14}r^2 = F$, which is equal to $\frac{\pi r^2}{2}$, if we take $\pi = 3\frac{1}{14}$. For the other segments the formula is accurate to two decimals; see Schapira, p. 20, note 7. If we take $\pi = 3$, then the formula is reduced to $(c + h)\frac{h}{2}$, in which form it was known to the Chinese (c. 176 B. C.) and to the Hindu Mahavira (c. 850); see Smith, History of Mathematics, I, pp. 139, 164. Hero of Alexandria refers to this inaccurate formula of the ancients and improves it by the addition of $\frac{1}{14}\left(\frac{c}{2}\right)^2$ to $(c + h)\frac{h}{2}$; see Hero, III, p. 72 sq., p. 80, line 12, p. 83; IV, p. 357 seq. and p. 363 seq.; V, pp. 185-191; Cantor, I[4], p. 379. This formula is also found in Calumella's (c. 60 C. E.) works; see Cantor, ib. p. 549, but not in Savasorda's nor in al-Khowarizmi's geometry. In Babylonian mathematics we find computations of chord, arrow and diameter, but not of the arc; see Struve-Neugebauer, QS., B. 1, pp. 90-92.

15 For the finding of the area of the segment; see V, 5, 6.

16 A body with quadrilateral surfaces and right angles. Gov, or Govoh = "back," then Govyah = Guf = body.

18 Surfaces. Hero, def. 105, quoted by Heath, Euclid, III, p. 269, speaks of prisms having six faces.

19 Isaiah 6, 2.

20 See Gandz, "The Origin of Angle-Geometry," § 15, p. 469.

20a Here and in the following, §§ 6, 7, 9, 10, the term mishikhah is used for the volume of a body, too.

23 A cylinder.

24 A prism.

26 B. has Yesher v'shav, "straight and even." The meaning is that base and top are parallel. But conception and term of parallelism are still missing in M. ha-M.; see Gandz, The Origin of Angle-Geometry, p. 466.

then measure its roof[27] according to the [above] mentioned measure, and you will ascertain the area; and the result you will multiply into the depth. And the [result] is the bulk of the body.

§7. And the decreasing one[29] [like the ethrog][30], with a sharp top and flat bottom[31], be it quadrilateral, circular, or trilateral: you measure the area of the bottom, throw away two thirds of the area and hold one third, and multiply it into the height, and the result is the bulk of the body, from the top to the bottom[35].

Chapter III.

§1. There are five[1] kinds of quadrilaterals[3] as follows: (1) one with equal sides and angles; (2) one with un-

---

27 The area of the top or bottom.

29 *M'shokh,* "drawn together, contracted," as subsequently explained, a solid having a flat, plane base and tapering, being contracted to a point or acute top; cf. Hero, IV, p. 54 seq.: "A cone is a solid figure having a circle for its base that is *contracted* to a point."

30 Ms. B.: has v'ham'shokh k'ethrog and the word ethrog occurs there again in § 9. The word is known from the Talmudic literature. The *ethrog* is a kind of a citron which is nearly cone-shaped. It is prescribed for the religious observances of the Feast of Tabernacles. Similarly, in the later literature, the cone is called alonee and etz'trovlee, "in the shape of the fir — cone:" See Klatzkin, Thesaurus Philosophicus, I, pp. 48, 71.

31 Sof = "end, bottom, lowest part, basis;" al-Khowarizmi has a word = "lowest part, bottom." This definition, "having a sharp top and a flat bottom" certainly sounds more ancient and primitive than the definition given by Hero, above, note 29, and Euclid, Elements, XI, def. 12, 18-20, Heath, III, pp. 268, 270. The conception and term of the mathematical point do not occur in the Mishnat ha-Middot. In the Talmud we have the word n'kudah and khod for the dot and point in general, but not for the mathematical point.

35 The formula is $bh/3$. We know it on the authority of Archimedes that Eudoxus (c. 370 B. C.) was the first who proved this formula for the volume of the pyramid and cone; see Smith, I, p. 91, Cantor, I[4], p. 241. The Hindus, however, as late as in the time of Aryabhatta (c. 510) still had a wrong formula ($bh/2$) for the volume of the pyramid; see Smith, II, p. 293; Cantor, I[4], p. 645. Maimonides, Moreh N'Vokheem, I, 36, also speaks of the error of those that think the cone to be the half of the cylinder with the same base and height.

1 The same five kinds of quadrilaterals also in Euclid, I, definition 22; see Heath, Euclid, I, p. 188 seq. The Hindus have also five classes of quadrilaterals, but of different kind; see Cantor, I[4], pp. 651, 727. Al-Khowarizmi, § 9, follows the M. ha M.

3 The quadrilaterals are treated before the trilaterals like in I, 2, 3. The reason for that is that the triangle is regarded as half of the quadrangle; see I, 1; IV, 2. In Hero's works, too, the quadrangles precede the triangles; see Cantor, I[4], pp. 389, 391, 395, 506.

equal sides and equal angles[6]; (3) one with equal sides and unequal angles[7]; (4) one with <equal and> unequal sides and angles, [namely] with the two lengths equal for themselves and the two breadths [equal] for themselves; and (5) one with entirely unequal sides and angles.

Chapter IV.

§1. There are three kinds of triangles as follows: The upright[1] one, the acute and the open[2] one. What is that an upright one? Its two short sides are multiplied each into itself [and added to each other]. And the long side which is the base is multiplied into itself. Then the last [square] is equal to the first one. For example: Six from this side and eight from that side, [and ten from the long side]; and the result of these [two each multiplied] into itself is hundred, and [the result] of that[8] [side] into itself is hundred. (If[9]) one wants to measure[10] [let him multiply one] of the short ones into the half of the other one, either 8 into 3 or 6 into 4, and the result is the area.

§2. And the angle standing between the short ones is the upright[11]. And this [triangle] is the half of a quadrilateral with unequal sides and equal angles[12].

---

6 The rectangle.

7 The rhombus.

1 The name is taken from the solid upright standing triangle; see Gandz, Origin of Angle-Geometry, pp. 464 seq., 471 seq.

2 The obtuse. Above, III, 4, the oblique angles are called "narrow" and "broad;" see note 11 hereafter.

8 The hypotenuse, which is ten.

9 In round brackets is given the translation of the corrupt text, as presented by manuscript and editions. Subsequently, in square brackets the emendated text, as suggested by al-Khowarizmi's version, is given; see note 13.

10 The triangle.

11 The right angle is called the "upright angle" and is defined as standing between the short sides of the upright triangle. Similarly, in § 4 and 10, the acute and obtuse angles are described as occurring in the acute, respectively obtuse triangle; see "Origin of Angle-Geometry", pp. 467 seq., 471 seq. The M. ha M., by its character, is nearer to Egyptian than to Greek mathematics. It has here (see §§ 4-9) the division of the trilaterals according to the sides, equilateral, isosceles or scalene, but not the grouping according to the angles. On the contrary the angles are grouped after the shape of the trilaterals, where they occur.

12 The rectangle.

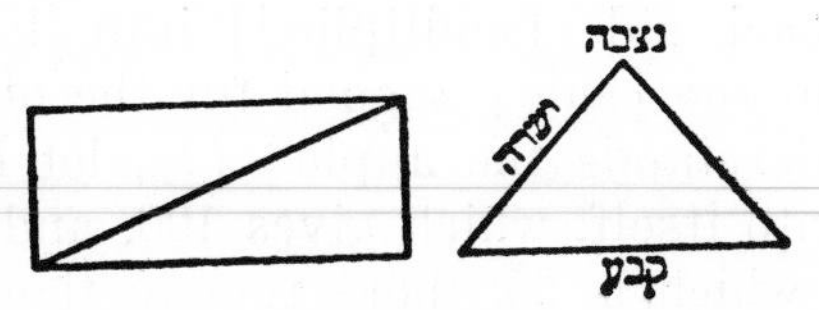

§5. If one wants to know the measure of the pillar in the equilateral [triangle], let him multiply one of the sides into itself [and the half of the other side into itself] and throw off the smaller [square] from the larger. The rest is the foundation[25] and what is found[26] is the pillar.

§6. How does one calculate in numbers[27]? Ten upon ten is 100, the half of the other side, which is 5, multiplied into itself is 25. And he throws off the small from the large, [hence] there remains 75 and this is the foundation and its root is 8 and a rest[29]. If one wants to measure let him multiply the root into the half of the bottom side[30] and the result of the computation is the area, which is 43 and a rest.

§7. (There[31]) are seven[32] other kinds of trilaterals. The

25 The square.

26 By extracting the root. Read perhaps v'ekro "and its root," like in the following paragraph.

27 Compare I, 6, note 42.

29 Shirim is the usual term in the Talmud for a small balance in fractions.

30 The base.

31 In round brackets is given the translation of the text as presented by the manuscript. It seems to be corrupt. The whole paragraph seems to be a variant to §§ 5-6, which is indicated by the gloss s.a., or sifrim akharim "a reading of other books," that came into the text; see note 20 to the Hebrew text. This variant differs from § 6 in one very important point. In § 6 the root of 75 is given as 8 and a balance; it is multiplied into 5 and said to give 43 and a rest. But since the balance of $\sqrt{75}$ over 8 is not mentioned, we do not know how the result of 43 and a balance is obtained. Here, however, 5 is brought under the root, and we have $5.\sqrt{75} = \sqrt{75.25} = \sqrt{1875} = 43\ldots$ This is the method of al-Khowarizmi, § 10h; the transformation of $a\sqrt{b}$ into $\sqrt{a^2b}$ is taught in al-Khowarizmi's "Algebra," pp. 19-20.

32 Steinschneider suggests that the word shivah was originally written for the letter zion indicating that it is the seventh Mishna. Schapira emendates into yashbah. If we maintain the reading shvah, however, this would give an interesting parallel to Hero. Hero, IV, pp. 38 and 92, speaks of six species of trilaterals, like Euclid; see Euclid, I, def. 20-21; Heath, Euclid, I, pp. 187-89. But on pp. 132, 150 and 269 ib. Hero mentions seven kinds of trilaterals. They are I. The equilateral; 2-4, the right, acute, and obtuse isosceles; 5-7, the right, acute, and obtuse scalene. Similarly, Proclus has 7 kinds; see Heath, ib., p. 188.

equilateral, each side [multiplied] into itself. What is said from the one [side] is good for the other one. The one who understands the apple[33] (?), let him multiply one [side] into itself, which gives 100, and throw away the quarter, which is 25, there remain then 75. (If one wants to measure.) [There are other ways in an equilateral triangle. Each side is [measuring ten, f. e.] ... If one wants to measure, let him multiply one [side] into itself, this gives 100, and throw away the quarter, which is 25, there remain then 75]; let him multiply 75 into 25, this is three quarters[35] into one quarter, this amounts to 1875; let him take the root of it, and this is the area and this is 43 and a rest. Thus you find here that the pillar[36] always falls upon the half of the base.

§8. You have, thus, found out the [area of the] equilateral and which is similar to it[37]. As for the calculation of the scalenes[38], however, there is nothing more difficult than that in the calculation of the area. If one is searching for them, let him closely consider either the sides or the pillar and the base[39].

---

33 The meaning is dark. May be "apple-numbers," or "algebra"? Cf. Heath, Greek Mathematics, I, p. 15 says: "Several of them (of the problems in the Greek anthology) are problems of dividing a number of apples or nuts among a certain number of persons."

35 This does not mean the transformation of common into decimal fractions, as Schapira thinks. It rather gives the general formula for the altitude, as $\sqrt{\frac{3a^2}{4}}$ and for the area as $\sqrt{\frac{3a^2}{4} \cdot \frac{a^2}{4}}$. The Heronian formulae for the equilateral triangle are $\frac{\sqrt{3}}{4} a^2$ and $\frac{a^2}{3} + \frac{a^2}{10}$ see Hero, III, p. 46 seq. and Cantor, I[4], pp. 376 and 399.

36 In the equilateral triangle.

37 The isosceles.

38 Literally khalofim = "the different, unequal ones," i. e.: the triangles with unequal sides.

39 In the following, only the first method, i. e.: to compute the area by the three sides, is given. But the method of finding out the height and its footpoints is not given.

§ 9. How[40] does one figure? For example: a triangle with unequal sides and acute angles[41], 15 from one side, 14 from the other side and 13 from the third side. Whoever wants to measure, let him seize the three of them together, they amount to 42: let him take the half [of it] and see how much greater it is than the first side, and let him multiply the half upon the difference, this is 21 into 6, which gives 126, and put it on the side; let him again, for the second time, take the half and see how much greater it is than the second side, and let him multiply the difference, which is 7, into the first 126, which amounts to 882, and put it on the side; let him again, for the third time, take the half and see how much greater it is than the third side, and let him multiply the difference, which is 8, into the last 882, and this amounts to 7056 and its root is 84, and this is the measure of the area.

Chapter V.

§ 1. There are three kinds of the circular [figures] as follows: The suspended one[2], the hill-like[3] and the flat one[4]. What is that the suspended one? That is one that stands on the root[5] of a circle from all the sides, [like] a sphere, or that the surface was like [that of] a water-

[40] Here the so called Heronian formula, $\Delta = \sqrt{s\ (s-a)\ (s-b)\ (s-c)}$, is given, in words of course. The formula $\sqrt{s\ (s-a)\ (s-b)\ (s-c)}$ and the method of finding the perpendiculars of a triangle when the sides are given are ascribed, on the authority of al-Biruni (c. 1000), to Archimedes (c. 225 B. C.); see Bibliotheca Mathematica, XI, 3 (1910-11), pp. 37-40, 69; Heath, Greek Mathematics, II, p. 103; Smith, History, II, p. 287; Tropfke, IV², p. 9. The Heronian formula became very popular. It is found in the Roman agrimensores; see Cantor, I⁴, pp. 555, 590. Brahmagupta (c. 628) gives one and the same formula for triangle and quadrilateral, namely $A = \sqrt{(s-a)(s-b)\ (s-c)\ (s-d)}$; in the triangle d is $= 0$.

[41] Here, exceptionally, the triangle is defined according to the angles; see above, note 11.

[2] The sphere.

[3] The hemisphere.

[4] The circle.

[5] Here used perhaps in the meaning of "side," or "circumference"; compare III, 2, where the side of a square is called root, because it stands upon it. Hence the root of a circle would be the point upon which it stands.

melon which is circular all around, provided that its rounding is equal in length, breadth and depth[5a]. How does one measure? Let him multiply the threads, the one into its own half, [and the result let him multiply into 3 + 1/7], and the result is the area[7]. And double it, because they[8] are its walls.

§2. What is that the hill-like one? That is one that stands on[8a] the half of the suspended one, like a hill or a vaulted tent, provided that it is even. If one wants to measure, let him multiply one of the threads [running] from one end to the other end into the half of the other one or into its own half, [and the result let him multiply into 3 + 1/7] and the result is the area.

§3. What is that the flat one? That is one that is put down [flatly] on the ground like a circular field or a circular figure. If one wants to measure, let him multiply the thread into itself and throw away from it the one seventh and the half of a seventh; the rest is the area, its roof. And if you want to know the circumference all around, multiply the thread into 3 and one seventh[13] and it amounts to 22[14]. And if you want to compute the area, take the half of the circumference which is 11 and multiply it into the half of the thread[15] which is 3 and a half, and it amounts to 38 and a half. It is the same [result] according to the first [method] and the last one.

[5a] A melon which is "circular all around" and the rounding of which "is equal in length, breadth and depth" is a spherical and not an elliptical one.

[7] Of the hemisphere.

[8] The two hemispheres.

[8a] See note 26a hereafter.

[13] On π as $3 + 1/7$ see the Introduction, notes 17, 18 and 20. On the history see still Tropfke, IV², pp. 196 seq., 205 seq.; Smith, "The History and transcendence of π" in Monographs on Modern Mathematics, New York 1927, pp. 389 sqq.; on the Babylonian value cf. Struve in QS, B 1, p. 85 seq., for the Egyptian value, see Struve, QS, A 1, pp. 177-79 and Neugebauer, QS. B 1, p. 429; for the Hindu value see B. Datta in Journal and Proceedings, Asiatic Society of Bengal, vol. 22, 1926, pp. 25-42.

[14] The diameter is assumed to be seven, like in II, 3, in order to obtain a whole number for the circumference.

[15] On the semidiameter.

§ 4. Now[16] it is written[17]: "And he made the molten sea of ten cubits from brim to brim, round in compass," and [nonetheless] its [circumference[18]] is thirty cubits, for it is written[19]: "And a line of thirty cubits compassed it round about." What is the meaning of the verse "and a line of thirty cubits" a. s. f.? [Nehemiah[20] says]: Since the people of the world[21] say that the circumference of a circle contains three times and a seventh of the thread, take off from that one seventh[22] for the thickness of the sea[23] on the two brims, then there remain "thirty cubits compass it round about." The seas, reservoirs and cisterns are equally [computed] according to this measure in length, breadth and depth. Thus you have learned the measure of the circular [figure].

§ 5. There are three kinds of the bow-figure, as follows: The even[26] one, the minor and the major one. What is that the even one? Each [arc] standing upon[26a] the half of the circle, neither less nor more than it. The minor? Each [arc] being less than half the circle. And the major? Each [arc] being greater than half the circle. The rule is as follows: Each [arc] which has an arrow standing [upon the half of the chord[27] is known to be an even one. Each [arc] having an arrow standing] [upon] less than half of the chord is known to be a minor one.

---

16 Here seems to begin a new paragraph, § 4. Because both manuscripts, M. (according to Schapira) and B. agree in heading the next § with hay = 5. Here the text in Ms. B. starts again.

17 I, Kings, 7, 23; II, Chronicles, 4, 2.

18 Kumto = "height" is apparently corrupt.

19 Loc. cit.

20 This is the reading of B. נחמיה אומר.

21 The gentiles, or the people devoted to secular things and secular learning, or b'nai aretz = "the landmeasurers." In B. the phrase is missing; it is perhaps a corruption of n'kham yah omer?

22 Of the diameter.

23 Of the walls of the sea. According to this explanation the diameter of 10 included the walls, while the circumference excluded them. This is typical for the harmonizing, scholastic, exegesis of Mishna and Midrash.

26 The semicircle, because it divides the circle into two even parts.

26a I. e.: equal to the half of the circle. "When the arrow is equal to the half of the chord."

27 The author apparently does not realize that the chord here is the diameter and that the diameter bisects the circle, or he does not care to say so.

And each [arc] having an arrow greater than half of the chord is known to be a major.

§ 6. If one wants to measure the even one, let him multiply the entire chord into itself and throw away from that the seventh and half of the seventh[28]. From the rest let him throw away the half. The result is the area.

§ 7. Concerning the other ones[29] you have to know the measure of their circle[30]. How does one figure? Let him multiply the half of the chord into itself, divide the product upon[31] the arrow and add the quotient to the arrow; the result is the thread of the circle[32]. Now let him take the half of this thread and multiply it into the

---

[28] That gives the area of the whole circle; see II, 3. Again, we would have expected the author to say that the chord is the diameter of the circle. The use of the formula shows that he knows it.

[29] The minor and the major.

[30] The diameter.

[31] El = "upon, through, by."

[32] See Euclid, Elements, III, 35; Heath, II, p. 71. $AE \cdot BE = CE \cdot DE$; hence $\frac{AE \cdot BE}{CE} = DE$; cf. also Savasorda's geometry, § 33, p. 16, and § 106, p. 65, note. The formula is: $\frac{\left(\frac{c}{2}\right)^2}{a} + a = 2r$, if we call the chord c, the arrow a, and the radius r. This formula can also be found by the following equation: $r^2 = \left(\frac{c}{2}\right)^2 + x^2$; $x = r - a$; hence, $r^2 = \left(\frac{c}{2}\right)^2 + r^2 - 2ra + a^2$; $2ra = \left(\frac{c}{2}\right)^2 + a^2$; $2r = \frac{\left(\frac{c}{2}\right)^2}{a} + a$.

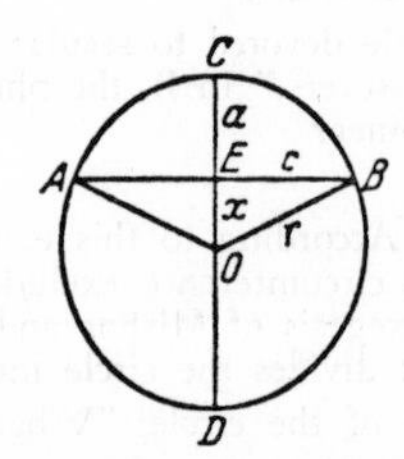

This formula occurs also in the works of Brahmagupta (c. 628) and Bhascara (c. 1150), quoted by Colebrooke, pp. 89 and 309, but without proof. Al-Karkhi, II, p. 24, and Savasorda, loc. cit., have the formula with the proof.

half of the [arc] and let him put the result aside[33]. Now let him see [how the arc-figure is]. Was it a minor-arc figure, let him throw away its arrow from the half-thread[34] of the circle and multiply the rest into the half-chord and subtract it from the side[35]; the rest is the area. And if it was a major arc-figure, let him throw away the half-thread of the circle from its own arrow and multiply the rest into the half chord and add it to the side[36]; the result is the area.

---

33 As the area of the sector, $br/2$ where b is the bow.

34 The radius.

35 From the product that was put aside as the area of the sector.

36 $\frac{br}{2} + \frac{(r - a)\, c}{2}$.

SIR ISAAC NEWTON

(1642—1727)

Isaac Newton, one of the greatest mathematicians and physicists of all time, was born at Woolsthorpe, England, on Christmas day in 1642. The inauspicious circumstances of his birth gave no hint of the brilliance of his career to come and of the eminence he was to achieve through his epoch-making scientific and mathematical discoveries. A few months before Newton was born, his father died. At birth Newton was so frail that small hope was entertained for his survival. His mother married a second time when he was only two years old, and he was left at Woolsthorpe at that tender age to be raised by his grandmother, Mrs. Ayscough. He was fourteen when his mother, widowed again, withdrew him from school so that he might be of some help to her on her farm. It may be placed to the credit of the charm and good sense of both his mother and Mrs. Ayscough, that a deep feeling of love and admiration between Newton and his mother persisted throughout his childhood and later, despite the long periods of separation. Quiet, introspective, and already inventive, Isaac showed little aptitude for the business of farming. In 1660, on the advice of his uncle, William Ayscough, he was returned to school to prepare for Cambridge.

In 1661 Newton entered Trinity College at Cambridge. Here his genius was soon recognized by the great Isaac Barrow, who accepted him first as a pupil, then as an assistant, and in 1669, as his successor in the Lucasian professorship of mathematics. Newton remained in continuous residence at Cambridge until 1696 except for a single period (1665—1666) during the Black Plague in London, when he returned once more to Woolsthorpe. The months spent at Woolsthorpe in uninterrupted study saw the beginnings of Newton's magnificent creative achievements in mathematics and science. The concepts of the calculus were clear to him at that time. His optical researches, including his work in establishing the composition of white light were begun in 1665. The development of his laws of motion and his idea of universal gravitation, his theory of the moon and of tidal effects were well under way in 1666.

Newton's contributions to the development of mathematics and science were widely known for many years before their appearance in print. The substance of his early works, such as the *Arithmetica Universalis* (publ. 1707) and his *Opticks* (publ. 1704), was presented in the lectures given by him at Cambridge in his capacity as Lucasian professor (from 1669). During the period 1666—1676, Newton wrote three important works presenting his method of fluxions, that is, his system of differential and integral calculus. Each of these treatises was in wide circulation among his friends long before publication. Newton's *De Analysi per Aequationes Numero Termi-*

norem Infinitas was written in 1669 and printed in 1711. His *Methodus Fluxionem et Serierum Infinitarum* was written about 1671 and printed in 1736, nine years after his death. His *Tractatus de Quadratura Curvarum,* written in 1676, was printed in 1704. The first of Newton's printed works to contain a presentation of his calculus was his *Philosophiae Naturalis Principia Mathematica* (1687, "Mathematical Principles of Natural Philosophy"), one of the greatest systematic treatises ever written. In the *Principia,* Newton used the Euclidean method of definitions, axioms and theorems to construct a mathematical system of mechanics based upon his new mathematics. Newton's mechanics became the basis of the scientific developments and technical progress of the centuries which followed.

In 1668 Newton completed the invention of his reflecting telescope. He presented a model of his telescope to the Royal Society in 1671 and shortly thereafter he was elected Fellow of the Royal Society. In 1689 and again in 1701 he was elected Member of Parliament, representing Cambridge University. He became president of the Royal Society in 1703, a position to which he was annually reelected to the end of his life. For about eighteen months in 1692—1694, Newton suffered from a serious nervous disorder after which he seemed to have lost interest in scientific researches, preferring to devote himself to studies in theology. In 1696 he accepted an appointment as Warden of the Mint with the special assignment of reforming the coinage which had depreciated because of the adulteration of its precious metal content. An excellent administrator, he was appointed Master of the Mint in 1699. Newton remained in London for more than thirty years occupied with his duties at the Mint, his theological writings and his problems in alchemy and chemistry. Occasionally he would be aroused to interrupt the routine of these activities for the purpose of disposing swiftly and brilliantly of a challenge to solve difficult problems issued by the mathematicians of the Continent. The calculus, Newton's chief contribution to the development of mathematics, an invaluable aid in the forward looking problems of satellites and space travel, continues to be applied to the analysis of the motion of all types of things, including rigid bodies, particles, fluids and gases.

●

TREATISE OF THE QUADRATURE OF CURVES

translated by JOHN STEWART

INTRODUCTION TO THE QUADRATURE OF CURVES.

1. I consider mathematical Quantities in this Place not as consisting of very small Parts; but as describ'd by a

continued Motion. Lines are describ'd, and thereby generated not by the Apposition of Parts, but by the continued Motion of Points; Superficies's by the Motion of Lines; Solids by the Motion of Superficies's; Angles by the Rotation of the Sides; Portions of Time by a continual Flux: and so in other Quantities. These Geneses really take Place in the Nature of Things, and are daily seen in the Motion of Bodies. And after this Manner the Ancients, by drawing moveable right Lines along immoveable right Lines, taught the Genesis of Rectangles.

2. Therefore considering that Quantities, which increase in equal Times, and by increasing are generated, become greater or less according to the greater or less Velocity with which they increase and are generated; I sought a Method of determining Quantities from the Velocities of the Motions or Increments, with which they are generated; and calling these Velocities of the Motions or Increments *Fluxions,* and the generated Quantities *Fluents,* I fell by degrees upon the Method of Fluxions, which I have made use of here in the Quadrature of Curves, in the Years 1665 and 1666.

3. Fluxions are very nearly as the Augments of the Fluents generated in equal but very small Particles of Time, and, to speak accurately, they are in the *first Ratio* of the nascent Augments; but they may be expounded by any Lines which are proportional to them.

4. Thus if the Area's ABC, ABDG be described by the Ordinates BC, BD moving along the Base AB with an uniform Motion, the Fluxions of these Area's shall be to one another as the describing Ordinates BC and BD, and may be expounded by these Ordinates, because that these Ordinates are as the nascent Augments of the Area's.

5. Let the Ordinate BC advance from it's Place into any new Place *bc.* Complete the Parallelogram BCE*b,* and draw the right Line VTH touching the Curve in C, and meeting the two Lines *bc* and BA produc'd in T and V: and B*b,* E*c* and C*c* will be *the* Augments now generated of the Absciss AB, the Ordinate BC and the Curve

Line AC*c*; and the Sides of the Triangle CET are in the *first Ratio* of these Augments considered as nascent, therefore the Fluxions of AB, BC and AC are as the Sides CE, ET and CT of that Triangle CET, and may be expounded by these same Sides, or, which is the same thing, by the Sides of the Triangle VBC, which is similar to the Triangle CET.

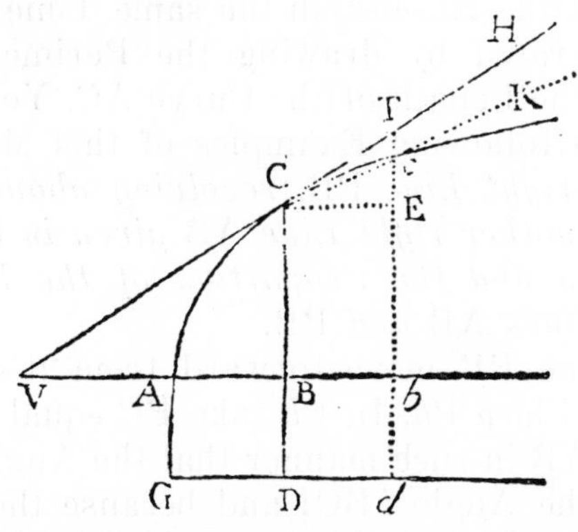

6. It comes to the same Purpose to take the Fluxions in the *ultimate Ratio* of the evanescent Parts. Draw the right Line C*c*, and produce it to K. Let the Ordinate *bc* return into it's former Place BC, and when the Points C and *c* coalesce, the right Line CK will coincide with the Tangent CH, and the evanescent Triangle CE*c* in it's ultimate Form will become similar to the Triangle CET, and it's evanescent Sides CE, E*c* and C*c* will be *ultimately* among themselves as the Sides CE, ET and CT of the other Triangle CET, are, and therefore the Fluxions of the Lines AB, BC and AC are in this same Ratio. If the Points C and *c* are distant from one another by any small Distance, the right Line CK will likewise be distant from the Tangent CH by a small Distance. That the right Line CK may coincide with the Tangent CH, and the ultimate Ratios of the Lines CE, E*c* and C*c* may be found, the Points C and *c* ought to coalesce and exactly coincide. The very smallest Errors in mathematical Matters are not to be neglected.

7. By the like way of reasoning, if a Circle describ'd

with the Center B and Radius BC be drawn at right Angles along the Absciss AB, with an uniform Motion, the Fluxion of the generated Solid ABC will be as that generating Circle, and the Fluxion of it's Superficies will be as the Perimeter of that Circle and the Fluxion of the Curve Line AC jointly. For in whatever Time the Solid ABC is generated by drawing that Circle along the Length of the Absciss, in the same Time it's Superficies is generated by drawing the Perimeter of that Circle along the Length of the Curve AC. You may likewise take the following Examples of this Method.

8. *Let the right Line* PB, *revolving about the given Pole* P, *cut another right Line* AB *given in Position*: *it is required to find the Proportion of the Fluxions of these right Lines* AB *and* PB.

Let the Line PB move forward from it's Place PB into the new Place P*b*. In P*b* take PC equal to PB, and draw PD to AB in such manner that the Angle *b*PD may be equal to the Angle *b*BC; and because the Triangles *b*BC, *b*PD are similar, the Augment B*b* will be to the Augment C*b* as P*b* to D*b*. Now let P*b* return into it's

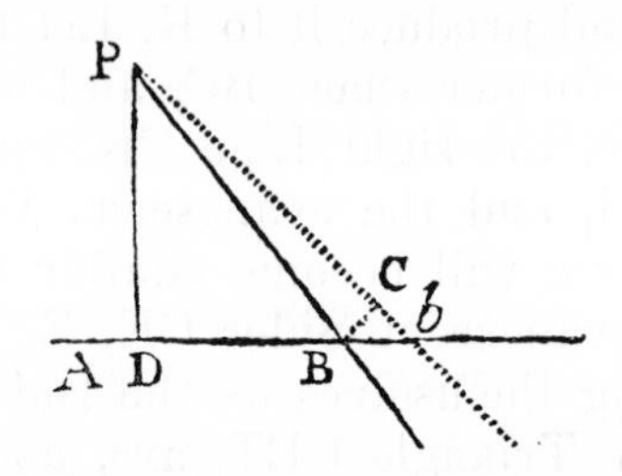

former Place PB, that these Augments may evanish, then the ultimate Ratio of these evanescent Augments, that is the ultimate Ratio of P*b* to D*b*, shall be the same with that of PB to DB, PDB being then a right Angle, and therefore the Fluxion of AB is to the Fluxion of PB in that same Ratio.

9. *Let the right Line* PB, *revolving about the given Pole* P, *cut other two right Lines given in Position,* viz. AB *and* AE *in* B *and* E: *the Proportion of the Fluxions of these right Lines* AB *and* AE *is sought.*

Let the revolving right Line PB move forward from it's Place PB into the new Place P*b*, so as to cut the Lines AB, AE in the Points *b* and *e*: and draw BC parallel to AE meeting P*b* in C, and it will be B*b* : BC :: A*b* : A*e*, and BC : E*e* :: PB : PE, and by joining the Ratios,

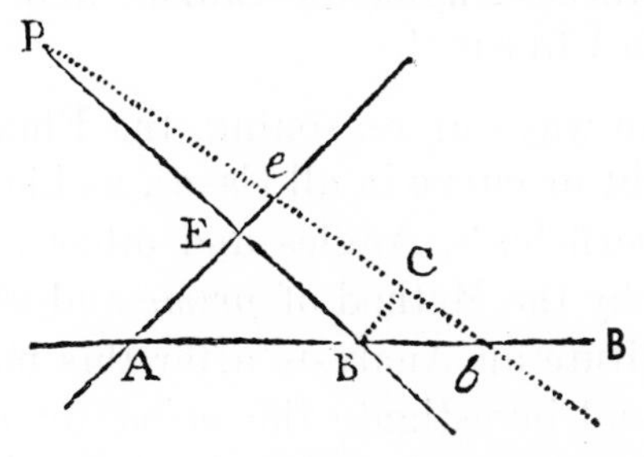

B*b* : E*e* :: A*b* × PB : A*e* × PE. Now let P*b* return into it's former Place PB, and the evanescent Augment B*b* will be to the evanescent Augment E*e* as AB × PB to AE × PE; and therefore the Fluxion of the right Line AB is to the Fluxion of the right Line AE in the same Ratio.

10. Hence if the revolving right Line PB cut any curve Lines given in Position in the Points B and E, and the right Lines AB, AE now becoming moveable, touch these Curves in the Points of Section B and E: the Fluxion of the Curve, which the right Line AB touches, shall be to the Fluxion of the Curve, which the right Line AE touches, as AB × PB to AE × PE. The same thing would happen if the right Line PB perpetually touch'd any Curve given in Position in the moveable Point P.

11. *Let the Quantity x flow uniformly, and let it be proposed to find the Fluxion of x^n.*

In the same Time that the Quantity x, by flowing, becomes $x + o$, the Quantity x^n will become $(x + o)^n$, that is, by the Method of infinite Series's, $x^n + nox^{n-1} + \frac{n^2 - n}{2}$ oox^{n-2} + &c. And the Augments o and $nox^{n-1} + \frac{n^2 - n}{2}$

$oox^{n-2} + \&c.$ are to one another as 1 and $nx^{n-1} + \frac{n^2 - n}{2} ox^{n-2} + \&c.$

Now let these Augments vanish, and their ultimate Ratio will be 1 to nx^{n-1}.

12. By like ways of reasoning, the Fluxions of Lines, whether right or curve in all Cases, as likewise the Fluxions of Superficies's, Angles and other Quantities, may be collected by the Method of *prime* and *ultimate* Ratios. Now to institute an Analysis after this manner in finite Quantities and investigate the *prime* or *ultimate* Ratios of these finite Quantities when in their nascent or evanescent State, is consonant to the Geometry of the Ancients: and I was willing to show that, in the Method of Fluxions, there is no necessity of introducing Figures infinitely small into Geometry. Yet the Analysis may be performed in any kind of Figures, whether finite or infinitely small, which are imagin'd similar to the evanescent Figures; as likewise in these Figures, which, by the Method of Indivisibles, use to be reckoned as infinitely small, provided you proceed with due Caution.

From the Fluxions to find the Fluents, is a much more difficult Problem, and the first Step of the Solution is equivalent to the Quadrature of Curves; concerning which I wrote what follows some considerable Time ago.

OF THE QUADRATURE of CURVES.

13. In what follows I consider indeterminate Quantities as increasing or decreasing by a continued Motion, that is, as flowing forwards, or backwards, and I design them by the Letters z, y, x, v, and their Fluxions or Celerities of increasing I denote by the same Letters

pointed $\dot{z}$, $\dot{y}$, $\dot{x}$, $\dot{v}$. There are likewise Fluxions or Mutations more or less swift of these Fluxions, which may be call'd the second Fluxions of the same Quantities z, y, x, v, and may be thus design'd $\ddot{z}$, $\ddot{y}$, $\ddot{x}$, $\ddot{v}$: and the first Fluxions of these last, or the third Fluxions of z, y, x, v are thus denoted $\dddot{z}$, $\dddot{y}$, $\dddot{x}$, $\dddot{v}$: and the Fourth Fluxions thus $\ddddot{z}$, $\ddddot{y}$, $\ddddot{x}$, $\ddddot{v}$. And after the same manner that $\dddot{z}$, $\dddot{y}$, $\dddot{x}$, $\dddot{v}$ are the Fluxions of the Quantities $\ddot{z}$, $\ddot{y}$, $\ddot{x}$, $\ddot{v}$, and these the Fluxions of the Quantities $\dot{z}$, $\dot{y}$, $\dot{x}$, $\dot{v}$; and these last the Fluxions of the Quantities z, y, x, v: so the Quantities z, y, x, v may be considered as the Fluxions of others, which I shall design thus $\acute{z}$, $\acute{y}$, $\acute{x}$, $\acute{v}$; and these and the Fluxions of others $\overset{\prime\prime}{z}$, $\overset{\prime\prime}{y}$, $\overset{\prime\prime}{x}$, $\overset{\prime\prime}{v}$; and these last still as the Fluxions of others $\overset{\prime\prime\prime}{z}$, $\overset{\prime\prime\prime}{y}$, $\overset{\prime\prime\prime}{x}$, $\overset{\prime\prime\prime}{v}$. Therefore $\overset{\prime\prime}{z}$, $\acute{z}$, z, $\dot{z}$, $\ddot{z}$, $\dddot{z}$, $\ddddot{z}$, $\ddddot{z}$, &c. design a Series of Quantities whereof every one that follows is the Fluxion of the one immediately preceding, and every one that goes before, is a flowing Quantity having that which immediately succeeds, for it's Fluxion.

OF ANALYSIS BY EQUATIONS OF AN INFINITE NUMBER OF TERMS

translated by JOHN STEWART

1. *The General Method, which I had devised some considerable Time ago, for measuring the Quantity of Curves, by means of Series, infinite in the Number of Terms, is rather shortly explained, than accurately demonstrated in what follows.*

2. Let the Base AB of any Curve AD have BD for it's perpendicular Ordinate; and call AB = x, BD = y, and

let a, b, c, &c. be given Quantities, and m and n whole Numbers. Then

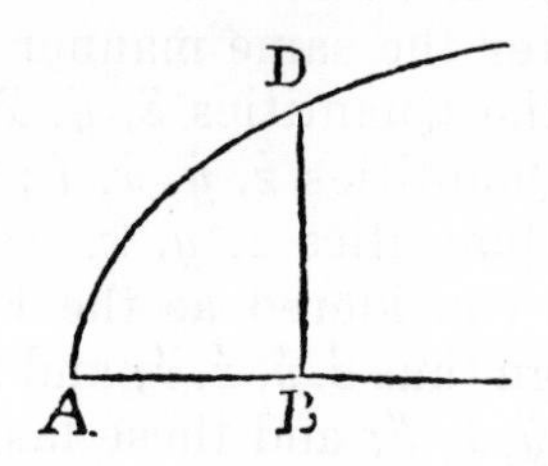

The Quadrature of Simple Curves.

RULE I.

3. If $ax^{m/n} = y$, it shall be $\frac{an}{m+n} x^{\frac{m+n}{n}}$ = Area ABD.

The thing will be evident by an Example.

1. If x^2 $(=1x^{\frac{2}{1}}) = y$, that is $a = 1 = n$, and $m = 2$; it shall be $1/3x^3$ = ABD.

2. Suppose $4\sqrt{x}$ $(= 4x^{\frac{1}{2}}) = y$; it will be $\frac{8}{3}x^{\frac{3}{2}} (= \frac{8}{3}\sqrt{x^3})$ = ABD.

3. If $\sqrt[3]{x^5}$ $(=x^{5/3}) = y$; it will be $\frac{3}{8}x^{8/3} (= \frac{3}{8}\sqrt[3]{x^8})$ = ABD.

4. If $\frac{1}{x^2}(= x^{-2}) = y$, that is if $a = 1 = n$, and $m = -2$;

It will be $\frac{1}{-1}x^{\frac{-1}{1}} (= -x^{-1}) = \frac{-1}{x}$ = αBD, infinitely ex-

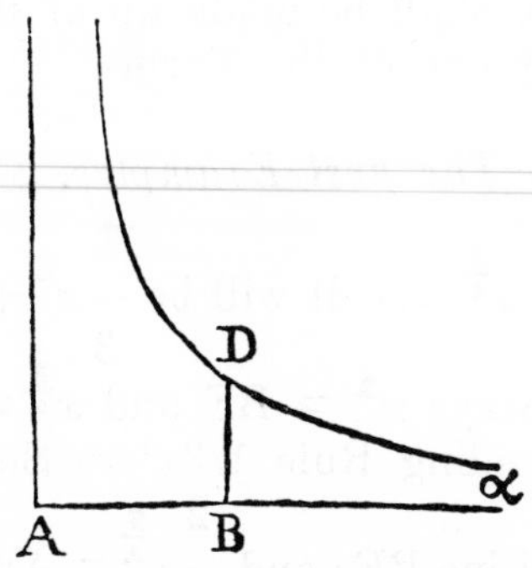

tended towards α, which the Calculation places negative, because it lies upon the other side of the Line BD.*

5. If $\frac{1}{\sqrt{x^3}}\left(x^{-\frac{3}{2}}\right) = y$; it will be $\left(\frac{2}{-1}x^{-\frac{1}{2}} =\right) \frac{2}{-\sqrt{x}} = \text{BD}\alpha$.

6. If $\frac{1}{x}\ (= x^{-1}) = y$; it will be $\frac{1}{0}x^{\frac{0}{1}} = \frac{1}{0}x^{0} = \frac{1}{0}\times 1 = \frac{1}{0}$ = an infinite Quantity; such as is the Area of the Hyperbola upon both sides of the Line BD.

The Quadrature of Curves Compounded of Simple Ones.

RULE II.

4. If the Value of y be made up of several such Terms,

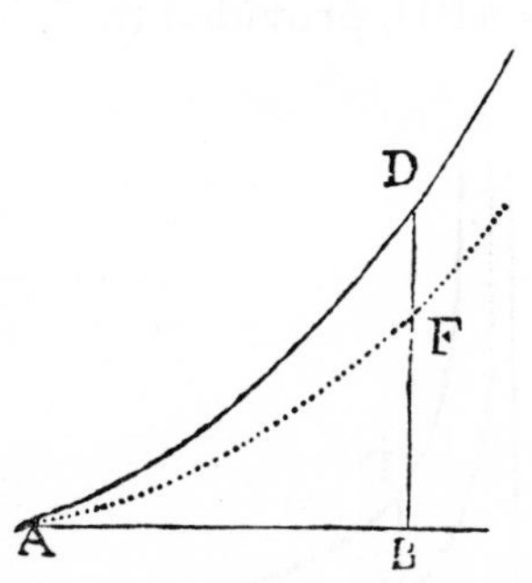

* Whatever is laid down by our Author with respect to the Position of Areas of Curves in this and the following Rules, is explained at full length in Sect. 5 of the preceding Treatise. Which see.

the Area likewise shall be made up of the Areas which result from every one of the Terms.

The first Examples.

5. If it be $x^2 + x^{\frac{3}{2}} = y$; it will be $\frac{1}{3}x^3 + \frac{2}{5}x^{\frac{5}{2}} =$ ABD.

For if it be always x^2 = BF and $x^{\frac{3}{2}}$ = FD, you will have by the preceding Rule $1/3x^3$ = Superficies AFB; described by the Line BF; and $\frac{2}{5}x^{\frac{5}{2}}$ = AFD described by DF; wherefore $\frac{1}{3}x^3 + \frac{2}{5}x^{\frac{5}{2}} =$ the whole Area ABD.

Thus if it be $x^2 - x^{\frac{3}{2}} = y$; it will be $\frac{1}{3}x^3 - \frac{2}{5}x^{\frac{5}{2}} =$ ABD. And if it be $3x - 2x^2 + x^3 - 5x^4 = y$; it will be $\frac{3}{2}x^2 - \frac{2}{3}x^3 + \frac{1}{4}x^4 - x^5 =$ ABD.

The second Examples.

6. If $x^{-2} + x^{-\frac{3}{2}} = y$; it will be $x^{-1} - 2x^{-\frac{1}{2}} = \alpha$BD. Or if it be $x^{-2} - x^{-\frac{3}{2}} = y$; it will be $-x^{-1} + 2x^{-\frac{1}{2}} = \alpha$BD.

And if you change the Signs of the Quantities, you will have the affirmative Value $(x^{-1} + 2x^{-\frac{1}{2}}$, or $x^{-1} - 2x^{-\frac{1}{2}})$ of the Superficies αBD, provided the whole of it fall above the Base ABα.

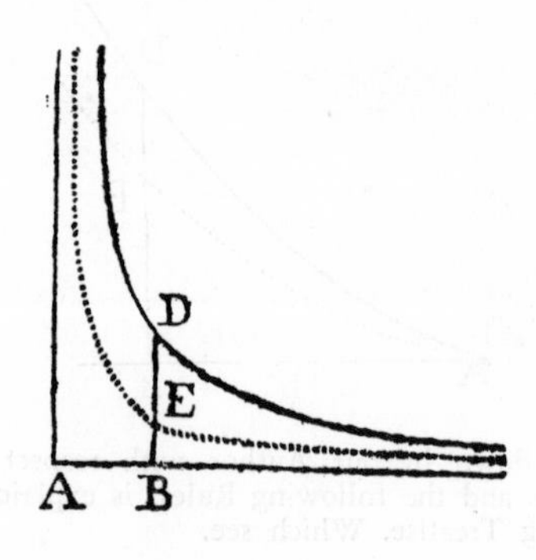

7. But if any Part fall below (which happens when the Curve decussates or crosses it's Base betwixt B and α,

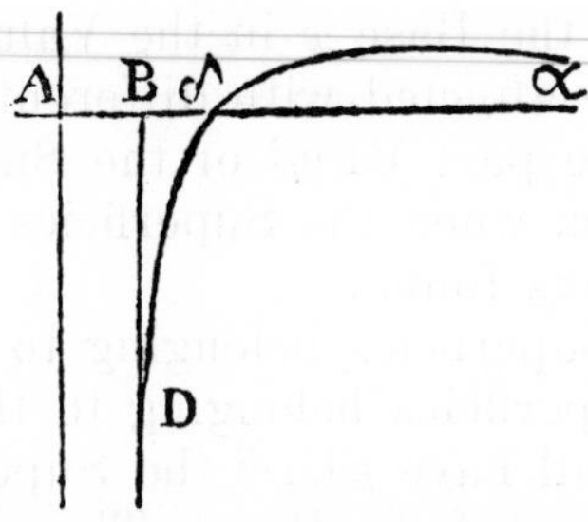

as you see here in δ) you are to subtract that Part from the Part above the Base; and so you shall have the Value of the Difference: but if you would have their Sum, seek both the Superficies's separately, and add them. And the same thing I would have observed in the other Examples belonging to this Rule.

The third Examples.

8. If $x^2 + x^{-2} = y$; it will be $\frac{1}{3}x^3 - x^{-1}$ = the Superficies described.

But here it must be remarked that the Parts of the said Superficies so found, lie upon opposite Sides of the Line BD.

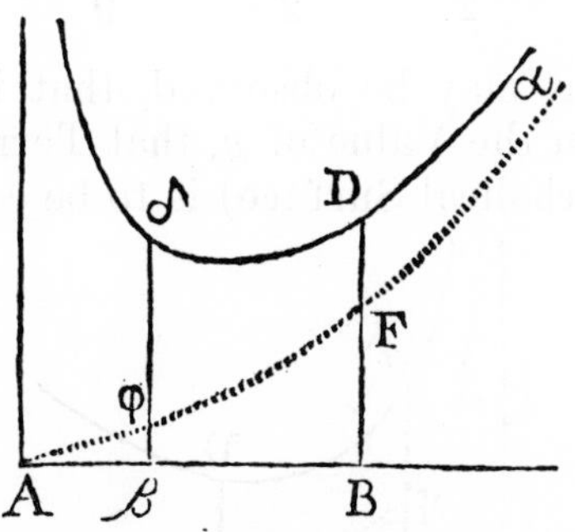

That is, putting x^2 = BF, and x^{-2} = FD; it shall be $\frac{1}{3}x^3$ = ABF the Superficies described by BF, and $-x^{-1}$ =DFα the Superficies described by DF.

9. And this always happens when the Indexes $\frac{m+n}{n}$ of the Ratios of the Base x in the Value of the Superficies sought, are affected with different Signs. In such Cases any middle part BD$\delta\beta$ of the Superficies (which only can be given, when the Superficies is infinite upon both Sides) is thus found.

Subtract the Superficies belonging to the lesser Base Aβ from the Superficies belonging to the greater Base AB, and you shall have βBDδ the Superficies insisting upon the difference of the Bases. Thus in this Example (see the preceding Fig.)

If AB = 2, and Aβ = 1; it will be βBDδ = 17/6:

For the Superficies belonging to AB (*viz.* ABF — DFα) will be 8/3 — 1/2 or 13/6; and the Superficies belonging to Aβ (*viz.* A$\phi\beta$ — $\delta\phi\alpha$) will be 1/3 — 1, or — 2/3: and their Difference (*viz.* ABF — DFα — A$\phi\beta$ + $\delta\phi\alpha$ = βBDδ) will be 13/6 + 2/3 or 17/6.

After the same manner, if Aβ = 1, and AB = x; it will be βBDδ = $2/3 + 1/3x^3 - x^{-1}$.

Thus if $2x^3 - 3x^5 - \frac{2}{3}x^{-4} + x^{-\frac{3}{5}} = y$, and $A\beta = 1$;

It will be $\beta BD\delta = \frac{1}{2}x^4 - \frac{1}{2}x^6 + \frac{2}{9}x^{-3} + \frac{5}{2}x^{\frac{2}{5}} - \frac{49}{18}$

10. Finally it may be observed, that if the Quantity x^{-1} be found in the Value of y, that Term (since it generates an hyperbolical Surface) is to be considered apart from the rest.

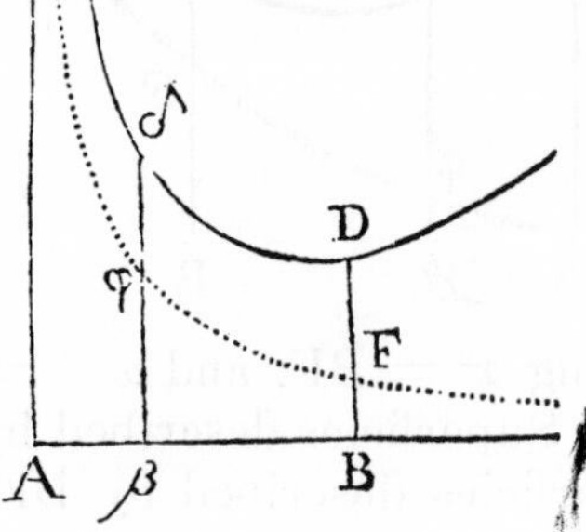

As if it were $x^2 + x^{-3} + x^{-1} = y$: let it be $x^{-1} = BF$, and $x^2 + x^{-3} = FD$; and $A\beta = 1$; and it will be $\delta\phi FD = \frac{1}{0} + \frac{1}{3}x^3 - \frac{1}{2}x^{-2}$, as being that which is generated by the Terms $x^2 + x^{-3}$.

Wherefore if the remaining Superficies $\beta\phi FB$, which is hyperbolical, be given by any Method of Computation, the whole βBDd will be given.

The Quadrature of All other Curves

RULE III.

11. But if the Value of y, or any of it's Terms be more compounded than the foregoing, it must be reduced into more simple Terms; by performing the Operation in Letters, after the same Manner as Arithmeticians divide in Decimal Numbers, extract the Square Root, or resolve affected Equations; and afterwards by the preceding Rules you will discover the Superficies of the Curve sought.

Examples, where you divide.

12. Let $\frac{aa}{b + x} = y$; *Viz.* where the Curve is an Hyperbola.

Now that that Equation may be freed from it's Denominator, I make the Division thus.

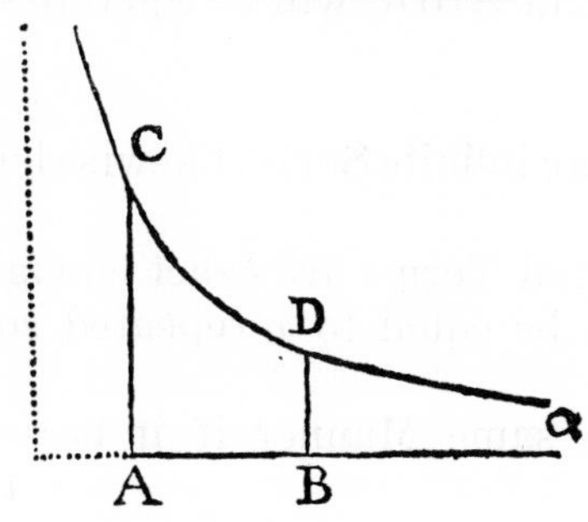

$$b+x)\,aa+0\left(\frac{aa}{b}-\frac{aax}{b^2}+\frac{aax^2}{b^3}-\frac{aax^3}{b^4}\ \&c.\right.$$

$$\begin{array}{l}
aa+\frac{aax}{b} \\
\hline
0-\frac{aax}{b}+0 \\
-\frac{aax}{b}-\frac{aax^2}{b^2} \\
\hline
0+\frac{aax^2}{b^2}+0 \\
+\frac{aax^2}{b^2}+\frac{aax^3}{b^3} \\
\hline
0-\frac{aax^3}{b^3}+0 \\
-\frac{aax^3}{b^3}-\frac{aax^4}{b^4} \\
\hline
0+\frac{aax^4}{b^4} \\
\&c.
\end{array}$$

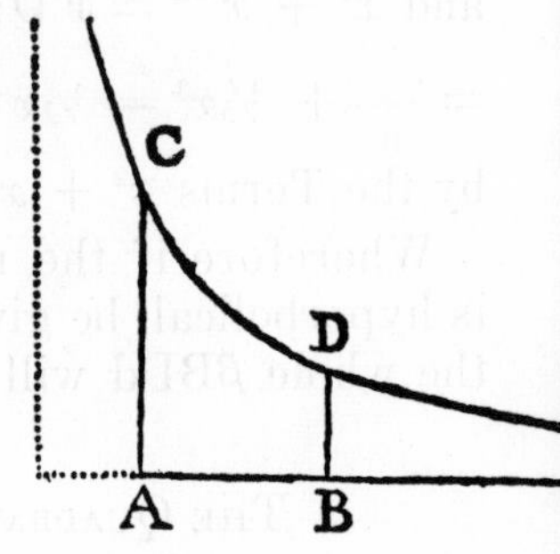

And thus in Place of this $y=\dfrac{aa}{b+x}$, a new Equation arises, *viz.* $y=\dfrac{a^2}{b}-\dfrac{a^2x}{b^2}+\dfrac{a^2x^2}{b^3}-\dfrac{a^2x^3}{b^4}$ &c. this Series being continued infinitely; and therefore (by the second Rule)

The Area sought ABDC will be equal to $\dfrac{a^2x}{b}-\dfrac{a^2x^2}{2b^2}+\dfrac{a^2x^3}{3b^3}-\dfrac{a^2x^4}{4b^4}$ &c. an infinite Series likewise but yet such, that a few of the initial Terms are exact enough for any Use, provided that b be equal to x repeated some few times.

13. After the same Manner if it be $\dfrac{1}{1+xx}=y$ by

dividing there arises $y = 1 - xx + x^4 - x^6 + x^8$ &c. Whence (by the second Rule)

$$\text{You will have ABDC} = x - \frac{1}{3}x^3 + \frac{1}{5}x^5 - \frac{1}{7}x^7 + \frac{1}{9}x^9 \text{ \&c.}$$

Or if x^2 be made the first Term in the Divisor, *viz.* (thus: $x^2 + 1$) there will arise $x^{-2} - x^{-4} + x^{-6} - x^{-8}$ &c for the Value of y; whence (by the second Rule)

$$\text{It will be BD}\alpha = -x^{-1} + \frac{1}{3}x^{-3} - \frac{1}{5}x^{-5} + \frac{1}{7}x^{-7} \text{ \&c.}$$

You must proceed in the first Way when x is small enough, but the second Way, when it is supposed great enough.

●

MATHEMATICAL PRINCIPLES OF NATURAL PHILOSOPHY

translated by Andrew Motte

the translation revised by Florian Cajori

Newton's Preface to the First Edition

Since the ancients (as we are told by *Pappus*) esteemed the science of mechanics of greatest importance in the investigation of natural things, and the moderns, rejecting substantial forms and occult qualities, have endeavored to subject the phenomena of nature to the laws of mathematics, I have in this treatise cultivated mathematics as far as it relates to philosophy. The ancients considered mechanics in a twofold respect; as rational, which proceeds accurately by demonstration, and practical. To practical mechanics all the manual arts belong, from which mechanics took its name. But as artificers do not work with perfect accuracy, it comes to pass that mechanics is so distinguished from geometry that what is perfectly accurate is called geometrical; what is less so, is called mechanical. However, the errors are not in the art, but in the artificers. He that works with less accuracy is an imperfect mechanic; and if any could work with perfect accuracy, he would be the most perfect mechanic of all, for the description of right lines and circles, upon which geometry is founded, belongs to mechanics. Geometry does not teach us to draw these lines, but requires them to be drawn, for it requires that the learner should first be taught to describe these accurately before he enters upon geometry, then it shows how by these operations problems may be solved. To describe right lines and circles are problems, but not geometrical problems. The solution of these problems is required from mechanics, and by geometry the use of them, when so solved, is shown; and it is the glory of geometry that from those few principles, brought from without, it is able to produce so many things. Therefore geometry is founded in mechanical practice, and is nothing but that part of universal mechanics which accurately proposes and demonstrates the art of measuring. But since the manual arts are chiefly employed in the moving of bodies, it happens that geometry is commonly referred to their magnitude, and mechanics to their motion. In this sense rational mechanics will be the science of motions resulting from any forces whatsoever, and of the forces required to produce any motions, accurately proposed and demonstrated. This part of mechanics, as far as it extended to the five powers which relate to manual arts, was cultivated by the ancients, who considered gravity (it not being a manual power) no otherwise than in moving weights by those powers. But I consider philosophy rather than arts and write not concerning manual but natural powers, and consider chiefly those things which relate to gravity, levity, elastic force, the resistance of fluids, and the like forces, whether attractive or impulsive; and therefore I offer this work as the mathematical principles of philosophy, for the whole burden of philosophy seems to consist in this—from the phenomena of motions to investigate the forces of nature, and then from these forces to demonstrate the other phenomena; and to this end the general propositions in the first and second Books are directed. In the third Book I give an example of this in the explication of the System of the World; for by the propositions mathematically demonstrated in the former Books, in the third I derive from the celestial phenomena the forces of gravity with which bodies tend to the sun and the several planets. Then from these forces, by other propositions which are also mathematical, I deduce the motions of the planets, the comets, the moon, and the sea. I wish we could derive the rest of the phenomena of Nature by the same kind of reasoning from mechanical principles, for I am induced by many reasons to suspect that they may all depend upon certain forces by which the particles of bodies, by some causes hitherto unknown, are either mutually impelled towards one another, and cohere in regular figures, or are repelled and recede from one another. These forces being unknown, philosophers have hitherto attempted the search of Nature in vain; but I hope the principles here laid down will afford some light either to this or some truer method of philosophy.

Book One

THE MOTION OF BODIES

SECTION I

The method of first and last ratios of quantities, by the help of which we demonstrate the propositions that follow.

LEMMA I

Quantities, and the ratios of quantities, which in any finite time converge continually to equality, and before the end of that time approach nearer to each other than by any given difference, become ultimately equal.

If you deny it, suppose them to be ultimately unequal, and let D be their ultimate difference. Therefore they cannot aproach nearer to equality than by that given difference D; which is contrary to the supposition.

LEMMA II

If in any figure AacE, *terminated by the right lines* Aa, AE, *and the curve* acE, *there be inscribed any number of parallelograms* Ab, Bc, Cd, &c., *comprehended under equal bases* AB, BC, CD, &c., *and the sides,* Bb, Cc, Dd, &c., *parallel to one side* Aa *of the figure; and the parallelograms* aKBl, bLcm, cMdn, &c., *are completed: then if*

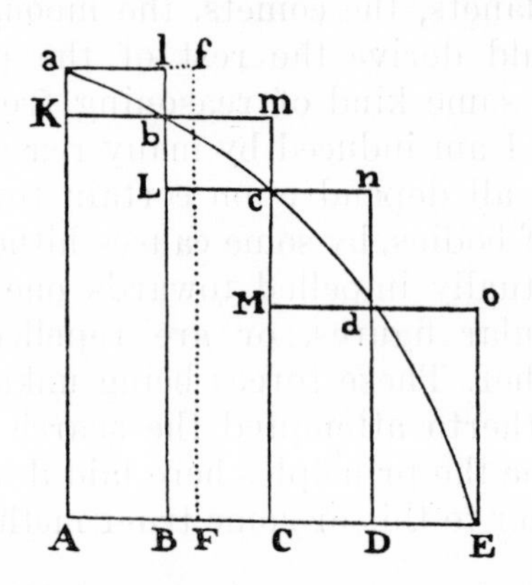

the breadth of those parallelograms be supposed to be diminished, and their number to be augmented in infinitum, *I say, that the ultimate ratios which the inscribed figure* AKbLcMdD, *the circumscribed figure* AalbmcndoE, *and curvilinear figure* AabcdE, *will have to one another, are ratios of equality.*

For the difference of the inscribed and circumscribed figures is the sum of the parallelograms K*l*, L*m*, M*n*, D*o*, that is (from the equality of all their bases), the rectangle under one of their bases K*b* and the sum of their altitudes A*a*, that is, the rectangle AB*la*. But this rectangle, because its breadth AB is supposed diminished *in infinitum,* becomes less than any given space. And therefore (by Lem. I) the figures inscribed and circumscribed become ultimately equal one to the other; and much more will the intermediate curvilinear figure be ultimately equal to either. Q.E.D.

LEMMA III

The same ultimate ratios are also ratios of equality, when the breadths AB, BC, DC, &c., *of the parallelograms are unequal, and are all diminished* in infinitum.

For suppose AF equal to the greatest breadth, and complete the parallelogram FA*af*. This parallelogram

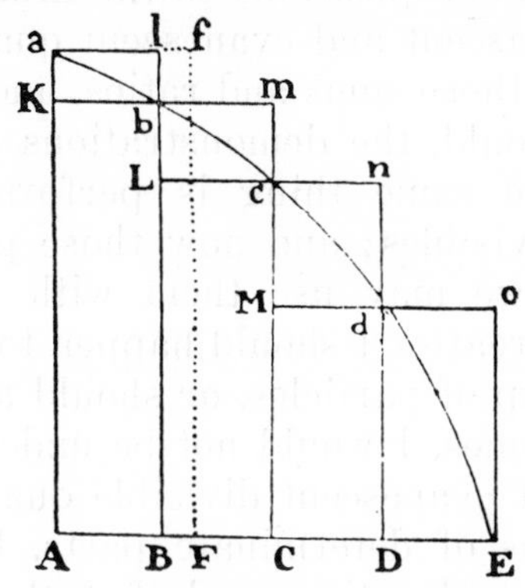

will be greater than the difference of the inscribed and circumscribed figures; but, because its breadth AF is diminished *in infinitum,* it will become less than any given rectangle. Q.E.D.

Cor. i. Hence the ultimate sum of those evanescent parallelograms will in all parts coincide with the curvilinear figure.

Cor. ii. Much more will the rectilinear figure comprehended under the chords of the evanescent arcs *ab, bc, cd,* &c., ultimately coincide with the curvilinear figure.

Cor. iii. And also the circumscribed rectilinear figure comprehended under the tangents of the same arcs.

Cor. iv. And therefore these ultimate figures (as to

their perimeters *ac*E) are not rectilinear, but curvilinear limits of rectilinear figures.

Those things which have been demonstrated of curved lines, and the surfaces which they comprehend, may be easily applied to the curved surfaces and contents of solids. These Lemmas are premised to avoid the tediousness of deducing involved demonstrations *ad absurdum,* according to the method of the ancient geometers. For demonstrations are shorter by the method of indivisibles; but because the hypothesis of indivisibles seems somewhat harsh, and therefore that method is reckoned less geometrical, I chose rather to reduce the demonstrations of the following Propositions to the first and last sums and ratios of nascent and evanescent quantities, that is, to the limits of those sums and ratios, and so to premise, as short as I could, the demonstrations of those limits. For hereby the same thing is performed as by the method of indivisibles; and now those principles being demonstrated, we may use them with greater safety. Therefore if hereafter I should happen to consider quantities as made up of particles, or should use little curved lines for right ones, I would not be understood to mean indivisibles, but evanescent divisible quantities; not the sums and ratios of determinate parts, but always the limits of sums and ratios; and that the force of such demonstrations always depends on the method laid down in the foregoing Lemmas.

Perhaps it may be objected, that there is no ultimate proportion of evanescent quantities; because the proportion, before the quantities have vanished, is not the ultimate, and when they are vanished, is none. But by the same argument it may be alleged that a body arriving at a certain place, and there stopping, has no ultimate velocity; because the velocity, before the body comes to the place, is not its ultimate velocity; when it has arrived, there is none. But the answer is easy; for by the ultimate velocity is meant that with which the body is moved, neither before it arrives at its last place and the motion ceases, nor after, but at the very instant it arrives; that is, that velocity with which the body arrives at its last place, and with which the motion ceases. And in like manner, by the ultimate ratio of evanescent quantities is to be understood the ratio of the quantities not before they vanish, nor afterwards, but with which they vanish. In like manner the first ratio of nascent quantities is that with which they begin to be. And the first or last sum is that with which they begin and cease to be (or to be augmented or diminished). There is a limit which the velocity at the end of the motion may attain, but not exceed. This is the ultimate velocity. And there is the like limit in all quantities and proportions that begin and cease to be. And since such limits are certain and definite, to determine the same is a problem strictly geometrical. But whatever is geometrical we may use in determining and demonstrating any other thing that is also geometrical.

Book Two

SECTION II, LEMMA II.

The moment of any genitum *is equal to the moments of each of the generating sides multiplied by the indices of the powers of those sides, and by their coefficients continually.*

I call any quantity a *genitum* which is not made by addition or subtraction of divers parts, but is generated or produced in arithmetic by the multiplication, division, or extraction of the root of any terms whatsoever; in geometry by the finding of contents and sides, or of the extremes and means of proportionals. Quantities of this kind are products, quotients, roots, rectangles, squares, cubes, square and cubic sides, and the like. These quantities I here consider as variable and indetermined, and increasing or decreasing, as it were, by a continual motion or flux; and I understand their momentary increments or decrements by the name of moments; so that the increments may be esteemed as added or affirmative moments; and the decrements as subtracted or negative ones. But take care not to look upon finite particles as such. Finite particles are not moments, but the very quantities generated by the moments. We are to conceive them as the just nascent principles of finite magnitudes. Nor do we in this Lemma regard the magnitude of the moments, but their first proportion, as nascent. It will be the same thing, if, instead of moments, we use either the velocities of the increments and decrements (which may also be called the motions, mutations, and fluxions of quantities), or any finite quantities proportional to those velocities. The coefficient of any generating side is the quantity which arises by applying the genitum to that side.

Wherefore the sense of the Lemma is, that if the moments of any quantities A, B, C, &c., increasing or decreasing by a continual flux, or the velocities of the mutations which are proportional to them, be called *a, b, c,* &c., the moment or mutation of the generated rectangle AB will be $a\mathrm{B} + b\mathrm{A}$; the moment of the generated content ABC will be $a\mathrm{BC} + b\mathrm{AC} + c\mathrm{AB}$; and the moments of the generated powers A^2, A^3, A^4, $\mathrm{A}^{1/2}$, $\mathrm{A}^{3/2}$, $\mathrm{A}^{1/3}$, $\mathrm{A}^{2/3}$, A^{-1}, A^{-2}, $\mathrm{A}^{-1/2}$ will be $2a\mathrm{A}$, $3a\mathrm{A}^2$, $4a\mathrm{A}^3$, $^1/_2 a\mathrm{A}^{-1/2}$, $^3/_2 a\mathrm{A}^{1/2}$, $^1/_3 a\mathrm{A}^{-2/3}$, $^2/_3 a\mathrm{A}^{-1/3}$, $-a\mathrm{A}^{-2}$, $-2a\mathrm{A}^{-3}$, $-^1/_2 a\mathrm{A}^{-3/2}$ respectively; and, in general, that the moment of any power $\mathrm{A}^{\frac{n}{m}}$ will be $\frac{n}{m} a\mathrm{A}^{\frac{n-m}{m}}$. Also, that the moment of the generated quantity $\mathrm{A}^2\mathrm{B}$ will be $2a\mathrm{AB} + b\mathrm{A}^2$; the moment of the generated quantity $\mathrm{A}^3\mathrm{B}^4\mathrm{C}^2$ will be $3a\mathrm{A}^2\mathrm{B}^4\mathrm{C}^2 + 4b\mathrm{A}^3\mathrm{B}^3\mathrm{C}^2 + 2c\mathrm{A}^3\mathrm{B}^4\mathrm{C}$; and the moment of the generated quantity $\frac{\mathrm{A}^3}{\mathrm{B}^2}$ or $\mathrm{A}^3\mathrm{B}^{-2}$ will be $3a\mathrm{A}^2\mathrm{B}^{-2} - 2b\mathrm{A}^3\mathrm{B}^{-3}$; and so on. The Lemma is thus demonstrated.[1]

Case 1. Any rectangle, as AB, augmented by a continual flux, when, as yet, there wanted of the sides A and B half their moments $\frac{1}{2}a$ and $\frac{1}{2}b$, was $\mathrm{A} - 1/2a$ into $\mathrm{B} - 1/2b$, or $\mathrm{AB} - 1/2a\,\mathrm{B} - 1/2b\,\mathrm{A} + \frac{1}{4}ab$; but as soon as the sides A and B are augmented by the other half-moments, the rectangle becomes $\mathrm{A} + \frac{1}{2}a$ into $\mathrm{B} + \frac{1}{2}b$,

[1] Appendix, Note 31.

or $AB + 1/2a\,B + 1/2b\,A + 1/4ab$. From this rectangle subtract the former rectangle, and there will remain the excess $aB + bA$. Therefore with the whole increments a and b of the sides, the increment $aB + bA$ of the rectangle is generated. Q.E.D.

CASE 2. Suppose AB always equal to G, and then the moment of the content ABC or GC (by Case 1) will be $gC + cG$, that is (putting AB and $aB + bA$ for G and g), $aBC + bAC + cAB$. And the reasoning is the same for contents under ever so many sides. Q.E.D.

CASE 3. Suppose the sides A, B, and C, to be always equal among themselves; and the moment $aB + bA$, of A^2, that is, of the rectangle AB, will be $2aA$; and the moment $aBC + bAC + cAB$ of A^3, that is, of the content ABC, will be $3aA^2$. And by the same reasoning the moment of any power A^n is naA^{n-1}. Q.E.D.

CASE 4. Therefore since $\frac{1}{A}$ into A is 1, the moment of $\frac{1}{A}$ multiplied by A, together with $\frac{1}{A}$ multiplied by a, will be the moment of 1, that is, nothing. Therefore the moment of $\frac{1}{A}$, or of A^{-1}, is $\frac{-a}{A^2}$. And generally since $\frac{1}{A^n}$ into A^n is 1, the moment of $\frac{1}{A^n}$ multiplied by A^n together with $\frac{1}{A^n}$ into naA^{n-1} will be nothing. And, therefore, the moment of $\frac{1}{A^n}$ or A^{-n} will be $-\frac{na}{A^{n+1}}$. Q.E.D.

CASE 5. And since $A^{1/2}$ into $A^{1/2}$ is A, the moment of $A^{1/2}$ multiplied by $2A^{1/2}$ will be a (by Case 3); and therefore, the moment of $A^{1/2}$ will be $\frac{a}{2A^{1/2}}$ or $^1/_2aA^{-1/2}$. And generally, putting $A^{\frac{m}{n}}$ equal to B, then A^m will be equal to B^n, and therefore maA^{m-1} equal to nbB^{n-1}, and maA^{-1} equal to nbB^{-1}, or $nbA^{-\frac{m}{n}}$; and therefore $\frac{m}{n}aA^{\frac{n-m}{n}}$ is equal to b, that is, equal to the moment of $A^{\frac{m}{n}}$. Q.E.D.

CASE 6. Therefore the moment of any generated quantity A^mB^n is the moment of A^m multiplied by B^n, together with the moment of B^n multiplied by A^m, that is, $maA^{m-1}B^n + nbB^{n-1}A^m$; and that whether the indices m and n of the powers be whole numbers or fractions, affirmative or negative. And the reasoning is the same for higher powers. Q.E.D.

COR. I. Hence in quantities continually proportional, if one term is given, the moments of the rest of the terms will be as the same terms multiplied by the number of intervals between them and the given term. Let A, B, C, D, E, F be continually proportional; then if the term C is given, the moments of the rest of the terms will be among themselves as —2A, —B, D, 2E, 3F.

COR. II. And if in four proportionals the two means are given, the moments of the extremes will be as those extremes. The same is to be understood of the sides of any given rectangle.

COR. III. And if the sum or difference of two squares is given, the moments of the sides will be inversely as the sides.

NICOMACHUS OF GERASA

(c. 100 A.D.)

Nicomachus of Gerasa, a celebrated Neo-Pythagorean, was the first mathematician to write a book dealing specifically and systematically with arithmetic as the science of numbers. This work, the *Introduction to Arithmetic,* exerted a powerful influence over the study of arithmetic for more than a millennium. In the middle ages and later, the authority of Nicomachus in the field of arithmetic was comparable to that of Euclid in geometry. Nicomachus is said to have written eleven works. Two of these have been preserved in complete form, the *Introduction to Arithmetic* containing an elementary theory of numbers and the *Manuale Harmonicum,* a treatise on music. Parts of a third work, the *Theologumena Arithmeticae,* written by him or wholly based on his work, are also extant. The remaining treatises ascribed to him, dealing with astronomy, mathematics, music, philosophy and biography, are known only through allusions to them by other authors and through references made to them by Nicomachus himself.

For the details of his life, historians have had as their sources only the extant writings of Nicomachus and the evidence given by occasional quotations from his works or the mention of his name by other writers. The date, or period in which he flourished, has therefore been deduced by considering, in the first place, that in his *Manuale Harmonicum,* Nicomachus mentions a certain Thrasyllus, a Platonist, who is known to have lived in the reign of Tiberius (14—37 A.D.). Hence, the *Manuale* could not have been written much earlier than 14 A.D. Secondly, the *Introduction to Arithmetic* was translated into Latin by Apuleius who lived under Antoninus Pius (138—161 A.D.). Hence, the *Introduction* could not have been written after 161 A.D., and we arrive at the conclusion that Nicomachus lived most likely c. 100 A.D. As for his personal life, many inferences may be drawn from the preface written by Nicomachus to his *Manuale Harmonicum.* This was in the form of a letter addressed to an unnamed lady of noble birth, at whose request and for whose benefit Nicomachus wrote the treatise. The cultured tone of the letter, the reference to a more detailed and more advanced treatise to be written for her in the future and the remarks concerning journeys undertaken by him, leaving him short of time, are all significant. Nicomachus may well be regarded as a highly learned scientist and philosopher possessing considerable grace of personality. The elementary nature of the material in his extant works may by no means be a true measure of the extent of his achievements. That he was sought after and highly respected for his knowledge by persons of high rank points up the great reputation for learning which he enjoyed in his own day. His interests were obviously not confined to Gerasa (a city in ancient Palestine) which, however, was probably the principal scene of his activity.

The commentaries of Iamblichus (4th century) and the versions of the *Introduction* contained in the *De Institutione Arithmetica* by Boethius (d. 524) made Nicomachus's work available to scholars familiar with Greek and Latin. Through the translation by Thabit Qor'ah (836—901), the *Introduction* became known in the East. Even if Proclus (d. 485 A.D.) had not listed Nicomachus as one of the "golden chain" of true philosophers, the *Theologumena Arithmeticae* and the *Introduction to Arithmetic* would have clearly revealed the Pythagorean philosophy underlying Nicomachus's arithmetical system. Nicomachus distinguishes between the wholly conceptual, immaterial number, which he regards as the "divine" number, and the number which measures material things, the "scientific" number. The *Introduction* implements the study of "scientific" numbers. Here, in a setting influenced by Pythagorean philosophy of numbers, he explains, defines and classifies numbers, and sets forth details of the principles governing their relations.

●

INTRODUCTION TO ARITHMETIC

translated by MARTIN LUTHER D'OOGE

BOOK I

The ancients, who under the leadership of Pythagoras first made science systematic, defined philosophy as the love of wisdom. Indeed the name itself means this, and before Pythagoras all who had knowledge were called 'wise' indiscriminately—a carpenter, for example, a cobbler, a helmsman, and in a word anyone who was versed in any art or handicraft. Pythagoras, however, restricting the title so as to apply to the knowledge and comprehension of reality, and calling the knowledge of the truth in this the only wisdom, naturally designated the desire and pursuit of this knowledge philosophy, as being desire for wisdom.

Therefore, if we crave for the goal that is worthy and fitting for man, namely, happiness of life—and this is accomplished by philosophy alone and by nothing else, and philosophy, as I said, means for us desire for wisdom, and wisdom the science of the truth in things, and of things some are properly so called, others merely share the name—it is reasonable and most necessary to distinguish and systematize the accidental qualities of things.

Things, then, both those properly so called and those that simply have the name, are some of them unified and continuous, for example, an animal, the universe, a tree, and the like, which are properly and peculiarly called 'magnitudes'; others are discontinuous, in a side-by-side arrangement, and, as it were, in heaps, which are called 'multitudes,' a flock, for instance, a people, a heap, a chorus, and the like.

Wisdom, then, must be considered to be the knowledge of these two forms. Since, however, all multitude and magnitude are by their own nature of necessity infinite —for multitude starts from a definite root and never ceases increasing; and magnitude, when division beginning with a limited whole is carried on, cannot bring the dividing process to an end, but proceeds therefore to infinity—and since sciences are always sciences of limited things, and never of infinites, it is accordingly evident that a science dealing either with magnitude, per se. or with multitude, per se, could never be formulated, for each of them is limitless in itself, multitude in the direction of the more, and magnitude in the direction of the less. A science, however, would arise to deal with something separated from each of them, with quantity, set off from multitude, and size, set off from magnitude.

Again, to start afresh, since of quantity one kind is viewed by itself, having no relation to anything else, as 'even,' 'odd,' 'perfect,' and the like, and the other is relative to something else and is conceived of together with its relationship to another thing, like 'double,' 'greater,' 'smaller,' 'half,' 'one and one-half times,' 'one and one-third times,' and so forth, it is clear that two scientific methods will lay hold of and deal with the whole investigation[1] of quantity; arithmetic, absolute quantity, and music, relative quantity.

And once more, inasmuch as part of 'size' is in a state of rest and stability, and another part in motion and revolution, two other sciences in the same way will accurately treat of 'size,' geometry the part that abides and is at rest, astronomy that which moves and revolves.

Without the aid of these, then, it is not possible to deal accurately with the forms of being nor to discover the truth in things, knowledge of which is wisdom, and evidently not even to philosophize properly.

Number is limited multitude or a combination of units or a flow of quantity made up of units; and the first division of number is even and odd.

The even is that which can be divided into two equal parts without a unit intervening in the middle; and the odd is that which cannot be divided into two equal parts because of the aforesaid intervention of a unit.

Now this is the definition after the ordinary conception; by the Pythagorean doctrine, however, the even number is that which admits of division into the greatest and the smallest parts at the same operation, greatest in size and smallest in quantity, in accordance with the natural contrariety[2] of these two genera; and the odd is that which does not allow this to be done to it, but is divided into two unequal parts.

In still another way, by the ancient definition, the even

---

[1] Nicomachus thus subdivides the subject matter and assigns the special fields of the four mathematical sciences: I, treating number (1) as such, absolutely, Arithmetic; and (2) relative number, Music; II, treating quantity (1) at rest, Geometry; (2) in motion, Astronomy. Proclus, *op. cit., Prol.,* p. 35. 21 ff., Friedl., gives the same division of the field of the mathematical sciences, using the same terms, in his report of the Pythagorean mathematics, probably drawing upon this work. It is to be noted that Nicomachus does not in fact adhere strictly to his classification, for he treats in this work of relative number, which falls in the domain of Music, and in the discussion of linear, plane and solid numbers he comes close to Geometry.

[2] That is, halves are the greatest possible parts of a term in magnitude; and there is a smaller number of them than of any other fractional part. Thus greater magnitude of factors is associated with a smaller number of them; this is the 'natural contrariety' of magnitude and quantity.

is that which can be divided[2] alike into two equal and two unequal parts, except that the dyad,[3] which is its elementary form, admits but one division, that into equal parts; and in any division whatsoever it brings to light only one species of number, however it may be divided, independent of the other. The odd[4] is a number which in any division whatsoever, which necessarily is a division into unequal parts, shows both the two species of number together, never without intermixture one with another, but always in one another's company.

By the definition in terms of each other, the odd is that which differs by a unit from the even in either direction, that is, toward the greater or the less, and the even is that which differs by a unit in either direction from the odd, that is, is greater by a unit or less by a unit.

Every number is at once half the sum of the two on either side of itself,[1] and similarly half the sum of those next but one in either direction, and of those next beyond them, and so on as far as it is possible to go. Unity alone, because it does not have two numbers on either side of it, is half merely of the adjoining number; hence unity is the natural starting point of all number.

By subdivision of the even,[2] there are the even-times even, the odd-times even, and the even-times odd. The even-times even and the even-times odd are opposite to one another, like extremes, and the odd-times even is common to them both like a mean term.

Now the even-times even is a number which is itself

---

[2] When an even number is divided into two parts, whether equal or unequal, these parts are always either both odd or both even ('only one species of number,' as Nicomachus says). Iamblichus, p. 12, 14 ff. Pistelli. See Heath, *History,* vol. I, p. 70.

[3] Iamblichus (p. 13, 7 ff. Pistelli) notes that the monad is distinguished from all the odd numbers by not even admitting division into unequal parts, and the dyad from the even numbers by admitting division into equal parts only.

[4] If an odd number is divided into two parts these will always be unequal and one odd, the other even ('the two species of number').

[1] Thus 5 is half the sum of $4 + 6$, $3 + 7$, $2 + 8$, etc.

[2] Euclid, among the definitions of *Elem.,* VII, defines the even-times even, even-times odd, odd-times even and odd-times odd (the latter is "one which is measured by an odd number an odd number of times"). Nicomachus confines himself to a tripartite division of the even only; Euclid's classification applies to all numbers.

capable of being divided into two equal parts, in accordance with the properties of its genus, and with each of its parts similarly capable of division, and again in the same way each of their parts divisible into two equals until the division of the successive subdivisions reaches the naturally indivisible unit. Take for example 64; one half of this is 32, and of this 16, and of this the half is 8, and of this 4, and of this 2, and then finally unity is half of the latter, and this is naturally indivisible and will not admit of a half.

It is a property of the even-times even that, whatever part of it be taken, it is always even-times even in designation, and at the same time, by the quantity of the units in it, even-times even in value; and that neither of these two things will ever share in the other class. Doubtless it is because of this that it is called even-times even, because it is itself even and always has its parts, and the parts of its parts down to unity, even both in name and in value; in other words, every part that it has is even-times even in name and even-times even in value.

Let us then set forth the odd numbers from 3 by themselves in due order in one series:

3, 5, 7, 9, 11, 13, 15, 17, 19, . . .

and the even-times even, beginning with 4, again one after another in a second series after their own order:

4, 8, 16, 32, 64, 128, 256, . . .

as far as you please. Now multiply by the first number of either series—it makes no difference which—from the beginning and in order all those in the remaining series and note down the resulting numbers; then again multiply by the second number of the same series the same numbers once more, as far as you can, and write down the results; then with the third number again multiply the same terms anew, and however far you go you will get nothing but the odd-times even numbers.

For the sake of illustration let us use the first term of the series of odd numbers and multiply by it all the terms in the second series in order, thus: 3×4, 3×8, 3×16, 3×32, and so on to infinity. The results will be 12, 24, 48, 96, which we must note down in one line. Then taking a new start do the same thing with the second number, 5×4, 5×8, 5×16, 5×32. The results will be 20, 40, 80, 160. Then do the same thing once more with 7, the third number, 7×4, 7×8, 7×16, 7×32. The results are 28, 56, 112, 224; and in the same way as far as you care to go, you will get similar results.

Odd numbers		3	5	7	9	11	13	15
Even-times even		4	8	16	32	64	128	256
Odd-times even numbers	Breadth	16	24	48	96	192	384	768
		20	40	80	160	320	640	1280
		28	56	112	224	448	896	1792
		36	72	144	288	576	1152	2304
		44	88	176	352	704	1408	2816
		Length						

Ed. Note. The encircled number should be 12.

Now when you arrange the products of multiplication by each term in its proper line, making the lines parallel, in marvelous fashion there will appear along the breadth of the table the peculiar property of the even-times odd, that the mean term is always half the sum of the extremes, if there should be one mean, and the sum of the means equals the sum of the extremes if two. But along the length of the table the property of the even-times even will appear; for the product of the extremes is equal to the square of the mean, should there be one mean term, or their product, should there be two. Thus this one species has the peculiar properties of them both, because it is a natural mixture of them both.

Again, while the odd is distinguished over against the even in classification and has nothing in common with it, since the latter is divisible into equal halves and the former is not thus divisible, nevertheless there are found three species of the odd, differing from one another, of which the first is called the prime and incomposite, that which is opposed to it the secondary and composite, and that which is midway between both of these and is viewed as a mean among extremes, namely, the variety which, in itself, is secondary and composite, but relatively is prime and incomposite.

Now the first species, the prime and incomposite, is found whenever an odd number admits of no other factor save the one with the number itself as denominator,[1] which is always unity; for example, 3, 5, 7, 11, 13, 17, 19, 23, 29, 31. None of these numbers will by any chance be found to have a fractional part with a denominator different from the number itself, but only the one with this as denominator, and this part will be unity in each case; for 3 has only a third part, which has the same denominator as the number and is of course unity, 5 a fifth, 7 a seventh, and 11 only an eleventh part, and in all of them these parts are unity.

As an illustration, let 9 be compared with 25. Each in itself is secondary and composite, but relatively to each other they have only unity as a common measure, and no factors in them have the same denominator, for the third part in the former does not exist in the latter nor is the fifth part in the latter found in the former.

The production of these numbers is called by Eratosthenes the 'sieve,' because we take the odd numbers mingled together and indiscriminate and out of them by this method of production separate, as by a kind of instrument or sieve, the prime and incomposite by themselves, and the secondary and composite by themselves, and find the mixed class by themselves.

The method of the 'sieve' is as follows. I set forth all the odd numbers in order, beginning with 3, in as long a series as possible, and then starting with the first I ob-

[1] As 1/3 in the case of 3.

serve what ones it can measure, and I find that it can measure the terms two places apart, as far as we care to proceed. And I find that it measures not as it chances and at random, but that it will measure the first one, that is, the one two places removed, by the quantity of the one that stands first in the series, that is, by its own quantity, for it measures it 3 times; and the one two places from this by the quantity of the second in order, for this it will measure 5 times; and again the one two places further on by the quantity of the third in order, or 7 times, and the one two places still farther on by the quantity of the fourth in order, or 9 times, and so *ad infinitum* in the same way.

Then taking a fresh start I come to the second number and observe what it can measure, and find that it measures all the terms four places apart, the first by the quantity of the first in order, or 3 times; the second by that of the second, or 5 times; the third by that of the third, or 7 times; and in this order *ad infinitum.*

Again, as before, the third term 7, taking over the measuring function, will measure terms six places apart, and the first by the quantity of 3, the first of the series, the second by that of 5, for this is the second number, and the third by that of 7, for this has the third position in the series.

And analogously throughout, this process will go on without interruption, so that the numbers[1] will succeed to the measuring function in accordance with their fixed position in the series; the interval separating terms measured is determined by the orderly progress of the even numbers from 2 to infinity, or by the doubling of the position in the series occupied by the measuring term, and the number of times a term is measured is fixed by the orderly advance of the odd numbers in series from 3.

---

[1] It is generally assumed (as by Heath, *History,* vol. I, p. 100) that in the 'sieve of Eratosthenes' only the odd prime numbers take on successively the measuring function, and indeed this is all that is necessary, for, e.g., 9 is a multiple of 3 and all its multiples are likewise multiples of 3. The text, however, seems to imply that all the odd numbers should be used, although perhaps Nicomachus did not intend that he should be so strictly interpreted.

Now a triangular number is one which, when it is analyzed into units, shapes into triangular form the equilateral placement of its parts in a plane. 3, 6, 10, 15, 21, 28, and so on, are examples of it; for their regular formations, expressed graphically, will be at once triangular and equilateral. As you advance you will find that such a numerical series as far as you like takes the triangular form, if you put as the most elementary form the one that arises from unity, so that unity may appear to be potentially a triangle, and 3 the first actually.

Their sides will increase by the successive numbers, for the side of the one potentially first is unity; that of the one actually first, that is, 3, is 2; that of 6, which is actually second, 3; that of the third, 4; the fourth, 5; the fifth, 6; and so on.

The triangular number is produced from the natural series of number set forth in a line, and by the continued addition of successive terms, one by one, from the beginning; for by the successive combinations and additions of another term to the sum, the triangular numbers in regular order are completed. For example, from this natural series, 1, 2, 3, 4, 5, 6, 7, 8, 9, 10, 11, 12, 13, 14, 15, I take the first term and have the triangular number which is potentially first, 1, a; then adding the next term I get the triangle actually first, for 2 plus 1 equals 3. In its graphic representation it is thus made up: Two units, side by side, are set beneath one unit, and the number three is made a triangle:

a
a a

Then when next after these the following number, 3, is added, simplified unto units, and joined to the former, it gives 6, the second triangle in actuality, and furthermore, it graphically represents this number:

a
a a
a a a

Again, the number that naturally follows, 4, added in and set down below the former, reduced to units, gives the one in order next after the aforesaid, 10, and takes a triangular form: 5, after this, then 6, then 7, and all the numbers in order, are added, so that regularly the sides of each triangle will consist of as many numbers as have been added from the natural series to produce it:

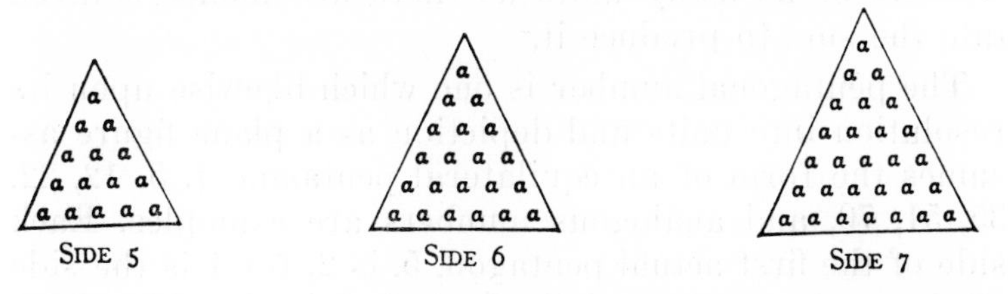

The square is the next number after this, which shows us no longer 3, like the former, but 4, angles in its graphic representation, but is none the less equilateral. Take, for example, 1, 4, 9, 16, 25, 36, 49, 64, 81, 100; for the representations of these numbers are equilateral, square figures, as here shown; and it will be similar as far as you wish to go:

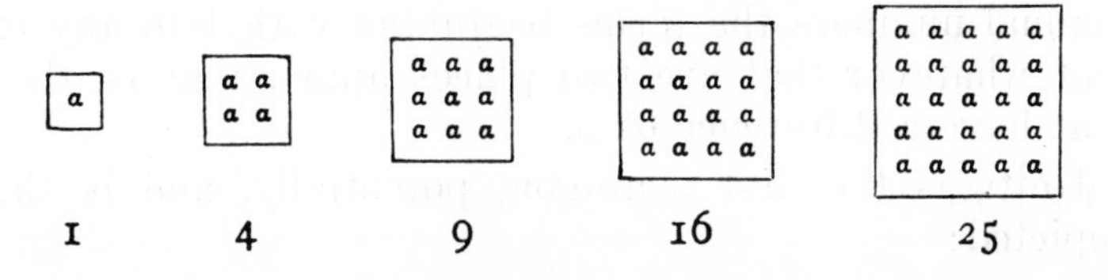

It is true of these numbers, as it was also of the preceding, that the advance in their sides progresses with the natural series. The side of the square potentially first, 1, is 1; that of 4, the first in actuality, 2; that of 9, actually the second, 3; that of 16, the next, actually the third, 4; that of the fourth, 5; of the fifth, 6, and so on in general with all that follow.

This number also is produced if the natural series is extended in a line, increasing by 1, and no longer the successive numbers are added to the numbers in order, as was shown before, but rather all those in alternate places, that is, the odd numbers. For the first, 1, is potentially the first square; the second, 1 plus 3, is the first in actuality; the third, 1 plus 3 plus 5, is the second in actuality; the fourth, 1 plus 3 plus 5 plus 7, is the third in actuality; the next is produced by adding 9 to the former numbers, the next by the addition of 11, and so on.

In these cases, also, it is a fact that the side of each consists of as many units as there are numbers taken into the sum to produce it.[2]

The pentagonal number is one which likewise upon its resolution into units and depiction as a plane figure assumes the form of an equilateral pentagon. 1, 5, 12, 22, 35, 51, 70, and analogous numbers are examples. Each side of the first actual pentagon, 5, is 2, for 1 is the side of the pentagon potentially first, 1; 3 is the side of 12, the second of those listed; 4, that of the next, 22; 5, that of the next in order, 35, and 6 of the succeeding one, 51, and so on. In general the side contains as many units as are the numbers that have been added together to produce the pentagon, chosen out of the natural arithmetical series set forth in a row. For in a like and similar manner, there are added together to produce the pentagonal numbers the terms beginning with 1 to any extent whatever that are two places apart, that is, those that have a difference of 3.

Unity is the first pentagon, potentially, and is thus depicted:

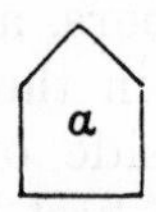

5, made up of 1 plus 4, is the second, similarly represented:

[2] So in the first square, 1, the side is 1 and only one term is taken to produce it. In the second, 4, the side is 2 and two terms are taken to produce it $(1 + 3)$. Generally, the algebraic sum of 1, 3, 5 . . . to n terms is n^2.

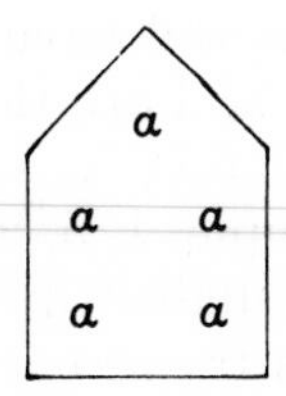

12, the third, is made up out of the two former numbers with 7 added to them, so that it may have 3 as a side, as three numbers have been added to make it. Similarly the preceding pentagon, 5, was the combination of two numbers and had 2 as its side. The graphic representation of 12 is this:

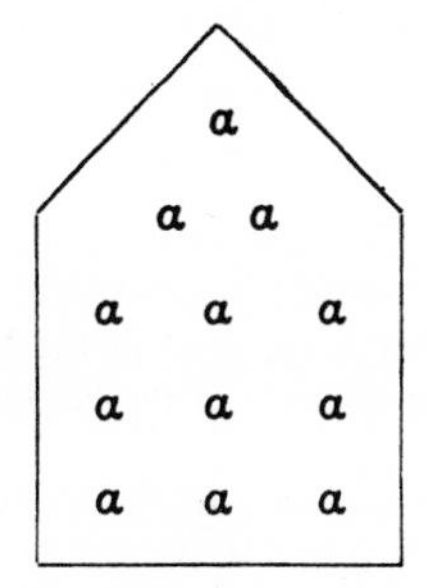

The other pentagonal numbers will be produced by adding together one after another in due order the terms after 7 that have the difference 3, as, for example, 10, 13, 16, 19, 22, 25, and so on. The pentagons will be 22, 35, 51, 70, 92, 117, and so forth.

The hexagonal, heptagonal, and succeeding numbers will be set forth in their series by following the same process, if from the natural series of number there be set forth series with their differences increasing by 1. For as the triangular number was produced by admitting into the summation the terms that differ by 1 and do not pass over any in the series; as the square was made by adding the terms that differ by 2 and are one place apart, and the pentagon similarly by adding terms with a difference of 3 and two places apart (and we have demonstrated these, by setting forth examples both of them and of the polygonal numbers made from them), so likewise the hexagons will have as their root-numbers[1] those which differ by 4 and are three places apart in the series, which added together in succession will produce[2] the hexagons. For example, 1, 5, 9, 13, 17, 21, and so on; so that the hexagonal numbers produced will be 1, 6, 15, 28, 45, 66, and so on, as far as one wishes to go.

The heptagonals, which follow these, have as their root-numbers terms differing by 5 and four places apart in the series, like 1, 6, 11, 16, 21, 26, 31, 36, and so on. The heptagons that thus arise are 1, 7, 18, 34, 55, 81, 112, 148, and so forth.

[1] That is, gnomons; the term being used in the broader sense.

[2] MS G gives the following diagram of the hexagonal number 15:

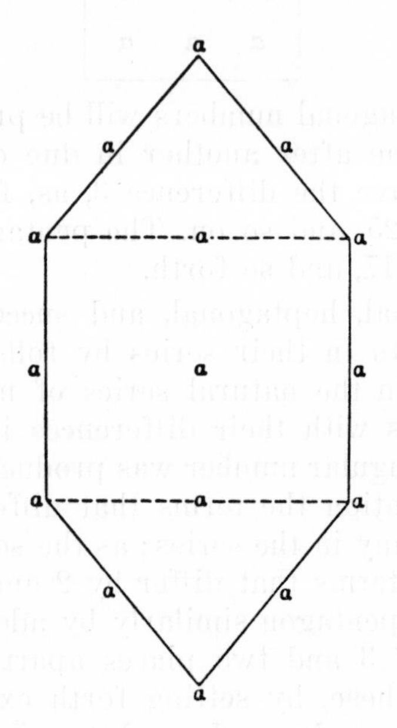

The octagonals[1] increase after the same fashion, with a difference of 6 in their root-numbers and corresponding variation in their total constitution.

In order that, as you survey all cases, you may have a rule generally applicable,[2] note that the root-numbers of any polygonal differ by 2 less than the number of the angles shown by the name of the polygonal—that is, by 1 in the triangle, 2 in the square, 3 in the pentagon, 4 in the hexagon, 5 in the heptagon, and so on, with similar increase.

[1] The following illustrations are from the same MS:

Derivation of heptagonals:

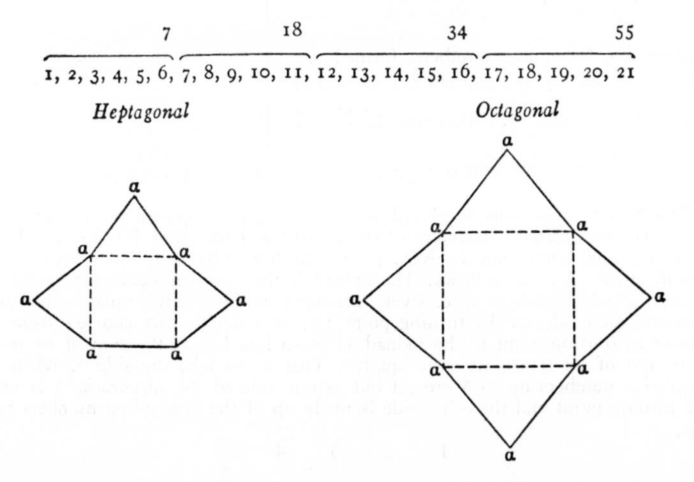

[2] Cf. also Theon, pp. 34, 6 and p. 40, 11 ff. The principle here stated by Nicomachus had already been given by Hypsicles (*ca.* 180 B.C.), whose theorem is cited by Diophantus (*De Polygonis Numeris, Prop.* IV) as follows: "If as many numbers as you please be set out at equal interval from 1, and the interval is 1, their sum is a triangular number; if the interval is 2, a square; if 3, a pentagonal; and generally the number of angles is greater by 2 than the interval."

Any square figure[1] diagonlly divided is resolved into two triangles and every square number is resolved into two consecutive triangular numbers, and hence is made up of two successive triangular numbers. For example, 1, 3, 6, 10, 15, 21, 28, 36, 45, 55, and so on, are triangular numbers and 1, 4, 9, 16, 25, 36, 49, 64, 81, 100, squares. If you add any two consecutive triangles that you please, you will always make a square, and hence, whatever square you resolve, you will be able to make two triangles of it.

Again, any triangle joined to any square figure makes a pentagon, for example, the triangle 1 joined with the square 4 makes the pentagon 5; the next triangle, 3 of course, with 9, the next square, makes the pentagon 12; the next, 6, with the next square, 16, gives the next pentagon, 22; 10 and 25 give 35; and so on.

---

[1] MS G gives the following figure as an illustration. The principle may be proved from the formulas of arithmetic progression,

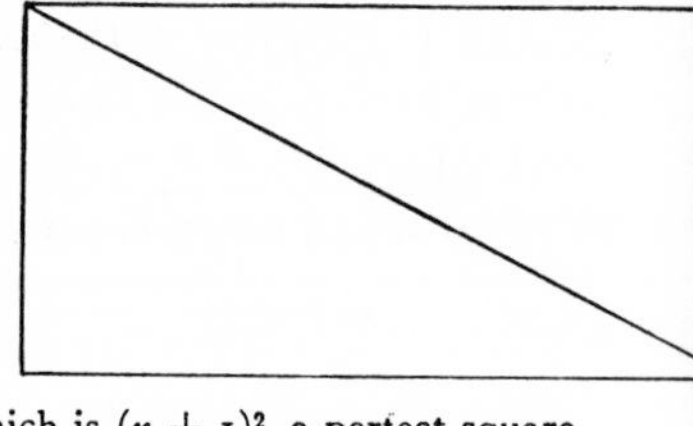

$$S = \frac{n}{2}(a + l),\ l = a + (n - 1)d.$$

Two successive triangular numbers, formed according to definition by the summation of n and $n + 1$ terms respectively, will therefore be $\frac{n^2 + n}{2}$ and $\frac{n^2 + 3n + 2}{2}$, and their sum is $n^2 + 2n + 1$, which is $(n + 1)^2$, a perfect square.

The Neo-Pythagoreans employed an interesting development of this principle to display the relative characters of the monad and the dyad (cf. *Theol. Arith.*, p. 9 Ast, and Iamblichus *In Nic.*, p. 75, 20 ff.). The matter is stated in the *Theol. Arith.*, *l. c.*, as follows: The monad is the cause of squares not only because the odd numbers successively arranged about it give squares, but also "because each side, as the turning point (*sc.* of a double race course) from the monad as starting point to the monad as finish line has as the sum of its going forth and of its return its own square". That is, to take the side 5, when the successive numbers up to 5 are set out as one side of the race-track, 5 is made the turning point and the other side is made up of the descending numbers to 1, e.g.,

1 2 3 4
5
1 2 3 4

the sum of the whole series is 25, or 5^2. The series 1 . . . 5, of course, is one triangular number, and the descending series 4 . . . 1 the immediately preceding one. From its resemblance to the double race course of the Greek games this proposition was apparently recognized under the name 'diaulos' (cf. Iamblichus, p. 75, 25). Its further application to the heteromecic numbers is not pertinent to the present subject.

Similarly,[3] if the triangles are added to the pentagons, following the same order, they will produce the hexagonals in due order, and again the same triangles with the latter will make the heptagonals in order, the octagonals after the heptagonals, and so on to infinity.

To remind us, let us set forth rows of the polygonals, written in parallel lines, as follows: The first row, triangles, the next squares, after them pentagonals, then hexagonals, then heptagonals, then if one wishes the succeeding polygonals.

Triangles	1	3	6	10	15	21	28	36	45	55
Squares	1	4	9	16	25	36	49	64	81	100
Pentagonals	1	5	12	22	35	51	70	92	117	145
Hexagonals	1	6	15	28	45	66	91	120	153	190
Heptagonals	1	7	18	34	55	81	112	148	189	235

You can also set forth the succeeding polygonals in similar parallel lines.

In general, you will find that the squares are the sum of the triangles above those that occupy the same place in the series, plus the numbers of that same class in the next place back;[1] for example, 4 equals 3 plus 1, 9 equals 6 plus 3, 16 equals 10 plus 6, 25 equals 15 plus 10, 36 equals 21 plus 15, and so on.

The pentagons are the sum of the squares above them in the same place in the series, plus the elementary triangles that are one place further back in the series; for example, 5 equals 4 plus 1, 12 equals 9 plus 3, 22 equals 16 plus 6, 35 equals 25 plus 10, and so on.

Again, the hexagonals are similarly the sums of the pentagons above them in the same place in the series plus the triangles one place back; for instance, 6 equals 5 plus 1, 15 equals 12 plus 3, 28 equals 22 plus 6, 45 equals 35 plus 10, and as far as you like.

---

[3] This proposition and the preceding are special cases of the theorem that the polygonal number of r sides with side n, plus the triangular number with side $n - 1$, makes the polygonal number with $r + 1$ sides and side n. Algebraically

$$\frac{n+1}{2}(2+nd)+\frac{n(n+1)}{2}=\frac{n+1}{2}[2+n(d+1)].$$

[1] That is, in the column next to the left.

The same applies to he heptagonals, for 7 is the sum of 6 and 1, 18 equals 15 plus 3, 34 equals 28 plus 6, and so on. Thus each polygonal number is the sum of the polygonal in the same place in the series with one less angle, plus the triangle, in the highest row, one place back in the series.

Naturally, then, the triangle is the element of the polygon[2] both in figures and in numbers, and we say this because in the table, reading either up or down or across, the successive numbers in the rows are discovered to have as differences the triangles in regular order.

Still further, every square plus its own side becomes heteromecic, or by Zeus, if its side is subtracted from it. Thus, 'the other' is conceived of as being both greater and smaller than 'the same,' since it is produced, both by addition and by subtraction, in the same way that the two kinds of inequality[1] also, the greater and the less, have their origin from the application of addition or subtraction to equality.

---

[2]*Theol. Arith.*, p. 8 Ast, states that the triangle is the element of both magnitudes and numbers and is made by the congress of the monad and the dyad.

[1] The results obtained by adding to or subtracting their sides from the square numbers are as follows:

$$4 + 2 = 6 = 2 \times 3$$
$$9 + 3 = 12 = 3 \times 4$$
$$16 + 4 = 20 = 4 \times 5$$
$$25 + 5 = 30 = 5 \times 6$$

or

$$m^2 + m = (m + 1)m$$

$$4 - 2 = 2 = 1 \times 2$$
$$9 - 3 = 6 = 2 \times 3$$
$$16 - 4 = 12 = 3 \times 4$$
$$25 - 5 = 20 = 4 \times 5$$

or

$$m^2 - m = (m - 1)m$$

OMAR KHAYYAM

(c. 1044—1123)

The phenomenal rise of the fame of Omar Khayyam, the astronomer-poet of Persia, in all parts of the civilized world began in 1859 with the anonymous publication of a hundred of his four line verses in a book entitled the *Rubaiyatt of Omar Khayyam.* The verses had been translated rather freely into English by Edward Fitzgerald, an English writer and student of Iranian philology. Within fifty years after the appearance of that edition, more than three hundred editions in English of the first and subsequent versions of the *Rubaiyatt* by Fitzgerald were published. Within seventy years after the first publication, more than thirteen hundred works connected with the *Rubaiyatt* had appeared. Of these almost two hundred were written in thirty three languages other than English. In 1900 the Omar Khayyam Club of America was organized in Boston, Mass., and interest in his writing continued undiminished. The enormous vogue for his poetry everywhere evoked a correspondingly widespread desire to know more intimately the details of the poet's life and work. In this quest some searched in the great libraries of the world hoping to find manuscripts of other works written by Omar. Others closely scrutinized his poetry and interpreted it. Fact and fancy mingled on a wide scale, and there was no lack of controversy over the factual story of Omar Khayyam's life, his quality as a poet and as a philosopher, as well as the depth and sincerity of his devotion to religious principles. Despite the emergence of certain apparently irreconcilable points of view, continued research has narrowed the differences, and substantial agreement has been found in some matters.

Omar's full name is Omar ibn Ibrahim al-Khayyam, Giyat ed-din Abu'l Fath (Ghiyath ud Din Abu'l Fatah 'Omar bin Ibrahim Khayyam). The date of his birth may have been as early as 1042. His family name, al-Khayyam, means "the tent-maker," but this occupation was most likely far back in his ancestry, his immediate forebears having been a literary family. Omar himself says, "Khayyam who stitched in the tents of science."

During his lifetime Omar was held in the highest esteem by princes, by scholars, and by the common man as the greatest scientist of his day. He was a teacher of scientific subjects, although his known pupils are few in number. By his own statement he preferred to learn rather than to teach. Omar was celebrated for his mastery of astrology and metaphysics, for his prodigious feats of memory, and for the mystical bent of his philosophy. His reform of the Persian calendar achieved extraordinary accuracy, greatly adding to Omar's stature in the field of science. His quatrains, too, were well known in his own lifetime. However, the same quatrains which were admired and enjoyed by many people, were found shocking by others, and some verses had the effect of bringing important enmities upon Omar. In his later years Omar gave up writing and went into seclusion for long periods.

It was the field of algebra which brought Omar the first complete success of his long career, and his contributions to this area of mathematics were of lasting scientific influence. His treatise on algebra became widely known through the translation (1931) of an Arabic manuscript in the library of Professor David Eugene Smith. This work, now known to us as *The Algebra of Omar Khayyam,* had been in use as a school text in Persia for hundreds of years. It continued in use until a very late date, especially in the more isolated regions of Persia. Far ahead of his time, in mathematical methods, Omar supported his algebraic solutions by geometrical constructions and proofs. Celebrated as the astronomer-poet of Persia, Omar Khayyam was also the first mathematician to study and classify cubic equations and to employ conic sections in their solution.

●

THE ALGEBRA OF OMAR KHAYYAM

Translated from the Arabic, with explanatory notes

by Daoud S. Kasir

CHAPTER I

DEFINITIONS

Algebra. By the help of God and with His precious assistance, I say that Algebra is a scientific art. The objects with which it deals are absolute numbers and measurable quantities which, though themselves unknown, are related to "things" which are known, whereby the determination of the unknown quantities is possible. Such a thing is either a quantity or a unique relation, which is only determined by careful examination. What one searches for in the algebraic art are the relations which lead from the known to the unknown, to discover which is the object of Algebra[1] as stated above. The perfection of this art consists in knowledge of the scientific method by which one determines numerical and geometric unknowns.

Measurable Quantities. By measurable quantities I mean continuous quantities of which there are four kinds, viz., line, surface, solid, and time, according to the customary terminology of the Categories[2] and what is expounded in metaphysics.[3] Some consider space a subdivision of surface, subordinate to the division of continuous quantities, but investigation has disproved this claim. The truth is that space is a surface only under circumstances the determination of which is outside the scope of the present field of investigation. It is not customary to include "time" among the objects of our algebraic studies, but if it were mentioned it would be quite admissible.

The Unknown. It is a practice among algebraists in connection with their art to call the unknown which is to be determined a "thing,"[4] the product obtained by multiplying it by itself a "square,"[5] and the product of the square and the "thing" itself a "cube." The product of the square multiplied by itself is "the square of the square," the product of its cube multiplied by its square "the cube of the square," and the product of a cube into itself "a cube of the cube," and so on, as far as the

BIBLIOGRAPHICAL AND EXPLANATORY NOTES

1. The author refers here to the algebraic relations existing between the known and the unknown quantities which the algebraist has to establish. For other Arabic definitions of algebra see *Haji Khalpha, Mohammed ibn Musa,* by Karpinski, p. 67; *Mukadamat ibn Khaldun,* p. 422 (Egypt).
2. *Category* of Aristotle, cap. 6; phys. lv, cap. 4 ult. According to Aristotle's definitions, point, line, and surface are first principles and must be assumed. Heath, *Euclid,* vol. I, pp. 155-156, 158, 159, 165, 170.
3. Here the author is referring to his book on metaphysics. See A. Christensen: *Un Traite de Metaphysique d'Omar. Le Monde Oriental,* 1908, vol. I, pp. 1-16.
4. The Arabic word *shai* (literally a "thing") here means the "unknown." Latin translators used the word *res.*
5. *Mal* (literally, "substances") is the word used by the author to indicate the second power of the unknown. Gherardo of Cremona (*c.* 1150) used *census,* which has the same meaning.

succession is carried out.[6] It is known from Euclid's book, the *Elements,*[7] that all the steps are in continuous proportion; i.e., that the ratio of one to the root is as the ratio of the root to the square and as the ratio of the square to the cube.[8] Therefore, the ratio of a number to a root is as the ratio of roots to squares, and squares to cubes, and cubes to the squares of the squares, and so on after this manner.[9]

Sources. It should be understood that this treatise cannot be comprehended except by those who know thoroughly Euclid's books, the *Elements* and the *Data,* as well as the first two books from Apollonius' work on *Conics.* Whoever lacks knowledge of any one of these books cannot possibly understand my work, as I have taken pains to limit myself to these three books only.

Algebraic Solutions. Algebraic solutions are accomplished by the aid of equations; that is to say, by the well-known method of equating these degrees one with the other. If the algebraist were to use the square of the square in measuring areas, his result would be figurative[10] and not real, because it is impossible to consider the square of the square as a magnitude of a measurable nature. What we get in measurable quantities is first one dimension, which is the "root"[11] or the "side"[12] in relation to its square; then two dimensions, which represent the surface and the (algebraic) square representing the square surface; and finally, three dimensions, which rep-

---

6. $x \cdot x = x^2, \quad x \cdot x \cdot x = x^3, \quad x^2 \cdot x^2 = x^4, \quad x^2 \cdot x^3 = x^5, \quad x^3 \cdot x^3 = x^6.$

7. *Elements of Euclid,* Heath, vol. II, p. 390.

8. E.g., $1 : x = x : x^2 = x^2 : x^3$.

9. E.g., $a : ax = ax : ax^2 = ax^2 : ax^3 = ax^3 : ax^4$, etc.

10. The literal translation of the Arabic word *majaz* is "path, way." The author means that a quantity raised to the fourth power cannot be represented geometrically and therefore has no real geometric meaning, while algebraically it has. In other words, the author meant by *majaz,* "hypothetical." See *Akrabu'l-Mawarid* (Beirut, 1889).

11. The Arab writers used also the word "root" for the first power of the unknown quantity in an equation.

12. *Dulu* (literally, side), meaning an unknown quantity, is represented geometrically by a line, while *mal* (square) is represented by a surface, and *muk'ab* (cube) by a solid.

resent the solid.[13] The cube in quantities is the solid bounded by six squares, and since there is no other dimension, the square of the square does not fall under measurable quantities. This is even more true in the case of higher powers.[14] If it is said that the square of the square is among measurable quantities, this is said with reference to its reciprocal value in problems of measurement and not because it in itself is measurable. This is an important distinction to make.

The square of the square is, therefore, neither essentially nor accidentally a measurable quantity, and is not as even and odd numbers, which are accidentally included in measurable quantities, depending on the way in which they represent continuous measurable quantities as discontinuous.

What is found in the books of algebra relative to these four geometric quantities—namely, the absolute numbers, the "sides," the squares, and the cubes—are three equations containing numbers, sides, and squares. We, however, shall present methods by which one is able to determine the unknown quantities in equations including four degrees concerning which we have just said that they are the only ones that can be included in the category of measurable quantities, namely, the number, the thing, the square, and the cube.

The demonstration[15] (of solutions) depending on the properties of the circle—that is to say, as in the two works of Euclid, the *Elements* and the *Data*—is easily effected; but what we can demonstrate only by the properties of conic sections should be referred to the first two books on conics.[16] When, however, the object of the prob-

---

13. The author's idea of dimension conforms fundamentally with that of Aristotle, Proclus, and al-Nairizi. See Heath, *Euclid*, vol. I, pp. 157-159.

14. It was Descartes who first defeated this method of reasoning, which had been universally accepted before him.

15. The author refers here to the demonstration of processes which constitute the solution.

16. The author is referring here to the above mentioned works of Apollonius.

lem is an absolute number,[17] neither we, nor any of those who are concerned with algebra, have been able to prove this equation—perhaps others who follow us will be able to fill the gap—except when it contains only the three first degrees, namely, the number, the thing, and the square.[18] For the numerical demonstration given in cases that could also be proved by Euclid's book, one should know that the geometric proof of such procedure does not take the place of its demonstration by number, if the object of the problem is a number and not a measurable quantity. Do you not see how Euclid proved certain theorems relative to proportions of geometric quantities in his fifth book, and then in the seventh book gave a demonstration of the same theorems for the case when their object is a number?[19]

CHAPTER II

TABLE OF EQUATIONS

The equations among those four quantities are either simple or compound. The simple equations are of six species:

i. A number equals a root.
ii. A number equals a square.
iii. A number equals a cube.
iv. Roots equal a square.
v. Squares equal a cube.
vi. Roots equal a cube.

Three of these six species are mentioned in the books of the algebraists. The latter said a thing is to a square as a square is to a cube. Therefore, the equality between

17. Or "if it is required to satisfy the proposed equation by a whole number." The author means here that cubic equations can be solved geometrically, but that neither he nor his predecessors could solve them algebraically. It was to Archimedes, al-Mahani, Thabit ibn Qorra, and al-Khazin that he referred here. It was not until the 16th century that Cardan and Tartaglia succeeded in solving cubic equations algebraically. Smith, *History of Mathematics,* vol. II, pp. 455 (footnote 2) and 459.

18. For example, as in $x^2 - 7x + 12 = 0$, where 12 is the number, x is the "thing," and x^2 is the square.

19. Compare, for example, Prop. 5 of Book V with Prop. 8 of Book VII.

the square and the cube is equivalent to the equality of the thing to the square. Again they said that a number is to a square as a root is to a cube. And they did not prove by geometry. As for the number which is equal to a cube there is no way of determining its side when the problem is numerical except by previous knowledge of the order of cubic numbers. When the problem is geometrical it cannot be solved except by conic sections.

CHAPTER V

PRELIMINARY THEOREMS FOR THE CONSTRUCTION OF CUBIC EQUATIONS

After presenting those species of equations which it has been possible to prove by means of the properties of the circle, i.e., by means of Euclid's book, we take up now the discussion of the species which cannot be proved except by means of the properties of conics. These include fourteen species: one simple equation, namely, that in which *a number is equal to a cube;* six trinomial equations; and seven tetranomial equations.

Let us precede this discussion by some propositions based on the book on *Conics* so that they may serve as a sort of introduction to the student and so that our treatise will not require familiarity with more than the three books already mentioned, namely, the two books of Euclid on the *Elements* and the *Data,* and the first two parts of the book on *Conics*.

Between two given lines it is required to find two other lines such that all four will form a continuous proportion.[1]

Let there be two straight lines (given) *AB, BC* (Fig. 14), and let them enclose the right angle *B*. Construct a parabola the vertex of which is the point *B,* the axis *BC,* and the parameter *BC*. Then the position of the conic *BDE* is known because the positions of its vertex and axis are known, and its parameter is given. It is tangent to the line *BA,* because the angle *B* is a right angle and it is equal to the angle of the ordinate, as was shown in the figure of the thirty-third proposition in the first book on *Conics*.[2] In the same manner construct another parab-

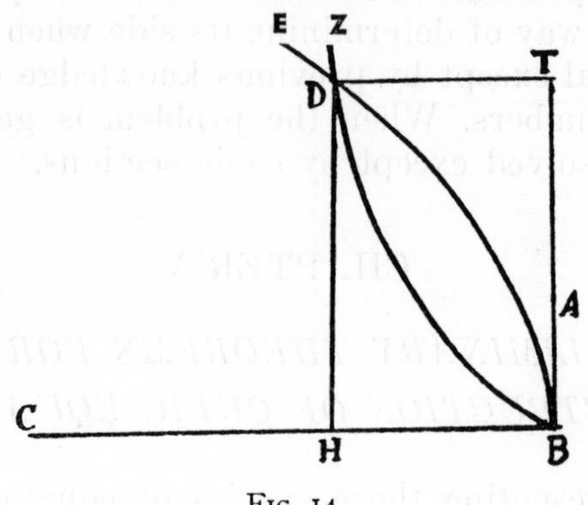

FIG. 14

ola, with vertex *B*, axis *AB*, and parameter *AB*. This will be the conic *BDZ*, as was shown also by Apollonius in the fifty-sixth proposition of the first book.[3] The conic *BDZ* is tangent to the line *BC*. Therefore, the two (parabolas) necessarily intersect. Let *D* be the point of intersection. Then the position of point *D* is known because the position of the two conics is known. Let fall from the point *D* two perpendiculars, *DH* and *DT*, on *AB* and *BC* respectively. These are known in magnitude, as was shown in the *Data*.[4] I say that the four lines *AB*, *BH*, *BT*, *BC* are in continuous proportion.

Demonstration

The square of *HD* is equal to the product of *BH* and *BC*, because the line *DH* is the ordinate of the parabola *BDE*. Consequently *BC* is to *HD*, which is equal to *BT*, as *BT* to *HB*. The line *DT* is the ordinate of the parabola *BDZ*. The square of *DT* (which is equal to *BH*) is equal to the product of *BA* and *BT*. Consequently *BT* is to *BH* as *BH* to *BA*. Then the four lines are in continuous proportion and the line *DH* is of known magnitude, as it is drawn from the point the position of which is known, to a line whose position is known, at an angle whose magnitude is known. Similarly, the length of *DT* is known.

Therefore, the two lines, BH and BT, are known and are the means of the proportion between the two lines, AB and BC; that is to say, AB to BH is as BH to BT and is as BT to BC. That is what we wanted to demonstrate.

Given (Fig. 15a) *the rectangular parallelepiped ABCDE, whose base is the square AD, and the square MH, construct on MH a rectangular parallelepiped equal to ABCDE.*

Let AB to MZ be as MZ to K and let AB to K be as ZT to ED.[5] Then make ZT perpendicular to the plane MH at the point Z and complete the solid $MZTH$. Then I say that this solid is equal to the given solid.

Demonstration

The square AC to the square MH is as AB to K. Then the square AC to the square MH is as ZT, which is the height of the solid MTH to ED, which is the height of the solid BE. Therefore the two solids are equal, for their bases are reciprocally proportional to their heights, as it was demonstrated in the eleventh book of the *Elements*.

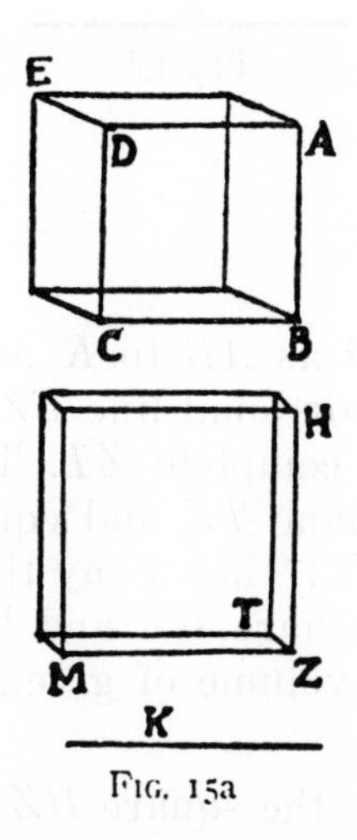

FIG. 15a

Whenever we speak of "a solid" we mean a rectangular parallelepiped and whenever we say "plane" we refer to the rectangle.

Given the solid ABCD (Fig. 15b), *whose base AC is a square, it is required to construct a solid whose base is a square, whose height is equivalent to a given line ET, and which is equal to the solid ABCD.*

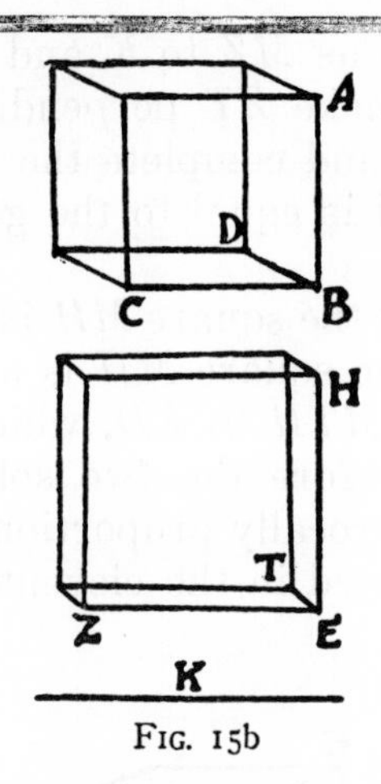

Fig. 15b

Let ET be to BD as AB to K and take between AB and K a mean proportional line EZ.[6] Make EZ perpendicular to ET and complete ZT. Then make EH perpendicular to the plane TZ and equal to EZ, and complete the solid $HETZ$. Then I say the volume of solid T, whose base is the square HZ and height the given line ET, is equal to the volume of given solid D.

Demonstration

The square AC to the square HZ is as AB to K. Consequently, the square AC to the square HZ is as ET to BD. Therefore the bases of the two solids are also reciprocally proportional to their heights and the solids then are equal. That is what we wanted to demonstrate.

After these preliminary proofs we shall be able to give the solution of the third species of the simple equation, *a cube is equal to a number.*[7]

Let the number be equal to the solid $ABCD$ (Fig. 16), and its base AC the square of one, as we have said previously. Its length is equal to the given number. It is desired to construct a cube equal to this solid. Take between the two lines AB and BD two mean proportionals.[8] These are known in magnitude, as has been demonstrated.[9] They are E and Z. Then draw HT equal to the line E and construct on it the cube $THKL$. This cube and its side are known in magnitude. Then I say that this cube is equal to the solid D.

Demonstration

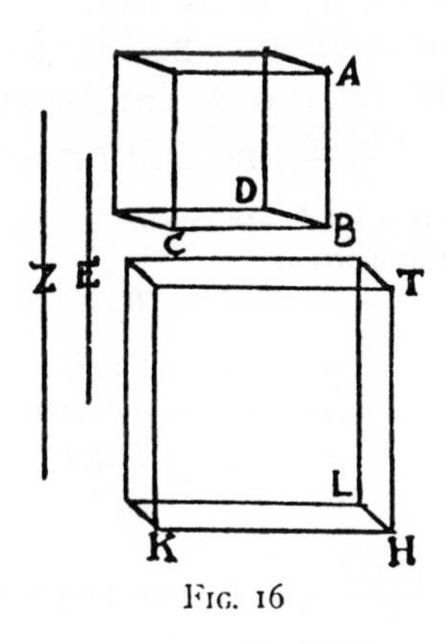

FIG. 16

The square AC to the square TK is twice the ratio AB to HK,[10] and twice the ratio of AB to HK is equal to the ratio AB to Z. But the first is to the third of the four lines as HK, the second, is to BD, the fourth. The bases (TK, AC) of the cube L and the solid D are then reciprocally proportional to their height. Then the solids are equal, which is what we wanted to demonstrate.

BIBLIOGRAPHICAL AND EXPLANATORY NOTES

1. $AB : x = x : y = y : BC$.

   In the parabola BDE $\overline{HD}^2 = \overline{BT}^2 = BH \cdot BC$, hence $BC : BT = BT : HB$.
   In the parabola BDZ $\overline{DT}^2 = \overline{HB}^2 = BA \cdot BT$, hence $BT : HB = HB : BA$.
   Consequently $BC : BT = BT : HB = HB : BA$ or $AB : BH = BH : BT = BT : BC$.

   This is the second of the two constructions of the problem attributed to Menaechmus.
2. Apollonius, ed. Oxford, 1710, fol., p. 57. The author refers here to the 32nd proposition of this book.
3. Apollonius, ed. Oxford, Book I, proposition 52.
4. See propositions 30, 25, 26.
5. That is, construct K from the proportion $AB : MZ = MZ : K$, in which $\overline{AB}^2$, MZ are known and ZT as the third term of $AB : K = ZT : ED$. The volume of $ABCDE = \overline{AB}^2 \cdot DE$. But $\overline{MZ}^2 \cdot ZT$ = volume of the parallelepiped on $MH = \overline{AB}^2 \cdot DE$, since the first proportion gives $\overline{MZ}^2 = AB \cdot K$ and the second $ZT = \frac{AB \cdot ED}{K}$. But $\overline{AB}^2 \cdot DE$ = volume of parallelepiped $ABCDE$. Hence the two solids are equal.
6. Construct K from the proportion

   $$ET : BD = AB : K,$$

   and EZ from

   $$AB : EZ = EZ : K.$$

   It follows that $\overline{AB}^2 : \overline{EZ}^2 = ET : BD$.

   Then $\overline{AB}^2 \cdot BD = \overline{EZ}^2 \cdot ET$.

   Or solid D = solid T.
7. $a = x^3$.
8. $AB = E^2 : Z$; $\overline{AB}^2 = \frac{AB \cdot E^2}{Z}$ (E, Z mean proportional lines)

   $$\overline{AB}^2 : E^2 = AB : Z$$

   But $AB : E = Z : BD$ gives

   $$AB : Z = E : BD$$

   Hence $\overline{AB}^2 : E^2 = E : BD$

   $\therefore$ $E^3 = \overline{AB}^2 : BD$, etc.
9. See p. 71, lines 14 ff. and footnote 1 above.
10. That is $(AB : HK)(AB : HK)$ or $\overline{AB}^2 : \overline{HK}^2$

CHAPTER VI

TRINOMIAL EQUATIONS

Capable of Being Proved by Means of the Properties of the Conic Sections

After this we are to work on the remaining six trinomial equations.

I. The first species. *A cube and sides are equal to a number.*

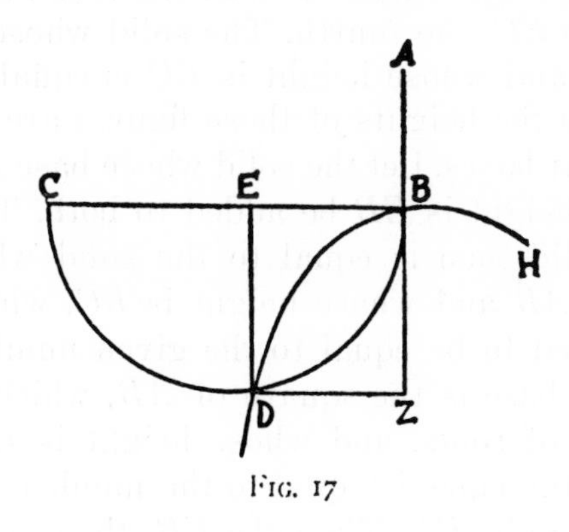

FIG. 17

Let the line AB (Fig. 17) be the side of a square equal to the given number of roots. Construct a solid whose base is equal to the square on AB, equal in volume to the given number. The construction has been shown previously. Let BC be the height of the solid. Let BC be perpendicular to AB. You know already what meaning is applied in this discussion to the phrase *solid number.* It is a solid whose base is the square of unity and whose height is equal to the given number; that is, the height is a line whose ratio to the side of the base of the solid is as the ratio of the given number to one. Produce AB to Z and construct a parabola whose vertex is the point B, axis BZ, and parameter AB. Then the position of the conic *HBD* will be known, as has been shown previously and it will be tangent to *BC*. Describe on *BC* a semicircle. It necessarily intersects the conic. Let the point of intersection be *D;* drop from *D,* whose position is known, two perpendiculars *DZ* and *DE* on *BZ* and *BC*. Both the position and the magnitude of these lines are known. The line *DZ* is an ordinate of the conic. Its square is then equal to the product of *BZ* and *AB*. Consequently, *AB* to *DZ,* which is equal to *BE,* is as *BE* to *ED,* which is equal to *ZB*. But *BE* to *ED* is as *ED* to *EC*. The four lines then are in continuous proportion, *AB, BE, ED, EC,* and consequently the square of the parameter *AB,* the first, is to the square of *BE,* the second, as *BE,* the second, is to *EC,* the fourth. The solid whose base is the square *AB* and whose height is *EC* is equal to the cube *BE,* because the heights of these figures are reciprocally equal to their bases. Let the solid whose base is the square of *AB* and height is *EB* be added to both. The cube *BE* plus the solid then is equal to the solid whose base is the square *AB* and whose height is *BC,* which solid we have assumed to be equal to the given number. But the solid whose base is the square of *AB,* which is equal to the number of roots, and whose height is *EB,* which is the side of the cube, is equal to the number of the given sides of the cube *EB*. The cube *EB,* then, plus the number of its given sides is equal to the given number, which was required.

This species does not present varieties of cases or impossible problems. It has been solved by means of the properties of the circle combined with those of the parabola.

II. The second species. *A cube and a number are equal to sides.*

Let the line *AB* (Fig. 18) be the side of a square equal to the number of the roots, and construct a solid having as its base the square of *AB* and equal to the given number, and let its height *BC* be perpendicular to *AB*. Describe a parabola having as its vertex the point *B* and

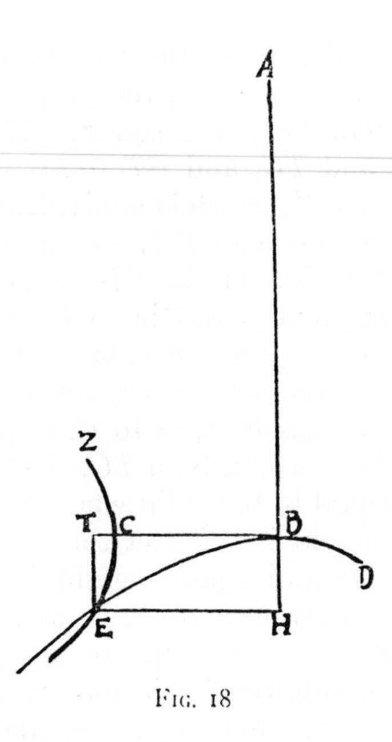

Fig. 18

its axis along the direction AB and its parameter AB. This is, then, the curve DBE, whose position is known. Construct also a second conic, namely, a hyperbola whose vertex is the point C and whose axis is along the direction of BC. Each one of its two parameters, the perpendicular and the oblique, is equal to BC. It is the curve ECZ. This hyperbola also is known in position, as was shown by Apollonius in the 58th proposition of his first book. The two conics will either meet or will not meet. If they do not meet, the problem is impossible of solution. If they do meet, they do it tangentially at a point or by intersection at two points.

Suppose they meet at a point and let it be at E, whose position is known. Then drop from it two perpendiculars ET and EH on the two lines BT and BH. The two perpendiculars are known unerringly in position and magnitude. The line ET is an ordinate of the hyperbola. Consequently, the square of ET is to the product of BT and TC as the parameter is to the oblique, as was demonstrated by Apollonius in the twentieth proposition of the first book. The two sides, the perpendicular and the oblique, are equal. Then the square ET is equal to the product of BT and TC, and BT to TE is as TE to TC. But the square of EH, which is equivalent to BT, is equal to the product of BH and BA, as was demonstrated in the second proposition of the first book of the treatise on conics. Consequently, AB is to BT as BT is to BH and as BH, which is equal to ET, is to TC. The four lines, AB, BT, ET, TC, then, are in continuous proportion, and the square of AB, the first, is to the square of BT, the second, as BT, the second, is to TC, the fourth. The cube of BT, then, is equal to the solid whose base is the square AB and whose height is CT. Let the solid whose base is the square of AB and whose height is BC, which was made equal to the given number, be added to both. Then the cube BT plus the given number is equal to the solid whose base is the square of AB and whose height is BT, which represents the number of the sides of the cube.

Thus it is shown that this species includes different cases and among its problems are some that are impossible. The species has been solved by means of the properties of the two conics, the parabola and the hyperbola.

PAPPUS

(c. 300 A.D.)

Pappus, a Greek geometer and scientist who lived in the reign of Diocletian (Roman Emperor 284—305), was a prolific writer on mathematical and scientific subjects, and a great teacher of the second Alexandrian school. Through the large numbers of pupils attracted to his side, he was a strong influence in the revival of interest in mathematics in his time. He was, moreover, a vital source of inspiration to mathematicians more than thirteen hundred years later when his surviving writings were a stimulating force upon the greatest scholars of the seventeenth century. Among them were Descartes, Fermat, Pascal and Desargues.

The works ascribed to Pappus by the Greek lexicographer, Suidas, indicate a breadth of learning on the part of the ancient author found only among the greatest of the ancient writers. In addition to Pappus's *Mathematical Collection,* originally in eight books, Suidas's list of works by Pappus contains *A Commentary on Ptolemy's Almagest, A Description of the Rivers of Libya, A Treatise on Military Engines* and *Commentaries on Aristarchus of Samos,* the last mentioned being concerned with the magnitudes and distances of the sun and moon. Of these, only the *Mathematical Collection* has been preserved. Although all of Book I and fragments of the other books of the *Collection* have been lost, the remaining parts of this extraordinary work form one of our richest sources of information about ancient mathematicians and the ancient science of mathematics.

The *Collection* became known in Europe through a Latin version and commentaries on it by Commandinus, published in 1588. In the *Collection,* Pappus gives a brief account of the contents of numerous older mathematical works which were held in high esteem in Alexandria. His famous *Treasury of Analysis* (*Mathematical Collection,* Book VII) contains a list of works written by Euclid, Apollonius, Aristaeus and Eratosthenes, which Pappus advises as most suitable for an advanced course of study in the method of analysis and synthesis. The procedure employed by Pappus in discussing individual problems has been of inestimable historical value. He first presents the solutions given by previous authors, then his own demonstrations, and finally various applications. The *Collection* also contains the celebrated Problem of Pappus taken by Descartes for the third appendix (La Geometrie) to his *Discours de la Methode.* As an illustration of the power of his *Methode,* Descartes solved the problem proposed by Pappus and in the course of the solution, he was led to the invention of analytic geometry. Pappus's efforts could not prevent the deterioration in the study of mathe-

matics in the centuries immediately following his death. However, mathematicians of a much later date eagerly studied all his available writings, and building upon his teachings, opened the way for the development of modern mathematics.

PAPPUS'S COLLECTION

From *Selections Illustrating the History of Greek Mathematics*

with an English translation by Ivor Thomas

(*f*) Extension of Pythagoras's Theorem

Pappus, Collection iv. 1. 1, ed. Hultsch 176. 9-178. 13

If ΑΒΓ be a triangle, and on ΑΒ, ΒΓ there be described any parallelograms ΑΒΔΕ, ΒΓΖΗ, and ΔΕ, ΖΗ be produced to Θ, and ΘΒ be joined, then the parallelograms ΑΒΔΕ, ΒΓΖΗ are together equal to the parallelogram contained by ΑΓ, ΘΒ in an angle which is equal to the sum of the angle ΒΑΓ, ΔΘΒ.

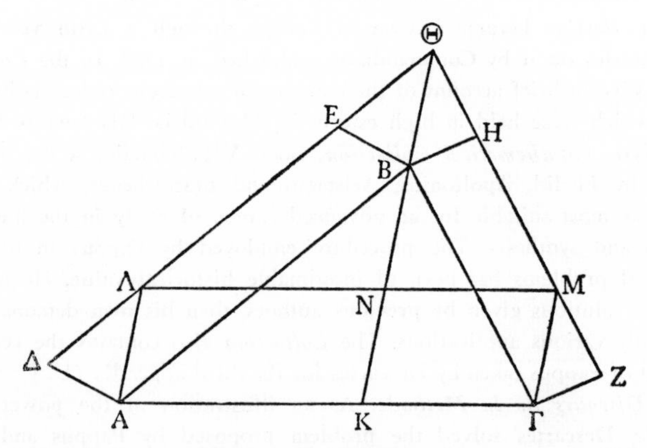

For let ΘΒ be produced to Κ, and through Α, Γ let ΑΛ, ΓΜ be drawn parallel to ΘΚ, and let ΛΜ be joined. Since

ΑΛΘΒ is a parallelogram, ΑΛ, ΘΒ are equal and parallel. Similarly ΜΓ, ΘΒ are equal and parallel, so that ΛΑ, ΜΓ are equal and parallel. And therefore ΛΜ, ΑΓ are equal and parallel; therefore ΑΛΜΓ is a parallelogram in the angle ΛΑΓ, that is an angle equal to the sum of the angles ΒΑΓ and ΔΘΒ; for the angle ΔΘΒ = angle ΛΑΒ. And since the parallelogram ΔΑΒΕ is equal to the parallelogram ΛΑΒΘ (for they are upon the same base ΑΒ and in the same parallels ΑΒ, ΔΘ), while ΛΑΒΘ = ΛΑΚΝ (for they are upon the same base ΛΑ and in the same parallels ΛΑ, ΘΚ), therefore ΑΔΕΒ = ΛΑΚΝ. By the same reasoning ΒΗΖΓ = ΝΚΓΜ; therefore the parallelograms ΔΑΒΕ, ΒΗΖΓ are together equal to ΛΑΓΜ, that is, to the parallelogram contained by ΑΓ, ΘΒ in the angle ΛΑΓ, which is equal to the sum of the angles ΒΑΓ, ΒΘΔ. And this is much more general than the theorem proved in the *Elements* about the squares on right-angled triangles.[a]

(*g*) Circles Inscribed in the ἄρβηλος

Ibid. iv. 14. 19, ed. Hultsch 208. 9-21

There is found in certain [books] an ancient proposi-

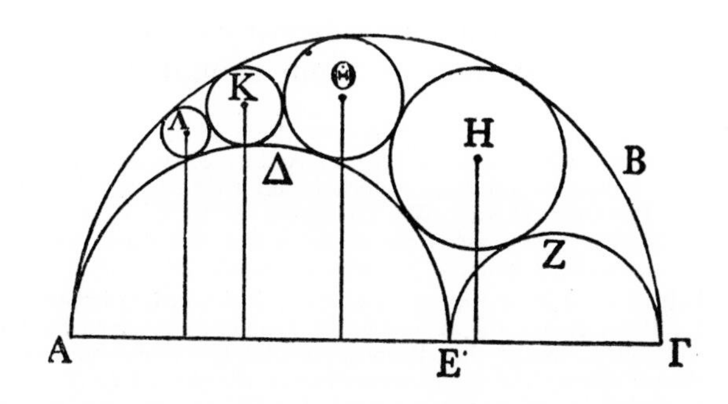

[a] Eucl. i. 47, *v.* vol. i. pp. 178-185. In the case taken by Pappus, the first two parallelograms are drawn outwards and the third, equal to their sum, is drawn inwards. If the areas of parallelograms drawn outwards be regarded as of opposite sign to the areas of those drawn inwards, the theorem may be still further generalized, for the algebraic sum of the three parallelograms is equal to zero.

tion to this effect: Let ΑΒΓ, ΑΔΕ, ΕΖΓ be supposed to be three semicircles touching each other, and in the space between their circumferences, which is called the "leather-worker's knife," let there be inscribed any number whatever of circles touching both the semicircles and one another, as those about the centres Η, Θ, Κ, Λ; to prove that the perpendicular from the centre Η to ΑΓ is equal to the diameter of the circle about Η, the perpendicular from Θ is double of the diameter of the circle about Θ, the perpendicular from Κ is triple, and the [remaining] perpendiculars in order are so many times the diameters of the proper circles according to the numbers in a series increasing by unity, the inscription of the circles proceeding without limit.[a]

(*i*) Isoperimetric Figures[b]

Ibid. v., Preface 1-3, ed. Hultsch 304. 5-308. 5

Though God has given to men, most excellent Megethion, the best and most perfect understanding of wisdom and mathematics, He has allotted a partial share to some of the unreasoning creatures as well. To men, as being endowed with reason, He granted that they should do everything in the light of reason and demonstration, but to the other unreasoning creatures He gave only this gift, that each of them should, in accordance

[a] Three propositions [about the "leather-worker's knife" are] in Archimedes' *Liber Assumptorum,* which has survived in Arabic. They are included as particular cases in Pappus's exposition, which is unfortunately too long for reproduction here. Professor D'Arcy W. Thompson (*The Classical Review,* lvi. (1942), pp. 75-76) gives reasons for thinking that this was a saddler's knife rather than a shoemaker's knife, as usually translated.

[b] The whole of Book v. in Pappus's *Collection* is devoted to isoperimetry. The first section follows closely the exposition of Zenodorus as given by Theon (*v. supra,* pp. 386-395), except that Pappus includes the proposition that *of all circular segments having the same circumference the semicircle is the greatest.* The second section compares the volumes of solids whose surfaces are equal, and is followed by a digression, on the semi-regular solids discovered by Archimedes. After some propositions on the lines of Archimedes' *De sph. et cyl.,* Pappus finally proves that *of regular solids having equal surfaces, that is greatest which has most faces.*

The introduction, here cited, on the sagacity of bees is rightly praised by Heath (*H.G.M.* ii. 389) as an example of the good style of the Greek mathematicians when freed from the restraints of technical language.

with a certain natural forethought, obtain so much as is needful for supporting life. This instinct may be observed to exist in many other species of creatures, but it is specially marked among bees. Their good order and their obedience to the queens who rule in their commonwealths are truly admirable, but much more admirable still is their emulation, their cleanliness in the gathering of honey, and the forethought and domestic care they give to its protection. Believing themselves, no doubt, to be entrusted with the task of bringing from the gods to the more cultured part of mankind a share of ambrosia in this form, they do not think it proper to pour it carelessly into earth or wood or any other unseemly and irregular material, but, collecting the fairest parts of the sweetest flowers growing on the earth, from them they prepare for the reception of the honey the vessels called honeycombs, [with cells] all equal, similar and adjacent, and hexagonal in form.

That they have contrived this in accordance with a certain geometrical forethought we may thus infer. They would necessarily think that the figures must all be adjacent one to another and have their sides common, in order that nothing else might fall into the interstices and so defile their work. Now there are only three rectilineal figures which would satisfy the condition, I mean regular figures which are equilateral and equiangular, inasmuch as irregular figures would be displeasing to the bees. For equilateral triangles and squares and hexagons can lie adjacent to one another and have their sides in common without irregular interstices. For the space about the same point can be filled by six equilateral triangles and six angles, of which each is 2/3 . right angle, or by four squares and four right angles, or by three hexagons and three angles of a hexagon, of which each is 1-1/3 . right angle. But three pentagons would not suffice to fill the space about the same point, and four would be more than sufficient; for three angles of the pentagon are less than four right angles (inasmuch as each angle is 1-1/5 . right angle), and four angles are greater than four right angles. Nor can three heptagons be placed about the same point so as to have their sides adjacent to each other; for three angles of a heptagon are greater than four right angles (inasmuch as each is 1-3/7 . right angle). And the same argument can be applied even more to polygons with a greater number of angles. There being, then, three figures capable by themselves of filling up the space around the same point, the triangle, the square and the hexagon, the bees in their wisdom chose for their work that which has the most angles, perceiving that it would hold more honey than either of the two others.

Bees, then, know just this fact which is useful to them, that the hexagon is greater than the square and the triangle and will hold more honey for the same expenditure of material in constructing each. But we, claiming a greater share in wisdom than the bees, will investigate a somewhat wider problem, namely that, *of all equilateral and equiangular plane figures having an equal perimeter, that which has the greater number of angles is always greater, and the greatest of them all is the circle having its perimeter equal to them.*

(*j*) Apparent Form of a Circle

Ibid. vi.[a] 48. 90-91, ed. Hultsch 580. 12-27

Let ABΓ be a circle with centre E, and from E let EZ be drawn perpendicular to the plane of the circle; I say that, if the eye be placed on EZ, the diameters of the circle appear equal.[b]

This is obvious; for all the straight lines falling from Z on the circumference of the circle are equal one to another and contain equal angles.

---

[a] Most of Book vi. is astronomical, covering the treatises in the *Little Astronomy*. The proposition here cited comes from a section on Euclid's *Optics*.

[b] As they will do if they subtend an equal angle at the eye.

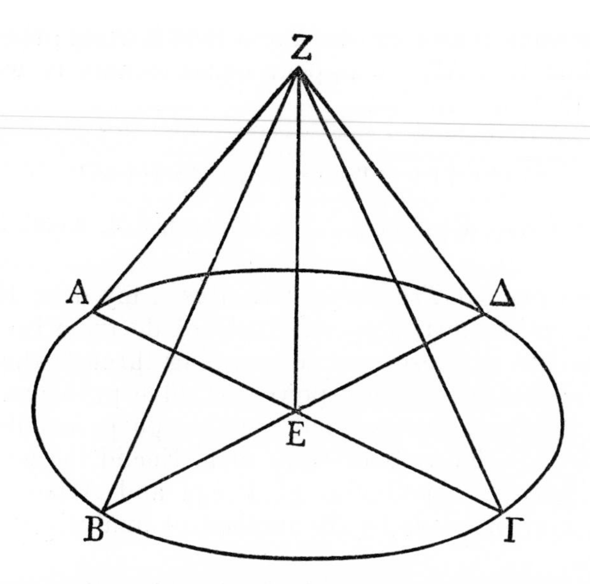

Now let EZ be not perpendicular to the plane of the circle, but equal to the radius of the circle; I say that, if the eye be at the point Z, in this case also the diameters appear equal.

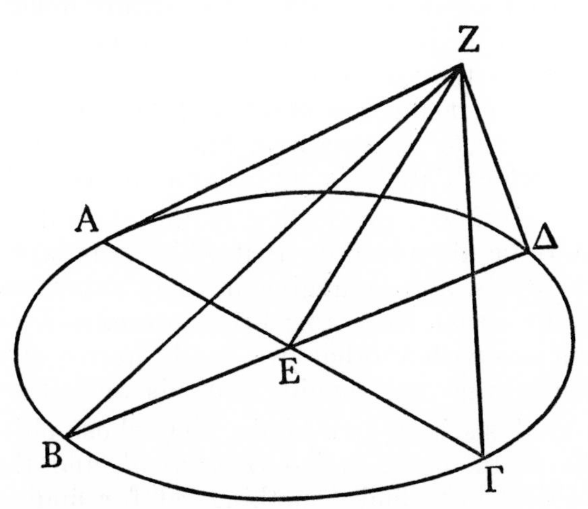

For let two diameters AΓ, BΔ be drawn, and let ZA, ZB, ZΓ, ZΔ be joined. Since the three straight lines EA, EΓ, EZ are equal, therefore the angle AZΓ is right. And by the same reasoning the angle BZΔ is right; therefore the diameters ΑΓ, ΒΔ appear equal. Similarly we may show that all are equal.

(*k*) The "Treasury of Analysis"

Ibid. vii., Preface 1-3, ed. Hultsch 634. 3-636. 30

The so-called *Treasury of Analysis,* my dear Hermodorus, is, in short, a special body of doctrine furnished for the use of those who, after going through the usual elements, wish to obtain power to solve problems set to them involving curves, and for this purpose only is it useful. It is the work of three men, Euclid the writer of the *Elements,* Apollonius of Perga and Aristaeus the elder, and proceeds by the method of analysis and synthesis.

Now *analysis* is a method of taking that which is sought as though it were admitted and passing from it through its consequences in order to something which is admitted as a result of synthesis; for in analysis we suppose that which is sought to be already done, and we inquire what it is from which this comes about, and again what is the antecedent cause of the latter, and so on until, by retracing our steps, we light upon something already known or ranking as a first principle; and such a method we call analysis, as being a reverse solution.

But in *synthesis,* proceeding in the opposite way, we suppose to be already done that which was last reached in the analysis, and arranging in their natural order as consequents what were formerly antecedents and linking them one with another, we finally arrive at the construction of what was sought; and this we call synthesis.

Now analysis is of two kinds, one, whose object is to seek the truth, being called *theoretical,* and the other, whose object is to find something set for finding, being called *problematical.* In the theoretical kind we suppose the subject of the inquiry to exist and to be true, and then we pass through its consequences in order, as though they also were true and established by our hypothesis, to something which is admitted; then, if that which is admitted be true, that which is sought will also be true, and the proof will be the reverse of the analysis, but if we come upon something admitted to be false, that which is sought will also be false. In the problematical kind we suppose that which is set as already known, and then we pass through its consequences in order, as though they were true, up to something admitted; then, if what is admitted be possible and can be done, that is, if it be what the mathematicians call *given,* what was originally set will also be possible, and the proof will again be the reverse of the analysis, but if we come upon something admitted to be impossible, the problem will also be impossible.

So much for analysis and synthesis.

This is the order of the books in the aforesaid *Treasury of Analysis*. Euclid's *Data,* one book, Apollonius's *Cutting-off of a Ratio,* two books, *Cutting-off of an Area,* two books, *Determinate Section,* two books, *Contacts,* two books, Euclid's *Porisms,* three books, Apollonius's *Vergings,* two books, his *Plane Loci,* two books, *Conics,* eight books, Aristaeus's *Solid Loci,* five books, Euclid's *Surface Loci,* two books, Eratosthenes' *On Means,* two books. In all there are thirty-three books, whose contents as far as Apollonius's *Conics* I have set out for your examination, including not only the number of the propositions, the conditions of possibility and the cases dealt with in each book, but also the lemmas which are required; indeed, I believe that I have not omitted any inquiry arising in the study of these books.

(*l*) Locus with Respect to Five or Six Lines[a]

Ibid. vii. 38-40, ed. Hultsch 680. 2-30

If from any point straight lines be drawn to meet at given angles five straight lines given in position, and

[a] It was by reflection on this passage that Descartes evolved the system of co-ordinates described in his *Geometrie.*

the ratio be given between the volume of the rectangular parallelepiped contained by three of them to the volume of the rectangular parallelepiped contained by the remaining two and a given straight line, the point will lie on a curve given in position. If there be six straight lines, and the ratio be given between the volume of the aforesaid solid formed by three of them to the volume of the solid formed by the remaining three, the point will again lie on a curve given in position. If there be more than six straight lines, it is no longer permissible to say "if the ratio be given between some figure contained by four of them to some figure contained by the remainder," since no figure can be contained in more than three dimensions. It is true that some recent writers have agreed among themselves to use such expressions, but they have no clear meaning when they multiply the rectangle contained by these straight lines with the square on that or the rectangle contained by those. They might, however, have expressed such matters by means of the composition of ratios, and have given a general proof both for the aforesaid propositions and for further propositions after this manner: *If from any point straight lines be drawn to meet at given angles straight lines given in position, and there be given the ratio compounded of that which one straight line so drawn bears to another, that which a second bears to a second, that which a third bears to a third, and that which the fourth bears to a given straight line—if there be seven, or, if there be eight, that which the fourth bears to the fourth—the point will lie on a curve given in position;* and similarly, however many the straight lines be, and whether odd or even. Though, as I said, these propositions follow the locus on four lines, [geometers] have by no means solved them to the extent that the curve can be recognized.

(*m*) Anticipation of Guldin's Theorem[a]

Ibid. vii. 41-42, ed. Hultsch 680. 30-682. 20

The men who study these matters are not of the same quality as the ancients and the best writers. Seeing that all geometers are occupied with the first principles of mathematics and the natural origin of the subject matter of investigation, and being ashamed to pursue such topics myself, I have proved propositions of much greater importance and utility . . . and in order not to make such a statement with empty hands, before leaving the argument I will give these enunciations to my readers. *Figures generated by a complete revolution of a plane figure about an axis are in a ratio compounded* (*a*) *of the ratio* [*of the areas*] *of the figures, and* (*b*) *of the ratio of the straight lines similarly drawn to the axes of rotation from the respective centres of gravity. Figures generated by incomplete revolutions are in a ratio compounded* (*a*) *of the ratio* [*of the areas*] *of the figures, and* (*b*) *of the ratio of the arcs described by the centres of gravity of the respective figures, the ratio of the arcs being itself compounded* (1) *of the ratio of the straight lines similarly drawn* [*from the respective centres of gravity to the axes of rotation*] *and* (2) *of the ratio of the angles contained about the axes of revolution by the extremities of these straight lines.* These propositions, which are practically one, include a large number of theorems of all sorts about curves, surfaces and solids, all of which are proved simultaneously by one demonstration, and include propositions never before proved as well as those already proved, such as those in the twelfth book of these elements.

[a] Paul Guldin (1577-1643), or Guldinus, is generally credited with the discovery of the celebrated theorem here enunciated by Pappus. It may be stated: *If any plane figure revolve about an external axis in its plane, the volume of the solid figure so generated is equal to the product of the area of the figure and the distance travelled by the centre of gravity of the figure.* There is a corresponding theorem for the area.

BENJAMIN PEIRCE

(1809—1880)

Benjamin Peirce, professor of astronomy and mathematics at Harvard University and leading mathematician of his day, was born at Salem, Mass., on April 4, 1809. His father, who had been a member first of the lower house and then of the upper house of the state legislature, was Librarian of Harvard University from 1826 to 1831, and the author (posthumously) of the History of Harvard University from its inception to the period of the Revolution. As an undergraduate, Benjamin came under the influence of Nathaniel Bowditch. His deep affection for Professor Bowditch continued undiminished in later years and it was to him that Peirce dedicated the greatest and most extensive of his texts, his *Analytic Mechanics.* "To the cherished and revered memory," he wrote, "of my master in science, Nathaniel Bowditch, the father of American geometry." Before graduating from Harvard, Peirce had already made a firm choice of a career, the teaching of mathematics. He was appointed tutor in mathematics at Harvard at the same time as Charles W. Eliot, and the two young mathematics tutors joined forces in securing the innovation of written final examinations in mathematics in the place of oral examinations which had formerly been held in the presence of visiting committees of the Board of Overseers. The practice of holding written examinations soon spread to other departments at Harvard and to other universities. Peirce was the first professor of mathematics who consistently encouraged his students to engage in mathematical research. Through the great series of text books which he wrote, Benjamin Peirce exerted a profound and lasting influence upon the teaching of mathematics in America.

Vastly more than teaching and text books filled Peirce's forty-nine active years at Harvard. In 1847 he was one of a committee of five to plan a program for the organization of the Smithsonian Institution. In that same year he received the degree of L.L.D. from the University of North Carolina. Thereafter not a year went by without his participation in some vitally important activity or without his receiving academic recognition from learned societies and universities both at home and abroad. An office of the American Nautical Almanac was established at Harvard so that without interrupting his duties as professor he was able to serve the Almanac as consulting astronomer (1849—1867). He was Director of the longitude determination for the United States Coast Survey from 1832 to 1867. He served as Superintendent of the Coast Survey from 1867 to 1874, and as the consulting geometer from 1874 to 1880. In 1870 he personally conducted an expedition to Sicily to observe the eclipse of the sun. He was instrumental in the establishment of the Dudley Observatory at Albany in 1855 and he was largely responsible for the institution of an observatory at Harvard. Possessing a huge fund of personal dynamism, Benjamin Peirce was active and influential in numerous scientific associations, some of which he helped to found. He was president of the American Association for the Advancement of Science in 1853. He was one of the fifty incorporators of the National Academy of Sciences and the chairman of the mathematics and physics class in 1864.

Each of Benjamin Peirce's four sons achieved professional distinction. James Mills Peirce, the eldest, was for forty years professor of mathematics at Harvard. Benjamin Mills Peirce was a mining engineer. Herbert Henry Peirce was a diplomat. Charles Sanders Peirce, the least successful financially of the entire family, has come to be regarded as the greatest and most original of American philosophers. The researches which led Benjamin Peirce to the publication of his memoir, *Linear Associative Algebra,* were undertaken by him upon the urging of his son, Charles. Stimulated by Charles's lively interest in the new mathematics being developed on a level of generality and application heretofore unknown, Benjamin Peirce wrote the memoir which he described as a "philosophic study of the laws of algebraic operation", developed from fundamental principles, no reference being made to other branches of mathematics. Introducing the work in 1870, Benjamin Peirce stated, "This work has been the pleasantest mathematical effort of my life. In no other have I seemed to myself to have received so full a reward for my mental labor in the novelty and breadth of the results." The method employed by Benjamin Peirce in his *Linear Associative Algebra* was extended and perfected by later writers, notably by H. E. Hawkes who wrote on hypercomplex numbers in seven units.

●

LINEAR ASSOCIATIVE ALGEBRA

A Memoir read before the National Academy of Sciences in Washington, 1870.

By Benjamin Peirce.

With Notes and Addenda, by C. S. Peirce, Son of the Author.

---

1. Mathematics is the science which draws necessary conclusions.

This definition of mathematics is wider than that which is ordinarily given, and by which its range is limited to quantitative research. The ordinary definition, like those of other sciences, is objective; whereas this is subjective. Recent investigations, of which quaternions is the most noteworthy instance, make it manifest that the old definition is too restricted. The sphere of mathematics is here extended, in accordance with the derivation of its name, to all demonstrative research, so as to include all knowledge strictly capable of dogmatic teaching. Mathematics is not the discoverer of laws, for it is not induction; neither is it the framer of theories, for it is not hypothesis; but it is the judge over both, and it is the arbiter to which each must refer its claims; and neither law can rule nor theory explain without the sanction of mathematics. It deduces from a law all its consequences, and develops them into the suitable form for comparison with observation, and thereby measures the strength of the argument from observation in favor of a proposed law or of a proposed form of application of a law.

Mathematics, under this definition, belongs to every enquiry, moral as well as physical. Even the rules of logic, by which it is rigidly bound, could not be deduced without its aid. The laws of argument admit of simple statement, but they must be curiously transposed before they can be applied to the living speech and verified by observation. In its pure and simple form the syllogism cannot be directly compared with all experience, or it would not have required an Aristotle to discover it. It must be transmuted into all the possible shapes in which reasoning loves to clothe itself. The transmutation is the mathematical process in the establishment of the law. Of some sciences, it is so large a portion that they have been quite abandoned to the mathematician,—which may not have been altogether to the advantage of philosophy. Such is the case with geometry and analytic mechanics. But in many other sciences, as in all those of mental philosophy and most of the branches of natural history, the deductions are so immediate and of such simple construction, that it is of no practical use to separate the mathematical portion and subject it to isolated discussion.

2. The branches of mathematics are as various as the sciences to which they belong, and each subject of physical enquiry has its appropriate mathematics. In every form of material manifestation, there is a corresponding form of human thought, so that the human mind is as wide in its range of thought as the physical universe in which it thinks. The two are wonderfully matched. But where there is a great diversity of physical appearance, there is often a close resemblance in the processes of deduction. It is important, therefore, to separate the intellectual work from the external form. Symbols must be adopted which may serve for the embodiment of forms of argument, without being trammeled by the conditions of external representation or special interpretation. The words of common language are usually unfit for this purpose, so that other symbols must be adopted, and mathematics treated by such symbols is called *algebra*. Algebra, then, is formal mathematics.

3. All relations are either qualitative or quantitative. Qualitative relations can be considered by themselves without regard to quantity. The algebra of such enquiries may be called logical algebra, of which a fine example is given by Boole.

Quantitative relations may also be considered by themselves without regard to quality. They belong to arithmetic, and the corresponding algebra is the common or arithmetical algebra.

In all other algebras both relations must be combined, and the algebra must conform to the character of the relations.

4. The symbols of an algebra, with the laws of combination, constitute its *language;* the methods of using the symbols in the drawing of inferences is its *art;* and their interpretation is its *scientific application*. This three-fold

analysis of algebra is adopted from President Hill, of Harvard University, and is made the basis of a division into books.

Book I.*

The Language of Algebra.

5. The language of algebra has its alphabet, vocabulary, and grammar.

6. The symbols of algebra are of two kinds: one class represent its fundamental conceptions and may be called its *letters,* and the other represent the relations or modes of combination of the letters and are called *the signs.*

7. The *alphabet* of an algebra consists of its letters; the *vocabulary* defines its signs and the elementary combinations of its letters; and the *grammar* gives the rules of composition by which the letters and signs are united into a complete and consistent system.

The Alphabet.

8. Algebras may be distinguished from each other by the number of their independent fundamental conceptions, or of the letters of their alphabet. Thus an algebra which has only one letter in its alphabet is a *single* algebra; one which has two letters is a *double* algebra; one of three letters a *triple* algebra; one of four letters a *quadruple* algebra, and so on.

This artificial division of the algebras is cold and uninstructive like the artificial Linnean system of botany. But it is useful in a preliminary investigation of algebras, until a sufficient variety is obtained to afford the material for a natural classification.

Each fundamental conception may be called a *unit;* and thus each unit has its corresponding letter, and the two words, unit and letter, may often be used indiscriminately in place of each other, when it cannot cause confusion.

* Only this book was ever written. [C. S. P.]

9. The present investigation, not usually extending beyond the sextuple algebra, limits the demand of the algebra for the most part to six letters; and the six letters, i, j, k, l, m and n, will be restricted to this use except in special cases.

10. *For any given letter another may be substituted,* provided a new letter represents a combination of the original letters of which the replaced letter is a necessary component.

For example, any combination of two letters, which is entirely dependent for its value upon both of its components, such as their sum, difference, or product, may be substituted for either of them.

This *principle of the substitution of letters* is radically important, and is a leading element of originality in the present investigation; and without it, such an investigation would have been impossible. It enables the geometer to analyse an algebra, reduce it to its simplest and characteristic forms, and compare it with other algebras. It involves in its principle a corresponding substitution of *units* of which it is in reality the formal representative.

There is, however, no danger in working with the symbols, irrespective of the ideas attached to them, and the consideration of the change of the original conceptions may be safely reserved for the *book of interpretation.*

11. In making the substitution of letters, the original letter will be preserved with the distinction of a subscript number.

Thus, for the letter i there may successively be substituted i_1, i_2, i_3, etc. In the final forms, the subscript numbers can be omitted, and they may be omitted at any period of the investigation, when it will not produce confusion.

It will be practically found that these subscript numbers need scarcely ever be written. They pass through the mind, as a sure ideal protection from erroneous substitution, but disappear from the writing with the same facility with which those evanescent chemical compounds, which are essential to the theory of transformation, escape the eye of the observer.

12. A *pure* algebra is one in which every letter is connected by some indissoluble relation with every other letter.

13. When the letters of an algebra can be separated into two groups, which are mutually independent, it is a *mixed algebra*. It is mixed even when there are letters common to the two groups, provided those which are not common to the two groups are mutually independent. Were an algebra employed for the simultaneous discussion of distinct classes of phenomena, such as those of sound and light, and were the peculiar units of each class to have their appropriate letters, but were there no recognized dependence of the phenomena upon each other, so that the phenomena of each class might have been submitted to independent research, the one algebra would be actually a mixture of two algebras, one appropriate to sound, the other to light.

It may be farther observed that when, in such a case as this, the component algebras are identical in form, they are reduced to the case of one algebra with two diverse interpretations.

The Vocabulary.

14. Letters which are not appropriated to the alphabet of the algebra* may be used in any convenient sense. But it is well to employ *the small letters* for expressions of common algebra, and *the capital letters* for those of the algebra under discussion.

There must, however, be exceptions to this notation; thus the letter D will denote the derivative of an expression to which it is applied, and Σ the summation of cognate expressions, and other exceptions will be mentioned as they occur. Greek letters will generally be reserved for angular and functional notation.

* See § 9.

15. The three symbols J, $ə$, and 6 will be adopted with the signification

$$\mathrm{J} = \sqrt{-1}$$

$ə =$ the ratio of circumference to diameter of circle $= 3.1415926536$

$6 =$ the base of Naperian logarithms $= 2.7182818285$, which gives the mysterious formula

$$\mathrm{J}^{-\mathrm{J}} = \sqrt{6^{ə}} = 4.810477381.$$

16. All the signs of common algebra will be adopted; but any signification will be permitted them which is not inconsistent with their use in common algebra; so that if by any process an expression to which they refer is reduced to one of common algebra, they must resume their ordinary signification.

17. The sign $=$, which is called that of equality, is used in its ordinary sense to denote that the two expressions which it separates are the same whole, although they represent different combinations of parts.

18. The signs $>$ and $<$ which are those of inequality, and denote "more than" or "less than" in quantity, will be used to denote the relations of a whole to its part, so that the symbol which denotes the part shall be at the vertex of the angle, and that which denotes the whole at its opening. This involves the proposition that the smaller of the quantities is included in the class expressed by the larger. Thus

$$B < A \text{ or } A > B$$

denotes that A is a whole of which B is a part, so that all B is A.†

If the usual algebra had originated in qualitative, instead of quantitative, investigations, the use of the symbols might easily have been reversed; for it seems that all conceptions involved in A must also be involved in B, so that B is more than A in the sense that it involves more ideas.

The combined expression

$$B > C < A$$

† The formula in the text implies, also, that some A is not B. [C. S. P.]

denotes that there are quantities expressed by C which belong to the class A and also to the class B. It implies, therefore, that some B is A and that some A is B.* The intermediate C might be omitted if this were the only proposition intended to be expressed, and we might write

$$B > < A.$$

In like manner the combined expression

$$B < C > A$$

denotes that there is a class which includes both A and B,† which proposition might be written

$$B < > A.$$

19. A vertical mark drawn through either of the preceding signs reverses its signification. Thus

$$A \neq B$$

denotes that B and A are essentially different wholes;

$$A \not> B \text{ or } B \not< A$$

denotes that all B is not A,‡ so that if they have only quantitative relations, they must bear to each other the relation of

$$A = B \text{ or } A < B.$$

20. The sign $+$ is called *plus* in common algebra and denotes *addition*. It may be retained with the same name, and the process which it indicates may be called addition. In the simplest cases it expresses a mere mixture, in which the elements preserve their mutual independence. If the elements cannot be mixed without mutual action and a consequent change of constitution, the mere union is still expressed by the sign of addition, although some other symbol is required to express the character of the mixture as a peculiar compound having properties different from its elements. It is obvious from the simplicity of the union recognized in this sign, that the order of the admixture of the elements cannot affect it; so that it may be assumed that

$$A + B = B + A$$

* This, of course, supposes that C does not vanish. [C. S. P.]

† The universe will be such a class unless A or B is the universe. [C. S. P.]

‡ The general interpretation is rather that either A and B are identical or that some B is not A. [C. S. P.]

and

$$(A + B) + C = A + (B + C) = A + B + C.$$

21. The sign — is called *minus* in common algebra, and denotes *subtraction*. Retaining the same name, the process is to be regarded as the reverse of addition; so that if an expression is first added and then subtracted, or the reverse, it disappears from the result; or, in algebraic phrase, it is *canceled*. This gives the equations

$$A + B - B = A - B + B = A$$

and

$$B - B = 0.$$

The sign minus is called the negative sign in ordinary algebra, and any term preceded by it may be united with it, and the combination may be called a *negative term*. This use will be adopted into all the algebras, with the provision that the derivation of the word negative must not transmit its interpretation.

22. The sign × may be adopted from ordinary algebra with the name of the sign of *multiplication*, but without reference to the meaning of the process. The result of multiplication is to be called the *product*. The terms which are combined by the sign of multiplication may be called *factors*; the factor which precedes the sign being distinguished as the *multiplier*, and that which follows it being the *multiplicand*. The words multiplier, multiplicand, and product, may also be conveniently replaced by the terms adopted by Hamilton, of *facient*, *faciend*, and *factum*. Thus the equation of the product is

multiplier × multiplicand = product;
or facient × faciend = factum.

When letters are used, the sign of multiplication can be *omitted* as in ordinary algebra.

23. When an expression used as a factor in certain combinations gives a product which vanishes, it may be called in those combinations a *nilfactor*. Where as the multiplier it produces vanishing products it is *nilfacient*, but where it is the multiplicand of such a product it is *nilfaciend*.

24. When an expression used as a factor in certain

combinations overpowers the other factors and is itself the product, it may be called an *idemfactor*. When in the production of such a result it is the multiplier, it is *idemfacient,* but when it is the multiplicand it is *idemfaciend.*

25. When an expression raised to the square or any higher power vanishes, it may be called *nilpotent;* but when, raised to a square or higher power, it gives itself as the result, it may be called *idempotent.*

The defining equation of nilpotent and idempotent expressions are respectively $A^n = 0$, and $A^n = A$; but with reference to idempotent expressions, it will always be assumed that they are of the form

$$A^2 = A,$$

unless it be otherwise distinctly stated.

26. *Division* is the reverse of multiplication, by which its results are verified. It is the process for obtaining one of the factors of a given product when the other factor is given. It is important to distinguish the position of the given factor, whether it is facient or faciend. This can be readily indicated by combining the sign of multiplication, and placing it before or after the given factor just as it stands in the product. Thus when the multiplier is the given factor, the correct equation of division is

$$\text{quotient} = \frac{\text{dividend}}{\text{divisor} \times}$$

and the equation of verification is

$$\text{divisor} \times \text{quotient} = \text{dividend}.$$

But when the multiplicand is the given factor, the equation of division is

$$\text{quotient} = \frac{\text{dividend}}{\times\ \text{divisor}}$$

and the equation of verification is

$$\text{quotient} \times \text{divisor} = \text{dividend}.$$

27. Exponents may be introduced just as in ordinary algebra, and they may even be permitted to assume the forms of the algebra under discussion. There seems to be no necessary restriction to giving them even a wider range and introducing into one algebra the exponents

from another. Other signs will be defined when they are needed.

The definition of the fundamental operations is an essential part of the vocabulary, but as it is subject to the rules of grammar which may be adopted, it must be reserved for special investigation in the different algebras.

The Grammar.

28. Quantity enters as a form of thought into every inference. It is always implied in the syllogism. It may not, however, be the direct object of inquiry; so that there may be logical and chemical algebras into which it only enters accidentally, agreeably to § 1. But where it is recognized, it should be received in its most general form and in all its variety. The algebra is otherwise unnecessarily restricted, and cannot enjoy the benefit of the most fruitful forms of philosophical discussion. But while it is thus introduced as a part of the formal algebra, it is *subject to every degree and kind of limitation in its interpretation.*

The free introduction of quantity into an algebra does not even involve the reception of its unit as one of the independent units of the algebra. But it is probable that without such a unit, no algebra is adapted to useful investigation. It is so admitted into quaternions, and its admission seems to have misled some philosophers into the opinion that quaternions is a triple and not a quadruple algebra. This will be the more evident from the form in which quaternions first present themselves in the present investigation, and in which the unit of quantity is not distinctly recognizable without a transmutation of the form.

29. The introduction of quantity into an algebra naturally carries with it, not only the notation of ordinary algebra, but likewise many of the rules to which it is subject. Thus, when a quantity is a factor of a product, it has the same influence whether it be facient or faciend, so that with the notation of § 14, there is the equation

$$Aa = aA,$$

and in such a product, the quantity a may be called the *coefficient*.

In like manner, terms which only differ in their coefficients, may be added by adding their coefficients; thus,

$$(a \pm b)\ A = aA \pm bA = Aa \pm Ab = A\ (a \pm b).$$

30. The exceeding simplicity of the conception of an equation involves the identity of the equations

$$A = B \text{ and } B = A$$

and the substitution of B for A in every expression, so that

$$MA \pm C = MB \pm C,$$

or that, *the members of an equation may be mutually transposed or simultaneously increased or decreased or multiplied or divided by equal expressions.*

31. How far the principle of § 16 limits the extent within which the ordinary symbols may be used, cannot easily be decided. But it suggests limitations which may be adopted during the present discussion, and leave an ample field for curious investigation.

The distributive principle of multiplication may be adopted; namely, the principle that the product of an algebraic sum of factors into or by a common factor, is equal to the corresponding algebraic sum of the individual products of the various factors into or by the common factor; and it is expressed by the equations

$$(A \pm B)\ C = AB \pm BC.$$
$$C\ (A \pm B) = CA \pm CB.$$

32. *The associative principle of multiplication* may be adopted; namely, that the product of successive multiplications is not affected by the order in which the multiplications are performed, provided there is no change in the relative position of the factors; and it is expressed by the equations

$$ABC = (AB)C = A(BC).$$

This is quite an important limitation, and the algebras which are subject to it will be called *associative.*

33. The principle that the value of a product is not affected by the relative position of the factors is called *the commutative principle,* and is expressed by the equation

$$AB = BA.$$

This principle is *not* adopted in the present investigation.

34. An algebra in which every expression is reducible to the form of an algebraic sum of terms, each of which consists of a single *letter* with a quantitative coefficient, is called *a linear* algebra. Such are all the algebras of the present investigation.

35. Wherever there is a limited number of independent conceptions, a linear algebra may be adopted. For a combination which was not reducible to such an algebraic sum as those of linear algebra, would be to that extent independent of the original conceptions, and would be an independent conception additional to those which were assumed to constitute the elements of the algebra.

36. An algebra in which there can be complete interchange of its independent units, without changing the formulae of combination, is a *completely symmetrical algebra;* and one in which there may be a partial interchange of its units is *partially symmetrical.* But the term symmetrical should not be applied, unless the interchange is more extensive than that involved in the distributive and commutative principles. An algebra in which the interchange is effected in a certain order which returns into itself is a *cyclic algebra.*

Thus, quaternions is a cyclic algebra, because in any of its fundamental equations, such as

$$i^2 = -1$$
$$ij = -ji = k$$
$$ijk = -1$$

there can be an interchange of the letters in the order

i, j, k, i, each letter being changed into that which follows it. The double algebra in which

$$i^2 = i, \quad ij = i$$
$$j^2 = j, \quad ji = j$$

is cyclic because the letters are interchangeable in the order i, j, i. But neither of these algebras is commutative.

37. When an algebra can be reduced to a form in which all the letters are expressed as powers of some one of them, it may be called a *potential algebra*. If the powers are all squares, it may be called *quadratic;* if they are cubes, it may be called *cubic;* and similarly in other cases.

Linear Associative Algebra.

38. *All the expressions of an algebra are distributive, whenever the distributive principle extends to all the letters of the alphabet.*

For it is obvious that in the equation

$$(i + j)(k + l) = ik + jk + il + jl$$

each letter can be multiplied by an integer, which gives the form

$$(ai + bj)(ck + dl) = acik + bcjk + adil + bdjl,$$

in which a, b, c and d are integers. The integers can have the ratios of any four real numbers, so that by simple division they can be reduced to such real numbers. Other similar equations can also be formed by writing for a and b, a_1 and b_1, or for c and d, c_1 and d_1, or by making both these substitutions simultaneously. If then the two first of these new equations are multiplied by J and the last by -1; the sum of the four equations will be the same as that which would be obtained by substituting for a, b, c and d, $a + J a_1$, $b + J b_1$, $c + J c_1$ and $d + J d_1$. Hence a, b, c and d may be any numbers, real or imaginary, and in general whatever mixtures A, B, C and D may represent of the original units under the form of an algebraic sum of the letters i, j, k, &c., we shall have

$$(A + B)(C + D) = AC + BC + AD + BD,$$

which is the complete expression of the distributive principle.

39. *An algebra is associative whenever the associative principle extends to all the letters of its alphabet.*

For if

$$A = \Sigma\,(ai) = ai + a_1 j + a_2 k + \&c.$$
$$B = \Sigma\,(bi) = bi + b_1 j + b_2 k + \&c.$$
$$C = \Sigma\,(ci) = ci + c_1 j + c_2 k + \&c.$$

it is obvious that

$$AB = \Sigma\,(ab_1 ij)$$
$$BC = \Sigma\,(bc_1 ij)$$
$$(AB)\mathrm{C} = \Sigma\,(ab_1 c_2 ijk) = A(BC) = ABC$$

which is the general expression of the associative principle.

CHARLES SANDERS PEIRCE

(1839—1914)

Charles Sanders Peirce, one of the most profound and original of American philosophers and mathematicians, founder of the philosophical school of pragmatism, was born at Cambridge, Mass., on September 10, 1839. The second son of Benjamin Peirce, famous Harvard professor of astronomy and mathematics, he belonged to a family which had been prominent in the affairs of Harvard University for generations. An extraordinarily precocious child, his formal schooling was supplemented by his father's teaching in mathematics and the physical sciences. His early interest in philosophy and logic, on the other hand, met with scant sympathy or approval in the scientific atmosphere of the Peirce household. Charles's training in chemistry, astronomy, geodesy and optics as well as in mathematics left him, as he said, "saturated through and through with the spirit of the physical sciences." In 1861 he accepted an appointment as a physicist and mathematician in the United States Coast Survey. Had his activities been restricted to the field of science alone, his accomplishments in this area would have been a sufficient mark of his genius. Peirce's work on astronomical problems and his investigations on the pendulum were especially well received both at home and abroad. Nevertheless, his strong leaning toward philosophy and the sensitivity of his creative powers were never to be overwhelmed. Throughout his life, by means of his personal contacts, lectures and essays, Charles Peirce was at the center of the development of philosophy in America. James, Royce, Dewey and others frequently acknowledged his influence upon them. Eventually, too, his activities in the newer mathematics instigated the researches undertaken and published by his father (Benjamin Peirce: *Linear Associative Algebra,* 1870).

Peirce retired from the Coast Survey after thirty years of service to devote himself to writing. He left without a pension. Despite a small inheritance and some income derived from his lectures, from the publication of essays, book reviews and numerous contributions to the Century Dictionary and to the Dictionary of Philosophy, he suffered financial hardships during the entire period of his retirement. After his death several hundreds of unpublished manuscripts were found. These came into the care of the Department of Philosophy at Harvard University and have since been edited and published as the Collected Papers of Charles Sanders Peirce. The range of subjects on which Peirce wrote was encyclopaedic, including not only logic and philosophy, but also topics in astrophysics, pure mathematics, philosophy of mathematics, probability, philology, criminology, telepathy, and optics. All of Peirce's writings were marked by originality of outlook. Intense in his advocacy of the scientific method, vigorously outspoken and unwilling to bridle his violent disapproval of certain popular philosophical beliefs, Peirce failed during his life to win large numbers of disciples. Later scholars were better prepared to evaluate his proposals and his new ideas, presented as they were in the strange but highly significant terms and symbols invented by him. The inspirational and stimulating force of his work has come to enjoy ever greater recognition, and interest in Charles Peirce's vital contributions to the field of logic and scientific method has mounted steadily.

●

ON THE ALGEBRA OF LOGIC

§3. FORMS OF PROPOSITIONS

173. In place of the two expressions $A -\!\!< B$ and $B -\!\!< A$ taken together we may write $A = B$;[2] in place of the two expres-

---

[2] There is a difference of opinion among logicians as to whether $-\!\!<$ or $=$ is the simpler relation. But in my paper on the *Logic of Relatives* [47n.], I have strictly demonstrated that the preference must be given to $-\!\!<$ in this respect. The term *simpler* has an exact meaning in logic; it means that whose logical depth is smaller; that is, if one conception implies another, but not the reverse, then the latter is said to be the simpler. Now to say that $A = B$ implies that $A -\!\!< B$, but not conversely. *Ergo*, etc. It is to no purpose to reply that $A -\!\!< B$ implies $A = (A \text{ that is } B)$; it would be equally relevant to say that $A -\!\!< B$ implies $A = A$. Consider an analogous case. Logical sequence is a simpler conception than causal sequence, because every causal sequence is a logical sequence but not every logical sequence is a causal sequence; and it is no reply to this to say that a logical sequence between two facts implies a causal sequence between some two facts whether the same or different. The idea that $=$ is a very simple relation is probably due to the fact that the discovery of such a relation teaches us that instead of two objects we have only one, so that it simpli-

sions $A \prec B$ and $B \overline{\prec} A$ taken together we may write $A<B$ or $B>A$; and in place of the two expressions $A \overline{\prec} B$ and $B \overline{\prec} A$ taken together [disjunctively] we may write $A \asymp B$.*

174. De Morgan, in the remarkable memoir with which he opened his discussion of the syllogism (1846, p. 380,†) has pointed out that we often carry on reasoning under an implied restriction as to what we shall consider as possible, which restriction, applying to the whole of what is said, need not be expressed. The total of all that we consider possible is called the *universe* of discourse, and may be very limited. One mode of limiting our universe is by considering only what actually occurs, so that everything which does not occur is regarded as impossible.

175. The forms $A \prec B$, or A implies B, and $A \overline{\prec} B$, or A does not imply B‡, embrace both hypothetical and categorical propositions. Thus, to say that all men are mortal is the same as to say that if any man possesses any character whatever then a mortal possesses that character. To say, 'if

fies our conception of the universe. On this account the existence of such a relation is an important fact to learn; in fact, it has the sum of the importances of the two facts of which it is compounded. It frequently happens that it is more convenient to treat the propositions $A \prec B$ and $B \prec A$ together in their form $A=B$; but it also frequently happens that it is more convenient to treat them separately. Even in geometry we can see that to say that two figures A and B are equal is to say that when they are properly put together A will cover B and B will cover A; and it is generally necessary to examine these facts separately. So, in comparing the numbers of two lots of objects, we set them over against one another, each to each, and observe that for every one of the lot A there is one of the lot B, and for every one of the lot B there is one of the lot A.

In logic, our great object is to analyse all the operations of reason and reduce them to their ultimate elements; and to make a calculus of reasoning is a subsidiary object. Accordingly, it is more philosophical to use the copula $\prec$ apart from all considerations of convenience. Besides, this copula is intimately related to our natural logical and metaphysical ideas; and it is one of the chief purposes of logic to show what validity those ideas have. Moreover, it will be seen further on that the more analytical copula does in point of fact give rise to the easiest method of solving problems of logic.

* I.e., $-(A=B)$.

† "On the Structure of the Syllogism, and on the Application of the Theory of Probabilities to Questions of Argument and Authority." *Transactions, Cambridge Philosophical Society*, vol. 8, pp. 379–408, (1849). The paper was read and dated 1846.

‡ I.e., it is false that $A \prec B$.

A, then B' is obviously the same as to say that from A, B follows, logically or extralogically. By thus identifying the relation expressed by the copula with that of illation, we identify the proposition with the inference, and the term with the proposition. This identification, by means of which all that is found true of term, proposition, or inference is at once known to be true of all three, is a most important engine of reasoning, which we have gained by beginning with a consideration of the genesis of logic.[1]

§4. THE ALGEBRA OF THE COPULA

182. From the identity of the relation expressed by the copula with that of illation, springs an algebra. In the first place, this gives us

$$x \multimap\!\!< x \qquad (1)$$

the principle of identity, which is thus seen to express that what we have hitherto believed we continue to believe, in the absence of any reason to the contrary. In the next place, this identification shows that the two inferences

$$\begin{array}{ccc} x & & \\ y & \text{and} & x \\ \therefore z & & \therefore y \multimap\!\!< z \end{array} \qquad (2)$$

are of the same validity. Hence we have

$$\{x \multimap\!\!< (y \multimap\!\!< z)\} = \{y \multimap\!\!< (x \multimap\!\!< z)\}.^{2} \qquad (3)$$

183. From (1) we have

$$(x \multimap\!\!< y) \multimap\!\!< (x \multimap\!\!< y),$$

whence by (2)

$$\begin{array}{cc} x \multimap\!\!< y & x \\ & \therefore y \end{array} \qquad (4)$$

---

[1] In consequence of the identification in question, in S —< P, I speak of S indifferently as *subject*, *antecedent*, or *premiss*, and of P as *predicate*, *consequent*, or *conclusion*.

[2] Mr. Hugh McColl (*Calculus of Equivalent Statements*, Second Paper, 1878, [*Proceedings*, *London Mathematical Society*, vol. 9, p. 183 (1877)]), makes use of the sign of inclusion several times in the same proposition. He does not, however, give any of the formulæ of this section.

is a valid inference.

184. By (4), if x and $x -\!\!< y$ are true y is true; and if y and $y -\!\!< z$ are true z is true. Hence, the inference is valid

$$x \qquad x -\!\!< y \qquad y -\!\!< z$$
$$\therefore z.$$

By the principle of (2) this is the same as to say that

$$x -\!\!< y \qquad y -\!\!< z$$
$$\therefore x -\!\!< z \tag{5}$$

is a valid inference.

●

A CONTRIBUTION TO THE PHILOSOPHY OF NOTATION*

§1. THREE KINDS OF SIGNS†

359. Any character or proposition either concerns one subject, two subjects, or a plurality of subjects. For example, one particle has mass, two particles attract one another, a particle revolves about the line joining two others. A fact concerning two subjects is a dual character or relation; but a relation which is a mere combination of two independent facts concerning the two subjects may be called *degenerate*, just as two lines are called a degenerate conic. In like manner a plural character or conjoint relation is to be called degenerate if it is a mere compound of dual characters.

360. A sign is in a conjoint relation to the thing denoted and to the mind. If this triple relation is not of a degenerate species, the sign is related to its object only in consequence of a mental association, and depends upon a habit. Such signs are always abstract and general, because habits are general rules to which the organism has become subjected. They are, for the most part, conventional or arbitrary. They include all general words, the main body of speech, and any mode of conveying a judgment. For the sake of brevity I will call them *tokens*.‡

*** *The American Journal of Mathematics*, vol. 7, No. 2, pp. 180–202, (1885); reprinted pp. 1–23.**

† See vol. 2, bk. II, for a detailed analysis of signs.

‡ More frequently called 'symbols'; the word 'token' is later (in 4.537) taken to apply to what in 2.245 is called a 'sinsign.'

361. But if the triple relation between the sign, its object, and the mind, is degenerate, then of the three pairs

sign	object
sign	mind
object	mind

two at least are in dual relations which constitute the triple relation. One of the connected pairs must consist of the sign and its object, for if the sign were not related to its object except by the mind thinking of them separately, it would not fulfill the function of a sign at all. Supposing, then, the relation of the sign to its object does not lie in a mental association, there must be a direct dual relation of the sign to its object independent of the mind using the sign. In the second of the three cases just spoken of, this dual relation is not degenerate, and the sign signifies its object solely by virtue of being really connected with it. Of this nature are all natural signs and physical symptoms. I call such a sign an *index*, a pointing finger being the type of the class.

The index asserts nothing; it only says "There!" It takes hold of our eyes, as it were, and forcibly directs them to a particular object, and there it stops. Demonstrative and relative pronouns are nearly pure indices, because they denote things without describing them; so are the letters on a geometrical diagram, and the subscript numbers which in algebra distinguish one value from another without saying what those values are.

362. The third case is where the dual relation between the sign and its object is degenerate and consists in a mere resemblance between them. I call a sign which stands for something merely because it resembles it, an *icon*. Icons are so completely substituted for their objects as hardly to be distinguished from them. Such are the diagrams of geometry. A diagram, indeed, so far as it has a general signification, is not a pure icon; but in the middle part of our reasonings we forget that abstractness in great measure, and the diagram is for us the very thing. So in contemplating a painting, there is a moment when we lose the consciousness that it is not the thing, the distinction of the real and the copy disappears, and it is

for the moment a pure dream — not any particular existence, and yet not general. At that moment we are contemplating an *icon*.

363. I have taken pains to make my distinction[1] of icons, indices, and tokens clear, in order to enunciate this proposition: in a perfect system of logical notation signs of these several kinds must all be employed. Without tokens there would be no generality in the statements, for they are the only general signs; and generality is essential to reasoning. Take, for example, the circles by which Euler represents the relations of terms. They well fulfill the function of icons, but their want of generality and their incompetence to express propositions must have been felt by everybody who has used them.* Mr. Venn† has, therefore, been led to add shading to them; and this shading is a conventional sign of the nature of a token. In algebra, the letters, both quantitative and functional, are of this nature. But tokens alone do not state what is the subject of discourse; and this can, in fact, not be described in general terms; it can only be indicated. The actual world cannot be distinguished from a world of imagination by any description. Hence the need of pronoun and indices, and the more complicated the subject the greater the need of them. The introduction of indices into the algebra of logic is the greatest merit of Mr. Mitchell's system.[1] He writes F_1 to mean that the proposition F is true of every object in the universe, and F_u to mean that the same is true of some object.‡ This distinction can only be made in some such way as this. Indices are also required to show in what manner other signs are connected together. With these two kinds of signs alone any proposition can be expressed; but it cannot be reasoned

[1] See *Proceedings, American Academy of Arts and Sciences*, vol. 7, p. 294, May 14, 1867. [1.558.]

* See 4.356.

† "On the Diagrammatic and Mechanical Representations of Propositions and Reasoning." *Philosophical Magazine*, ser. 5, vol. 10, pp. 1–15 (1880).

[1] *Studies in Logic*, by members of the Johns Hopkins University; Boston, Little, Brown and Co., 1883.

‡ *Ibid.*, p. 74.

upon, for reasoning consists in the observation that where certain relations subsist certain others are found, and it accordingly requires the exhibition of the relations reasoned within an icon. It has long been a puzzle how it could be that, on the one hand, mathematics is purely deductive in its nature, and draws its conclusions apodictically, while on the other hand, it presents as rich and apparently unending a series of surprising discoveries as any observational science. Various have been the attempts to solve the paradox by breaking down one or other of these assertions, but without success. The truth, however, appears to be that all deductive reasoning, even simple syllogism, involves an element of observation; namely, deduction consists in constructing an icon or diagram the relations of whose parts shall present a complete analogy with those of the parts of the object of reasoning, of experimenting upon this image in the imagination, and of observing the result so as to discover unnoticed and hidden relations among the parts. For instance, take the syllogistic formula,

$$\begin{array}{r} \text{All } M \text{ is } P \\ S \text{ is } M \\ \therefore\ S \text{ is } P. \end{array}$$

This is really a diagram of the relations of S, M, and P. The fact that the middle term occurs in the two premisses is actually exhibited, and this must be done or the notation will be of no value. As for algebra, the very idea of the art is that it presents formulæ which can be manipulated, and that by observing the effects of such manipulation we find properties not to be otherwise discerned. In such manipulation, we are guided by previous discoveries which are embodied in general formulæ. These are patterns which we have the right to imitate in our procedure, and are the *icons par excellence* of algebra. The letters of applied algebra are usually tokens, but the x, y, z, etc., of a general formula, such as

$$(x+y)z=xz+yz,$$

are blanks to be filled up with tokens, they are indices of tokens. Such a formula might, it is true, be replaced by an abstractly stated rule (say that multiplication is distributive); but no application could be made of such an abstract statement without translating it into a sensible image.

§3. FIRST-INTENTIONAL LOGIC OF RELATIVES

392. The algebra of Boole affords a language by which anything may be expressed which can be said without speaking of more than one individual at a time. It is true that it can assert that certain characters belong to a whole class, but only such characters as belong to each individual separately. The logic of relatives considers statements involving two and more individuals at once. Indices are here required. Taking, first, a degenerate form of relation, we may write $x_i y_j$ to signify that x is true of the individual i while y is true of the individual j. If z be a relative character z_{ij} will signify that i is in that relation to j. In this way we can express relations of considerable complexity. Thus, if

$$\begin{matrix} 1, & 2, & 3, \\ 4, & 5, & 6, \\ 7, & 8, & 9, \end{matrix}$$

are points in a plane, and l_{123} signifies that 1, 2, and 3 lie on one line, a well-known proposition of geometry* may be written

$$l_{159} \prec l_{267} \prec l_{348} \prec l_{147} \prec l_{258} \prec l_{369} \prec l_{123} \prec l_{456} \prec l_{789}.$$

In this notation is involved a *sixth icon.*

393. We now come to the distinction of *some* and *all*, a distinction which is precisely on a par with that between truth and falsehood; that is, it is descriptive.

All attempts to introduce this distinction into the Boolian algebra were more or less complete failures until Mr. Mitchell† showed how it was to be effected. His method really con-

---

* If the six vertices of a hexagon lie three and three on two straight lines, the three points of intersection of the opposite sides lie on a straight line.

† *Op. cit.*, p. 79.

sists in making the whole expression of the proposition consist of two parts, a pure Boolian expression referring to an individual and a Quantifying part saying what individual this is. Thus, if k means 'he is a king,' and h, 'he is happy,' the Boolian

$$(\bar{k}+h)$$

means that the individual spoken of is either not a king or is happy. Now, applying the quantification, we may write

$$\text{Any } (\bar{k}+h)$$

to mean that this is true of any individual in the (limited) universe, or

$$\text{Some } (\bar{k}+h)$$

to mean that an individual exists who is either not a king or is happy. So

$$\text{Some } (kh)$$

means some king is happy, and

$$\text{Any } (kh)$$

means every individual is both a king and happy. The rules for the use of this notation are obvious. The two propositions

$$\text{Any } (x) \quad \text{Any } (y)$$

are equivalent to

$$\text{Any } (xy).$$

From the two propositions

$$\text{Any } (x) \quad \text{Some } (y)$$

we may infer $\qquad$ Some (xy).[1]

Mr. Mitchell has also a very interesting and instructive extension of his notation for *some* and *all*, to a two-dimensional universe, that is, to the logic of relatives. Here, in order to render the notation as iconical as possible we may use Σ for *some*, suggesting a sum, and Π for *all*, suggesting a product. Thus $\Sigma_i x_i$ means that x is true of some one of the individuals denoted by i or

$$\Sigma_i x_i = x_i + x_j + x_k + \text{etc.*}$$

In the same way, $\Pi_i x_i$ means that x is true of all these individuals, or

$$\Pi_i x_i = x_i x_j x_k, \text{ etc.†}$$

If x is a simple relation, $\Pi_i \Pi_j x_{ij}$ means that every i is in this relation to every j, $\Sigma_i \Pi_j x_{ij}$ that some one i is in this relation to every j, $\Pi_j \Sigma_i x_{ij}$ that to every j some i or other is in this relation, $\Sigma_i \Sigma_j x_{ij}$ that some i is in this relation to some j. It is to be remarked that $\Sigma_i x_i$ and $\Pi_i x_i$ are only *similar* to a sum and a product; they are not strictly of that nature, because the individuals of the universe may be innumerable.

---

[1] I will just remark, quite out of order, that the quantification may be made numerical; thus producing the numerically definite inferences of DeMorgan and Boole. Suppose at least $\frac{2}{3}$ of the company have white neckties and at least $\frac{3}{4}$ have dress coats. Let w mean 'he has a white necktie,' and d 'he has a dress coat.' Then, the two propositions are

$$\tfrac{2}{3}\,(w) \text{ and } \tfrac{3}{4}\,(d).$$

These are to be multiplied together. But we must remember that xy is a mere abbreviation for $\overline{\bar{x}+\bar{y}}$, and must therefore write

$$\overline{\overline{\tfrac{2}{3}w} + \overline{\tfrac{3}{4}d}}.$$

Now $\overline{\frac{2}{3}w}$ is the denial of $\frac{2}{3}w$, and this denial may be written $\underline{(>\frac{1}{3})\bar{w}}$, or more than $\frac{1}{3}$ of the universe (the company) have not white neckties. So $\overline{\frac{3}{4}d} = (>\frac{1}{4})\bar{d}$. The combined premisses thus become

$$\overline{(>\tfrac{1}{3})\bar{w} + (>\tfrac{1}{4})\bar{d}}.$$

Now $(>\frac{1}{3})\bar{w} + (>\frac{1}{4})\bar{d}$ gives $\qquad$ May be $(\frac{1}{3}+\frac{1}{4})(\bar{w}+\bar{d})$.

Thus we have $\qquad$ $\overline{\text{May be } (\tfrac{7}{12})(\bar{w}+\bar{d})}$,

and this is $\qquad$ (At least $\frac{5}{12}$)$(\bar{w}+\bar{d})$,

which is the conclusion.

* This is the seventh icon?

† This is the eighth icon?

394. At this point, the reader would perhaps not otherwise easily get so good a conception of the notation as by a little practice in translating from ordinary language into this system and back again. Let l_{ij} mean that i is a lover of j, and b_{ij} that i is a benefactor of j. Then

$$\Pi_i \Sigma_j l_{ij} b_{ij}$$

means that everything is at once a lover and a benefactor of something; and $$\Pi_i \Sigma_j l_{ij} b_{ji}$$

that everything is a lover of a benefactor of itself.

$$\Sigma_i \Sigma_k \Pi_j (l_{ij} + b_{jk})$$

means that there are two persons, one of whom loves everything except benefactors of the other (whether he loves any of these or not is not stated). Let g_i mean that i is a griffin, and c_i that i is a chimera, then

$$\Sigma_i \Pi_j (g_i l_{ij} + \bar{c}_j)$$

means that if there be any chimeras there is some griffin that loves them all; while $$\Sigma_i \Pi_j g_i (l_{ij} + \bar{c}_j)$$

means that there is a griffin and he loves every chimera that exists (if any exist). On the other hand,

$$\Pi_j \Sigma_i g_i (l_{ij} + \bar{c}_j)$$

means that griffins exist (one, at least), and that one or other of them loves each chimera that may exist; and

$$\Pi_j \Sigma_i (g_i l_{ij} + \bar{c}_j)$$

means that each chimera (if there is any) is loved by some griffin or other.

●

NOMENCLATURE AND DIVISIONS OF DYADIC RELATIONS*

§1. NOMENCLATURE

573. A dyadic relation proper is either such as can only have place between two subjects of different universes of discourse (as the membership of a natural person in a corporation), or is such as can subsist between two objects of the same universe. A relation of the former description may be termed

* Printed separately in eight pages, circa 1903, apparently intended as the second part of *A Syllabus of Certain Topics of Logic*, published as a supplement to the Lowell Lectures of 1903. See vol. 1, bk. II, ch. 1, note.

a *referential relation;* a relation of the latter description, a *rerelation.*[1]

574. A rerelation may either be such as can only subsist between characters or between laws (such as the relation of "essentially depending upon"), or it may be such as can subsist between two existent individual objects. In the former case, it may be termed a *modal* relation (not a good term), in the latter case an *existential relation.* The author's writings on the logic of relations[2] were substantially restricted to existential relations; and the same restriction will be continued in the body of what here follows. A note at the end of this section will treat of modal relations.

575. The number of different species of existential relations for which technical designations are required is so great that it will be best to adopt names for them which shall, by their form, furnish technical definitions of them, in imitation of the nomenclature of chemistry. The following rules will here be used. Any name (for which in this statement of the rules of word-formation we may put *x*), having been adopted for all relations of a given description, the preposition *extra* (or *ex*, or *e*) will be prefixed to that name ("extra *x*") in order to form a name descriptive of any relation to which the primitive name does not apply; the preposition *contra* will be prefixed (forming "contra-*x*,") to make a name applicable only to such relations as consist precisely in the non-subsistence of corresponding relations to which the primitive name does apply; the preposition *juxta* will be prefixed so as to bear the sense of *contra-extra*, or (what is the same) *extra-contra;* the preposition *red* (or *re*)

[1] It is far better to invent a word for a purely technical conception than to use an expression liable to be corrupted by being employed by loose writers. I reduplicate the first syllable of relation to form this word, with little reference to the meaning of the syllable as a preposition. Still, relations of this kind are the only ones that might be asserted of the same relates transposed; and the reduplication of the preposition *re* connotes such transposition.

[2] I must, with pain and shame, confess that in my early days I showed myself so little alive to the decencies of science that I presumed to change the name of this branch of logic, a name established by its author and my master, Augustus De Morgan, to "the logic of relatives." I consider it my duty to say that this thoughtless act is a bitter reflection to me now, so that young writers may be warned not to prepare for themselves similar sources of unhappiness. I am the more sorry, because my designation has come into general use.

will be prefixed to form a name applicable to a relation if, and only if, the correlate of it stands to its relate in a relation to which the primitive name applies, so that, in other words, a "red-x" is a relation the converse of an x; the preposition *com* (or *con*, or *co*,) will be prefixed to form the general name of any relation which consists in its relate and correlate alike standing in one relation of the primitive kind to one and the same individual correlate; the preposition *ultra* will be prefixed to form a name applicable only to a relation which subsists between any given relate and correlate only in case the former stands in a relation of the primitive kind to some individual to which the latter does not stand in that same relation; the preposition *trans* will be used so as to be equivalent to *contra-red-ultra*, or (what is the same) *recontrultra*, so that A will be in a relation "*trans-x*" to B, if, and only if, there is an x-relation in which A stands to whatever individual there may be to which B stands in that very same relation; and the preposition *super* to form the name of a relation which is, at once, *ultra* and *trans*, in respect to the very same relation of the primitive kind. Any of these prepositions may be prefixed, in the same sense, occasionally (and where no misunderstanding could result) not only to names of classes of relations and their cognates, but also to relative terms. But it is chiefly the prepositions *com*, *ultra*, *trans* and *super*, that will be so used. For example, taking the relative term "loves," there will be little occasion to use the first four of the following expressions, especially, the first and third, which become almost meaningless, while the last four will often be convenient.

1. A *extra-loves* B; that is, stands in some other relation, whether loving besides or not;

2. A *contra-loves* B; that is, does not love B;

3. A *juxta-loves* B; that is, stands in some other relation than that of not loving, whether loving or not;

4. A *reloves* B; that is, is loved by;

5. A *coloves* B; that is, loves something loved by;

6. A *ultraloves* B; that is, loves something not loved by;

7. A *transloves* B; that is, loves whatever may be loved by;

8. A *superloves* B; that is, loves whatever may be loved by and something else.*

* I.e., 1. extraloves $a\bar{l}b$
2. contraloves $-(alb)$
3. juxtaloves $-(a\bar{l}b)$
4. reloves $a\breve{l}b$
5. coloves $(alc)(c\breve{l}b)$
6. ultraloves $(alc)(c\overset{\times}{\bar{l}}b)$
7. transloves $-[(a\bar{l}c)(c\breve{l}b)]$
8. superloves $\{-[(a\bar{l}c)(c\breve{l}b)\mathbf{I}(ald)(d\overset{\times}{\bar{l}}b)]\}$

§2. FIRST SYSTEM OF DIVISIONS

578. An existential dyadic relation may be termed a *lation** to express its possibly subsisting between two existing individuals. . . .

*The following schedule may be of aid in this section:

1. $\Sigma_i\Sigma_j r_{ij}$ — lation
2. $\Sigma_i\Sigma_j \bar{r}_{ij}$ — contralation;
3. $\Pi_i\Pi_j \bar{r}_{ij}$ — extralation; $r=0$
4. $\Pi_i\Pi_j r_{ij}$ — juxtalation; $r=\infty$
5. $\Sigma_i\Pi_j r_{ij}$ — perlation
6. $\Sigma_i\Pi_j \bar{r}_{ij}$ — contraperlation
7. $\Pi_i\Sigma_j \bar{r}_{ij}$ — extraperlation
8. $\Pi_i\Sigma_j r_{ij}$ — juxtaperlation
9. $\Sigma_j\Pi_i r_{ij}$ — reperlation
10. $\Sigma_j\Pi_i \bar{r}_{ij}$ — contrareperlation
11. $\Pi_j\Sigma_i \bar{r}_{ij}$ — extrareperlation
12. $\Pi_j\Sigma_i r_{ij}$ — juxtareperlation
13. $\Sigma_i\Pi_j\Sigma_k r_{ik} \cdot r_{jk}$ — conlation
14. $\Sigma_i\Pi_j\Sigma_k r_{ik} . \bar{r}_{jk}$ — ultralation
15. $\Pi_i\Sigma_j\Pi_k - (\bar{r}_{ik} . r_{jk})$ — translation
16. $\Pi_i\Pi_j\Pi_k\Sigma_l - (\bar{r}_{ik} . r_{jk})(r_{il} . \bar{r}_{jl})$ — superlation
17. $\Sigma_i\Sigma_j r_{ij\infty}$ — essential perlation
18. $\Sigma_i\Sigma_j r_{\infty ij}$ — essential reperlation
19. $\Sigma_i\Sigma_j \bar{r}_{ij\infty}$ — contressentiperlation

$1=-3, 5=-7, 9=-11; 2=-4; 6=-8; 10=-12, 5 \prec 12; 9 \prec 8; 6 \prec 11;$
$10 \prec 7; 17.18 \prec 3 \curlyvee 4.$

THE SIMPLEST MATHEMATICS

239. The philosophical mathematician, Dr. Richard Dedekind,‡ holds mathematics to be a branch of logic. This would not result from my father's definition, which runs, not that mathematics is the science of *drawing* necessary conclusions — which would be deductive logic — but that it is the science

‡ *Was sind und was sollen die Zahlen; Vorwort;* (1888.)

which *draws* necessary conclusions. It is evident, and I know as a fact, that he had this distinction in view. At the time when he thought out this definition, he, a mathematician, and I, a logician, held daily discussions about a large subject which interested us both; and he was struck, as I was, with the contrary nature of his interest and mine in the same propositions. The logician does not care particularly about this or that hypothesis or its consequences, except so far as these things may throw a light upon the nature of reasoning. The mathematician is intensely interested in efficient methods of reasoning, with a view to their possible extension to new problems; but he does not, *quâ* mathematician, trouble himself minutely to dissect those parts of this method whose correctness is a matter of course. The different aspects which the algebra of logic will assume for the two men is instructive in this respect. The mathematician asks what value this algebra has as a calculus. Can it be applied to unravelling a complicated question? Will it, at one stroke, produce a remote consequence? The logician does not wish the algebra to have that character. On the contrary, the greater number of distinct logical steps, into which the algebra breaks up an inference, will for him constitute a superiority of it over another which moves more swiftly to its conclusions. He demands that the algebra shall analyze a reasoning into its last elementary steps. Thus, that which is a merit in a logical algebra for one of these students is a demerit in the eyes of the other. The one studies the science of drawing conclusions, the other the science which draws necessary conclusions.

240. But, indeed, the difference between the two sciences is far more than that between two points of view. Mathematics is purely hypothetical: it produces nothing but conditional propositions. Logic, on the contrary, is categorical in its assertions. True, it is not merely, or even mainly, a mere discovery of what really is, like metaphysics. It is a normative science. It thus has a strongly mathematical character, at least in its methodeutic division; for here it analyzes the problem of how, with given means, a required end is to be pursued. This is, at most, to say that it has to call in the aid of mathematics; that it has a mathematical branch. But so much may be said of every science. There is a mathematical

logic, just as there is a mathematical optics and a mathematical economics. Mathematical logic is formal logic. Formal logic, however developed, is mathematics. Formal logic, however, is by no means the whole of logic, or even its principal part. It is hardly to be reckoned as a part of logic proper. Logic has to define its aim; and in doing so is even more dependent upon ethics, or the philosophy of aims, by far, than it is, in the methodeutic branch, upon mathematics. We shall soon come to understand how a student of ethics might well be tempted to make his science a branch of logic; as, indeed, it pretty nearly was in the mind of Socrates. But this would be no truer a view than the other. Logic depends upon mathematics; still more intimately upon ethics; but its proper concern is with truths beyond the purview of either.

THE PERUVIAN QUIPU

(Highest Development in the 15th and 16th Centuries)

The Peruvian quipu or knot record was a remarkable development and extension of the primitive practice of recording numbers and reckoning by means of knots in cord. Tradition assigns the origin of the quipu to very early times. Authentic examples of the ancient quipus have been found principally in the coastal desert plains of Peru between the Andes Mountains and the Pacific Ocean, in the vicinity of the City of Lima. The discovery of knot records in Peru in the sixteenth century was all the more astonishing inasmuch as the quipus were found in common use at a time when the centralized governmental organization was highly complex. The Peruvian people, despite their possession of a rich and expressive language, had no system of writing. Knowledge of the quipu was restricted to the Inca tribesmen who held dominion over a widespread area in the northeastern part of South America, and to their selected functionaries. Chosen on the basis of their capabilities, the latter were trained in the uses of the quipu and were paid, usually, through exemption from the payment of taxes.

When the Spaniards first observed the use of the quipu among the Incas in the 16th century, they found the system of recording numbers by knots with its decimal place values in a highly developed form. The thickness of the strands and their color were given special meanings. White represented silver, yellow represented gold and red, soldiers or war. Each district under the rule of the Incas had its own specially trained *Quipu-camayu* (He who has charge of the accounts). Some villages had as many as twenty or thirty such individuals whose duty it was to record by means of the quipu amounts of tribute, the size and type of flocks, items relating to the administration of justice, and so on. A network of communication posts to which runners (*chasquis*) were assigned, facilitated the flow of information to the capital at Cuzco from all parts of the Inca dominion. Frequently the report which was coded in the quipu was supplemented by carefully memorized oral messages. Although Peruvian culture reached a level of considerable complexity, involving a strict class system, governmental records of crops and herds, and amazing feats of architecture, no writing materials or written symbols had been evolved. Hence, the quipus fulfilled a double purpose, serving on the one hand for mathematical accounting, and on the other as memoranda of historical events, ceremonies, negotiations for peace or war, and the like.

Recently, archaeological researches have revealed great new finds. Objects of great artistry made of gold, silver, copper and *tumbaga,* an alloy of these metals, have been unearthed. Great mountain fortresses reached by perilous stone steps and guarded by stone walls on steep slopes, have been revealed with their artificial terraces, hanging gardens, irrigation canals and stone sculptures. The metal work of the ancient Peruvian goldsmith, as well as the sculptured statues express the worship of deities requiring human sacrifice, though it is known that this practice in later times was gradually being abandoned. One of the most important of the early historical accounts of the Inca Civilization is the *Royal Commentaries* written by Garcilasso de la Vega (b. 1539) whose father was a Spanish cavalier and whose mother was an Inca princess. Garcilasso lived among the Incas until he was twenty years of age and his intimate knowledge of the Incas is one of our most important sources of information concerning the Inca Civilization. His work describes the organization of the Inca state, the selection of officials forming the liaison between the Incas and the general population, and the Indian way of life in which money was unknown and barter was the means of trading. He laid great stress on the gentle nature of the people, their honesty and fair dealing.

In the centuries succeeding the Spanish conquest, the spread of the knowledge of writing generally eliminated the need for the quipu. Nevertheless, its use persisted in some areas and examples of the quipu in its modern form can still be found.

THE ANCIENT QUIPU

From *The Ancient Quipu or Peruvian Knot Record*
by L. Leland Locke

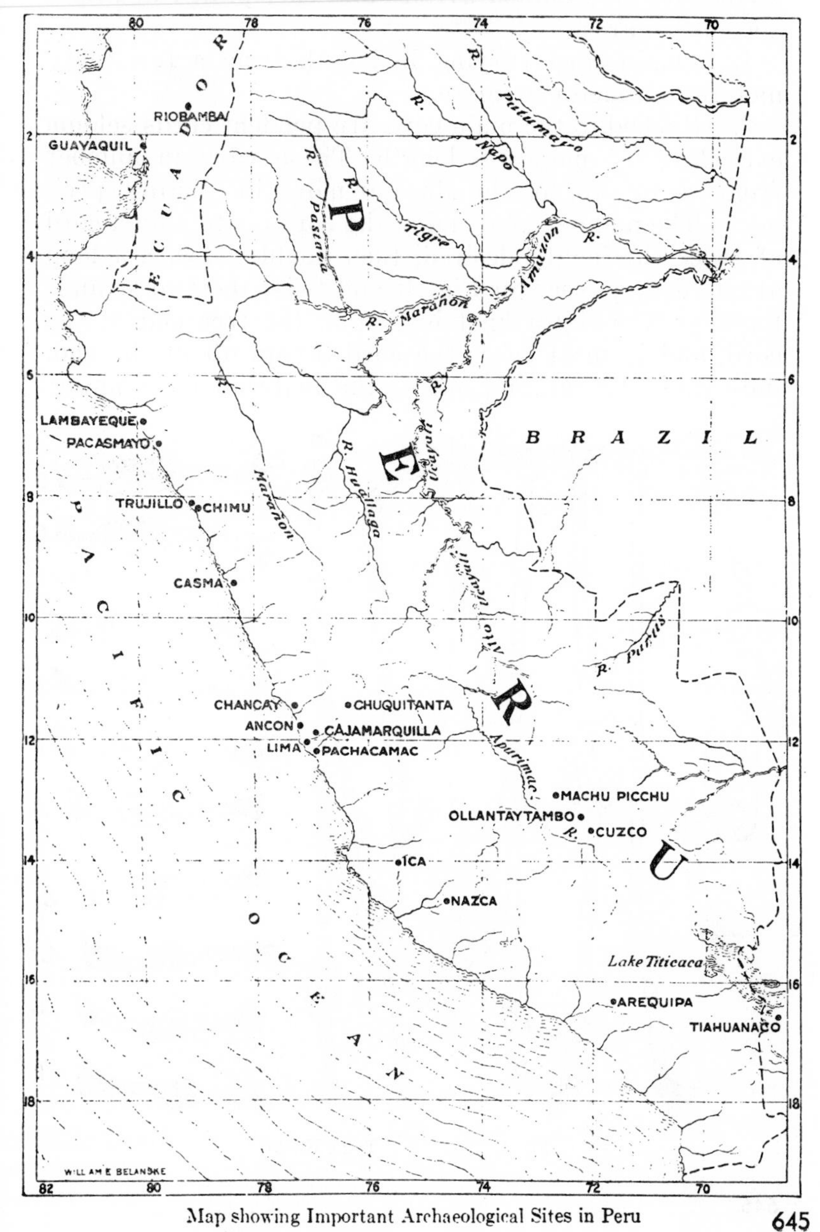

Map showing Important Archaeological Sites in Peru

DESCRIPTION OF THE QUIPU.

The characteristics of the ancient quipu, both as described by the Spanish writers and exemplified in extant specimens, are:—

1. A main cord varying in length from a few centimeters to a meter or more.

2. Attached to the main cord are pendent cords seldom exceeding 0.5 meter in length. These vary in number from one or two, to a hundred or more, in existing specimens. The manner of forming the cords is to spin a cord of twice the length desired, then double it, with a loop at one end, as seen in Fig. 1, and twist the two strands together. Usually a knot is tied in the free end of the cord, and in most cases the cord tapers off at the end, indicating the running out of the material in spinning.

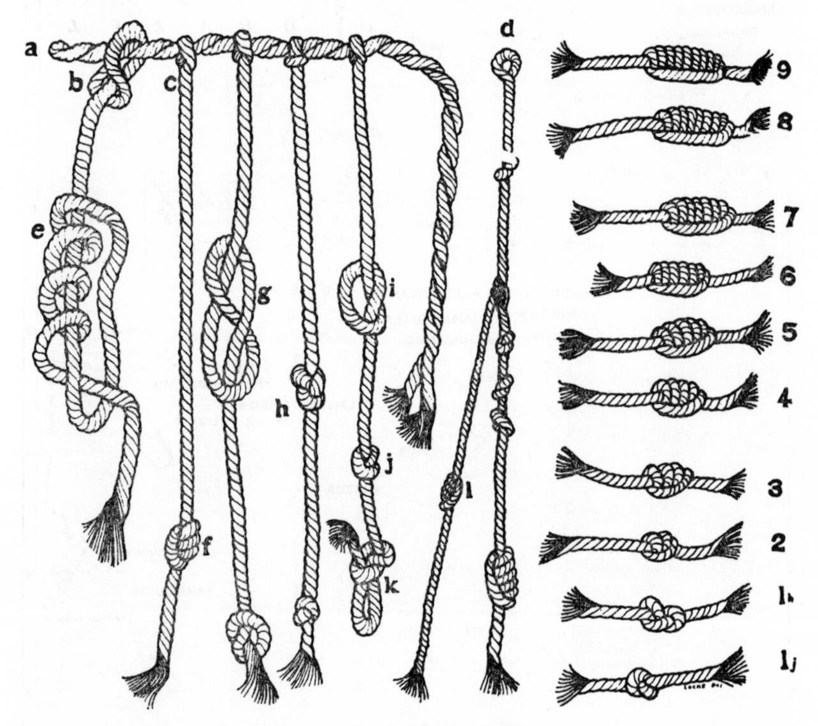

Fig. 1. Method of Tying Knots.

Both cotton and wool were used, natural white and buff being available in both materials.

The pendent strands are attached to the main cord by passing the free end over the main cord and through the loop formed by doubling, and then drawing taut. . . . The pendent strands are variously distributed along the main cord, usually as close together as possible, sometimes with small spaces between the groups, or the single strands.

3. Knots are tied in the pendent strands at varying distances from the main cord. In the better types these groups of knots are arranged roughly in rows across the quipu.

4. In nearly all of the ancient quipu short subsidiary cords are attached to the pendent strands, upon which are indicated numbers that disturb the main count of the quipu.

The subsidiary cord is attached to the pendent strand in the same manner as the pendent strand is fastened to the main cord, except that in most cases it is inserted between the two strands and therefore looped around half of the pendent strand. This is illustrated in Fig. 1d.

5. Character of the knots. Fig. 1 shows the forms of the knot and the mode of tying which exist in the specimens studied. The single or overhand knot (*i, j*), indicates 1 if it is in the row farthest from the main cord, 10 if it occurs in the next nearer row, 100 in the next row, etc. Not more than nine single knots are found in one group, the number system being strictly decimal. The figure eight knot occurs frequently.

The long knot, used to express the repetition of units of the same order in place of a cluster of single knots, has been likened by Mr. Frank H. Cushing to the appearance of the closed fist. It is formed by tying the overhand knot and passing the end through the loop of the knot as many times as there are units to be denoted. One end is then drawn taut, thus coiling the other about the strand the required number of times. There seems to have been no fixed practice as to which end is drawn taut, the upper fixed end, or the lower free end. As this would lower or raise the knot on the cord, it is possible that the device was used to keep the knots of one order relatively the same distance from the main cord. In some of the cruder specimens it is apparent that both ends have been pulled, as described earlier. The loop has apparently no numerical significance, but, from the manner of its appearance, it may have had some such use as the red line used by bookkeepers in closing an account.

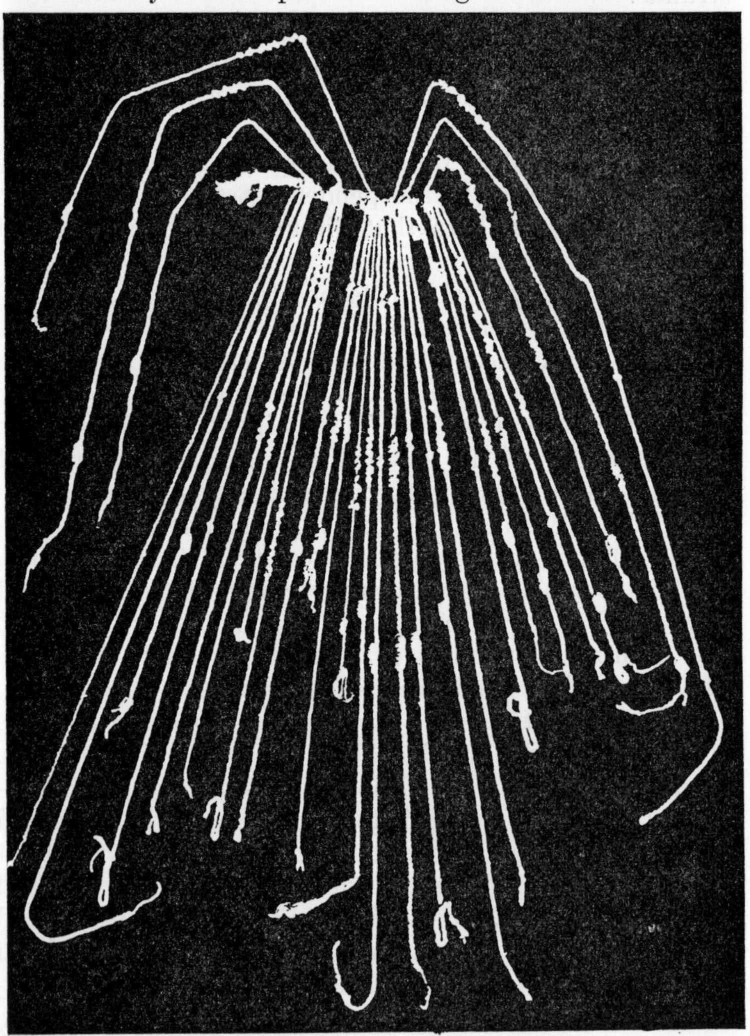

Example of the Highest Development of the Quipu. Quipu No. 1, from Chancay.

This specimen (Frontispiece) in the Bandelier collection in the American Museum of Natural History is one of three from Huando, north of Lima. This village was of the Chancay tribe, which was subdued by the Inca and from which tribute was levied. This is an example of the most highly developed form of the quipu, and is important in that it gives an accurate key to the numerical character of the knots.

The characteristics of this and the other two specimens from this locality are:—

1. The use of the long knot for ones only, and groups of single knots for the higher orders.

2. The use of the loop on the first (or last) cord of a group.

3. The pendent cords are grouped (in this specimen in fours, in the others in sixes) by passing a top cord through the top loops of the four (or six) pendent strands. See Fig. 2.

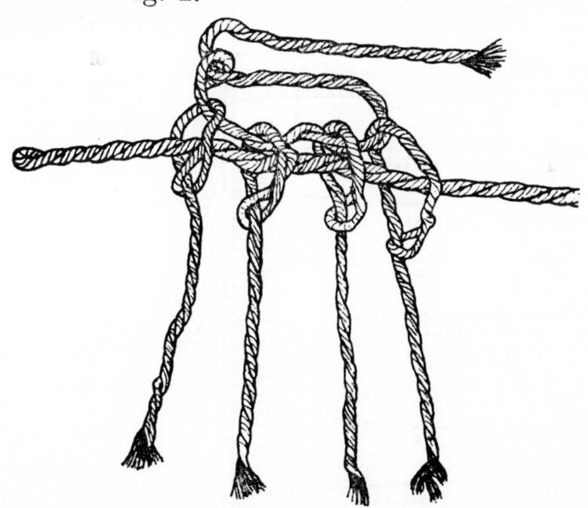

Fig 2. Mode of attaching the Top Cord upon which the Numbers of the Pendent Strands are summed.

4. *The top strand sums the numbers on the group of pendent strands through which it is passed.*

5. The ones, tens, and hundreds are arranged in rows

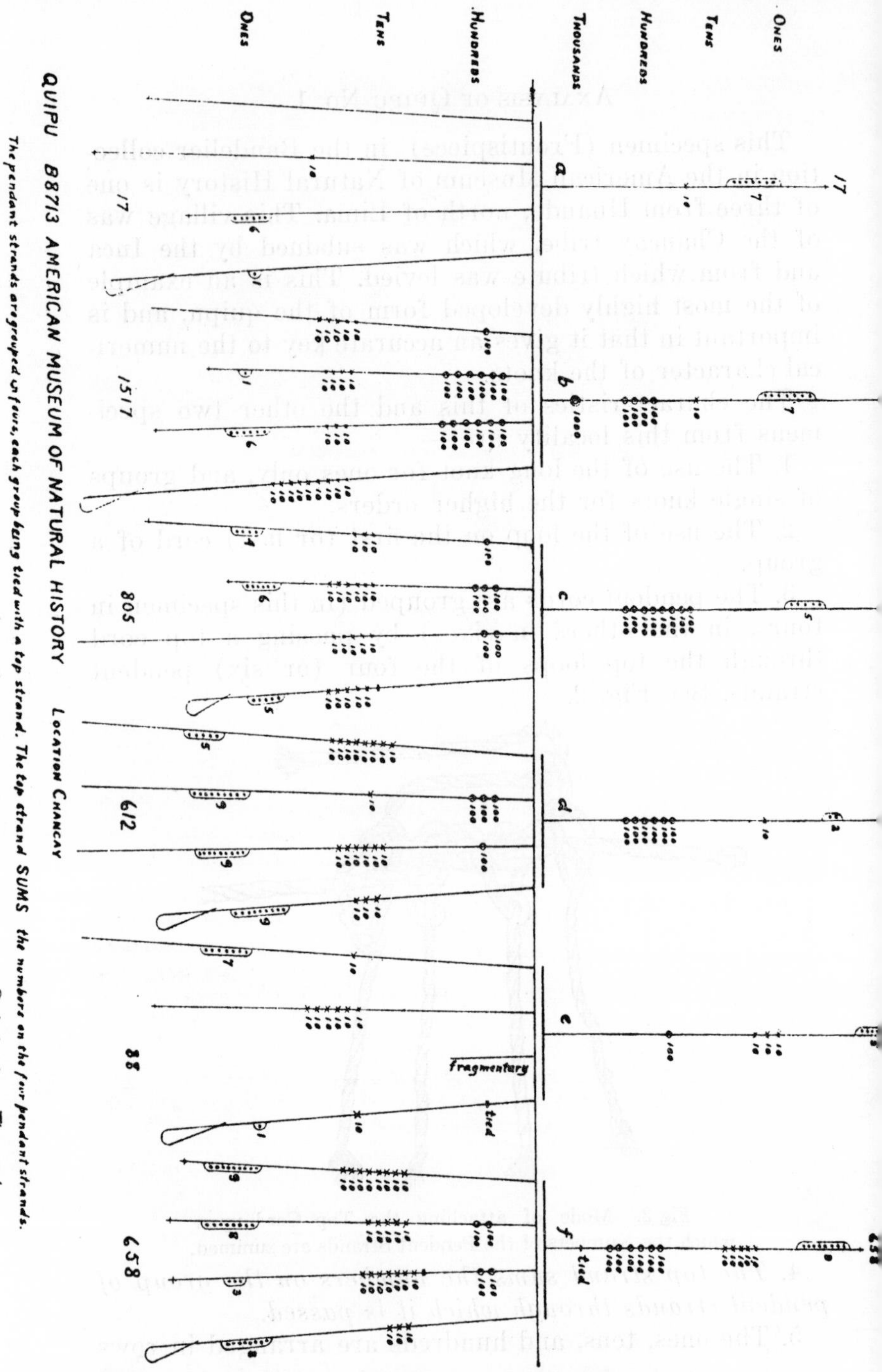
ONES
TENS
HUNDREDS
THOUSANDS
HUNDREDS
TENS
ONES
a
b
c
d
e
f
17
1517
805
612
88
658
Fragmentary
tied
QUIPU B8713 AMERICAN MUSEUM OF NATURAL HISTORY
LOCATION CHANCAY
The pendant strands are grouped in fours, each group being tied with a top strand. The top strand SUMS the numbers on the four pendant strands.
indicates Ones, each dot is a single one. Each x indicates a Ten. Each O indicates a Hundred. ⊙ indicates a Thousand

Fig. 3. Numerical Value of Knots in Quipu No. 1.

across the quipu, "as a good accountant arranges them in columns."

6. The auxiliary strand appears in two of the three specimens of this type.

A comparison with the Uhle or Bastian modern quipus would suggest that this specimen is a record of four types of things covering six years or periods.

The frontispiece is a photograph of this quipu and Fig. 3 is a line diagram of the arrangement of knots.

The accompanying table gives the knot readings and colors.

TABLE OF KNOT READINGS AND COLORS, QUIPU NO. 1

(Compare with Frontispiece and Fig. 3)

Strands	1000's	100's	10's	1's	Color
Main cord	....	....	....	....	White and dark brown
1	....	....	....	....	Brown
2	....	....	1	....	White
3	....	....	....	6	White
4	....	....	....	1	White
Sum	....	....	1	7	
a	....	....	1	7	Very light brown
1	....	1	5	....	White and reddish brown
2	....	6	4	1	White and light brown
3	....	6	3	6	White and dark brown
4[1]	....	....	9	....	White and dark brown
Sum	1	13	21	7	
	....	5	1	7	
b	1	4	1	7	White and light brown
1	....	1	3	4	Brown
2	....	3	6	6	Brown
3	....	2	5	....	Brown
4	....	....	5	5	Brown (darker)
Sum	....	6	19	15	
	....	8	0	5	
c	....	8	....	5	Light brown, reddish

[1]Fragmentary subsidiary cord (?); discrepancy of 100 in count.

Table of Knot Readings and Colors, Quipu No. 1

Strands	1000's	100's	10's	1's	Color
1	....	....	8	7	Blue
2	....	3	1	9	Blue
3	....	1	6	9	Blue
4	....	....	3	7	Blue
Sum	....	4	18	32	
		6	1	2	
d		6	1	2	Light brown, yellowish
1	....	....	1	7	Light blue and white
2	....	....	6	....	Light blue and white
3	Frag.	....	4(?)	7(?)	Light blue and white
4	....	....	1	1	Light blue and white
Sum	....	....	12(?)	15(?)	
	....	1	3	5	
e	....	1	3	5	Light and dark brown
1	....	....	8	9	Light brown
2	....	2	5	8	Light brown
3	....	2	7	3	Light brown
4	....	....	3	8	Light brown
Sum	....	4	23	28	
	....	6	5	8	
f	....	6	5	8	Light brown

MODERN QUIPU

Two specimens of the modern quipu have been secured by Dr. Max Uhle. One of these, which is on exhibition at the University of Pennsylvania Museum, was described by Dr. Uhle in the Bulletin of the Free Museum of Science and Art of the University of Pennsylvania, December, 1897. (See Fig. 11.)

The quipu was obtained in April, 1895 from an Indian, who was in charge of the flocks of a farm at Cutusuma,

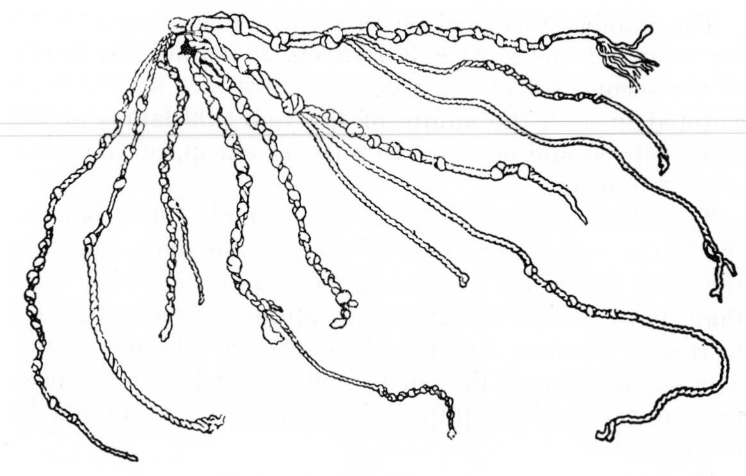

Fig. 11.

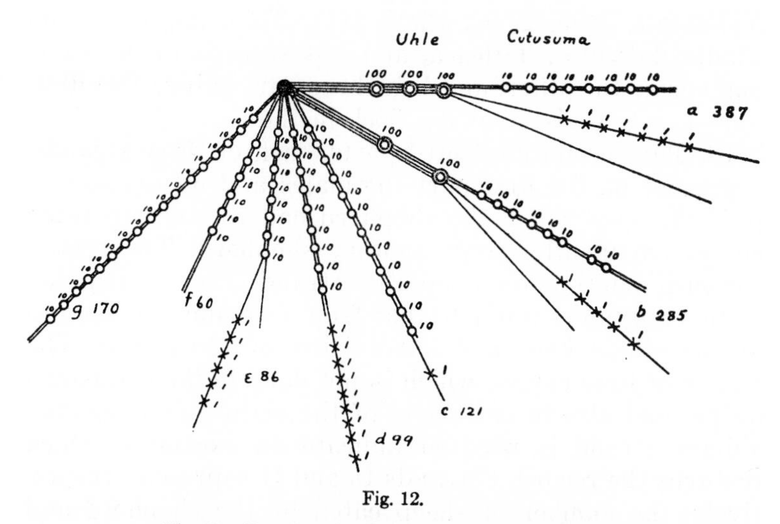

Fig. 12.

Fig. 11. Drawing of a Modern Quipu. After Uhle.
Fig. 12. Diagram of Quipu No. 40, shown in Fig. 11.

near Lake Titicaca, and consists of white strings of sheep wool. The Indian informed Dr. Uhle that the number of females is indicated on the border of the quipu, and that of the males in the center.

The number recorded on this quipu (as is seen in the key drawing and key) is 387 sheep, 285 rams, 121 lambs of the second set of the year, (the first set having been counted in with the adults of the year) 99 lambs of the third set, 86 and 60 and 170 milking sheep, of the three sets of lambs.

The illustration shows that the decimal system is used, the knots indicating hundreds, tens, and ones, but that the cord is divided to record the tens on a string finer than that used for the hundreds, and still further divided to record the ones. Further the knots are all single knots. The subdivision of the cords is not found on any specimen of the ancient quipu which has been examined by the writer.

The other specimen secured by Dr. Uhle was forwarded to Professor Bastian, at Berlin, and was described by him from notes furnished by Dr. Uhle (*Ethnologisches Notizblatt,* 1895, 2, 80, Plate III). This quipu is from Challa, Island of Titicaca, and was secured in the same manner as the other, and is a three-part quipu. The first, part I, is a register of the flock in the care of the shepherd. The second and third parts, each of three strands, represent on the first part the males and on the second part the ewes which the shepherd had received in three successive months from another shepherd. The record for each month is on a separate strand. The construction of this quipu is similar to that from Cutusuma in the use of the single knot and subdivision of the string. The maker utilizes colors, which is not done in the Cutusuma quipu, and also in two parts of the main quipu the subsidiary strand is used to indicate an exception which disturbs the record. (Strands I*b* and II represent, respectively, the number of sheep eaten by the shepherd and by the owner of the farm). This was a familiar feature of the ancient quipu. Cf. Figs. 13, 14, 15.

A comparison of these modern quipu with the ancient reveals the following facts:—

1. The decimal system and the relative placing of the hundreds, tens and ones is preserved.

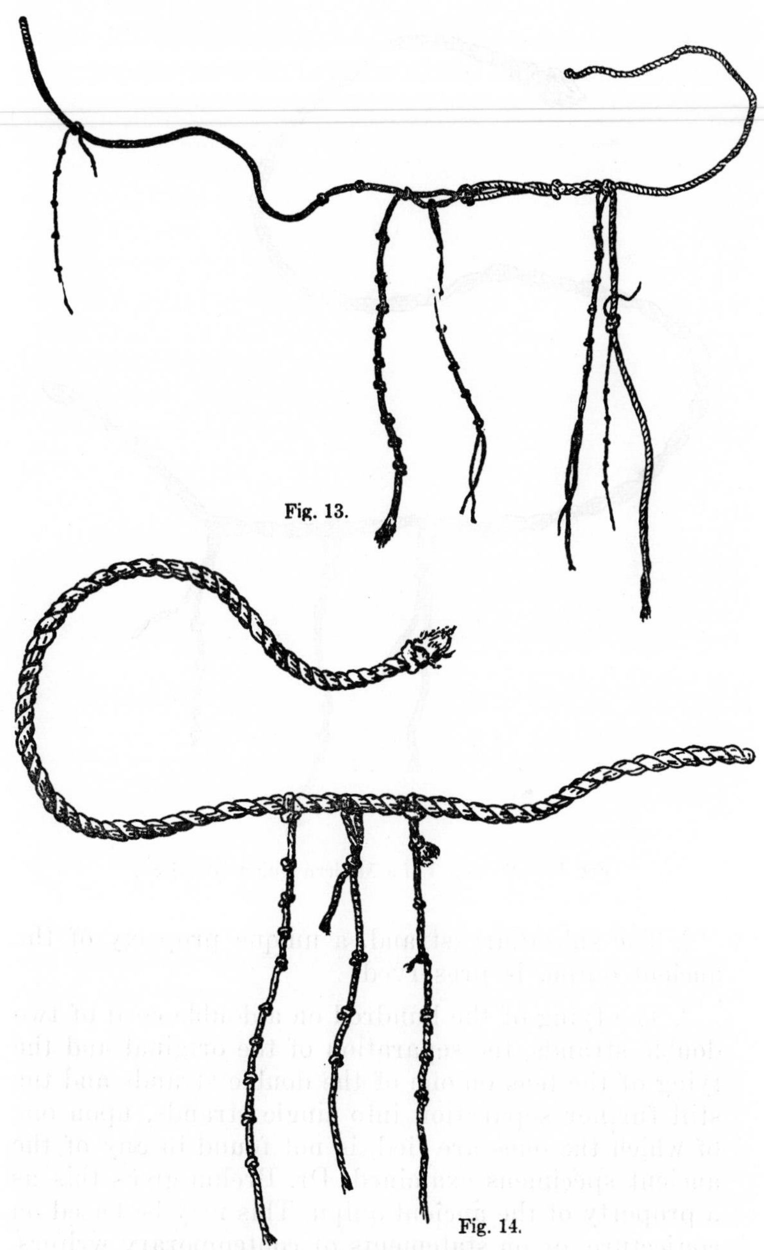

Fig. 13. Section 1 of a Modern Quipu (Bastian).
Fig. 14. Section 2 of a Modern Quipu (Bastian).

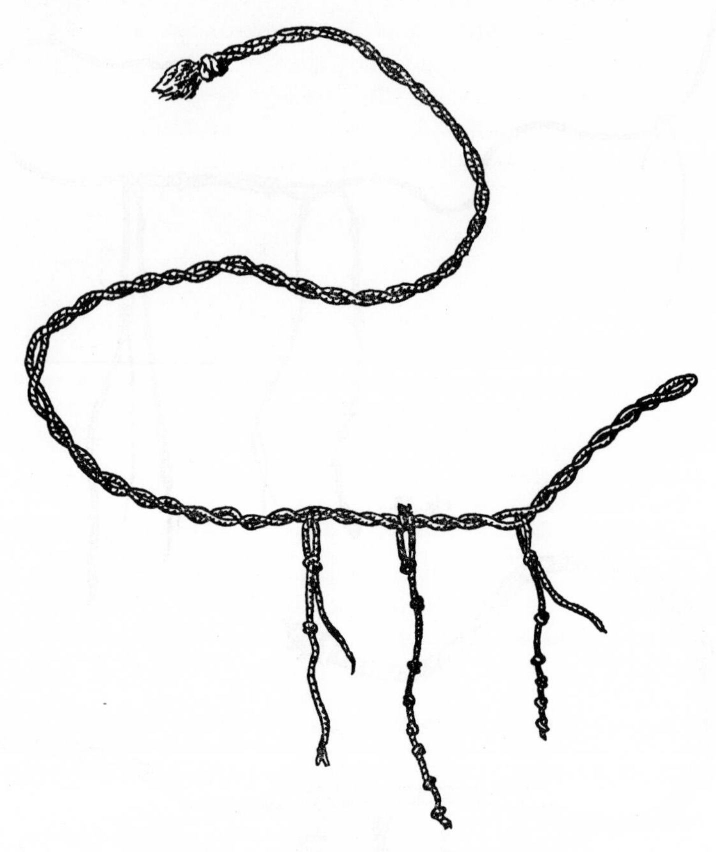

Fig. 15. Section 3 of a Modern Quipu (Bastian).

2. The subsidiary strand, a unique property of the ancient quipu, is preserved.

3. The tying of the hundred on a double cord of two double strands, the separation of the original and the tying of the tens on one of the double strands and the still further separation into single strands, upon one of which the ones are tied, is not found in any of the ancient specimens examined. Dr. Brehm gives this as a property of the ancient quipu. This may be based on conjecture, or on statements of contemporary writers, or on the examination of specimens. The writer has

been unable to find any such corroborative evidence.

4. The main strand is found in parts II and III of the Bastian quipu but is not used in either the principal part I, nor in the Uhle quipu.

5. The long knot and the mode of attaching to the main strand have been lost.

EXCERPTS

From the *Royal Commentaries*

by Garcilasso de la Vega

The ordinary judges gave a monthly account of the sentences they had pronounced to their superiors, and these to others, there being several grades of judges, according to the importance of the cases.

The way of making these reports to the Ynca, or to those of his Supreme Council, was by means of knots, made on cords of various colours, by which means the signification was made out, as by letters. The knots of such and such colours denoted that such and such crimes had been punished, and small threads of various colours attached to the thicker cords signified the punishment that had been afflicted, and in this way they supplied the want of letters.

The accountants were very accurate. Quipu means to knot or a knot and it was also understood as an account, because the knots supplied an account of everything. The Indians made strings of various colors. Some were all of one color, others of two combined, others of three, others more; and these colors, whether single or combined, all had a meaning. The strings were closely laid up in three or four strands, about the girth of an iron spindle, and three quarters of a vara (about two feet) long. They were strung on a thicker cord from which they hung in the manner of a fringe. The thing to which a string referred was understood by its color, for instance a yellow string referred to gold, a white to silver, and a red one to soldiers. Things which had no color were arranged according to their importance, beginning with that of most consequence, and proceeding in order to the most insignificant; each under its generic head, such as the different kinds of grain under corn, and the pulses in the same way. We will place the cereals and pulses of Spain in their order, as an example. First would come wheat, next barley, next beans, next millet. In the same way, when they recorded the quantity of arms. First they placed those that were considered the most noble, such as lances, next darts, next bows and arrows, then shields, then aces and then slings. In enumerating the vassals, they first gave account of the natives of each village, and next of those of the whole province combined. On the first string they put only men of sixty and upwards, in the second those of fifty, in the third those of forty and so on down to babies at the breast. The women were counted in the same order.

Some of these strings had other finer ones of the same color attached to them, to serve as supplements or exceptions to the chief record. Thus if the main strand of men of a certain age had reference to married people, the supplementary strand gave the number of widowers of the same age in that year. For these accounts were made up annually and only related to one year. The knots indicated units, tens, hundreds, thousands, and tens of thousands, but they rarely or never went beyond that; because each village was taken by itself, and each district, and neither ever reached to a number beyond tens of thousands, though there were plenty within that limit. But if it were necessary to record a number equal to hundreds of thousands, they could do it, for in their language they were able to express any number known in arithmetic; but as they had no occasion to go beyond tens of thousands, they did not use higher numbers. These numbers were counted by knots made on the threads, each number being divided from the next. But the knots for each number were made together in one company, like the knots represented in the girdle of the ever blessed Patriarch, St. Francis; and this could easily be done as there were never more than nine, seeing that the units, tens, etc., do not exceed that number. On the uppermost knot they put the highest number, which was tens of thousands, and so on to the units. The knots of each number, and each thread, were placed in a line with each other exactly in the way a good accountant places his figures to make a long addition sum.

These knots or Quipus were in charge of Indians, who were called Quipu-camayu, which means "He who has charge of the accounts." Although there was, at the time, little difference of character among the Indians, because owing to their gentle dispositions and excellent government all might be called good, yet the best and those who had given the longest proofs of their fitness, were selected for these and other offices. They were not given away from motives of favoritism, because these Indians were never influenced by such considerations, but from considerations of special fitness. Nor were these either sold nor farmed out, for they knew nothing of renting, buying, or selling, having no money they exchanged one article of food for another, and no more; for they neither sold clothes, nor houses nor estates.

The Quipu-camayus being so trustworthy and honest, as we have described—their number was regulated according to the population in each village; for however small the village might be, there were four accountants in it, and from that number up to twenty or thirty; though all used the same register. Thus as only one account was kept, one accountant would have been sufficient; but the Incas desired that there should be several in each village to act as checks upon each other, and they said that where there were so many all must be in fault or none.

PLATO

(c. 428—c. 347 B.C.)

Plato, one of the greatest and most influential philosophers of all time, was a descendant of the highest ranking families of Athens, tracing his ancestry back on his father's side to Codrus and on his mother's side to the law-giver Solon. He was born at Athens c. 428 B.C. An outstanding example of the ancient Greek ideal of universal culture, he applied himself successfully to every branch of science and art, achieving extraordinary skill in gymnastics, as well. Although he was named Aristocles after his grandfather, he was known generally by his nickname, Plato, which is said to have been given to him by his wrestling master because of his strong build and unusually strong shoulders. At the age of twenty Plato attached himself to Socrates with whom he studied for eight years and whose favorite pupil he became. About 400 B.C., after Socrates had been forced to drain the poison cup, Plato, threatened with persecution for his Socratic views, fled from Athens. He continued to travel and study for approximately twelve years, filling out his mathematical and scientific education and taking ever increasing interest in theology and in the theories of the universe and immortality. He remained in Egypt for a long time and there he may have had some contact with the books of Moses.

Invited to Sicily by Dionysius the Elder, Plato, so far from flattering the tyrant of Syracuse, was outspokenly critical. Angry and suspicious, Dionysius allowed himself to be dissuaded from punishing Plato with death, only to sell him into slavery. Ransomed by his friends, Plato returned at length to Athens where he was warmly received. He declined all offers of public office, desiring to devote himself wholly to philosophy. It was at this time that he organized the Academy, a school to which he imparted an impetus so vital and powerful that it was to continue to be an active center of learning far into the sixth century A.D. Apart from two voyages to Sicily in vain attempts to establish a model government there under Dionysius the Younger, Plato spent his remaining years in Athens writing and teaching.

Convinced that knowledge of mathematics was beneficial in many fields of endeavor and moreover, that it was essential preparation to the understanding of philosophy, Plato required some knowledge of mathematics of any who wished to enter his Academy. Members of the Academy were encouraged by him to undertake mathematical investigations and the advances in mathematics of his century and the next one were all connected directly or indirectly with the Academy. Adored by his scholars, known for his complete dedication to philosophy and for his exemplary moral conduct, Plato inspired the devotion of disciples all over the world. His writings, almost all of them in the form of dialogue, possess in addition to depth of philosophical insight a poetic charm and grace of style which may be said to go far toward explaining the admiration which his works awakened and the excellent state of preservation in which they have come down to us. Plato's *Dialogues* are interspersed everywhere with references to mathematics and with illustrations from mathematics. Taken together, Plato's mathematical illustrations serve to illuminate his philosophy, as was his intention. They present, in addition, a comprehensive view of the problems with which Greek mathematicians were concerned and their mathematical way of thinking.

●

DIALOGUES OF PLATO

translated by B. Jowett

PHILEBUS.

Soc. Then now let us divide the arts of which we were speaking into two kinds; the arts which, like music, are less exact in their results, and those which, like carpentering, are more exact.

Pro. Let us make that division.

Soc. Of the latter class, the most exact of all are those which I mentioned at first.

Pro. I see that you mean arithmetic, and the kindred arts of weighing and measuring.

Soc. Certainly, Protarchus; but are not these also distinguishable into two kinds?

Pro. What are the two kinds?

Soc. In the first place, arithmetic is of two kinds; one of which is popular, and the other philosophical.

Pro. How would you distinguish them?

Soc. There is a wide distinction between them, Protarchus; some arithmeticians reckon unequal units; as for example, two armies, two oxen; the one a very large and the other a very small two. The party who are opposed to them insists that every unit in ten thousand must be the same as every other unit.

Pro. Undoubtedly there is, as you say, a great difference among the votaries of the science; and there may be reasonably supposed to be two sorts of arithmetic.

Soc. And what of the arts of computation and mensuration which are used in building and trading,—when we compare them with philosophical geometry and exact calculation, shall we say that they are one or two?

Pro. On the analogy of what has preceded, I should be of opinion that they were two.

Soc. Right; but do you understand why I have discussed the subject?

Pro. I think so, but I should like to be told by you.

Soc. The argument has all along been seeking a parallel to pleasure, and true to that original design, has gone on to ask whether one sort of knowledge is purer than another, as one pleasure is purer than another.

Pro. Clearly; that was the intention.

Soc. And has not the argument in what has preceded, already shown that the arts have different provinces, and vary in their degree of certainty?

Pro. Very true.

Soc. And just now did not the argument first designate a particular art by a common term, thus making us believe in the unity of art; and then again, as if speaking of two different things, proceed to enquire whether the art as pursued by philosophers, or as pursued by non-philosophers, has more of certainty and purity?

Pro. That is the question which the argument is at this moment asking.

Soc. And how, Protarchus, shall we answer the enquirer?

Pro. O Socrates, we have reached a point at which the difference of clearness in different kinds of knowledge is enormous.

Soc. Then the answer will be the easier.

Pro. Certainly; and let us say in reply, that those arts

into which arithmetic and mensuration enter, far surpass all others; and that of these the arts or sciences which are animated by the pure philosophic impulse are infinitely superior in accuracy and truth about measures and numbers.

Soc. Then this is your judgment; and this is the answer which, upon your authority, we will give to all masters of the art of misinterpretation?

Pro. What answer?

Soc. That there are two arts of arithmetic, and two of mensuration; and also several other arts which in like manner have this double nature, and yet only one name.

THEAETETUS.

Soc. Then now is the time, my dear Theaetetus, for me to examine, and for you to exhibit; since although Theodorus has praised many a citizen and stranger in my hearing, never did I hear him praise any one as he has been praising you.

Theaet. I am glad to hear it, Socrates; but what if he was only in jest?

Soc. Nay, he is not given to jesting; and I cannot allow you to retract your assent on that ground. For if you do, he will have to clear himself on oath, and I am sure that no one will accuse him of false witness. Do not be shy then, but stand to your word.

Theaet. I will do as you wish.

Soc. In the first place, I should like to ask what you learn of Theodorus: something of geometry, I suppose?

Theaet. Yes.

Soc. And astronomy and harmony and calculation?

Theaet. I do my best.

Soc. Yes, my boy, and so do I; and my desire is to learn of him, and of anybody who seems to understand these things. And I get on pretty well in general; but there is a little matter which I want you and the company to aid me in investigating. Will you answer me a question: 'Is not learning growing wiser about that which you learn?'

Theaet. Of course.

Soc. And by wisdom the wise are wise?

Theaet. Yes.

Soc. And is that different from knowledge?

Theaet. What is different?

Soc. Wisdom; are not men wise in that which they know?

Theaet. Certainly.

Soc. Then wisdom and knowledge are the same?

Theaet. Yes.

Soc. And this is the very difficulty which I can never explain to myself—What is knowledge? Can we answer that question? What do you say? and which of us will answer first? whoever misses shall sit down, as at a game of ball, and shall be donkey, as the boys say, to the rest of the company; he who lasts out his competitors in the game without missing, shall be our king, and shall have the right of asking any questions which he likes. . . . Why is there no reply? I hope, Theodorus, that I am not betrayed into rudeness by my love of conversation? I only want to make us talk and be friendly and sociable.

Theod. The reverse of rudeness, Socrates: but I would rather that you would ask one of the young fellows; for the truth is, that I am not in the habit of playing at your game of question and answer, and I am too old to learn; the young will be more apt, and they will improve more than I shall, for youth is always able to improve. Having already made a beginning with him, I would advise you to detain Theaetetus, and interrogate him.

Soc. Do you hear, Theaetetus, what Theodorus says? the philosopher, whom you would not like to disobey, and whose word ought to be a command to a young man, bids me interrogate you. Take courage, then, and nobly say what you think that knowledge is.

Theaet. Well, Socrates, I will answer as you and he bid me; and if I make a mistake, you will doubtless correct me.

Soc. We will, if we can.

Theaet. Then, I think that the sciences which I learn from Theodorus—geometry, and those which you just now mentioned—are knowledge; and I would include the art of the cobbler and other craftsmen; these, all and each of them, are knowledge.

Soc. Too much, Theaetetus, too much; the nobility and liberality of your own nature make you give many and diverse things, when I am asking for one simple thing.

Theaet. What do you mean, Socrates?

Soc. Perhaps nothing. I will endeavour, however, to explain what I believe to be my meaning: When you speak of cobbling, you mean the art of making shoes?

Theaet. That is my meaning.

Soc. And when you speak of carpentering, you mean the art of making wooden implements?

Theaet. Yes.

Soc. In both cases you define the subject-matter of each of the two arts?

Theaet. True.

Soc. But that, Theaetetus, was not the question: we wanted to know not the subjects, nor yet the number of the arts or sciences, for we were not going to count them, but we wanted to know the nature of knowledge in the abstract. Am I not right?

Theaet. Perfectly right.

Soc. Take the following example: Suppose that a person were to ask about some very common and obvious thing—for example, What is clay? and we were to reply, that there is a clay of potters, there is a clay of oven-makers, there is a clay of brick-makers; would not the answer be ridiculous?

Theaet. Truly.

Soc. In the first place, there would be an absurdity in assuming that he who asked the question would understand from our answer the meaning of the word 'clay,' merely because we added 'of the image-makers,' or of any other workers. For how can a man understand the name of anything, when he does not know what it is?

Theaet. Of course not.

Soc. Then he who does not know what science or knowledge is, has no knowledge of the art or science of making shoes?

Theaet. None.

Soc. Nor of any other science?

Theaet. No.

Soc. And when a man is asked 'what science or knowledge is,' to give as an answer the name of some art or science, is ridiculous; for the question is, 'What is knowledge?' and he replies, 'a knowledge of this and that.'

Theaet. True.

Soc. Moreover, he might answer shortly and simply, but he makes an enormous circuit. For example, when asked about the clay, he might have said simply, that 'clay is moistened earth'—whose clay is not to the point.

Theaet. Yes, Socrates, there is no difficulty as you put the question. You mean, if I am not mistaken, something like what occurred to me and to my friend here, your namesake Socrates, in a recent discussion.

Soc. What was that, Theaetetus?

Theaet. Theodorus was writing out for us something about roots, such as the roots of three or five feet, showing that in linear measurement (i.e. comparing the sides of the squares) they are incommensurable by the unit: he selected the irrational roots of the numbers up to seventeen, but he went no farther; and as there are innumerable roots, the notion occurred to us of attempting to include them all under one name or class.

Soc. And did you find such a class?

Theaet. I think that we did; but I should like to have your opinion.

Soc. Let me hear.

Theaet. We divided all numbers into two classes; those which are made up of equal factors multiplying into one another, which we represented as squares and called squares or equilateral numbers;—that was one class.

Soc. Very good.

Theaet. The intermediate numbers, such as three and five, and every other number which is made up of unequal factors, either of a greater multiplied by a less, or of a less multiplied by a greater, and when regarded as a figure, is contained in unequal sides;—all these we represented as oblong figures, and called them oblong numbers.

Soc. Capital; and what followed?

Theaet. The lines, or sides, which are the roots of (or whose squares are equal to) the equilateral plane numbers, were called by us lengths or magnitudes; and the lines which are the roots of (or whose squares are equal to) the oblong numbers, were called powers or roots; the reason of this latter name being, that they are commensurable with the others [i.e. with the so-called lengths or magnitudes] not in linear measurement, but in the value of their squares; and the same about solids.

Soc. Excellent, my boy; I think that you fully justify the praises of Theodorus, and that he will not be found guilty of false witness.

Theaet. But I am unable, Socrates, to give you a similar answer about knowledge, which is what you appear to want; and therefore Theodorus is a deceiver after all.

Soc. Well, but suppose that you were running a course, and some one said in praise of you, that he had never known any youth who was as good a runner, and afterwards you were beaten in a race by a grown-up man, who was a great runner—would his praise be any the less true?

Theaet. Certainly not.

Soc. And is the discovery of the nature of knowledge really a little matter, as I just now said, or one requiring great skill?

Theaet. Requiring the greatest, I should say.

Soc. Well, then, be of good cheer; do not say that Theodorus was mistaken about you, but do your best to ascertain the true nature of knowledge, as well as of other things.

Theaet. I am eager enough, Socrates, if that would bring to light the truth.

Soc. Come, you made a good beginning just now; let your own answer about roots be your model, and as you comprehended them all in one class, try and bring the many sorts of knowledge under one definition.

STATESMAN.

Str. Then we must suppose that the great and small exist and are discerned in both these ways, and not, as we were saying before, only relatively to one another, but there must also be another comparison of them with the mean or ideal standard; would you like to hear the reason why?

Y. Soc. Certainly.

Str. If we assume the greater to exist only in relation to the less, there will never be any comparison of either with the mean.

Y. Soc. True.

Str. And would not this doctrine be the ruin of all the arts and their creations; would not the art of the Statesman and the aforesaid art of weaving disappear? For all these arts are on the watch against excess and defect, not as unrealities, but as real evils, which occasion a difficulty in action; and the excellence of beauty of every work of art is due to this observance of measure.

Y. Soc. Certainly.

Str. But if the science of the Statesman disappears, there will be no possibility of finding out the royal science.

Y. Soc. Very true.

Str. Well, then, as in the Sophist we extorted the inference that not-being had an existence, because here was the point at which the argument eluded our grasp, so in this we must endeavour to show that the greater and less are not only to be measured with one another, but also have to do with the production of the mean; for if this is not admitted, neither a statesman nor any other man of action can be an undisputed master of his science.

Y. Soc. Yes, we must certainly do again what we did then.

Str. But this, Socrates, is a greater work than the other, of which we only too well remember the length. I think, however, that we may fairly assume something of this sort:—

Y. Soc. What?

Str. That we shall some day require this notion of a standard with a view to the demonstration of absolute truth; meanwhile, the argument that the very existence of the arts must be held to depend on the possibility of measuring more or less, not only with one another, but also with a view to the attainment of the mean, seems to afford a grand support and satisfactory proof of the doctrine which we are maintaining; for if there are arts, there is a standard of measure, and if there is a standard of measure, there are arts; but if either is wanting, there is neither.

Y. Soc. True; and what is the next step?

Str. The next step clearly is to divide the art of measurement into two parts, and place in the one part all the arts which measure number, length, depth, breadth, swiftness, with their opposites; and to have another part in which they are measured with the mean, and the fit, and the opportune, and the due, and with all those words, in short, which denote a mean or standard removed from the extremes.

THE REPUBLIC.

But what branch of knowledge is there, my dear friend, which is of the desired nature; since all the useful arts were reckoned mean by us?

. . . and yet if music and gymnastic are excluded, and the arts are also excluded, what remains?

Well, I said, there may be nothing left; and then we shall have to take something which is of universal application.

What may that be?

A something which all arts and sciences and intelligences use in common, and which every one ought to learn among the elements of education.

What is that?

The little matter of distinguishing one, two, and three—in a word, number and calculation:—do not all arts and sciences necessarily partake of them?

Yes.

Then the art of war partakes of them?

To be sure.

Then Palamedes, when he appears in the play, proves Agamemnon ridiculously unfit to be a general. Did you never remark how he declares that he had invented number, and had numbered and set in array the ranks of the army at Troy; which implies that they had never been numbered before, and Agamemnon must be supposed literally to have been incapable of counting his own feet—how could he if he was ignorant of number? And if that is true, what sort of general must he have been?

I should say a very strange one, certainly.

Must not a warrior, then, I said, in addition to his military skill, have a knowledge of arithmetic?

Certainly he must, if he is to have the least understanding of military tactics, or indeed, I should rather say, if he is to be a man at all.

I should like to know whether you have the same notion which I have of this study?

What is your notion?

It appears to me to be a study which leads naturally to reflection, and is of the kind which we are seeking, but has never been rightly used; for it is really of use in drawing us towards being.

Will you explain your meaning? he said.

I will try, I said; and I wish you would consider and help me, and say 'yes' or 'no' when I attempt to distinguish in my own mind what branches of knowledge have this attracting power, in order that we may have clearer proof that arithmetic is one of them.

Explain, he said.

I mean to say that objects of sense are of two kinds; some of them do not invite thought because the sense is an adequate judge of them; while in the case of other objects there is a mistrust of the senses which imperatively demands enquiry.

You must be referring, he said, to the manner in which the senses are imposed upon by distance, and by painting in light and shade.

No, I said, that is not my meaning.

Then what is your meaning?

When speaking of uninviting objects, I mean those which do not pass from one sensation to another; inviting objects are those which give opposite sensations; in this latter case the sense coming upon the object, whether at a distance or near, gives no more vivid idea of anything in particular than of its opposite. An illustration will make my meaning clearer:—here are three fingers—a little finger, a second finger, and a middle finger.

Very good.

You may suppose that they are seen quite close. And here comes the point.

What is that?

Each of them equally appears a finger, whether seen in the middle or at the extremity, whether white or black, or thick or thin—it makes no difference; a finger is a finger all the same. And in all these cases the ordinary soul is not compelled to ask of thought the question what is a finger? for the sight never intimates to her that a finger is other than a finger.

True.

And therefore, I said, there is nothing here which invites or excites intelligence.

There is not, he said.

But is this equally true of the greatness and smallness of the fingers? Can sight adequately perceive them? and is no difference made by the circumstance that one of the fingers is in the middle and another at the extremity?

And in like manner does the touch adequately perceive the qualities of thickness or thinness, or softness or hardness? And so of the other senses; do they give perfect intimations of such matters? Is not their mode of operation rather on this wise—the sense which is concerned with the quality of hardness is necessarily concerned also with the quality of softness, and only intimates to the soul that the same thing is felt to be hard and soft?

Very true, he said.

And must not the soul be perplexed at this intimation of a hard which is also soft? What, again, is the meaning of light and heavy, if that which is light is also heavy, and that which is heavy, light?

Yes, he said, these intimations are very curious and have to be explained.

Yes, I said, and in these perplexities the soul naturally summons to her aid calculation and intelligence, that she may see whether the several objects announced are one or two.

True.

And if they turn out to be two, is not each of them one, and different?

Certainly.

And if each is one, and both are two, she will conceive the two as in a state of division, for if they were undivided they could only be conceived of as one?

True.

The eye certainly did behold both small and great, not divided but confused.

Yes.

Whereas the thinking mind, intending to light up the chaos, was compelled to reverse the process, and look at small and great as separate and not confused.

Very true.

And was not this the beginning of the enquiry 'What is great?' and 'What is small?'

Exactly so.

Here began the distinction of the visible and the intelligible.

Most true.

And that is an illustration of my meaning in describing impressions as inviting to the intellect, or the reverse —the inviting impressions are simultaneous with opposite impressions.

I understand, he said, and agree with you.

And to which class do unity and number belong?

I do not know, he replied.

Think a little and you will see that what has preceded will supply the answer; for if simple unity, and that only, can be adequately perceived by the sight or by any other sense, then, as we were saying in the case of the fingers, there will be nothing to attract towards being; but when there is some contradiction always present, and one is the reverse of one and involves the conception of plurality, then thought begins to be aroused within, and the soul perplexed and wanting to arrive at a decision asks 'What is absolute unity?' And this is the way in which the study of the one has a power of drawing and converting the mind to the contemplation of true being.

And surely, he said, this occurs notably when we look at one, for the same thing is seen by us as one and as infinite in multitude?

Yes, I said; and this being true of one must be equally true of all number?

Certainly.

And all arithmetic and calculation have to do with number?

Yes.

And they are conductors to truth?

Yes, in an eminent degree.

Then this is the sort of knowledge of which we are in search, having a double use, military and philosophical; for the man of war must learn the art of number that he may know how to array his troops, and the philosopher also, because he has to rise out of the sea of change and lay hold of true being, if he would be an arithmetician.

That is true.

And our guardian is both warrior and philosopher?

Certainly.

Then this is a kind of knowledge which legislation may fitly prescribe; and we must endeavour to persuade the principal men of our State to go and learn arithmetic, not as amateurs, but they must carry on the study until they see the nature of numbers in the mind only; nor again, in the spirit of merchants or traders, with a view to buying or selling, but for the sake of their military use, and of the soul herself; and because this will be the easiest way for her to pass from becoming to truth and being.

That is excellent, he said.

Yes, I said, and now having spoken of it, I must add how charming the science is! and in how many ways it conduces to our desired end, if pursued in the spirit of a philosopher, and not of a shopkeeper!

How do you mean?

I mean, as I was saying, that arithmetic has a very great and elevating effect, compelling the soul to reason about abstract number, and rebelling against the introduction of visible or tangible objects into the argument. You know how steadily the masters of the art repel and ridicule any one who attempts to divide absolute unity when he is calculating, and if you divide, they multiply[1], taking care that one shall continue one and not become lost in fractions.

That is very true.

Now, suppose a person were to say to them: O my friends, what are these wonderful numbers about which you are reasoning, in which, as you say, there is a unity such as you require, and each unit is equal, invariable, indivisible,—what would they answer?

---

[1] Meaning either (1) that they integrate the number because they deny the possibility of fractions; or (2) that division is regarded by them as a process of multiplication, and thus the unity and indivisibility of one is still maintained.

They would answer, as I suppose, that they were speaking of those numbers which are only realized in thought.

Then you see that this knowledge may be truly called necessary, necessitating as it does the use of the pure intelligence in the attainment of pure truth?

Yes; that is a marked characteristic of it.

And have you further remarked, that those who have a natural talent for calculation are generally quick at every other kind of knowledge; and even the dull, if they have had an arithmetical training, gain in quickness, if not in any other way?

Very true, he said.

And indeed, you will not easily find a more difficult study, and not many as difficult.

You will not.

And, for these reasons, arithmetic is a kind of knowledge in which the best natures should be trained, and which must not be given up.

I agree.

Let this then be made one of our subjects of education. And next, shall we enquire whether the kindred science also concerns us?

You mean geometry?

Yes.

Certainly, he said; that part of geometry which relates to war is clearly our concern; for in pitching a camp, or taking up a position, or closing or extending the lines of an army, or any other military manœuvre, whether in actual battle or on a march, there will be a great difference in a general, accordingly as he is or is not a geometrician.

Yes, I said, but for that purpose a very little of either geometry or calculation will be enough; the question is rather of the higher and greater part of geometry, whether that tends towards the great end—I mean towards the vision of the idea of good; and thither, as I was saying, all things tend which compel the soul to turn her gaze towards that place, where is the full perfection of being, of which she ought, by all means, to attain the vision.

True, he said.

Then if geometry compels us to view being, it concerns us; if becoming only, it does not concern us?

Yes, that is what we assert.

Nevertheless, such a conception of the science is in flat contradiction to the ordinary language of geometricians, as will hardly be denied by those who have any acquaintance with their study: for they speak of squaring and applying and adding, having in view use only, and absurdly confuse the necessities of geometry with those of daily life; whereas knowledge is the real object of the whole science.

Certainly, he said.

Then must not a further admission be made?

What admission?

The admission that this knowledge at which geometry aims is of the eternal, and not of the perishing and transient.

That, he replied, may be readily allowed, and is true.

Then, my noble friend, geometry will draw the soul towards truth, and create the spirit of philosophy, and raise up that which is now unhappily allowed to fall down.

Nothing will be more effectual.

Then nothing should be more effectually enacted than that the inhabitants of your fair city should learn geometry. Moreover the science has indirect effects, which are not small.

Of what kind are they? he said.

There are the military advantages of which you spoke, I said; and in all departments of study, as experience proves, any one who has studied geometry is infinitely quicker of apprehension than one who has not studied it.

Yes, he said, the difference between a geometrician and one who is not a geometrician is very great indeed.

Then shall we propose this as a second branch of knowledge which our youth will study?

Let us make the proposal, he replied.

And suppose we make astronomy the third—what do you say?

I am strongly inclined to it, he said; the observation of the seasons and of months and years is quite essential to husbandry and navigation, and not less essential to military tactics.

I am amused, I said, at your fear of the world, which makes you guard against the appearance of insisting upon useless studies; and I quite admit the difficulty of believing that in every man there is an eye of the soul which, when by other pursuits lost and dimmed, is by these purified and re-illumined; and is more precious far than ten thousand bodily eyes, for by this alone is truth seen. Now there are two classes of persons: one class who will agree with you and will take your words as a revelation; another class who have no understanding of them, and to whom they will naturally seem to be idle tales. And you had better decide at once with which of the two you are arguing; or perhaps, you will say with neither, and that your chief aim in carrying on the argument is your own improvement; at the same time not grudging to others any benefit which they may derive.

I think that I should prefer to carry on the argument on my own behalf.

Then take a step backward, for we have gone wrong in the order of the sciences.

What was the mistake? he said.

After plane geometry, I said, we took solids in revolution, instead of taking solids in themselves; whereas after the second dimension the third, which is concerned with cubes and dimensions of depth, ought to have followed.

That is true, Socrates; but these subjects seem to be as yet hardly explored.

Why, yes, I said, and for two reasons:—in the first place, no government patronises them, which leads to a want of energy in the study of them, and they are difficult; in the second place, students cannot learn them unless they have a teacher. But then a teacher can hardly be found, and even if he could, as matters now stand, the students, who are very conceited, would not mind him. That, however, would be otherwise if the whole State patronised and honoured these studies; then they would find disciples, and there would be continuous and earnest search, and discoveries would be made; since even now, disregarded as they are by the world, and maimed of their fair proportions, and although none of their votaries can tell the use of them, still these studies force their way by their natural charm, and very likely they may emerge into light.

Yes, he said, there is a remarkable charm in them. But I do not clearly understand the change in the order. First you began with a geometry of plane surfaces?

Yes, I said.

And you placed astronomy next, and then you made a step backward?

Yes, and I have delayed you by my haste; the ludicrous state of solid geometry made me pass over this branch and go on to astronomy, or motion of solids.

True, he said.

Then assuming that the science now omitted would come into existence if encouraged by the State, let us go on to astronomy, which will be fourth.

The right order, he replied.

GORGIAS.

Soc. And yet I do not believe that you really mean to call any of these arts rhetoric; although the precise expression which you used was, that rhetoric is an art which operates and is perfected through the medium of discourse; and an adversary who wished to be captious might take a fancy to say, 'And so, Gorgias, you call arithmetic rhetoric.' But I do not think that you *would* call arithmetic rhetoric, any more than you would call geometry rhetoric.

Gor. You are quite right, Socrates, in your apprehension of my meaning.

Soc. Well, then, let me now have the rest of my answer:—seeing that rhetoric is one of those arts which works mainly by the use of words, and there are other arts which also use words, tell me what is that quality in words with which rhetoric is concerned:—Suppose that a person asks me about some of the arts which I was mentioning just now; he might say, 'Socrates, what is arithmetic?' and I should reply to him, as you replied to me just now, that arithmetic is one of those arts which is perfected by words. And then he would proceed: 'With what?' and I should say, With the knowledge of odd and even numbers, and how many there are of each. And if he asked again: 'And what is the art of calculation?' I should say, That also is one of the arts which is concerned wholly with words. And if he further said, 'Concerned with what?' I should say in the clerk's phrase, 'as aforesaid,' like arithmetic, but with a difference, and the difference is that the art of calculation considers not only the quantities of odd and even numbers, but also their relation to themselves and to one another. And suppose, again, I were to say that astronomy is only words—he would ask, 'Words about what, Socrates?' and I should answer, that astronomy tells us about the motions of the stars and sun and moon, and their relative swiftness.

Gor. Very true, Socrates; I admit that.

Soc. And now let us have from you, Gorgias, the truth about rhetoric: which you would admit (would you not?) to be one of those arts which operate and are perfected through the medium of words?

Gor. True.

Soc. Tell me, I say, what about? To what class of things do the words which rhetoric uses relate?

LAWS.

The legislator is to consider all these things, and to bid the citizens, as far as possible, not to lose sight of numerical order; for no single instrument of youthful education has such mighty power, both as regards domestic economy and politics, and in the arts, as the study of arithmetic. Above all, arithmetic stirs up him who is by nature sleepy and dull, and makes him quick to learn, retentive, shrewd, and aided by art divine he makes progress quite beyond his natural powers. All these, if only the legislator, by laws and institutions, can banish meanness and covetousness from the souls of the disciples, and enable them to profit by them, will be excellent and suitable instruments of education. But if he cannot, he will unintentionally create in them, instead of wisdom, the habit of craft, which evil tendency may be observed in the Egyptians and Phoenicians, and many other races, through the general illiberality of their pursuits and possessions, whether some unworthy legislator of theirs has been the cause, or some impediment of chance or nature.

Ath. All freemen, I conceive, should learn as much of these branches of knowledge as every child in Egypt is taught when he learns his alphabet. In that country arithmetical games have been actually invented for the use of children, which they learn as a pleasure and amusement. They have to distribute apples and garlands, using the same number sometimes for a larger and sometimes for a lesser number of persons; and they arrange pugilists and wrestlers as they pair together by lot or remain over, and show the order in which they follow. Another mode of amusing them is by distributing vessels, some in which gold, brass, silver, and the like are mixed, others in which they are unmixed; as I was saying, they adapt to their amusement the numbers in common use, and in this way make more intelligible to their pupils the arrangements and movements of armies and expeditions, and in the management of a household they make people more useful to themselves, and more wide awake; and again in measurements of things which have length, and breadth, and depth, they free us from that natural ignorance of all these things which is so ludicrous and disgraceful.

PROCLUS

(410—485)

Proclus, Diadochus Platonicus, Greek philosopher, mathematician and astronomer, was the foremost representative of the later Neo-Platonic school in Athens. At the age of thirty he became head of the Athenian Academy whose long, though broken history began with its founding by Plato early in the fourth century B.C. The name "Diadochus Platonicus" was given to Proclus as a mark of his eminence not only because he was Plato's successor as head of the Academy but also because he epitomized many of the personal traits and ideals of his predecessor. Both Plato and Proclus were born of aristocratic and wealthy families, and each used his wealth unselfishly. Both possessed extraordinary intellectual powers; both were exceptionally gifted in physical strength and personal charm; both were motivated in their actions by high moral principles. The fame and influence of the Academy increased in Proclus's time through his forceful and untiring efforts in demonstrating the basic values of Plato's teachings. Proclus was deeply devoted to the old pagan religion.

Proclus was born in Byzantium in 410. Shortly after his birth his parents brought him to their native city of Xanthus in Lycia. He received his early education in Xanthus. Intended to follow his father's profession, the study of law, he was sent to Alexandria where he attended the Roman schools. At the same time he received instruction from the Greek masters, Leonas the rhetorician and Orion the grammarian. Philosophy and rhetoric proved to be more to his liking than Roman law, and, when Leonas left Alexandria on a mission to Byzantium, Proclus accompanied him on this voyage.

When he returned to Alexandria, Proclus turned to the study of mathematics and the doctrines of Aristotle. Later, upon hearing that Athens was the seat of the most brilliant teaching in philosophy, he left Alexandria for Athens. He was not yet twenty when Syrianus brought him to Plutarch, then head of the Academy in Athens. The aging Plutarch, profoundly moved by the manners and the scholarly attainments of young Proclus, accepted him as a pupil, and took him into his home as his own son. Proclus was initiated by Plutarch into the art of writing commentaries on the great philosophers. After Plutarch's death, Proclus became the companion of Syrianus under whom he studied the philosophy of Plato and by whom he was trained to assume the responsibilities of the head of the Academy. At the age of twenty eight, Proclus had already completed a great number of detailed treatises and commentaries. To his skill in poetry and philosophy were added a wide knowledge of the sciences. Some called him the "prince of all sciences".

While Proclus's main interest was in the exposition of Plato's writings, he encouraged the study of the sciences, giving particular attention to mathematics and astronomy. His writings include commentaries on scientific treatises which he believed were a proper part of the education of his pupils preparatory to their introduction to philosophy. Among these works are his *Commentaries on Book I of Euclid's Elements.* Writing for beginners in geometry, Proclus presented digests or the paraphrased contents of the works of the previous writers, adding his own comments and also his contributions to the subject (as in the case of his attempt to prove Euclid's parallel postulate). One of the two principal sources of our information about the origins of Greek mathematics, this work is of extreme historical interest. Many of the ancient treatises which were available to Proclus and which were described by him in the *Commentaries* are now lost. His recitals of their texts are in some instances invaluable evidence corroborating other sources. There are also some texts cited by him, which would be completely unknown to us but for his inclusion of them in his *Commentaries.*

●

PROCLUS'S SUMMARY[1]

From *Selections Illustrating the History of Greek Mathematics*

with an English Translation by IVOR THOMAS

Proclus, *On Euclid* i., ed. Friedlein 64. 16-70. 18

Since it behoves us to examine the beginnings both of the arts and of the sciences with reference to the present cycle [of the universe], we say that according to most accounts geometry was first discovered among the Egyptians,[2] taking its origin from the measurement of areas.

[1] This commentary is one of the two main sources for the history of Greek geometry, the other being the *Collection* of Pappus.

[2] The Egyptian origin of geometry is taught by Herodotus, ii. 109, where it is asserted that Sesostris (Ramses II, *c.* 1300 B.C.) divided the land among the Egyptians in equal rectangular plots, on which an annual tax was levied; when therefore the river swept away a portion of a plot, the owner applied for a reduction of tax, and surveyors had to be sent down to report. In this he saw the origin of geometry, and this story may be the source of Proclus's account, as also of the similar accounts in Heron, *Geometrica* 2, ed. Heiberg 176. 1-13, Diodorus Siculus i. 69, 81 and Strabo xvii. c. 3. Aristotle also finds the origin of mathematics among the Egyptians, but in the existence of a leisured class of priests, not in a practical need (*Metaphysica* A 1, 981 b 23).

For they found it necessary by reason of the rising of the Nile, which wiped out everybody's proper boundaries. Nor is there anything surprising in that the discovery both of this and of the other sciences should have its origin in a practical need, since everything which is in process of becoming progresses from the imperfect to the perfect. Thus the transition from perception to reasoning and from reasoning to understanding is natural. Just as exact knowledge of numbers received its origin among the Phoenicians by reason of trade and contracts, even so geometry was discovered among the Egyptians for the aforesaid reason.

Thales[1] was the first to go to Egypt and bring back to Greece this study; he himself discovered many propositions, and disclosed the underlying principles of many others to his successors, in some cases his method being more general, in others more empirical. After him Ameristus,[2] the brother of the poet Stesichorus, is mentioned as having touched the study of geometry, and Hippias of Elis[1] spoke of him as having acquired a rep-

---

[1] Thales (*c.* 624—547 B.C.), one of the "Seven Wise Men" of ancient Greece, is universally acknowledged as the founder of Greek geometry, astronomy and philosophy. His greatest fame in antiquity rested on his prediction of the total eclipse of the sun of May 28, 585 B.C., which led to the cessation of hostilities between the Medes and Lydians and a lasting peace (Herodotus i. 74); what Thales probably did was to predict the *year* in which the eclipse would take place, an achievement by no means beyond the astronomical powers of the age. Thales was noted for his political sense. He urged the separate states of Ionia, threatened by the encroachment of the Lydians, to form a federation with a capital at Teos; and his successful dissuasion of his fellow-Milesians from accepting the overtures of Croesus, king of the Lydians, may have had an influence on the favourable terms later granted to Miletus by Cyrus, king of the Persians, though the main reason for this preferential treatment was probably commercial. In philosophy Thales taught that the all is water.

[2] The name is uncertain. Stesichorus, the lyric poet, flourished *c.* 611 B.C.

[1] The well-known Sophist, born about 460 B.C., whose various accomplishments are described in Plato's *Hippias Minor.* He claimed to have gone once to the Olympic Games with everything that he wore made by himself, as well as all kinds of works in prose and verse of his own composition. His system of mnemonics enabled him to remember any string of fifty names which he had heard once. The unmathematical Spartans, however, could not appreciate his genius, and from them he could get no fees. His chief mathematical discovery was the curve known as the quadratrix, which could be used for trisecting an angle or squaring the circle.

utation for geometry. After these Pythagoras[2] transformed this study into the form of a liberal education, examining its principles from the beginning and tracking down the theorems immaterially and intellectually; he it was who discovered the theory of proportionals[3] and the construction of the cosmic figures. After him Anaxagoras of Clazomenae[4] touched many questions affecting geometry, and so did Oenopides of Chios,[5] being a little younger than Anaxagoras, both of whom Plato mentioned in the *Rivals* as having acquired a reputation for mathematics.

After them Hippocrates of Chios,[1] who discovered the quadrature of the lune, and Theodorus of Cyrene[2] became distinguished in geometry. For Hippocrates is the first of those mentioned as having compiled *elements*.[3] Plato, who came after them, made the other branches of mathematics as well as geometry take a very great step forward by his zeal for them; and it is obvious how he filled his writings with mathematical arguments and everywhere stirred up admiration for mathematics in those who took up philosophy. At this time also lived

---

[2] The life of Pythagoras is shrouded in mystery. He was probably born in Samos about 582 B.C. and migrated about 529 B.C. to Crotona, the Dorian colony in southern Italy, where a semi-religious brotherhood sprang up round him. This brotherhood was subjected to severe persecution in the fifth century B.C., and the Pythagoreans then took their doctrines into Greece proper.

[3] Friedlein's reading is, "irrationals," but there is grave difficulty in believing that Pythagoras could have developed a theory of irrationals; in fact, a Pythagorean is said to have been drowned at sea for his impiety in disclosing the existence of irrationals.

[4] *c.* 500—428 B.C. Clazomenae was a town near Smyrna. All we know about the mathematics of Anaxagoras is that he wrote on the squaring of the circle while in prison and may have written a book on perspective (Vitruvius, *De architectura* vii. praef. 11).

[5] Oenopides was primarily an astronomer, and Eudemus is believed to have credited him with the discovery of the obliquity of the ecliptic and the period of the Great Year (Theon of Smyrna, ed. Hiller 198. 14-16). In mathematics Proclus attributed to him the discovery of Eucl. i. 12 and i. 23.

[1] Hippocrates was in Athens from about 450 to 430 B.C.

[2] Our chief knowledge of Theodorus comes from the *Theaetetus* of Plato, whose mathematical teacher he is said to have been (Diog. Laert. ii. 103).

[3] Proclus (*in Eucl.* i., ed. Friedlein 72 *et seq.*) explains that the *elements* in geometry are leading theorems having to those which follow the relation of an all-pervading principle; he compares them with the letters of the alphabet in relation to language; and they have, indeed, the same name in Greek.

Leodamas of Thasos[5] and Archytas of Taras and Theaetetus of Athens, by whom the theorems were increased and an advance was made towards a more scientific grouping.

Younger than Leodamas were Neoclides and his pupil Leon, who added many things to those known before them, so that Leon was able to make a collection of the *elements* in which he was more careful in respect both of the number and of the utility of the things proved; he also discovered *diorismi,* showing when the problem investigated can be solved and when not. Eudoxus of Cnidos, a little younger than Leon and an associate of Plato's school, was the first to increase the number of the so-called general theorems; to the three proportions he added another three, and increased the number of theorems about the section, which had their origin with Plato, applying the method of analysis to them. Amyclas of Heraclea,[2] one of the friends of Plato, and Menaechmus,[3] a pupil of Eudoxus who had associated with Plato, and his brother Dinostratus[4] made the whole of geometry still more perfect. Theudius of Magnesia seemed to excel both in mathematics and in the rest of philosophy; for he made an admirable arrangement of *elements* and made many particular propositions more general. Again, Athenaeus of Cyzicus, who lived about those times, became famous in other branches of mathematics but mostly in geometry. They spent their time together in the Academy, conducting their investigations in common. Hermotimus of Colophon advanced farther the investigations begun by Eudoxus and Theaetetus; he discovered many propositions in the *Ele-*

[5] All we know about him is that Plato is said to have explained or communicated to him the method of analysis (Diog. Laert. iii. 24, Procl. *in Eucl.* i., ed. Friedlein 211. 19-23).

[2] The correct spelling appears to be Amyntas, though Diogenes Laertius (iii. 46) speaks of Amyclas of Heraclea as a pupil of Plato and in another place (ix. 40) says that a certain Pythagorean Amyclas dissuaded Plato from burning the works of Democritus. Heraclea was in Pontus.

[3] He discovered the conic sections.

[4] He applied the quadratrix (probably discovered by Hippias) to the squaring of the circle.

ments and compiled some portion of the theory of loci. Philippus of Medma,[1] a disciple of Plato and by him diverted to mathematics, not only made his investigations according to Plato's directions but set himself to do such things as he thought would fit in with the philosophy of Plato.

Those who have compiled histories carry the development of this science up to this point. Not much younger than these is Euclid, who put together the *Elements,* arranging in order many of Eudoxus's theorems, perfecting many of Theaetetus's, and also bringing to irrefutable demonstration the things which had been only loosely proved by his predecessors. This man lived in the time of the first Ptolemy; for Archimedes, who came immediately after the first Ptolemy, makes mention of Euclid; and further they say that Ptolemy once asked him if there was in geometry a way shorter than that of the elements; he replied that there was no royal road to geometry.[2] He is therefore younger than the pupils of Plato, but older than Eratosthenes and Archimedes. For these men were contemporaries, as Eratosthenes[1] some-

---

[1] Almost certainly the same as Philippus of Opus, who is said to have revised and published the *Laws* of Plato and (wrongly) to have written the *Epinomis.* Suidas notes a number of astronomical and mathematical works by him.

[2] Not much more is known about the life of Euclid than is contained in this passage (see Heath, *The Thirteen Books of Euclid's Elements,* vol. i., pp. 1-6 and *H.G.M.* i. 354-357). The summary of Euclid's achievement in the *Elements* is a very fair one, agreeing with the considered judgement of Heath (*H.G.M.* i. 217): "There is therefore probably little in the whole compass of the *Elements* of Euclid, except the new theory of proportion due to Eudoxus and its consequences, which was not in substance included in the recognized content of geometry and arithmetic by Plato's time, although the form and arrangement of the subject-matter and the method employed in particular cases were different from what we find in Euclid" (*cf. H.G.M.* i. 357). As Plato died in 347 B.C., and Archimedes was born in 287 B.C., Euclid must have flourished about 300 B.C.; Ptolemy I reigned from 306 to 283 B.C. Had not the confusion been common in the Middle Ages, it would scarcely be necessary to point out that this Euclid is to be distinguished from Euclid of Megara, the philosopher, who lived about 400 B.C. A story about there being no royal road to geometry is also told of Menaechmus and Alexander (Stobaeus, *Ecl.* ii 31, ed. Wachsmuth 115).

[1] Eratosthenes was born about 284 B.C. His ability in many branches of knowledge, but failure to achieve the highest place in any, won for him the nicknames "Beta" and "Pentathlos." He became tutor to Philopator, son of Ptolemy Euergetes and librarian at Alexandria. He wrote a book *Platonicus* and another *On Means* (both lost). His greatest achievement was his measurement of the circumference of the earth to a surprising degree of exactitude (see Heath, *H.G.M.* i. 106-108, *Greek Astronomy,* pp. 109-112).

where says. In his aim he was a Platonist, being in sympathy with this philosophy, whence it comes that he made the end of the whole *Elements* the construction of the so-called Platonic figures.[2] There are many other mathematical writings by this man, wonderful in their accuracy and replete with scientific investigations. Such are the *Optics* and *Catoptrics,* and the *Elements of Music,* and again the book *On Divisions.*[3] He deserves admiration pre-eminently in the compilation of his *Elements of Geometry* on account of the order and of the selection both of the theorems and of the problems made with a view to the elements. For he included not everything which he could have said, but only such things as he could set down as elements. And he used all the various forms of syllogisms, some getting their plausibility from the first principles, some setting out from demonstrative proofs, all being irrefutable and accurate and in harmony with science. In addition to these he used all the dialectical methods, the *divisional* in the discovery of figures, the *definitive* in the existential arguments, the *demonstrative* in the passages from first principles to the things sought, and the *analytic* in the converse process from the things sought to the first principles. And the various

---

[2] It is true that the final book of the *Elements,* as written by Euclid, dealt with the construction of the cosmic, or Platonic, figures, but the whole work was certainly not designed with a view to their construction. Euclid, however, may quite well have been a Platonist.

[3] Euclid's *Optics* survives and is available in the Teubner text in two recensions, one probably Euclid's own, the other by Theon of Alexandria. It is possible that Proclus has attributed to Euclid a treatise on *Catoptrics* (Mirrors) which was really Theon's; a treatise by Euclid on this subject is not otherwise known. Two musical treatises attributed to Euclid are extant, the *Sectio Canonis* and the *Introductio Harmonica;* the latter, however, is definitely by Cleonides, a pupil of Aristoxenus, and it is not certain that the former is Euclid's own. The book *On Divisions* (*of Figures*) has survived in an Arabic text discovered by Woepcke at Paris and published in 1851; see R. C. Archibald, *Euclid's Book on Division of Figures with a restoration based on Woepcke's text and the Practica Geometriae of Leonardo Pisano* (Cambridge 1915). A Latin translation (probably by Gherard of Cremona, 1114-1187) from the Arabic was known in the Middle Ages, but the Arabic cannot have been a direct translation from Euclid's Greek. The general character of the treatise is indicated by Procl. *in Eucl.* i., ed. Friedlein 144. 22-26, as the division of figures into like and unlike figures.

species of conversions,[2] both of the simpler (propositions) and of the more complex, are in this treatise accurately set forth and skilfully investigated, what wholes can be converted with wholes, what wholes with parts and conversely, and what as parts with parts. Again, mention must be made of the continuity of the proofs, the disposition and arrangement of the things which precede and those which follow, and the power with which he treats each detail.

[2] Geometrical conversion is to be distinguished from logical conversion, as described by Aristotle, *Cat.* xii. 6 and elsewhere. An analysis of the conversion of geometrical propositions is given by Proclus (*in Eucl.* i., ed. Friedlein, 252. 5 *et seq.*). In the leading form of conversion, also called conversion *par excellence,* the conversion is simple, the hypothesis and conclusion of one theorem becoming the conclusion and hypothesis of the converse theorem. The other form of conversion is more complex, being that where several hypotheses are combined into a single enunciation so as to lead to a single conclusion. In the converse proposition the conclusion of the original proposition is combined with the hypotheses of the original proposition, less one, so as to lead to the omitted hypothesis as the new conclusion. An example of the first species of conversion is Euclid i. 6, which is the converse of Euclid i. 5, and Heath's notes thereon are most valuable (*The Thirteen Books of Euclid's Elements,* vol. i. pp. 256-257); an example of partial conversion is given by Euclid i. 8, which is a converse to i. 4.

ROBERT RECORDE

(c. 1510—1558)

Robert Recorde, eminent physician and mathematician, founder of the English school of mathematics, lived at a time of social change, of economic expansion and of religious strife in England. An active participant in the turbulent life of his times, Recorde rose to a position of great trust and responsibility. The legacies he left behind in money and goods were very small. His scientific legacy to the English people is easily enumerated. It is less easily assessed in terms of its vast and ramified effects on the spread of education in England. A courageous man with the rare gift of loyalty and compassion, the span of his life was not without its tragedy.

Robert Recorde was born of a good family in Tenby, Pembroke, Wales. The exact date of his birth is not known, but it is recorded that he entered the University of Oxford in 1525 and that he was made fellow of All-Souls College in 1531. After teaching at Oxford for some time, he went to Cambridge to study medicine and there, in 1545, he received his M.D. degree. Recorde was at the height of his career in the reigns of Henry VIII, Edward VI, and Mary I. It is said that he was physician to Edward VI and Queen Mary. As early as 1549, in King Edward's reign, Recorde was Comptroller of His Majesty's Mint at Bristol. In 1551 a record was made of the action of the Privy Council giving instructions to him for service as Surveyor of the King's Mines and Monies in Ireland. Recent investigations point to some irregularities or inefficiencies connected with his duties in the latter office, and we know that there were charges brought against him arising from the controversies and complaints concerning his administration of the office. It is known, too, that at the risk of incurring the displeasure of Queen Mary, should his action be found out, Recorde attended his friend Edward Underhill imprisoned in Newgate by the Queen's Council, during Underhill's illness. Recorde's work as a teacher, writer, and physician was ended in 1557 by his imprisonment in the King's Bench Prison. His will, in which he described himself as "Robert Recorde, doctor of physicke, though sicke in body, yet whole of minde," was probated in June 1558. Such valuables as remained to him were bequeathed in part to Arthur Hilton, Under-Marshal of the King's Bench, "Where," Recorde stated, "I now remaine prisoner." Nothing has been found to indicate the reason for Recorde's imprisonment.

Robert Recorde published four mathematical text books. Each of them was an example of his unparalleled genius for filling the needs of his times. The long sustained popularity of his texts rested on three principal bases. First, his books contained sound mathematics. Second, they were written in English which was capable of being readily understood. Third, they reflected the author's unusual capacity for presenting lucid, logical, interesting theoretical explanations and appropriate applications. His *The Grounde of Artes,* on the elements of arithmetic, gained an immediate popularity which it enjoyed undiminished through twenty-eight editions from 1542 to 1699. His *The Castle of Knowledge* (printed 1556) was the first astronomy text in English to present the Copernican theory. His *The Pathwaie to Knowledge* (printed 1551) was an excellent shortened version of Euclid's *Elements.* His *The Whetstone of Witte* (printed 1557) was the first text in English to be devoted to the principles of algebra, the "Cossike Arte." In *The Whetstone of Witte,* Recorde introduced the modern sign $=$ for equality, and his method for extracting roots of algebraic expressions. The last pages of *The Whetstone* achieve, in addition, a totally unexpected dramatic value and emotional effect beginning with the knock at the door which brings the algebra lesson and the author's career to an end.

To help in understanding the extensive influence of Robert Recorde's texts, parts of his *The Whetstone of Witte* are given as printed in 1557. This original edition, exceedingly rare now, is accessible in modern libraries through the medium of microfilm. In perusing its beautiful pages of old "black-letter" type the reader will need to be aware, for the most part, of only a few differences between Recorde's spelling and our own. Note, for example, that the letter *i* at the beginning of a word stands for the modern *j,* that although a *v* is used at the beginning of a word, it is replaced by a *u* in the interior parts of a word, that the letters *ie* are frequently used where we would use *y,* and that the long *s* of the Middle-English period is used in accordance with common practice in the 16th century printing.

THE PREFACE
to the gentle Reader.

The excellencie of nomber.

Although nomber be infinite in increasyng: so that there is not in all the worlde, any thing that can excede the quantitie of it: Nother the grasse on the grounde, nother the droppes of water in the sea, no not the small graines of Sande through the whole masse of the yearth: yet maie it seme by good reason, that noe man is so experte in *Arithmetike*, that can nomber the commodities of it. Wherefore I maie truely saie, that if any imperfection bee in nomber, it is bicause that nomber, can scarsely nomber, the commodities of it self. For the moare that any experte man, doeth weigh in his mynde the benifites of it, the more of them shall he see to remain behinde. And so shall he well perceiue, that as nomber is infinite, so are the commodities of it as infinite. And if any thyng doe or maie exceade the whole worlde, it is nomber, whiche so farre surmounteth the measure of the worlde, that if there were infinite worldes, it would at the full cōprehend them all. This nomber also hath other prerogatiues, aboue all naturalle thynges, for neither is there certaintie in any thyng without it, nother good agremente where it wanteth. Whereof no man can doubte, that hath been accustomed in the Bookes of Plato, Aristotell, and other auncient Philosophers, where he shall see, how thei searche all secrete knowledge and hid misteries, by the aide of nomber.

¶The ſeconde parte of Arithmetike, containyng the extraction of Rootes in diuerſe kindes, with the Arte of Coſſike nombers, and of Surde nombers alſo, in ſondrie ſortes.

¶The interlocutors, Maſter. Scholar.

The Maſter.

See your deſire can not bee ſatiſfied, neither your requeſt ſtaied, untill I maie iuſtly aunſwere you, that I can teache you no more: whiche aunſwere maie ſtaie your requeſt, although it content not your deſire.

Scholar. I beſeche God of his mercie, to withſtande all ſuche occaſion: except it maie be more to your owne contentation and profite, then it would be pleaſaunt to the louers of learnyng.

Maſter. Yet a iuſte excuſe maie ſtande for my declaration: As if ignoraunce doe inforce me to ſtaie my trauell.

Scholar. Your owne ignorauce, I truſt, you will not allege: and as for the ignorauce of other, it ought to bee no ſtaie: ſith the ignoraunte multitude doeth, but as it was euer wonte, enuie that knowledge, whiche thei can not attaine, and wiſhe all men ignoraunt, like unto themſelf, but all gentle natures, contemneth ſuche malice: and deſpiſeth theim as blinde wormes, whom nature doeth plague, to ſtay the poiſone of their venemous ſtynge.

Maſter. We ſhall not nede to ſtande on this talke, but trauell with knowledge to vanquiſhe ignoraūce: And beleue that the *pricke* of knowledge, is more of force then the ſtynge of ignoraunce:

A.i.

The Arte
Of Coßike nombers.

Ombers *Coßike*, are soche as bee contracte unto a denomination of some *Coßike* signe as 1. nomber. 1. roote. 1. square 1. Cube. &c.

But as for cõpendiousnesse in the use of theim, there bee certain figures set for to signifie them: so I thinke it good to expresse unto you those figures, before wee enter any farther, to thintente we maie procede alwaies in certentie, and knowe the thynges that wee intermedle withall: for thei are the signes of all the arte, that foloweth here to be taught.

And although there be many kindes of irrationall nombers, yet those figures that serue in *Coßike nõbers*, bee the figures also of all irrtionalle nombers, and therfore being ones well knowen, thei serue in bothe places commodiously.

These therfore be their signes, and significations briefly touched: for their nature is partly declared before.

℈. Betokeneth nomber absolute: as if it had no signe.

ꝛ. Signifieth the roote of any nomber.

ʒ. Representeth a square nomber.

ℭ. Expresseth a Cubike nomber.

ʒʒ. Is the signe of a square of squares, or Zenzizenzike.

ſʒ. Standeth for a Sursolide.

ʒℭ. Doeth signifie a Zenzicubike, or a square of Cubes.

bſʒ. Doeth betoken a seconde Sursolide.

ʒʒʒ. Doeth represent a square of squares squared

ly,

ly, oꝛ a *zenzizenzizenzike*.

ℭℭ. Signifieth a *Cube* of *Cubes*.

ʒ./ſʒ. Expꝛesseth a *Square* of *Surſolides*.

c/ſʒ. Betokeneth a thirde *Surſolide*.

ʒ.ʒ.ℭ. Repꝛeſenteth a *Square* of *Squared Cubes*: oꝛ a *Zenzizenzicubike*.

D/ſʒ. Standeth foꝛ a fourthe *Surſolide*.

ʒ. Sb ſʒ. Is the ſigne of a *ſquare* of ſeconde *Surſolides*

ℭ/ſʒ. Signifieth a *Cube* of *Surſolides*.

ʒʒ.ʒʒ. Betokeneth a *Square* oꝛ *ſquares*, ſquaredly ſquared.

E/ſʒ. Is the fiftte *Surſolide*.

ʒ.ℭℭ. Expꝛeſſeth a ſquare of *Cubike Cubes*.

F/ſʒ. Is the ſixte *Surſolide*.

ʒ.ʒ./ſʒ. Doeth repꝛeſente a ſquare of ſquared ſurſolides.

ℭ b/ſʒ. Standeth foꝛ a Cube of ſeconde *Surſolides*.

ʒ.c/ſʒ. Is a ſquare of thirde *Surſolides*.

g/ſʒ. Doeth betoken the ſeuenthe *Surſolide*.

ʒʒ.ʒ.ℭ. Signifieth a ſquare of ſquares, of ſquared Cubes.

And though I maie pꝛoceade infinitely in this ſoꝛte, yet I thinke it ſhall be a rare chaunce, that you ſhall nede this moche: and therfoꝛe this maie ſuffice. Notwithſtandynge, I will anon tell you, how you maie cotinue theſe nombers, by pꝛogreſſion, as farre as you liſte.

And farther you ſhal underſtande, that many men doe euer moꝛe call ſquare nombers *zenzikes*, as a ſhoꝛter and apter name, other men call thoſe ſquares the *firſte quantities*, and the *cubes* thei call *ſeconde quantities* ſquares of ſquares thei call *thirde quantities*, and ſurſolides *fourthe quantities*. And ſo namyng them all quantities (excepte nombers and rootes) thei doe adde to them foꝛ a difference, an oꝛdinall name of nomber, as thei doe goe in oꝛder ſucceſſiuely.

As here foloweth in example.

z.	Firste.	Quantities.	And so forthe, of as many as maie bee reckened.
ce.	Seconde.		
zz.	Thirde.		
sz.	Fourthe.		
zce.	Fifte.		
bsz.	Sixte		
zzz.	Seuenthe.		
cece.	Eighte.		
zsz.	Nineth.		
csz.	Tenthe.		
zzce.	Eleuenthe		
dsz.	Twelfthe.		

But althoughe somemen accompte this the more easie waie: bicause the other names be comberouse, yet those other names before, do expresse the qualitie of the nomber, better then these later names doe.

Scholar. I thanke you double, sith you are contente to teache me double names: for so shall I be acquainted with bothe formes, as I shall chaunce on them in other mennes bookes.

Therfore now you maie procead to numeration: whiche I thinke it nexte.

Master. There be other. 2. signes in often vse, of whiche the firste is made thus + and betokeneth more: the other is thus made — and betokeneth lesse.

Of extraction of rootes.

Master.

As in nombers *Abstracte*, euery nomber is not a rooted nomber, but some certaine onely emongest theim, so in nombers *Cossike*, all nombers haue not rootes: but soche onely emongest simple *Cossike* nombers are rooted, whose nomber hath a roote, agreable to the figure of his denomination.

So that. 16. ℭ. is not a Square nomber, nother hath any roote. For although. 16. bee a square nomber, and hath. 4. for his roote, yet the denomination (whiche is. ℭ.) hath noe square roote: but. 16. ʒ. is a square nomber: and hath. 4. 𝔯, for his roote.

Likewaies. 8. ℭ. is a *Cubike* nomber, and his roote is. 2. 𝔯: but. 8. ʒ. hath noe roote. For bicause. 8. hath no square roote, agreable to the signe. ʒ. nother is it a *Cubike* nomber, although it haue a *Cubike* roote, bicause the roote is disagreable from the signe. ʒ.

Scholar. I perceiue that in these nombers, as wel as in all other, the roote beeyng multiplied by it self, will make the nomber, whose roote it is. And therefore can no nomber be called square, or *Cubike*, or any waies els a rooted nomber, excepte the roote of the nomber agree with his signe: Whereby I perceiue well, that. 32. ſʒ. is a rooted nomber, forbicause that 32. hath a *Surſolide* roote, agreable to the signe. So likewaies. 125. ℭ. is a rooted nomber, seyng 5. is the *Cubike* roote of. 125. But. 27. ʒ. is no rooted nōber.

Master. Thus you vnderstande sufficiently, the iudgemente of rooted nombers, and their knowlege, in simple *Coßike* nōbers, that be vtterly vncōpounde. Wherfore, for extraction of their rootes, take this brief order.

Extracte

Extracte the roote of your nomber, as if it were absolute, and put to it. ꝛ. for the denomination.

So. 27. *Cubes* hath for his roote. 3. ꝛ.

And. 49. z. hath. 7. ꝛ. for his roote.

Again, the roote of. 216. &. is. 6. ꝛ.

Scholar. This I perceiue. And by like reason, the roote of. 243. sz. is. 3. ꝛ. But why dooe you name nōbers *Coßike* utterly uncompounde? For as I understande, that there bee nombers compounde, in their signes, so I see that thei maie haue rootes also.

As. 16. zz. hath for his roote. 2. ꝛ. And likewaies. 64. z&. hath. 2. ꝛ. for his roote.

Master. And dooe you not see, that those compounde nombers, maie haue moare rootes then one? Sith. 16. zz. hath for his square roote. 4. z. as wel as it hath. 2. ꝛ. for his *zenzizenzike* roote.

So. 4. zz. hath for his Square roote. 2. z. And hath no *zenzizenzike* ꝛ agreable to his whole signe.

Likewaies. 9. z&. hath no *zenzicubike* roote, accordyng to his whole signe: but it hath a square roote agreable to parte of the signe, and that is. 3 &.

Scholar. I see that also. And so hath. 8. z&. noe *zenzicubike* roote, but a *Cubike* roote: whiche is. 2. z.

Master. Therfore in cōpoūde signes, if the signe maie haue soche a roote, as the nomber will yelde, it is a rooted nomber, els not.

Whereby you maie perceiue, that if any nomber cōpounde in signe, haue a roote agreable to his whole signe, then maie it haue also, as many rootes, as ther be partes in that compounde signe.

Of square rootes.

Exãple of. 529ʓ& —+— 184ʓʓ —+— 16ʓ. whiche is a *Square* nomber, made by multiplication of. 23.& —+— 4.ꝛ. by it self. This nomber maie haue his Roote orderly extracted thus.

529.ʓ& —+— 184ʓʓ —+— 16ʓ (23& + 4ꝛ
23 46.&.

In the firste nomber, I finde the *Square* roote to bee 23. And for his denomination, I take halfe the *Coßike* signe ʓ&, and that is. &. For as. &. multiplied by &. doeth make. ʓ&. So in diuision by. ʓ. and in extraction of *Square* rootes, I shall take the. &. for the halfe of ʓ& and the denomination of his roote: and so set it doune in the *quotiente*.

Then I shall double the nomber *Abstracte* of that *quotiente* (kepyng his *Coßike* signe vnaltered) and that double shall I set euermore vnder the nexte nomber, toward the righte hande. As here, you see, I haue set 46 (whiche is the double of 23) with his signe &. vnder the seconde nomber. And there I perceiue, I maie haue it. 4. tymes, if I doe diuide (as I ought) 184. by 46. And that. 4. I sette in the *quotiente*, with the signe —+—, and the denomination. ꝛ: seyng. ʓʓ. diuided by. &. doeth yelde. ꝛ.

Laste of all, I muste multiplie that parte of the *quotiente*, 4.ꝛ. by it self, and it will yelde. 16.ʓ. whiche beyng subtracted also (as it should) leaueth nothyng remainyng of the square nomber.

This order must you kepe in all square nombers, how greate so euer thei be. As in this seconde exãple.

—90ʓʓ.
25ʓ& —+— 80ßʓ —— 26ʓʓ —— 144& —+— 81ʓ (5& + 8ʓ —— 9ꝛ
5.&. 10& —+— 64ʓʓ.
—+— 10& —+— 16ʓ. —— 9.ꝛ.

The

The roote of the firſt nomber is. 5 ℭ. whiche I ſet in a *quotiente*.

Then doe I double that. 5, and it maketh. 10, to be ſette vnder. 8. with his denomination, whiche is. ℭ. like to the roote.

That. 10. ℭ. maie be founde in. 80. ʃʒ. 8. times, and therfore I ſet. 8. in the *quotiente*, with the ſigne —+— and the denomination. ℨ. And then doe I multiplie that. 8. ℨ. ſquaredly, whiche giueth. —+— 64. ℨℨ. to be ſubtracted out of ——— 26. ℨℨ. and ſo remaineth ——— 90. ℨℨ.

After this I double all the *quotiente* again, wherof commeth —+— 10. ℭ. —+— 16. ℨ. And bicauſe there is a remainer, ouer the nomber that I wrought laſte, I muſt ſet. 10. ℭ. vnder the remainer, and the other nomber in order, as you ſee it ſet.

Then ſeke I how often tymes maie. 10. ℭ. diuide 90. ℨℨ. and I finde the *quotiente* to be ——— 9. 𝓇. And likewaies —+— 16 ℨ. multiplied by ——— 9 𝓇 doeth make ——— 144. ℭ. equalle to the ſomme ouer it: And ſo ſubtracteth it cleane. Wherfore to ende that worke, I multiplie the laſte *quotiente*, by it ſelf ſquare, and it yeldeth. —+— 81. ℨ. whiche is to bee ſubtracted out of the like ſomme, in the ſquare nomber: and ſo reſteth nothyng. Wherfore I iuſtly affirme, that the firſte nomber is a ſquare nomber, and hath for his roote. 5. ℭ. —+— 8. ℨ. ——— 9. 𝓇.

Scholar. That maie I ſone proue, if I multiplie

5 ℭ. —+— 8 ℨ. ——— 9. 𝓇.
5 ℭ. —+— 8 ℨ. ——— 9. 𝓇.

---

25 ℨℭ —+— 40 ʃʒ ——— 45 ℨℨ
—+— 40 ʃʒ —+— 64 ℨℨ
81. ℨ. ——— 72. ℭ ——— 45 ℨℨ
——— 72. ℭ.

---

25 ℨℭ —+— 80 ʃʒ ——— 26 ℨℨ ——— 144 ℭ —+— 81 ℨ.

Dd. ii. that

that roote by it ſelf, as here I haue doen it. Wherby I haue not onely confirmed it to be a ſquare nomber: but alſo I haue eſpied, that you vſed the nomber not so plainly ſet doune, as the particulare multiplication did make it: but rather as a reaſonable reduction would expreſſe it. I meane in the . ȝ. ȝ. where the particulare multiplication hath —+— 64.ȝ.ȝ. and ——90ȝ.ȝ. For whiche twoo nombers you ſette one, that reſulteth of the bothe, that is ——26ȝ.ȝ.

Maſter. But if you would take the nōber in that ſorte, the woorke would be not onely all one: but alſo ſomewhat plainer to bee perceiued of a learner. And therefore for your pleaſure, I will ſet forthe here, the example of that woorke. And loe, here it is.

ȝ.cc+80ȝ+64ȝȝ——90ȝȝ——144ȝ+81ȝ (ſcc+8ȝ—9
.cc 10cc+64ȝȝ 10.cc.—+—16.

Scholar. By comparynge theſe bothe formes of woorke together, I dooe better vnderſtande, the reaſon of the firſte woorke.

The rule of equation, commonly called Algebers Rule.

be rule of equation.

HEtherto haue I taughte you, the common formes of worke, in nombers *Denominate*. Whiche rules are vsed also in nõbers *Abstracte*, & likewaies in *Surde* nombers. Although the formes of these workes be seueralle, in eche kinde of nomber. But now will I teache you that rule, that is the principall in *Coßike* workes: and for whiche all the other dooe serue.

This Rule is called the Rule of *Algeber*, after the name of the inuentoure, as some men thinke: or by a name of singular excellencie, as other iudge. But of his vse it is rightly called, the rule of *equation*: bicause that by *equation* of nombers, it dooeth dissolue doubtefull questions: And vnfolde intricate ridles. And this is the order of it.

The somme of the rule of equation:

WHen any question is propoũded, apperteinyng to this rule, you shall imagin a name for the nomber, that is to bee soughte, as you remember, that you learned in the rule of false position. And with that nomber shall you procede, accordyng to the question, vntil you finde a Coßike nomber, equalle to that nomber, that the question expresseth, whiche you shal reduce

reduce euermore to the leaste nombers. And then diuide the nomber of the lesser denomination, by the nomber of the greateste denomination, and the quotient doeth aunswere to the question. Except the greater denominatiō, doe beare the signe of some rooted nōber. For then must you extract the roote of that quotiente, accordyng to that signe of denomination.

Scholar. It semeth that this rule is all one, with the rule of false position: and therefore mighte so bee called: seyng it taketh a false nōber, to worke with al.

Master. This rule doeth farre excell that other. And dooeth not take a false nomber, but a true nomber for his position, as it shall bee declared anon. Wherby it maie bee thoughte, to bee a rule of wonderfull inuention, that teacheth a manne at the firste worde, to name a true nomber, before he knoweth resolutely, what he hath named.

But bicause that name is common to many nombers (although not in one question) and therfore the name is obscure, till the worke doe detect it, I thinke this rule might well bee called, the rule of darke position, or of straunge position: but not of false position.

And for the more easie and apte worke in this arte wee dooe commonly name that darke position. 1. — . And with it doe we worke, as the question intendeth, till we come to the *equation*.

Alwaies willyng you to remember, that you reduce your nombers, to their leaste denominations, and smalleste formes, before you procede any farther.

And again, if your *equation* be soche, that the greateste denomination *Cosike*, be ioined to any parte of a compounde nomber, you shall tourne it so, that the nomber of the greateste signe alone, maie stande as equalle to the reste.

And this is all that neadeth to be taughte, concernyng this woorke.

Howbeit, for easie alteratiō of *equations*. I will propounde a fewe exāples, bicause the extraction of their rootes, maie the more aptly bee wroughte. And to auoide the tediouse repetition of these woordes: is equalle to: I will sette as I doe often in woorke use, a paire of paralleles, or Gemowe lines of one lengthe, thus: ═══, bicause noe.2. thynges, can be moare equalle. And now marke these nombers.

1. $14.\mathfrak{ze}. + .15.\vartheta = 71.\vartheta.$

2. $20.\mathfrak{ze}. - .18.\vartheta = .102.\vartheta.$

3. $26.\mathfrak{z} + 10\mathfrak{ze} = 9.\mathfrak{z} - 10\mathfrak{ze} + 213.\vartheta.$

4. $19.\mathfrak{ze} + 192.\vartheta = 10\mathfrak{z} + 108\vartheta - 19\mathfrak{ze}.$

5. $18.\mathfrak{ze} + 24.\vartheta. = 8.\mathfrak{z}. + 2.\mathfrak{ze}.$

6. $34\mathfrak{z} - 12\mathfrak{ze} = 40\mathfrak{ze} + 480\vartheta - 9.\mathfrak{z}.$

Scholar. Now I perceiue that in Addition, and Subtraction of *Surdes*, the last nombers that did result of that worke, were *vniuersalle rootes*.

Master. You saie truthe. But harke what meaneth that hastie knockyng at the doore?

Scholar. It is a messenger.

Master. What is the message? tel me in mine eare. Yea sir is that the mater? Then is there noe remedie, but that I must neglect all studies, and teaching, for to withstande those daungers. My fortune is not so good, to haue quiete tyme to teache.

Scholar. But my fortune and my fellowes, is moche worse, that your vnquietnes, so hindereth our knowledge. I praie God amende it.

Master. I am inforced to make an ende of this mater: But yet will I promise you, that whiche you shall chalenge of me, whē you see me at better laiser: That I will teache you the whole arte of *vniuersalle rootes*. And the extraction of rootes in all *Square Surdes*: with the demonstration of theim, and all the former workes.

If I mighte haue been quietly permitted, to reste but a litle while lōger, I had determined not to haue ceased, till I had ended all these thinges at large. But

now

now farewell. And applie your studie diligently in this that you haue learned. And if I maie gette any quietnesse reasonable, I will not forget to performe my promise with an augementation.

Scholar. My harte is so oppressed with pẽsiuenes, by this sodaine vnquietnesse, that I can not expresse my grief. But I will praie, with all theim that loue honeste knowledge, that God of his mercie, will sone ende your troubles, and graunte you soche reste, as your trauell doeth merite.
And al that loue learnyng: saie therto. Amen.

Master. Amen, and Amen.

¶ Imprinted at London, by Jhon Kyngston.

Anno domini. 1557.

THE RHIND MATHEMATICAL PAPYRUS

(c. 1650 B.C.)

The Rhind Mathematical Papyrus is the largest of the ancient Egyptian mathematical papyri extant and the earliest to be extensively studied. It was found at Thebes in a room of a ruined building near the Ramesseum. In 1858 it was purchased by the English archaeologist, A. Henry Rhind, after whom it is named. Through the agency of the British Museum which purchased the papyrus from the Rhind estate in 1864, it has been made available in facsimile form for detailed study by scholars of Egyptology and mathematics. Originally a single scroll about eighteen and a half feet long and approximately thirteen inches high, it was received at first in two parts, a middle portion having been lost. Fragments of the missing portion were found in 1922 in a wholly unexpected place, among the medical papyri of the Edwin Smith collection in New York. The plates published in Professor T. Eric Peet's work on the *Rhind Mathematical Papyrus* (1923) now show the New York fragments in place, and the papyrus in virtually complete form.

The scroll containing the ancient mathematical treatise is made of papyrus three layers thick. The color is a fine light brown and the hieratic script of the text is beautifully written in a strong, bold hand, the greatest part of it in black ink. The title, the first words of the sections and certain numbers are in red ink which still retains the brightness of its color.

The scribe, whose name, A'h-mose (or Aah-mes, or Ahmes) means "A'h (the moon-god)-is-born," stated that he had written this "book" in the thirty third year of the reign of the pharaoh 'A-user-Re, of the Hyksos dynasty (i.e., c. 1650 B.C.), and that it was a copy of an earlier work which had been written in the time of King Ne-ma'et-Re. The latter, known to us as King Amen-em-het III was the ruler of Egypt from 1849 to 1801 B.C. Hence, the mathematical problems and processes of the Rhind represent methods which were in use during the period of the Middle Kingdom. Many of the problem types in the Rhind Papyrus are also to be found in the Moscow Papyrus and other papyrus fragments dating from 1850 B.C.

A chief feature of the ancient Egyptian mathematics is a highly original procedure for operating with fractions. The use of the Egyptian method of representing fractions survived to a very late date. Their process of multiplication, restricted to doubling and selective addition, combined with a limitation in the representation of fractions to the use of unit fractions and 2/3, led to the need of a table of doubled unit fractions. This was given as a table of the division of 2 by odd numbers. The Egyptians used a decimal system of notation, they made frequent use of the *Regula falsi,* they verified their numerical answers, but had no procedure which was in the nature of a

general proof. The geometrical problems were mensurational. Researches involving related Mesopotamian cultures confirm the view that the level and extent of Egyptian mathematics as shown in the Rhind Papyrus is representative of the mathematics of its period. The influence of Egyptian arithmetical methods can be observed in the later Greek papyri of the Hellenistic period.

●

THE RHIND MATHEMATICAL PAPYRUS

From *The Rhind Mathematical Papyrus*

by Thomas Eric Peet

INTRODUCTORY

DESCRIPTION OF THE PAPYRUS.

The Rhind Papyrus as it now lies in the British Museum consists of two pieces separately mounted between sheets of plate glass and numbered 10057 and 10058 respectively. These two pieces once formed a single roll, and were probably separated in modern times by an unskilful unroller.

The two sheets in the British Museum, Fig. 1, may be described as follows:—

Papyrus 10058.

Present length 206 cm., height 33 cm.

Recto. The recto consists of five pages of papyrus, each about 395 mm. broad, except the first, and the last, which is incomplete. The gumming is admirably done. At the right-hand end there is a blank space of about 10 cm., after which the title begins in vertical columns. This is followed by a double vertical black line, and from this point leftwards the sheet is ruled in black into six horizontal registers or bands throughout. The whole of this

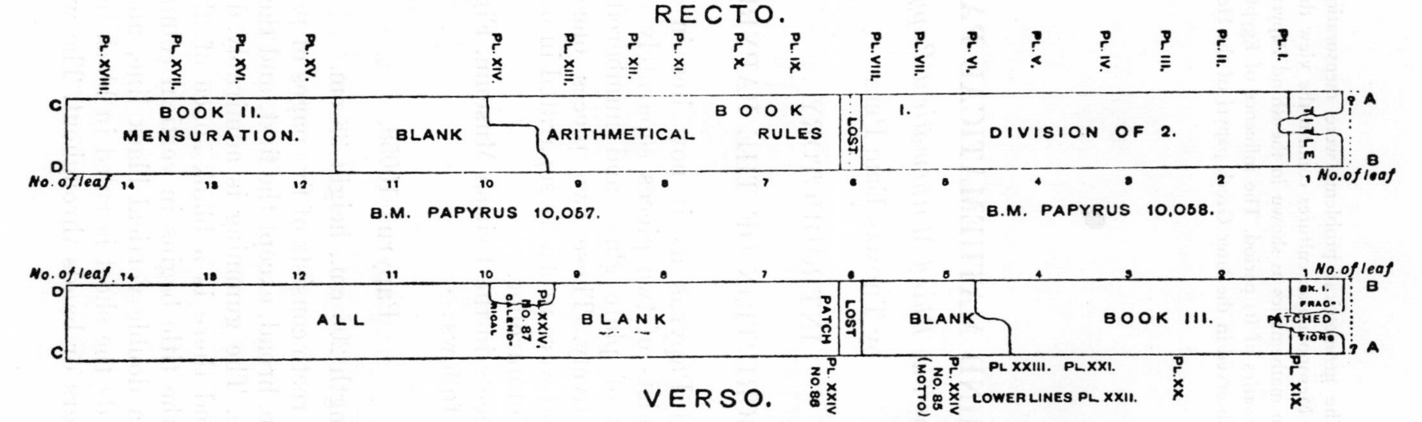

Fig. 1 (after GRIFFITH, *P.S.B.A.*, XVI, Pl. 1.) The plate numbers refer to the *B.M.Facs.*

recto is devoted, with the exception of the title already referred to, to the division of 2 by the odd numbers from 3 to 101.

Verso. This face is very heavily patched, not only at the blank left-hand end, but also on the right: this patching was clearly done in ancient times, and where signs had disappeared on a lost fragment they have been written in in very black ink on the patches by a later hand. At 18 cm. from the right-hand end is a double vertical ruling in black, as on the recto. Left of this the papyrus is ruled out into six horizontal registers. The writing begins at the same end as on the other face. On the right, outside the double line, is the carelessly written No. 61. It is followed by Nos. 62 to 84, and to the left of this last the papyrus is blank to its end (57 cm. away), except for the curious No. 85, written upside down near the bottom and about half-way along the blank space.

Papyrus 10057.

Present length 319 cm., height 33 cm. or just over, the edge being actually under the framing.

Recto. The pages are from 39 to 40 cm. broad, and the gumming is very accurate. The left-hand end is fragmentary. The whole face is ruled out in six horizontal registers. Problem No. 1 begins the recto and we run without a break up to No. 40; after which there is a blank of about 55 cm.: No. 41 begins a fresh page, and the problems continue up to No. 60, which ends the recto.

Verso. This face is quite blank except for the calendrical entry No. 87, which is written near the top about halfway along. At the right-hand end the papyrus has been patched with a piece of another papyrus bearing the fragment of accounts numbered No. 86.

The following is a synopsis of the contents:—

Table of resolution of fractions with numerator 2.

Book I. Arithmetic.

Nos. 1-6. Division of various numbers of loaves equally between 10 men.

Nos. 7-20. First group of completion-calculations (*sekem*) involving multiplication of fractions.

Nos. 21-23. Second group of completion-calculations, involving simple addition of fractions.

Nos. 24-34. Arithmetical solution by trial of equations of the first degree. (Eisenlohr's *hau*-calculations.)

Nos. 35-38. Similar equations involving the bushel or *hekat*.

Nos. 39 and 40. Division of loaves between men in unequal proportions.

Book. II. Mensuration.

Part I. Volumes and cubic content in corn.

Nos. 41-43. Cylindrical containers.

Nos. 44-46. Rectangular parallelopipedal containers.

No. 47. Expression in correct form of 1/10, 1/20, up to 1/100 of a *hekat*, disguised as a sum in cubic content.

Part II. Areas.

No. 48. Area of square and circle compared.

No. 49. Rectangle.

No. 50. Circle.

No. 51. Triangle.

No. 52. Truncated triangle.

No. 53. Trapezoid (?).

Nos. 54 and 55. Division of given area of land into equal-sized fields.

Part III. Batter, or angle of slope.

Nos. 56-59. Batter of pyramid.

No. 60. Slope of a cone (?).

Book III. Miscellaneous problems in arithmetic.

No. 61. Multiplication of fractions (probably out of place, see above).

No. 62. Proportionate values of precious metals.

No. 63. Division of loaves in unequal proportions.

No. 64. Division of barley into shares in arithmetical progression.

No. 65. Division of loaves in unequal proportions.

No. 66. Daily portion of a yearly ration of fat.

No. 67. Reckoning of livestock.

No. 68. Division of 100 *hekat* of corn in unequal proportions.

Nos. 69-78. So-called *pefsu*-reckonings. Conversion of grain into bread and beer, and the barter of these last.

No. 79. Geometrical progression.

No. 80-1. Conversion of fractions of the *hekat* (1/2, 1/4, 1/8, etc.) into *henu*.

No. 82-3. Food estimate for a poultry yard.

No. 84. Estimate of food of an ox-stall.

Additions.

No. 85. Unintelligible group of signs.

No. 86. Fragment of accounts.

No. 87. Calendrical entries.

From *The Rhind Mathematical Papyrus*

Vol. I by Arnold B. Chace

with the assistance of Henry P. Manning,

Vol. II by Arnold B. Chace,

Ludlow Bull and Henry P. Manning.

FREE TRANSLATION AND COMMENTARY.[1]

Title, Date, and Scribe

Accurate reckoning. The entrance into the knowledge of all existing things and all obscure secrets. This book was copied in the year 33, in the fourth month of the inundation season, under the majesty of the king of Upper and Lower Egypt, 'A-user-Re', endowed with life, in likeness to writings of old made in the time of the king of Upper and Lower Egypt, Ne-mat'et-Re'. It is the scribe A'h-mose who copies this writing.

[1] In the following pages I have endeavored to give in clear smooth English a free translation of the Rhind papyrus with some notes explaining details. In some places I have put in words or clauses that are omitted from the original, but found in other problems of the same group, or are required to express what I believe is the true meaning of the Egyptian. In some places where parts of a solution are misplaced I have arranged them in their proper order (see, for example, Problems 32 and 69). More particularly, I have corrected numerical mistakes and careless slips in the way of writing numbers. The reader will find the exact words of the original in the Literal Translation, and all corrections that have been made in the Free Translation may be found by a comparison of the two.

Notes giving explanations or interpretations of the text, except such as have been included in the Introduction, are placed in the following pages with the problems to which they refer. Notes relating to the Egyptian language or writing are placed with the Literal Translation.

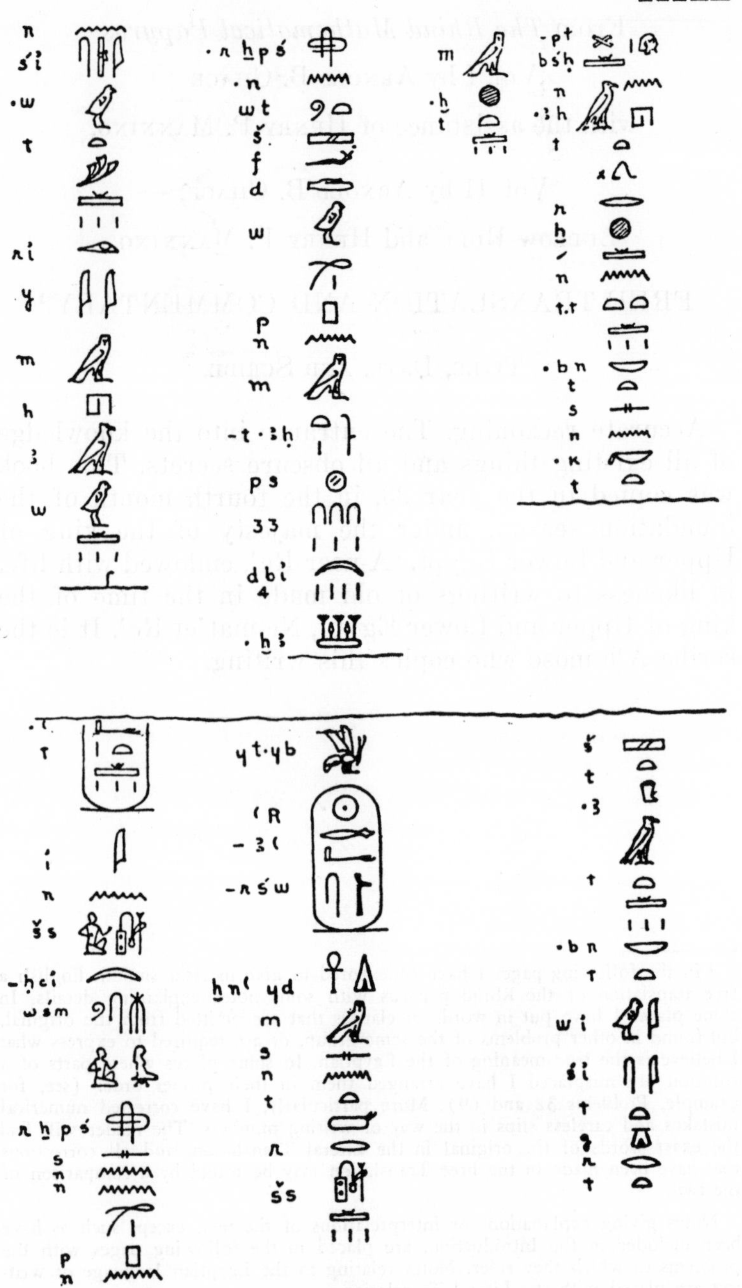

Photograph 1, *Columns* 1-3 *B. M. Facsimile, Plate* 1

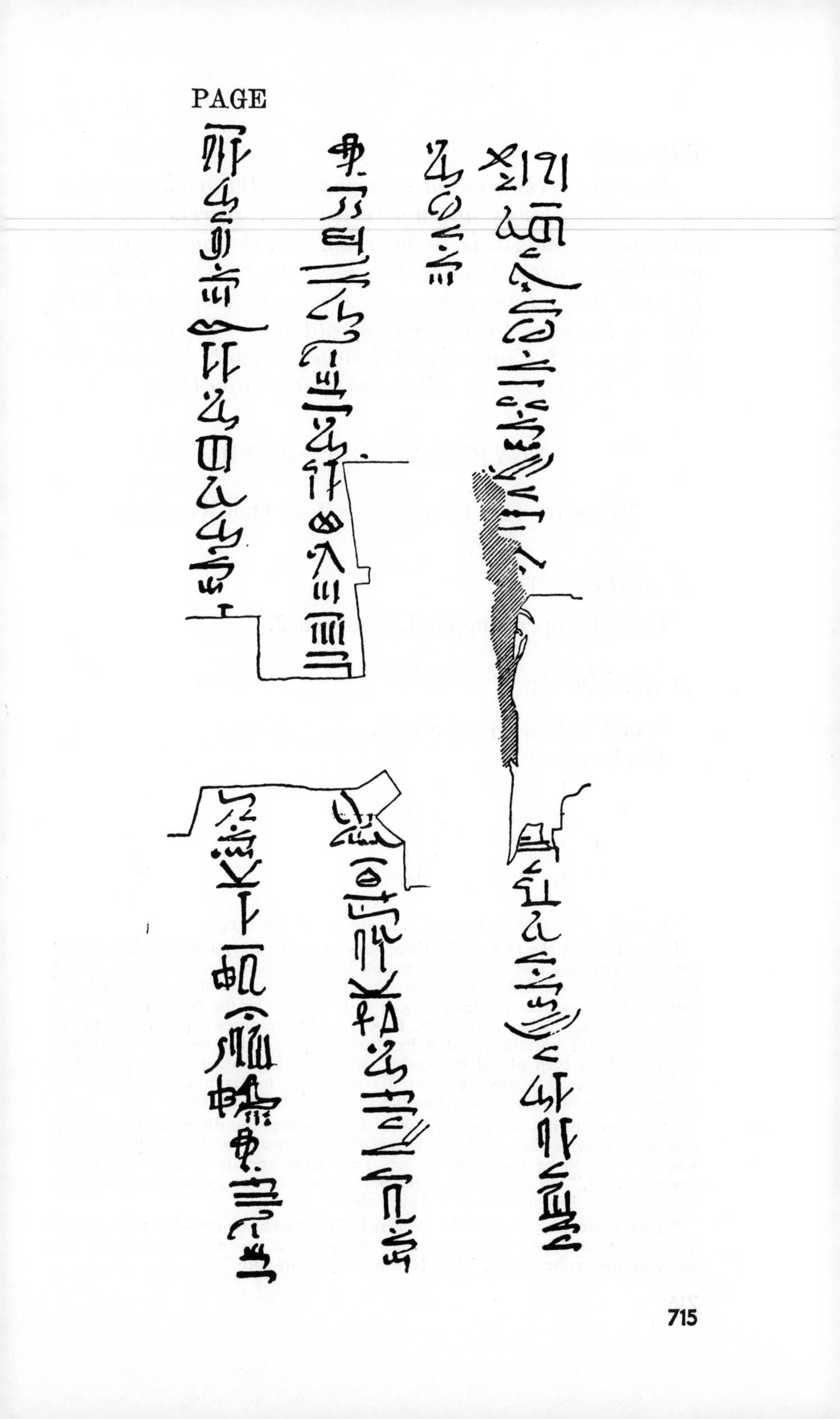

PAGE

Title-page

Accurate reckoning[1] *of entering into things, knowledge of existing things all, mysteries . . . secrets all. Now was copied book this in year 33, month four of the inundation*[4]*-season [under the majesty of the] King of [Upper and] Lower Egypt, 'A-user-Re*[5]*, endowed with life, in likeness to writings of old made in the time of the King of Upper [and Lower] Egypt, [Ne-ma]'et-[Re'].*[6] *Lo the scribe A'h-mose writes copy thus.*

EGYPTIAN ARITHMETIC

Table of the Division of 2 by Odd Numbers

2 divided by 3

Get 2 by operating on 3. $\bar{\bar{3}}$ of 3 is 2.

2 divided by 5

$\bar{3}$ of 5 is 1 $\bar{\bar{3}}$, $\overline{15}$ of 5 is $\bar{3}$.

Working out:

1	5
$\bar{\bar{3}}$	3 $\bar{3}$
1\ $\bar{3}$	1 $\bar{\bar{3}}$
\ $\overline{15}$	$\bar{3}$.

---

[1] Literally: "head of reckoning," *i.e.* approved reckoning.

[4] The *Akhet* is the first of the three seasons of the Egyptian year. It has been generally assumed that it was the season of inundation, partly because of the meaning of a word with a similar stem and partly because of the general belief that the Egyptian year originally began with the rise of the Nile. This view is set forth above, volume 1, page 44. However, the meanings of the names of the seasons are still uncertain, and it has been suggested that the New Year may originally have been placed in October, when the inundation begins to subside and the first quickly-growing crops are beginning to germinate, and that the *Shomu,* rather than the *Akhet,* was the season of the inundation.

[5] In proper names compounded with divine names the divine name (in this case written with the sun-disk) is usually, as a mark of honor, placed first, whether it is to be read first or not. This name appears to mean "Great-of-strength-is-Re'," but the syntax of the phrases and sentences often used as names by the ancient Egyptians, is not always clear.

[6] This name may perhaps be rendered, "He-who-belongs-to-the-truth-of-Re'." This is the so-called "praenomen" or "throne-name" of Amen-em-het III. The name of the scribe means, "A'h (the moon-god)-is-born."

2 divided by 7

1/4 of 7 is 1 1/2 1/4, 1/28 of 7 is 1/4.

1	7			
1/2	3 1/2		1	7
\1/4	1 1/2 1/4		2	14
^{2}\4	28	1/4	4	28.

2 divided by 9

1/6 of 9 is 1 1/2, 1/18 of 9 is 1/2.

1	9	
2/3	6	
1/3	3	
\1/6	1 1/2	
\2	18	1/2.

2 divided by 11

1/6 of 11 is 1 2/3 1/6, 1/66 of 11 is 1/6.

1	11				
2/3	7 1/3		1	11	
1/3	3 2/3		\2	22	
\1/6	1 2/3 1/6		\4	44	
		Total	6	66	1/6.

2 divided by 13

1/8 of 13 is 1 1/2 1/8, 1/52 of 13 is 1/4, 1/104 of 13 is 1/8.

1	13	
1/2	6 1/2	
1/4	3 1/4	
\1/8	1 1/2 1/8	
\4	52	1/4
\8	104	1/8.

2 divided by 15

1/10 of 15 is 1 1/2, 1/30 of 15 is 1/2.

1	15
\ 1/10	1 1/2
\ 1/30	1/2.

2 divided by 17

Get 2 by operating on 17. 1/12 of 17 is 1 1/3 1/12, 1/51 of 17 is 1/3, 1/68
17 is 1/4.

Working out:

1	17			
2/3	11 1/3			
1/3	5 2/3		\ 1	17
1/6	2 1/2 1/3		\ 2	34
\ 1/12	1 1/4 1/6	Total	3	51
Remainder	1/3 1/4		4	68

In the fourth line of the multiplication the author might have said 2 2/3 1/6, and t
the last line would have been 1 1/3 1/12, and he uses this form, in giving his answer ab
for the part that 1/12 of 17 makes towards 2. Somewhat similarly in the case of 23
changes 1 1/2 1/4 1/6 to 1 2/3 1/4.

2 divided by 97

1/56 of 97 is 1 1/2 1/8 1/14 1/28, 1/679 of 97 is 1/7, 1/776 of 97 is 1/8.

	1	97	
Find	\ 1/56	1 1/2 1/8 1/14 1/28	
	\ 7	679	1/7
	\ 8	776	1/8.

2 divided by 99

1/66 of 99 is 1 1/2, 1/198 of 99 is 1/2.

	1	99	
Find	\ 2/3	66	1 1/2
	\ 2	198	1/2.

2 divided by 101

Get 2 by operating on 101. $\frac{1}{101}$ of 101 is 1, $\frac{1}{202}$ of 101 is $\frac{1}{2}$, $\frac{1}{303}$ of 101 is $\frac{1}{3}$, $\frac{1}{606}$ of 101 is $\frac{1}{6}$.

Working out:

\1	101	1
\2	202	$\frac{1}{2}$
\3	303	$\frac{1}{3}$
\6	606	$\frac{1}{6}$.

TABLE OF THE DIVISION OF THE NUMBERS 1-9 BY 10

Table						
	1	divided	by	10	gives	$\frac{1}{10}$
	2	"	"	"	"	$\frac{1}{5}$
	3	"	"	"	"	$\frac{1}{5}$ $\frac{1}{10}$
	4	"	"	"	"	$\frac{1}{3}$ $\frac{1}{15}$
	5	"	"	"	"	$\frac{1}{2}$
	6	"	"	"	"	$\frac{1}{2}$ $\frac{1}{10}$
	7	"	"	"	"	$\frac{2}{3}$ $\frac{1}{30}$
	8	"	"	"	"	$\frac{2}{3}$ $\frac{1}{10}$ $\frac{1}{30}$
	9	"	"	"	"	$\frac{2}{3}$ $\frac{1}{5}$ $\frac{1}{30}$.

Problem 1

Example of dividing 1 *loaf among* 10 *men.*

Each man receives $\frac{1}{10}$.

Proof. Multiply $\frac{1}{10}$ by 10.

Do it thus:	1	$\frac{1}{10}$
	\2	$\frac{1}{5}$
	4	$\frac{1}{3}$ $\frac{1}{15}$
	\8	$\frac{2}{3}$ $\frac{1}{10}$ $\frac{1}{30}$

Total 1 loaf, which is correct.

Problem 2

Divide 2 *loaves among* 10 *men.*

Each man receives $\frac{1}{5}$.

Proof. Multiply $\frac{1}{5}$ by 10.

Do it thus:		
	1	$\frac{1}{5}$
	\2	$\frac{1}{3}$ $\frac{1}{15}$
	4	$\frac{2}{3}$ $\frac{1}{10}$ $\frac{1}{30}$
	\8	1 $\frac{1}{3}$ $\frac{1}{5}$ $\frac{1}{15}$

Total 2 loaves, which is correct.

Problem 3

Divide 6 *loaves among* 10 *men.*

Each man receives $\frac{1}{2}$ $\frac{1}{10}$.

Proof. Multiply $\frac{1}{2}$ $\frac{1}{10}$ by 10.

Do it thus:		
	1	$\frac{1}{2}$ $\frac{1}{10}$
	\2	1 $\frac{1}{5}$
	4	2 $\frac{1}{3}$ $\frac{1}{15}$
	\8	4 $\frac{2}{3}$ $\frac{1}{10}$ $\frac{1}{30}$

Total 6 loaves, which is correct.

Problem 4

Divide 7 *loaves among* 10 *men.*

Each man receives $\frac{2}{3}$ $\frac{1}{30}$.

Proof. Multiply $\frac{2}{3}$ $\frac{1}{30}$ by 10; the result is 7.

Do it thus:		
	1	$\frac{2}{3}$ $\frac{1}{30}$
	\2	1 $\frac{1}{3}$ $\frac{1}{15}$
	4	2 $\frac{2}{3}$ $\frac{1}{10}$ $\frac{1}{30}$
	\8	5 $\frac{1}{2}$ $\frac{1}{10}$

Total 7 loaves, which is correct.

Problem 22

Complete $\frac{2}{3}$ $\frac{1}{30}$ *to* 1.

Applied to 30, $\frac{2}{3}$ $\frac{1}{30}$ is 21. 30 exceeds 21 by 9. Multiply 30 so as to get 9.

1	30
\ $\frac{1}{10}$	3
\ $\frac{1}{5}$	6
Total	9.

Therefore $\frac{1}{5}$ $\frac{1}{10}$ is to be added to make the completion.

For proof add them all together, namely,

$\frac{2}{3}$ $\frac{1}{5}$ $\frac{1}{10}$ $\frac{1}{30}$, making 1;

for, applied to 30, these fractions are equal to

20 6 3 1, making 30.

Problem 24

A quantity and its $\frac{1}{7}$ *added together become* 19. *What is the quantity?*

Assume 7.

\1	7
\ $\frac{1}{7}$	1
Total	8.

As many times as 8 must be multiplied to give 19, so many times 7 must be multiplied to give the required number.

1	8
\2	16
$\frac{1}{2}$	4
\ $\frac{1}{4}$	2
\ $\frac{1}{8}$	1

Total 2 $\frac{1}{4}$ $\frac{1}{8}$.

\1	2 $\frac{1}{4}$ $\frac{1}{8}$
\2	4 $\frac{1}{2}$ $\frac{1}{4}$
\4	9 $\frac{1}{2}$

Do it thus: The quantity is 16 $\frac{1}{2}$ $\frac{1}{8}$,

$\frac{1}{7}$ 2 $\frac{1}{4}$ $\frac{1}{8}$,

Total 19.

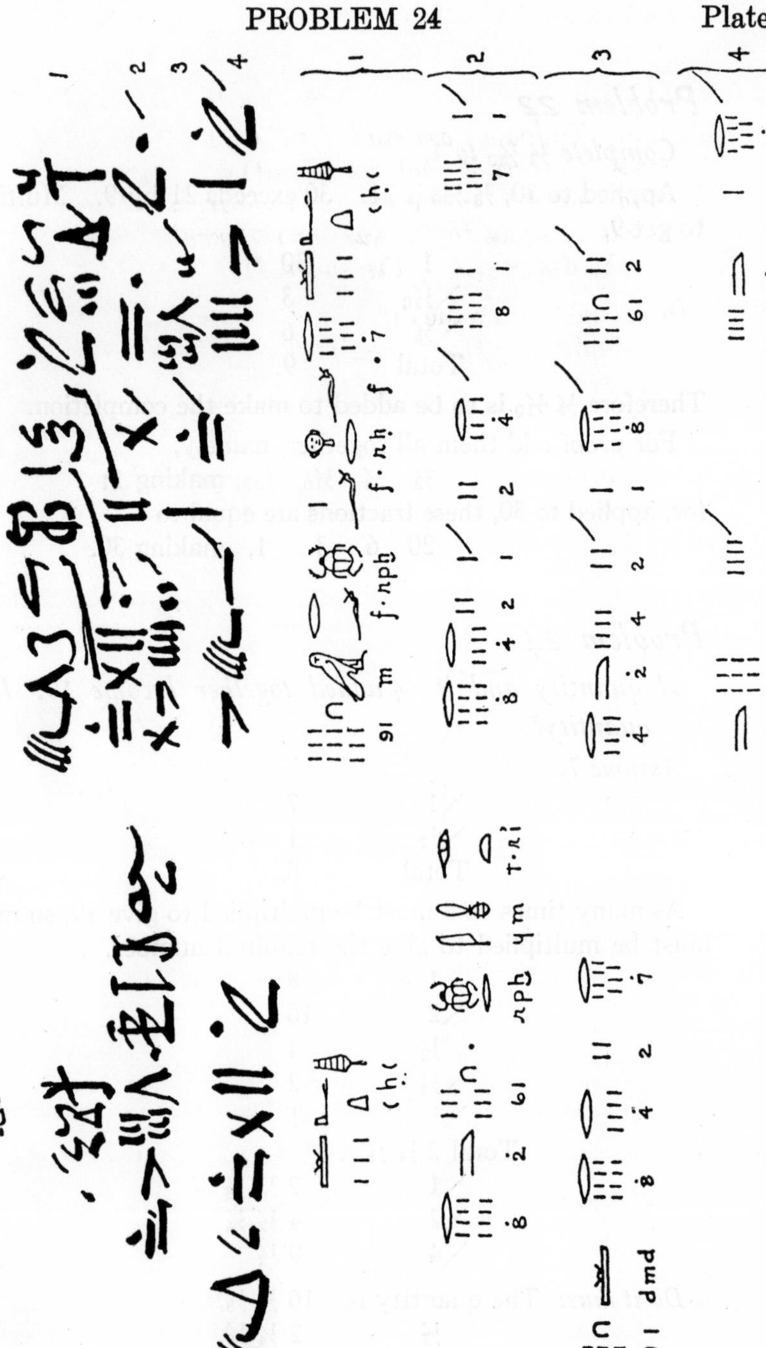

Photograph XII, *Register* 1

B.M. Facsimile, Plate I

Problem 40

Divide 100 *loaves among* 5 *men in such a way that the shares received shall be in arithmetical progression and that* 1/7 *of the sum of the largest three shares shall be equal to the sum of the smallest two. What is the difference of the shares?*

Do it thus: Make the difference of the shares 5½. Then the amounts that the 5 men receive will be

23   17½   12   6½   1,   total 60.

As many times as is necessary to multiply 60 to make 100, so many times must these terms be multiplied to make the true series.

\1	60
\⅔	40.

The total, 1 ⅔, times 60 makes 100.

Multiply by 1 ⅔

	23	it becomes	38 ⅓
	17 ½	" "	29 ⅙
	12	" "	20
	6 ½	" "	10 ⅔ ⅙
	1	" "	1 ⅔
Total	60	" "	100.

-b- -a-

1 2 3 4

w·y rh ḥ 3 n 7 5 s n 001 w·3t

32 w·y rh 2 s n

2 71 w n w t 4 tp

21

2 6 2 5 w n w t rph y m t·ri

06 dmd 1

3 83 m f·rh·rph 32 ps r 06 1

6 92 2 71 04 3

02 21 -ḥ3w k·[n]ḥ·ri

6 3 01 2 6 3 1 m pt

0.01 dmd 3 1 06 dmd 1

Photographs XVI-XVII, *Register* 2 *B. M. Facsimile, Plates* XI-XII

Problem 56

If a pyramid is 250 *cubits high and the side of its base* 360 *cubits long, what is its* seked?

Take 1/2 of 360; it makes 180. Multiply 250 so as to get 180; it makes 1/2 1/5 1/50 of a cubit. A cubit is 7 palms. Multiply 7 by 1/2 1/5 1/50.

1	7
1/2	3-1/2
1/5	1-1/3 1/15
1/50	1/10 1/25

The *seked* is 5-1/25 palms.

Problem 57

If the seked *of a pyramid is* 5 *palms* 1 *finger per cubit and the side of its base* 140 *cubits, what is its altitude?*

Divide 1 cubit by the *seked* doubled, which is 10-1/2. Multiply 10-1/2 so as to get 7, for this is a cubit: 7 is 2/3 of 10-1/2. Operate on 140, which is the side of the base: 2/3 of 140 is 93-1/3. This is the altitude.

In this inverse problem . . . the author doubles the *seked* instead of taking 1/2 of the side of the base, and instead of dividing the *seked* doubled by 7 and dividing the side of the base by the result, he divides 7 by the *seked* doubled and multiplies the side of the base by the result, which amounts to the same thing.

Problem 58

If a pyramid is 93-1/3 *cubits high and the side of its base* 140 *cubits long, what is its* seked?

Take 1/2 of 140, which is 70. Multiply 93-1/3 so as to get 70. 1/2 is 46-2/3, 1/4 is 23-1/3. Make thou 1/2 1/4 of a cubit. Multiply 7 by 1/2 1/4. 1/2 of 7 is 3-1/2, 1/4 is 1-1/2 1/4, together 5 palms 1 finger. This is its *seked*.

The working out:

1	93-1/3
\1/2	46-2/3
\1/4	23-1/3

Total 1/2 1/4.

Photographs XXI-XXII, *Register* 1 *B. M. Facsimile, Plate* XV

Make thou 1/2 1/4 of a cubit; a cubit is 7 palms.

1	7
1/2	3 1/2
1/4	1 1/2 1/4
Total	5 palms 1 finger

This is its *seked.*

Problem 61

Table for multiplication of fractions.

2/3 of 2/3 is 1/3 1/9
1/3 " 2/3 " 1/6 1/18
2/3 " 1/3 " 1/6 1/18
2/3 " 1/6 " 1/12 1/36
2/3 " 1/2 " 1/3
1/3 " 1/2 " 1/6
1/6 " 1/2 " 1/12
1/12 " 1/2 " 1/24

1/9 of 2/3 is 1/18 1/54; 1/9, 2/3 of it is 1/18 1/54

. . . .

1/5, 1/4 of it is 1/20
1/7, 2/3 " " " 1/14 1/42
1/7, 1/2 " " " 1/14
1/11, 2/3 " " " 1/22 1/66, 1/3 of it is 1/33
1/11, 1/2 " " " 1/22, 1/4 " " " 1/44.

Peet points out . . . that the above table contains two forms of statement which have an interesting significance. In the first four lines we find forms of the type, 2/3 of 2/3 is 1/3 1/9, while in the last five are such forms as, 1/5, 1/4 of it is 1/20. In the ninth line both forms are given, the statement being made twice, while the four lines that immediately precede seem to have been originally in the second form but to have been changed to the first; see Literal Translation. The reason for the second form is that of the fractions in this table the only ones that were legitimate multipliers are 2/3 and 1/2 and fractions obtained from them by halving. Thus the Egyptian could not directly say, "1/5 of 1/4" but only "1/5, 1/4 of it." He could have used the second form in all of these cases, but when he has a legitimate multiplier he prefers the first form, and so the author, perceiving after they were written that lines 5-8, like the first four, involve only these multipliers, changed them to the first form.

Problem 61*B*

Rule for getting 2/3 *of the reciprocal of an odd number.*

To get 2/3 of 1/5 take the reciprocals of 2 times 5 and 6 times 5, and in the same way get 2/3 of the reciprocal of any odd number.

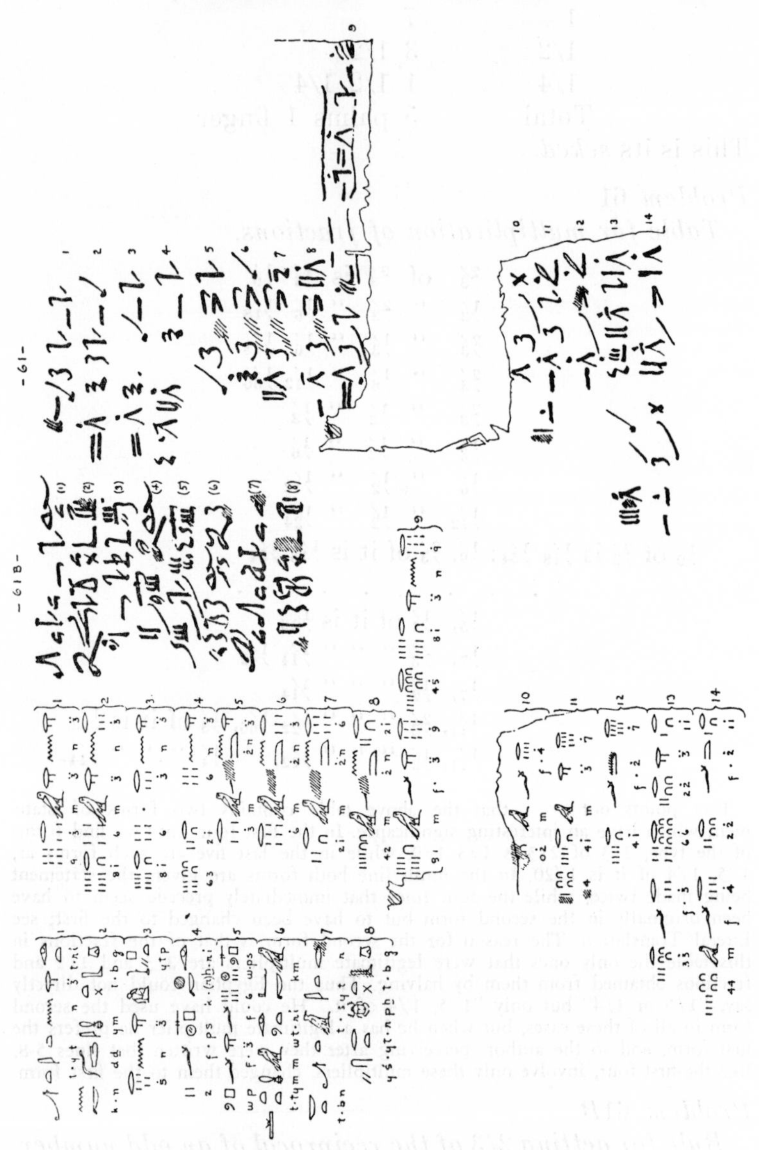

Photograph XXIII, *Right Half*
B. M. Facsimile, Plate XVI

Problem 62

Example of reckoning the contents of a bag of various precious metals. Suppose it is said to thee, A bag containing equal weights of gold, silver and lead, has been bought for 84 sha'ty. *What is the amount in it of each precious metal, that which is given for a* deben *of gold being* 12 sha'ty, *for a* deben *of silver* 6 sha'ty, *and for a* deben *of lead* 3 sha'ty?

Add that which is given for a *deben* of each precious metal. The result is 21 *sha'ty*. Multiply 21 so as to get 84, the 84 *sha'ty* for which this bag was bought. The result is 4, which is the number of *deben* of each precious metal.

Do it thus:

Multiply 12 by 4 getting 48 *sha'ty* for the gold in the bag,

Multiply 6 by 4 getting 24 *sha'ty* for the silver,

Multiply 3 by 4 getting 12 *sha'ty* for the lead,

Multiply 21 by 4 getting 84 *sha'ty* altogether.

The *sha'ty* was a seal, and the word here represents a unit of value (see Weill, 1925). The *deben* was a unit of weight, equal to about 91 grammes. The papyrus does not say that the bag contains equal weights of gold, silver, and lead, but in the solution the author proceeds as if this condition was understood.

Problem 79

Sum the geometrical progression of five terms, of which the first term is 7 *and the multiplier* 7.

The sum according to the rule. Multiply 2801 by 7.

1	2801
2	5602
4	11204
Total	19607.

The sum by addition.

houses	7
cats	49
mice	343
spelt	2401
hekat	16807
Total	19607.

In the second column the author places before the successive powers of 7 the words, houses, cats, mice, spelt and *hekat.* Eisenlohr regards these words as names given to the powers of 7. Another interpretation is that the problem intended is like this: In each of 7 houses are 7 cats, each cat kills 7 mice, each mouse would have eaten 7 ears of spelt, and each ear of spelt will produce 7 *hekat* of grain; how much grain is thereby saved? But the author adds all of these quantities together, showing that he is more interested in the numerical problem of the sum of these numbers.

This interpretation, coupled with the number 7, reminds us of the children's rhyme, of which one version is the following:

"As I was going to Saint Ives,
I met a man with seven wives.
Every wife had seven sacks,
Every sack had seven cats,
Every cat had seven kits;
Kits, cats, sacks and wives,
How many were there going to Saint Ives?"[1]

Here, again, it is suggested that the sum total of a geometrical progression be calculated but there is a "joker" in the actual wording of the first and last lines.

Rodet (1882, page 111) found in the *Liber Abaci* of Leonardo of Pisa (see Bibliography, 1857) a problem of a geometrical progression expressed in much the same way, and having the ratio 7, and he suggests that Problem 79, absurd as is its heterogeneous addition, has perpetuated itself through all the centuries from the times of the ancient Egyptians.

[1] *Every Child's Mother Goose,* with Introduction by Carolyn Wells, New York, 1918, page 111.

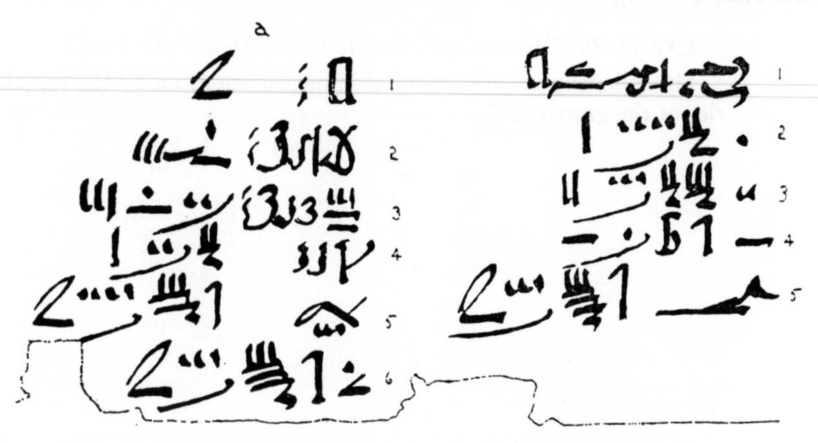

Line	Number	Word	Number	Word
1	7	ω·ηp		ηp - t·ymî t·ʿω
2	94	ω·ωym	108,2	1
3	343	ω·ωnp	206,5	2
4	103,2	t·db	402,11	4
5	708,61	t·3kḥ	706,91	dmd
6	706,91	dmd		

Photographs XXV-XXVI, *Register* 6 *B. M. Facsimile, Plate* XVIII

Problem 80

Express the "Horus eye" fractions in terms of the hînu.

The following vessels are used[1] in measuring grain by the functionaries of the granary:

1	*hekat*	makes	10	*hînu*
½	"	"	5	"
¼	"	"	2 ½	"
⅛	"	"	1 ¼	"
1/16	"	"	½ ⅛	"
1/32	"	"	¼ 1/16	"
1/64	"	"	⅛ 1/32	"

Problem 81

Another reckoning. Express fractions of a hekat *as "Horus eye" fractions and in terms of the* hînu.

Now

½	*hekat*	makes	5	*hînu*
¼	"	"	2 ½	"
⅛	"	"	1 ¼	"
1/16	"	"	½ ⅛	"
1/32	"	"	¼ 1/16	"
1/64	"	"	⅛ 1/32	"

a Now

½ ¼ ⅛	*hekat*		makes	8 ½ ¼	*hînu*		
½ ¼	"		"	7 ½	"		
½ ⅛ 1/32	"	3 ⅓ *ro*	"	6 ⅔	"	it is ⅔	of a *hekat*
½ ⅛	"		"	6 ¼	"	" " ½ ⅛	" " "
¼ ⅛	"		"	3 ½ ¼	"	" " ¼ ⅛	" " "
¼ 1/16 1/64	"	1 ⅔ "	"	3 ⅓	"	" " ⅓	" " "
¼	"		"	2 ½	"	" " ¼	" " "
⅛ 1/16	"	4 "	"	2	"	" " ⅕	" " "
⅛ 1/32	"	3 ⅓ "	"	1 ⅔	"	" " ⅙	" " "

b Now

⅛ 1/16	"	4 "	"	2	"	" " ⅕	" " "
1/16 1/32	"	2 "	"	1	"	" " 1/10	" " "
1/32 1/64	"	1 "	"	½	"	" " 1/20	" " "
1/64	"	3 "	"	¼	"	" " 1/40	" " "
1/16	"	1 ⅓ "	"	⅔	"	" " 1/15	" " "

[1] This interpretation is suggested by Gunn.

SIMON STEVIN

(1548—1620)

The extremely versatile mathematician, scientist and engineer, Simon Stevin, who more than any other single individual, was responsible for the widespread adoption of the decimal system, was born in Bruges, Flanders, in 1548. A leading figure in the Dutch school of mathematics and science, and an outstanding representative of the great scholars of the closing years of the Late Renaissance, he combined a genius for theoretical investigation with extraordinary practical skill and inventiveness. He gave himself not only to writing theoretical treatises but also to the construction of mills, the improvement of sluices and locks, and to the organization of commercial enterprises whose business was based on his inventions. Numerous patents were issued to him. The invention which brought him his greatest fame during his lifetime was a "sailing chariot" capable of carrying twenty five people. Set on wheels, it had a steering mechanism and was equipped with sails under which it was propelled like a sailing vessel at sea. An account of a trip made by Stevin's sailing chariot made him a popular figure all over Europe.

Stevin served as the mathematical and scientific tutor of the Stadtholder, Prince Maurice of Orange. During the long and close relationship between Prince Maurice and Stevin, the prince exhibited the utmost confidence in his tutor, and Stevin's influence grew with the rising tide of the prince's fortunes. Stevin wrote text books on all the mathematical and scientific subjects in which the prince was interested. Here, too, his inventiveness was evident, for each of his texts contained some innovation or improvement introduced by him. In a period of intermittent warfare, and of expanding economy, Stevin was sensitive to the growing need for technical instruction on the part of increasing numbers of merchants, surveyors, navigators and the like, to whom Latin was not available. Convinced that the Dutch language was excellently suited to scientific purposes, and that moreover the use of the Dutch language in science would contribute to the greatness of the nation, he wrote many of his works in Dutch, enriching the language with words of his own invention. In 1600, at the request of Prince Maurice, he directed the organization of a school of engineering at the University of Leyden, where Dutch, rather than Latin, was the language of instruction. Drawing upon his knowledge of commercial mathematics, Stevin urged that a separation be effected between governmental accounts and Prince Maurice's personal accounts, and on his advice, a system of double entry bookkeeping was instituted.

Stevin held rather modest official posts throughout his life. In 1592 he was in charge of the waterways of the Delft. He served in the States Army for some years under the title of "engineer". In 1603, Maurice recommended him for the post of Quartermaster of the States Army, and under this appointment he was in charge of laying out military camps and of their internal organization. This was the post which he held to the end of his life.

During the years 1582—1586 Stevin prepared a number of works for publication. These included his *Tables of Interest,* his *Problemata Geometria,* his *L'Arithmetique,* his *De Thiende,* his *Pratique d'Arithmetique* and four books on mechanics slanted towards mathematics. Of all these publications, *De Thiende* was by far the work of greatest importance. It contained a complete decimal system consistently applied to integers and fractions. In it Stevin demonstrated the simplicity, feasibility and advantage of the system, addressing himself to astronomers, surveyors, bankers, merchants, to any and all who dealt with measure. At the close of the treatise he added a plea for the application of the decimal system to all weights and measures and to coinage. *De Thiende,* written originally in Dutch, was published in 1585. In that same year, it was also published in French. An English translation by Robert Norton was printed in 1608 and soon thereafter numerous reprints and versions appeared, with the accompanying wide dissemination and implementation of Stevin's ideas.

•

DE THIENDE

From *The Principal Works of Simon Stevin*

Vol. II, edited by DIRK J. STRUIK

THE ART OF TENTHS
or
Decimal Arithmetic,
Teaching how to perform all computations
whatsoever by whole numbers without
fractions, by the four principles of
common arithmetic, namely: addition,
subtraction, multiplication, and
division.
Invented by the excellent mathematician,
SIMON STEVIN.
Published in English with some additions
by
Robert Norton, Gentleman.
Imprinted at London by S.S. for Hugh
Astley, and are to be sold at his
shop at St. Magnus' Corner. 1608.[1]

---

[1] This English translation of *De Thiende* was prepared by Richard Norton and published in 1608. The booklet contains a literal translation, almost certainly from the French version, with some additions: a) a short preface "to the courteous reader", b) a table for the conversion of sexagesimal fractions into decimal ones, and c) a short exposition on integers, how to write them, to perform the main species and to work with the rule of three. This exposition is taken from Stevin's *L'Arithmetique.* In using Norton's translation we have modernized the spelling and corrected some misprints.

The translator, Richard Norton, was the son of the British lawyer and poet Thomas Norton (1532—1584) and a nephew of Archbishop Cranmer. The father is remembered as the co-author of what is said to be the first English tragedy in blank verse, *Gorboduc* (acted in 1561) and as a translator of psalms and of Calvin's *Institutes.* The son, according to the *Dictionary of National Biography 41* (1895), was an engineer and gunner in the Royal service, became engineer of the Tower of London in 1627 and died in 1635. He wrote several texts on mathematics and artillery, supplied tables of interest to the 1628 edition of Robert Recorde's *Grounde of Arts* and seems to have been the author of the verses signed Ro: Norton, printed at the beginning of Captain John Smith's *Generall historie of Virginia, New England and the Summer Isles,* London, 1624.

On Norton see also E. J. R. Taylor, *The Mathematical Practitioners of Tudor and Stuart England.* Cambridge, Un. Press 1954, XI + 442 pp.

Norton calls Stevin's method both *Dime* and *The Art of Tenths* in the title, but in the text only uses the term *Dime.*

We reproduce this translation of *De Thiende* through the courtesy of the Houghton Library of Harvard University, Cambridge, Mass.

THE PREFACE OF SIMON STEVIN.

To Astronomers, Land-meters, Measurers of Tapestry, Gaugers, Stereometers in general, Money-Masters, and to all Merchants, SIMON STEVIN wishes health.

Many, seeing the smallness of this book and considering your worthiness, to whom it is dedicated, may perchance esteem this our conceit absurd. But if the proportion *be considered, the small quantity hereof compared to human imbecility, and the great utility unto high and ingenious intendments, it will be found to have made comparison of the extreme* terms, *which permit not any conversion of proportion. But what of that? Is this an admirable invention? No certainly: for it is so mean as that it scant deserves the name of an invention, for as the countryman by chance sometime finds a great treasure, without any use of skill or cunning, so hath it happened herein. Therefore, if any will think that I vaunt myself of my knowledge, because of the explicitation of these utilities, out of doubt he shows himself to have neither judgment, understanding, nor knowledge, to discern simple things from ingenious inventions, but he (rather) seems envious of the common benefit; yet howsoever, it were not fit to omit the benefit hereof for the inconvenience of such calumny. But as the mariner, having by hap found a certain unknown island, spares not to declare to his Prince the riches and profits thereof, as the fair fruits, precious minerals, pleasant champion*[2]*, etc., and that without imputation of self-glorification, even so shall we speak freely of the great use of this invention; I call it great, being greater than any of you expect to come from me. Seeing then that the* matter *of this Dime (the cause of the name whereof shall be declared by the first* definition *following) is number, the use and effects of which yourselves shall sufficiently witness by your continual experiences, therefore it were*

[2] Champion, comp. French "champagne", field, landscape. Comp. e.g. Deut. XI, 30, author. transl. of 1611: "the Canaanites which dwell in the campions".

not necessary to use many words thereof, for the astrologer *knows that the world is become by* computation astronomical (*seeing it teaches the pilot the elevation of the* equator *and of the* pole, *by means of the declination of the sun, to describe the true longitudes, latitudes, situations and distance of places, etc.*) *a paradise, abounding in some places with such things as the earth cannot bring forth in other. But as* the sweet is never without the sour, *so the travail in such computations cannot be unto him hidden, namely in the busy multiplications and divisions which proceed of the* 60*th* progression *of* degrees, minutes, seconds, thirds, etc. *And the surveyor or land-meter knows what great benefit the world receives from his science, by which many dissensions and difficulties are avoided which otherwise would arise by reason of the unknown capacity of land; besides, he is not ignorant* (*especially whose business and employment is great*) *of the troublesome multiplications of rods, feet, and oftentimes of inches, the one by the other, which not only molests, but also* (*though he be very well experienced*) *causes error, tending to the damage of both parties, as also to the discredit of landmeter or surveyor, and so for the money-masters, merchants, and each one in his business. Therefore how much they are more worthy, and the means to attain them the more laborious, so much the greater and better is this* Dime, *taking away those difficulties. But how? It teaches* (*to speak in a word*) *the easy performance of all reckonings, computations, & accounts, without broken numbers, which can happen in man's business, in such sort as that the four principles of arithmetic, namely addition, subtraction, multiplication, & division, by whole numbers may satisfy these effects, affording the like facility unto those that use counters. Now if by those means we gain the time which is precious, if hereby that be saved which otherwise should be lost, if so the pains, controversy, error, damage, and other inconveniences commonly happening therein be eased, or taken away, then I leave it willingly unto your judgment to be censured; and for that, that some* *may say that certain inventions at the first seem good, which when they come to be practised effect nothing of worth, as it often happens to the searchers of strong moving*[3], *which seem good in small proofs and models, when in great, or coming to the effect, they are not worth a button: whereto we answer that herein is no such doubt, for experience daily shows the same, namely by the practice of divers expert land-meters of Holland, unto whom we have shown it, who (laying aside that which each of them had, according to his own manner, invented to lessen their pains in their computations) do use the same to their great contentment, and by such fruit as the nature of it witnesses the due effect necessarily follows. The like shall also happen to each of yourselves using the same as they do. Meanwhile live in all felicity.*

THE ARGUMENT.

THE DIME has two parts, that is Definitions & Operations. By the first definition is declared what *Dime* is, by the second, third, and fourth what *commencement, prime, second,* etc. and *dime numbers* are. The operation is declared by four propositions: the addition, subtraction, multiplication, and division of dime numbers. The order whereof may be successively represented by this Table.

THE DIME *has two parts*	*Definitions, as what is*	*Dime,* *Commencement,* *Prime, Second, etc.* *Dime number.*
	Operations or Practice of the	*Addition,* *Subtraction,* *Multiplication,* *Division.*

[3] This is a translation of the Dutch "roersouckers", after Stevin's French version: "chercheurs de fort mouvements". It probably stands for people who start moving things, take initiative, comp. the archaic Dutch expressions "roermaker", "roerstichter" (information from Prof. Dr. C. G. N. De Vooys). The Dutch has "vonden der roersouckers", where "vonden" stands for "findings, inventions", and the whole expression for something like "widely proclaimed innovations".

And to the end the premises may the better be explained, there shall be hereunto an APPENDIX adjoined, declaring the use of the Dime in many things by certain examples, and also definitions and operations, to teach such as do not already know the use and practice of numeration, and the four principles of common arithmetic in whole numbers, namely addition, subtraction, multiplication, & division, together with the Golden Rule, sufficient to instruct the most ignorant in the usual practice of this art of Dime or decimal arithmetic.

THE FIRST PART.

Of the Definitions of the Dimes.

THE FIRST DEFINITION

Dime is a kind of arithmetic, invented by the tenth progression, consisting in character of ciphers, whereby a certain number is described and by which also all accounts which happen in human affairs are dispatched by whole numbers, without fractions or broken numbers.

Explication

Let the certain number be one thousand one hundred and eleven, described by the characters of ciphers thus 1111, in which it appears that each 1 is the 10th part of his precedent character 1; likewise in 2378 each unity of 8 is the tenth of each unity of 7, and so of all the others. But because it is convenient that the things whereof we would speak have names, and that this manner of computation is found by the consideration of such tenth or dime progression, that is that it consists therein entirely, as shall hereafter appear, we call this treatise fitly by the name of *Dime,* whereby all accounts happening in the affairs of man may be wrought and effected without fractions or broken numbers, as hereafter appears.

THE SECOND DEFINITION

Every number propounded is called COMMENCEMENT, whose sign is thus ◎.

Explication

By example, a certain number is propounded of three hundred sixty-four: we call them the 364 *commencements,* described thus 364◎, and so of all other like.

THE THIRD DEFINITION

And each tenth part of the unity of the COMMENCEMENT *we call the* PRIME, *whose sign is thus* ①, *and each tenth part of the unity of the prime we call the* SECOND, *whose sign is* ② *and so of the other: each tenth part of the unity of the precedent sign, always in order one further.*

Explication

As 3 ① 7 ② 5 ③ 9 ④, that is to say: 3 *primes,* 5 *thirds,* 9 *fourths,* and so proceeding infinitely, but to speak of their value, you may note that according to this definition the said numbers are 3/10, 7/100, 5/1000, 9/10000, together 3759/10000, and likewise 8 ◎ 9 ① 3 ② 7 ③ are worth 8,9/10, 3/100, 7/1000, together 8-937/1000, and so of other like. Also you may understand that in this *dime* we use no fractions, and that the multitude of signs, except ◎, never exceed 9, as for example not 7 ① 12 ②, but in their place 8 ① 2 ②, for they value as much.

THE FOURTH DEFINITION

The numbers of the second and third definitions beforegoing are generally called DIME NUMBERS.

The End of the Definitions

THE SECOND PART OF THE DIME.

Of the Operation or Practice.

THE FIRST PROPOSITION: OF ADDITION

Dime numbers being given,
how to add them to find their sum.

THE EXPLICATION PROPOUNDED: There are 3 orders of dime numbers given, of which the first 27 ⓪, 8 ①, 4 ②, 7 ③, the second 37 ⓪, 6 ①, 7 ②, 5 ③, the third 875 ⓪, 7 ①, 8 ②, 2 ③.

THE EXPLICATION REQUIRED: We must find their total sum.

CONSTRUCTION

The numbers given must be placed in order as here adjoining, adding them in the vulgar manner of adding of whole numbers in this manner. The sum (by the first problem of our French Arithmetic[5]) is 941304, which are (that which the signs above the numbers do show) 941 ⓪ 3 ① 0 ② 4 ③. I say they are the sum required. Demonstration: The 27 ⓪ 8 ① 4 ② 7 ③ given make by the 3rd

			⓪	①	②	③
	2	7	8	4	7
	3	7	6	7	5
8	7	5	7	8	2
9	4	1	3	0	4

definition before 27, 8/10, 4/100, 7/1000, together 27 847/1000 and by the same reason the 37 ⓪ 6 ① 7 ② 5 ③ shall make 37 675/1000 and the 875 ⓪ 7 ① 8 ② 2 ③ will make 875 782/1000, which three numbers make by common addition of vulgar arithmetic 941 304/1000. But

[5] *L'Arithmetique* (1585) Work V p. 81.

so much is the sum 941 ⓪ 3 ① 0 ② 4 ③; therefore it is the true sum to be demonstrated. Conclusion: The dime numbers being given to be added, we have found their sum, which is the thing required.

NOTE that if in the number given there want some signs of their natural order, the place of the defectant shall be filled. As, for example, let the numbers given be 8 ⓪ 5 ① 6 ② and 5 ⓪ 7 ②, in which the latter wanted the sign of ①; in the place thereof shall 0 ① be put. Take then for that latter number given 5 ⓪ 0 ① 7 ②, adding them in this sort.

	⓪	①	②
	8	5	6
	5	0	7
1	3	6	3

This advertisement shall also serve in the three following propositions, wherein the order of the defailing figures must be supplied, as was done in the former example.

THE SECOND PROPOSITION: OF SUBTRACTION

A dime number being given to subtract, another less dime number given: out of the same to find their rest. EXPLICATION PROPOUNDED: Be the numbers given 237 ⓪ 5 ① 7 ② 8 ③ & 59 ⓪ 7 ① 3 ② 9 ③. THE EXPLICATION REQUIRED: To find their rest. CONSTRUCTION: The numbers given shall be placed in this sort, subtracting according to vulgar manner of subtraction of whole numbers, thus.

		⓪	①	②	③
2	3	7	5	7	8
	5	9	7	3	9
1	7	7	8	3	9

The rest is 177839, which values as the signs over them do denote 177 ⓪ 8 ① 3 ② 9 ③. I affirm the same to be the rest required.

Demonstration: the 237 ⓪ 5 ① 7 ② 8 ③ make (by the third definition of this Dime) 237 5/10, 7/100, 8/1000, together 237 578/1000, and by the same reason the 59 ⓪ 7 ① 3 ② 9 ③ value 59 739/1000, which subtracted from 237 578/1000, there rests 177 839/1000, but so much doth 177 ⓪ 8 ① 3 ② 9 ③ value; that is then the true rest which should be made manifest. CONCLUSION: a dime being given, to subtract it out of another dime number, and to know the rest, which we have found.

THE THIRD PROPOSITION: OF MULTIPLICATION

A dime number being given to be multiplied, and a multiplicator given: to find their product.
THE EXPLICATION PROPOUNDED: Be the number to be multiplied 32 ⓪ 5 ① 7 ②, and the multiplicator 89 ⓪ 4 ① 6 ②.
THE EXPLICATION REQUIRED: To find the product. CONSTRUCTION: The given numbers are to be placed as here is shown, multiplying according to the vulgar manner of multiplication by whole numbers, in this manner, giving the product 29137122. Now to know how much they value, join the two last signs together as the one ② and the other ② also, which together make ④, and say that the last sign of the product shall be ④, which being known, all the rest are also known by their continued order. So that the product required is 2913 ⓪ 7 ① 1 ② 2 ③ 2 ④.

					⓪	①	②
				3	2	5	7
				8	9	4	6
			1	9	5	4	2
		1	3	0	2	8	
	2	9	3	1	3		
2	6	0	5	6			
2	9	1	3	7	1	2	2
			⓪	①	②	③	④

DEMONSTRATION: The number given to be multiplied, 32 ⓪ 5 ① 7 ② (as appears by the third definition of this Dime), 32, 5/10, 7/100, together 32-57/100; and by the same reason the multiplicator 89 ⓪ 4 ① 6 ② value 89 46/100 by the same, the said 32 57/100 multiplied gives the product 2913 7122/10000. But it also values 2913 ⓪ 7 ① 1 ② 2 ③ 2 ④.

It is then the true product, which we were to demonstrate. But to show why ② multiplied by ② gives the product ④, which is the sum of their numbers, also why ④ by ⑤ produces ⑨, and why ⓪ by ③ produces ③, etc., let us take 2/10 and 3/100, which (by the third definition of this Dime) are 2 ① 3 ②, their product is 6/1000, which value by the said third definition 6 ③; multiplying then ① by ②, the product is ③, namely a sign compounded of the sum of the numbers of the signs given.

CONCLUSION

A dime number to multiply and to be multiplied being given, we have found the product, as we ought.

NOTE

If the latter sign of the number to be multiplied be unequal to the latter sign of the multiplicator, as, for example, the one 3 ④ 7 ⑤ 8 ⑥, *the other* 5 ① 4 ②, *they shall be handled as aforesaid, and the disposition thereof shall be thus.*

		④	⑤	⑥	
		3	7	8	
			5	4	②
	1	5	1	2	
1	8	9	0		
2	0	4	1	2	
④	⑤	⑥	⑦	⑧	

THE FOURTH PROPOSITION: OF DIVISION

A dime number for the dividend and divisor being given: to find the quotient.

EXPLICATION PROPOSED: Let the number for the dividend be 3 ⓪ 4 ① 4 ② 3 ③ 5 ④ 2 ⑤ and the divisor 9 ① 6 ②.

EXPLICATION REQUIRED: To find their quotient.

CONSTRUCTION: The numbers given divided (omitting the signs) according to the vulgar manner of dividing of whole numbers, gives the quotient 3587; now to know what they value, the latter sign of the divisor ② must be subtracted from the latter sign of the dividend, which is ⑤, rest ③ for the latter sign of the latter character of the quotient, which being so known, all the rest are also manifest by their continued order, thus 3 ⓪ 5 ① 8 ② 7 ③ are the quotient required.

DEMONSTRATION: The number dividend given 3 ⓪ 4 ① 4 ② 3 ③ 5 ④ 2 ⑤ makes (by the third definition of this Dime) 3, 4/10, 4/100, 3/1000, 5/10000, 2/100000, together 3 44352/100000, and by the same reason the divisor 9 ① 6 ② values 96/100, by which 3 44352/100000 being divided, gives the quotient 3 587/1000; but the said quotient values 3 ⓪ 5 ① 8 ② 7 ③, therefore it is the true quotient to be demonstrated.

CONCLUSION : A dime number being given for the dividend and divisor, we have found the quotient required.

NOTE: *If the divisor's signs be higher than the signs of the dividend, there may be as many such ciphers* 0 *joined to the dividend as you will, or as many as shall be necessary: as for example,* 7② *are to be divided by* 4 ⑤, *I place after the* 7 *certain* 0, *thus* 7000, *dividing them as afore said, and in this sort it gives for the quotient* 1750 ⓪.

~~3~~ ~~2~~
~~7~~ ~~0~~ ~~0~~ ~~0~~ (1750 ⓪
~~4~~ ~~4~~ ~~4~~ ~~4~~

It happens also sometimes that the quotient cannot be expressed by whole numbers, as 4 ① *divided by* 3 ② *in this sort, whereby appears that there will infinitely come*

```
    1 1 1 (1              ⓪ ① ②
    4 0 0 0 0 0 0     (1  3  3  3
    3 3 3 3
```

3's, *and in such a case you may come so near as the thing requires, omitting the remainder. It is true, that* 13 ⓪ 3 ① 3 1/3 ② *or* 13 ⓪ 3 ① 3 ② 3 1/3 ③ *etc. shall be the perfect quotient required. But our invention in this Dime is to work all by whole numbers. For seeing that in any affairs men reckon not of the thousandth part of a mite, es, grain, etc., as the like is also used of the principal geometricians and astronomers in computations of great consequence, as Ptolemy and Johannes Montaregio*[6], *have not described their tables of arcs, chords or sines in extreme perfection (as possibly they might have done by multinomial numbers), because that imperfection (considering the scope and end of those tables) is more convenient than such perfection.*

NOTE 2. *The extraction of all kinds of roots may also be made by these dime numbers; as, for example, to extract the square root of* 5 ② 2 ③ 9 ④, *which is performed in the vulgar manner of extraction in this sort, and the root shall be* 2 ① 3 ②, *for the moiety or half of the latter sign of the numbers given is always the latter sign of the root; wherefore, if the latter sign given were of a number impair, the sign of the next following shall be*

```
 1
 5 2 9
 -----
 2  3
 -----
   4
```

[6] See the Introduction to *De Thiende,* esp. footnote 5 and to the *Driehouckhandel.* Johannes Montaregio, or Ian van Kuenincxberghe, Iehan de Montroial, is best known under his latinized name Iohannes Regiomontanus (1436—1476). This craftsman, humanist, astronomer and mathematician of Nuremberg, born near Konigsberg in Franconia (hence his name), influenced the development of trigonometry as an independent science for more than a century by his tables and his *De triangulis omnimodis libri quinque* (first published in 1533). The sines, for Regiomontanus as well as for Stevin, were half chords, not ratios. On Regiomontanus see E. Zinner, *Leben und Wirken des Johannes Muller von Konigsberg genannt Regiomontanus,* Schriftenreihe zur buyr. Landesgesch. 31, Munchen, 1938, XIII + 294 pp.

added, and then it shall be a number pair; and then extract the root as before. Likewise in the extraction of the cubic root, the third part of the latter sign given shall be always the sign of the root; and so of all other kinds of roots.

THE END OF THE DIME

THE APPENDIX

THE PREFACE

Seeing that we have already described the Dime, we will now come to the use thereof, showing by 6 articles how all computations which can happen in any man's business may be easily performed thereby; beginning first to show how they are to be put in practice in the casting up of the content or quantity of land, measured as follows.

THE FIRST ARTICLE:

OF THE COMPUTATIONS OF LAND-METING.

Call the perch or rod[7] also *commencement,* which is 1 ⓪, dividing that into 10 equal parts, whereof each one shall be 1 ①; then divide each prime again into 10 equal parts, each of which shall be 1 ②; and again each of them into 10 equal parts, and each of them shall be 1 ③, proceeding further so, if need be. But in land-meting, divisions of seconds will be small enough. Yet for such things as require more exactness, as roofs of lead, bodies, etc., there may be thirds used, and for as much as the greater number of land-meters use not the pole, but a chain line of three, four or five perch long, marking

[7] The English "perch" or "rod" and the Dutch "roede" are both measures of area and of length. For information on the precise meaning of the many measures mentioned in Stevin's book one may consult the *Oxford Dictionary of the English language.*

upon the yard of their cross staff[8] certain feet 5 or 6 with fingers, palms, etc., the like may be done here; for in the place of their five or six feet with their fingers, they may put 5 or 6 *primes* with their *seconds*.

This being so prepared, these shall be used in measuring, without regarding the feet and fingers of the pole, according to the custom of the place; and that which must be added, subtracted, multiplied or divided according to this measure shall be performed according to the doctrine of the precedent examples.

As, for example, we are to add 4 triangles or surfaces of land, whereof the first 345 ⓪ 7 ① 2 ②, the second 872 ⓪ 5 ① 3 ②, the third 615 ⓪ 4 ① 8 ②, the fourth 956 ⓪ 8 ① 6 ②.

			⓪	①	②
	3	4	5	7	2
	8	7	2	5	3
	6	1	5	4	8
	9	5	6	8	6
2	7	9	0	5	9

* * *

THE SECOND ARTICLE: OF THE COMPUTATIONS OF THE MEASURES OF TAPESTRY OR CLOTH

The ell of the measurer of tapestry or cloth shall be to him 1 ⓪, the which he shall divide (upon the side

[8] The Dutch *rechtcruys,* in Stevin's French version *croix rectangulaire,* translated *cross-staff,* was an instrument used by surveyors for setting out perpendiculars by lines of sight, crossing each other at right angles. It was also known as *surveyor's cross.* The cross was horizontal and supported by a pole, the *yard* of our text, on which Stevin wants to measure off a decimal scale. A variant of this cross was a graduated horizontal circle with a pointer (alidade) along which sighting could be performed, but even in the variations the basic rectangular cross remained.

Surveyors also used chains for measuring distances, or setting out perpendiculars, in which case they used the so-called 6, 8 and 10 rule, a popular application of Pythagoras' theorem.

The surveyor's cross is mentioned in many books on surveying. In N. Bion, *Traite de la construction et des principaux usages des instruments de mathematique,* Nouvelle edition, La Haye 1723, p. 133 we find it referred to as "equerre d'arpenteur", with a picture (information from Dr. P. H. van Cittert).

whereon the partitions which are according to the ordinance of the town is not set out) as is done above on the pole of the land-meter, namely into 10 equal parts, whereof each shall be 1 ⓪, then each 1 ① into 10 equal parts, of which each shall be 1 ②, etc. And for the practice, seeing that these examples do altogether accord with those of the first article of land-meting, it is thereby sufficiently manifest, so as we need not here make any mention again of them.

THE THIRD ARTICLE: OF THE COMPUTATIONS SERVING TO GAUGING, AND THE MEASURES OF ALL LIQUOR VESSELS

One ame (which makes 100 pots Antwerp) shall be 1 ⓪, the same shall be divided in length and deepness into 10 equal parts (namely equal in respect of the wine, not of the rod; of which the parts of the depth shall be unequal), and each part shall be 1 ① containing 10 pots; then again each 1 ① into 10 parts equal as afore, and each will make 1 ② worth 1 pot; then each 1 ② into 10 equal parts, making each 1 ③.

* * *

THE FOURTH ARTICLE: OF COMPUTATIONS OF STEREOMETRY IN GENERAL

True it is that gaugery, which we have before declared, is stereometry (that is to say, the art of measuring of bodies), but considering the divers divisions of the rod, yard or measure of the one and other, and that and this do so much differ as the genus and the species: they ought by good reason to be distinguished. For all stereometry is not gaugery. To come to the point, the stereometrian shall use the measure of the town or place, as the yard, ell, etc. with his ten partitions, as is described in the first and second articles; the use and practice thereof (as is before shown) is thus: Put case we have a quadrangular rectangular column to be measured, the length whereof is 3 ① 2 ②, the breadth 2 ① 4 ②, the height 2 ⓪ 3 ① 5 ②. The question is how much the substance or matter of that pillar is. Multiply (according to the doctrine of the 4th proposition of this Dime) the length by the breadth, & the product again by the height in this manner.

And the product appears to be 1 ① 8 ② 4 ④ 8 ⑤.

```
            ① ②
            3 2
            2 4
          -------
          1 2 8
          6 4
          -------
          7 6 8      ④
          2 3 5      ②
          -------
        3 8 4 0
      2 3 0 4
    1 5 3 6
    -----------
    1 8 0 4 8 0
    ① ② ③ ④ ⑤ ⑥
```

* * *

THE SIXTH ARTICLE:

OF THE COMPUTATIONS OF MONEY-MASTERS, MERCHANTS, AND OF ALL ESTATES IN GENERAL.

. . . The examples hereof are vulgar computations, which do almost continually happen to every man, to whom it were necessary that the solution so found were of each accepted for good and lawful. Therefore, considering the so great use, it would be a commendable thing, if some of those who expect the greatest commodity would solicit to put the same in execution to effect, namely that joining the vulgar partitions that are now in weight, measures, and moneys (continuing still each capital measure, weight, and coin in all places unaltered) that the same tenth progression might be lawfully ordained by the superiors for everyone that would use the same; it might also do well, if the values of moneys, principally the new coins, might be valued and reckoned upon certain *primes, seconds, thirds,* etc.

SUN-TSU

(c. Third Century)

Sun-Tsu, an ancient Chinese mathematician of considerable power, was the author of a mathematical work, the *Sun-Tsu Suan-ching,* "Arithmetic Classic of Sun-Tsu", a treatise referred to as authoritative by almost every subsequent Chinese writer on mathematics. It was the first of the ancient Chinese works to consider the solution of indeterminate problems and it is the source of the famous "Chinese remainder problem", where a number is sought such that if it is divided by certain divisors, then corresponding given remainders are obtained. The date at which Sun-Tsu lived is in some doubt. He was at one time identified with the military writer Sun-Wu-Tsu (or Sun-Tsu) of the fifth or sixth century B.C., whose treatise on the Art of War was the subject of many commentaries over the centuries. This identification has been definitely rejected on philological grounds, and Sun-Tsu, the mathematician, has been placed as belonging to the third century, at the end of the Han or the beginning of the Wei Dynasty. There are some authorities who believe that he may have lived as early as the first century A.D.

The *Sun-Tsu Suan-ching* is an elaborately constructed treatise in three books. It was based, in all likelihood, upon the earlier "Arithmetical Rules in Nine Sections", but the work shows substantial progress over the older treatise in the depth and extent of the author's understanding of mathematical techniques. Sun-Tsu's explanation of the decimal number system employed in his arithmetic involved the knowledge and use of calculating rods. His authority in this area was unchallenged for many centuries. In later times, when a new practice arose for the arrangement of the calculating pieces representing the even and odd places in a number, his name was attached to the "old method", being referred to as the *Son-shi-Reppu-ho,* "the method of arrangement of Sun-Tsu." Beginning with an exposition of metrological units and elementary operations in the *Sun-Tsu Suan-ching,* and proceeding to the method of extracting a square root, Sun-Tsu included all the topics that were taught in the "Nine Sections". The introduction of the solution of indeterminate problems in this work was an important innovation. Sun-Tsu's rule for the solution of an indeterminate problem, *Ta-Yen* (or *T'ai-yen*), "Great Extension" or "Great Generalization", was given under the heading *Wuh-puh-chi-soo,* "Unknown Numerical Quantities." Stated in four lines of rhyme, the rule was followed by the problem itself and a brief solution. The *Sun-tsu Suan-ching* became widely known in the West through Alexander Wylie's famous and highly informative article, "Jottings on the Science of Chinese Arithmetic."

THE SUN-TSU SUAN-CHING

From *The Development of Mathematics in China and Japan*

by Yoshio Mikami

Sun-Tsu ascribes, in the preface of his work, the origin of all things, material as well as intellectual, to the science of numbers or of calculation.

At the beginning of Sun-Tsu's treatise he gives the names of great and small numbers and of the measures and weights.

We here quote from Sun-Tsu's text:

"The measure originates with *hu*. What is one *hu?* The silkworm vomits its string, which measures (in diameter) one *hu*. Ten *hu* make one *mi*; ten *mi* one *hao;* ten *hao* one *li;* ten *li* one *fen;* ten *fen* one *t'sun;* ten *t'sun* one *ch'o* or one foot; ten feet one *chang;* ten *chang* one *yin*. And 50 feet make one *tuan,* 40 feet one *p'i,* 6 feet one *p'ou* or one pace, 240 paces one *mou,* and 300 paces one *li* or one Chinese mile.

"The weight originates with one grain of panicum maliaceum; ten of such grains make one *t'sen*; ten *t'sen* one *shu*; 24 *shu* one *liang*; 16 *liang* one *chin*; 30 *chin* one *chun*; and 4 chun one *shih.*

"The solid measure originates in a *su* or a grain of millet; six such grains make one *kuei*; ten *kuei* one *t'so*; ten *t'so* one *ch'ao*; ten *ch'ao* one *shao*; ten *shao* one *ho*; ten *ho* one *shong*; ten *shong* one *tou*; ten *tou* one *hu*; which contains 60,000,000 grains of millet."

Sun-Tsu takes $\pi = 3$, and the ratio of the side and the diagonal of a square to be 5 to 7.

The weights of gold, silver, jewel, copper, lead, iron and stone are given to be one *chin,* 14, 12, 7-1/2, 9-1/2, 6 and 3 *liangs,* respectively, for one *t'sun* cube.

Sun-Tsu does not explain expressly the use of the calculating pieces, but what he records in the first book of his treatise seems to indicate clearly the recourse being taken to that sort of abacus.

The calculating pieces are made of small bamboo or wooden pieces of two colours, red and black, representing the positive and the negative numbers. The pieces that were used in the later growth of mathematics were some 1-1/2 inches long and a sixth part of their length broad. But in old times much longer pieces made of bamboo were in use, as is recorded in the *Han Shu,* written by Pan Ku at the end of the 1st Christian century. Although we are not certain how long the abacus had been used in China, yet we are sure that it was not first brought into use during the ages of the Han Dynasty; it had most likely been employed from time immemorial in China. A passage in the illustrious book, *Tso Ch'uan*, serves to confirm this view; and the event told there relates to an occurrence in the year 542 B. C.

Sun-Tsu says in the first book of his treatise:

"In making calculations we must first know positions of numbers. Unity is vertical and ten horizontal; the hundred stands while the thousand lies; and the thousand and the ten look equally, and so also the ten thousand and the hundred."

This stage in Sun-Tsu is nothing but a description of the arrangement of the calculating pieces. These pieces are usually arranged in the following manner:

The first five numbers are represented by 1, 2, 3, 4 and 5 of these pieces, that are arranged vertically, while in the arrangement of the numbers from 6 to 9 one piece taken in the horizontal position over other vertical pieces is taken for 5. Thus:

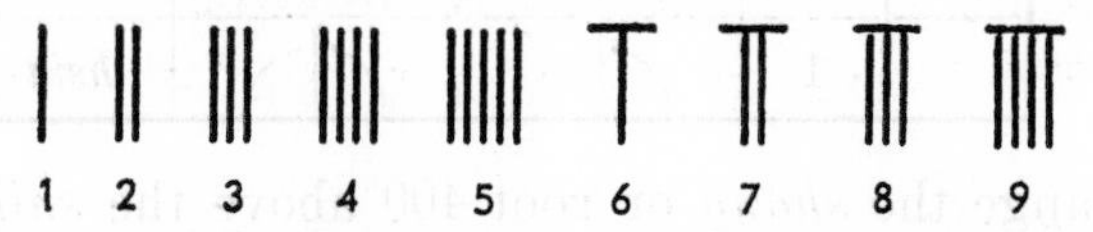

This way of arrangement is referred to in Sun-Tsu's work in the paragraph that follows that which we have just quoted; and it is also in sound accordance with what we can conjecture from the obscure passage in the *Tso*

Ch'uan mentioned above. Moreover, this was the very way that was followed in subsequent ages.

The figures in the ten's column are arranged with the calculating pieces in the following manner:

𝍩 𝍪 𝍫 𝍬 𝍭 𝍮 𝍯 𝍰 𝍱

For hundreds and higher numbers these arrangements are repeated alternately, but nothing new comes in. Thus the number 6728 will be arranged as annexed.

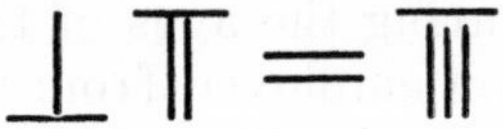

𝍮𝍦𝍪𝍧

The explanation of the extraction of the square-root found in the second book of Sun-Tsu:

"Arrange the area 234567 paces square and make it the *shih*.

"Next borrow a unit calculator, and make it the *hsia-fa*.".[1])

Thus:

2	3	4	5	6	7	*shih*
					1	*hsia-fa*

"Advance it over every one column, thus dividing the *shih* in groups, until it reaches the hundred's place."

Thus:

2	3	4	5	6	7	*shih*
	1					*hsia-fa*

"Arrange the *shang* or root 400 above the *shih*.

"Subjoin 40000[2]) under the *shih* and above the *hsia-fa*, and make it the *fang-fa*.

---

[1] The word *hsia* means below or under.

[2] This is the product of the root and the *hsia-fa*.

"With it multiply the root 400 and subtract the product from the *shih*." Thus:

4		0		0	root
7	4	5	6	7	*shih*
4	0	0	0	0	*fang-fa*
1					*hsia-fa*

"The subtraction being done, double the *fang-fa,* and draw it back one column, and the *hsia-fa* two columns." Thus:

4		0		0	root
7	4	5	6	7	*shih*
	8	0	0	0	*fang-fa*
		1			*hsia-fa*

"Again arrange 80 for the root next to the previous digit.

"Subjoin 800 under the *fang-fa* and above the *hsia-fa*; nominate it the *lien-fa*.

"Multiply the *fang-fa* and the *lien-fa* by the root 80, and subtract the products from the *shih*." Thus:

4		8		0	root
	4	1	6	7	*shih*
	8	0			*fang-fa*
		8			*lien-fa*
		1			*hsia-fa*

"When these subtractions are done, double the *lien-fa,* and add to the *fang-fa*.

"Draw back the *fang-fa* one column, and the *hsia-fa* two columns."

Here the *lien-fa* is understood to be got rid of. And thus the arrangement becomes:

4		8		0	root
	4	1	6	7	*shih*
		9	6	0	*fang-fa*
				1	*hsia-fa*

"Again, arrange 4 in the next column of the previous root.

"Subjoin 4 under the *fang-fa* and above the *hsia-fa*, and name it the *yu-fa*.[1])

"Multiply the *fang, lien,* and *yu*[2]) by the root 4, and subtract the products from the *shih*." Thus:

4		8		4	root
		3	1	1	*shih*
		9	6	0	*fang-fa*
				4	*yü-fa*
				1	*hsia-fa*

"This being over, double the *yu-fa* and add it to the *fang-fa*.

"Thus we get 484 for the root in the above and 968 (for the *hsia-fa*[3]), the remainder being 311."

"One side (of the square) is therefore 484-311/968 paces."

We here state one or two problems from Sun-Tsu's "Arithmetical Classic", Book 3.

"A woman was washing dishes in a river, when an official whose business was overseeing the waters de-

[1] This is the same as the previous *lien-fa,* only that it is differently named.

[2] This passage may seem somewhat strange, but it means that the *fang-fa* and the *yu-fa* are to be multiplied by 4 in the root.

[3] This is not in the same meaning as previously.

manded of her: 'Why are there so many dishes here?'—'Because a feasting was entertained in the house', the woman replied. Thereupon the official inquired of the number of the guests. 'I don't know', the woman said, 'how many guests had been there; but every two used a dish for rice between them; every three a dish for broth; every four a dish for meat; and there were sixty-five dishes in all."

"Rule. Arrange the 65 dishes, and multiply by 12, when we get 780. Divide it by 13, and thus we obtain the answer."

"There are certain things whose number is unknown. Repeatedly divided by 3, the remainder is 2; by 5 the remainder is 3; and by 7 the remainder is 2. What will be the number?"

This problem reduces to the indeterminate equations

$$3\,m_1 + 2 = 5\,m_2 + 3 = 7\,m_3 + 2,$$

of which the solution is

$m_1 = 5 \times 7r + 7, \quad m_2 = 21r + 4, \quad m_3 = 3 \times 5r + 3,$
for $r = 0, 1, 2, 3, \ldots$.

Sun-Tsu tries to solve this problem thus:

"The remainder divided by 3 is 2, and so take 140. The remainder divided by 5 is 3, and so take 63. The remainder divided by 7 is 2. and so take 30. Adding these together we get 233. Therefrom subtract 210, and we obtain the answer."

Sun-Tsu thus satisfied himself with a single solution of the problem.

Further adds Sun-Tsu: "In general, take 70, when the remainder of the repeated divisions by 3 is 1; take 21, when the remainder of the repeated divisions by 5 is 1; and take 15, when the remainder of the repeated divisions by 7 is 1. When the sum of these numbers is above 106, subtract 105, before we get the answer."

All the subjects treated by Sun-Tsu were those that had been given in the "Arithmetic in Nine Sections", but the problem of indeterminate analysis first appeared in the above in Sun-Tsu.

We find in Sun-Tsu a problem of finding the least common multiple. It is this:

"There are three sisters, of whom the eldest comes home once in every 5 days, the middle in every 4 days, and the youngest in every 3 days. In how many days will all the three meet together?"

The answer is 60 days.

To solve it Sun-Tsu gives the rule in these words:

"Arrange the 5 days of the eldest sister, the 4 days of the middle and the 3 days of the youngest in the right column. Opposite to each of these arrange unity on the left column. Then cross multiply (the numbers on the right), when we get the numbers of their returning. Thus the eldest comes 12 times, the middle 15 times and the youngest 20 times. If we multiply these numbers by the numbers of days in which the sisters once come back, we shall obtain the desired answer."

The last problem in the "Arithmetical Classic" of Sun-Tsu is one that relates to fortune-telling. Thus:

"A pregnant woman, who is 29 years of age, is expected to give birth to a child in the 9th month of the year. Which should be her child, a son or a daughter?"

Sun-Tsu gives to this problem the rule:

"Take 49; add the month of her child-bearing; subtract her age. From what now remains, subtract the heaven 1, subtract the earth 2, subtract the man 3, subtract the four seasons 4, subtract the five elements 5, subtract the six laws 6, subtract the seven stars 7, subtract the eight winds 8, subtract the nine provinces 9. If then the remainder be odd, the child shall be a son; and if even, a daughter."

Yuan Yuan desires in his "Biographical Collections" to ascribe this one problem to a subsequent addition, not to the original text of Sun-Tsu, since it appears to him too unbecoming for so able a writer as Sun-Tsu.

JAMES JOSEPH SYLVESTER

(1814—1897)

James Joseph Sylvester, one of the foremost mathematicians of the nineteenth century, an innovator in the theory of numbers, analysis, differential equations, and higher algebra, was born in London, England, on September 13, 1814. His mathematical genius was early in evidence and long lived. At the age of fifteen he won a prize of five hundred dollars for his solution of a problem proposed to him by the Directors of the Lotteries Contractors of the United States. At the age of eighty-two, his talent, zeal and vision undimmed, he was creating mathematics in number theory.

At the age of fourteen, Sylvester studied for a semester under Professor De Morgan in the University of London. He then entered the Royal Institution at Liverpool where he was so outstanding in mathematics that a special class was created for him. About two years later, he entered St. John's College, Cambridge. Sylvester graduated at St. John's College in 1837 as Second Wrangler. Nevertheless, he was denied a degree because, as a Jew, he was unable to pass the prescribed test of faith. Later, he was granted a degree at the University of Dublin, and in 1871, he also received his degree at Cambridge. At the unusually early age of twenty-five, Sylvester was elected Fellow of the Royal Society. After some fruitless attempts to secure a teaching position, Sylvester worked for a period of ten years, as an actuary for an insurance company in London. During this time he also studied law, and he was called to the Bar in 1850. Sylvester and Cayley met through their activities connected with the study of law. Their lifelong friendship grew out of their common interest in mathematics, and the mutual admiration and respect of each for the extraordinary capacities of the other. Sylvester's interest in pure mathematics having been rekindled through his discussions with Cayley, he applied for and received an appointment as professor of mathematics at the Royal Military Academy at Woolwich. Some sixteen years later, he was retired. "Superannuated" at Woolwich at the age of fifty six, Sylvester was actually on the threshold of many more years of vital activity. In the next few years he wrote on a variety of topics, including problems of link-motion. He invented a skew pantograph, and he published a pamphlet, *The Laws of Verse,* on the construction of poetry. In 1875 he became the first professor of mathematics at the new Johns Hopkins University at Baltimore, Md., where for six years, he was surrounded by numerous hard working and happy students. In 1876 he founded and became the editor of the American Journal of Mathematics. In 1883, at the age of seventy, he returned to England to fill the Savilian chair of geometry at Oxford University.

A vigorous and stimulating personality, Sylvester was an accomplished linguist with considerable talent in poetry and music. An eloquent speaker and writer, he is known to have held an audience spellbound for an hour and a half merely with the material introductory to the main text of his lecture. His mathematical papers were published in scientific periodicals all over the world. He was prolific in the creation of new mathematics and of new terminology as it was needed. He introduced almost all of the terminology in the theory of invariants. Terms in common use today such as invariant, covariant, Hessian, contravariant, combinant, commutant, concomitant, are but a few of those due to him. In his generous appreciation of the work of others, in his philosophical view of mathematics as an unlimited field of endeavor for the imagination and for invention, Sylvester encouraged his students, colleagues and readers, imparting to them his boundless enthusiasm, his method, and his power.

●

PRESIDENTIAL ADDRESS TO SECTION 'A' OF THE BRITISH ASSOCIATION

[*Exeter British Association Report* (1869), pp. 1—9.]*

From *The Collected Papers of James Joseph Sylvester, Vol. II*

It is said of a great party leader and orator in the House of Lords that, when lately requested to make a speech at some religious or charitable (at all events a non-political) meeting, he declined to do so on the ground that he could not speak unless he saw an adversary before him—somebody to attack or reply to. In obedience to a somewhat similar combative instinct, I set to myself the task of considering certain recent utterances of a most distinguished member of this Association, one whom I no less respect for his honesty and public spirit

[* The Address was also reprinted by the Author in a volume issued by Longmans, Green and Co., London, 1870, of which the earlier portion deals with the Laws of Verse. Some additional notes to the Address there given are reproduced at the end of this volume.]

than I admire for his genius and eloquence, but from whose opinions on a subject which he has not studied I feel constrained to differ. Goethe has said—

> "Verstaendige Leute kannst du irren sehn
> In Sachen, naemlich, die sie nicht verstehn."

Understanding people you may see erring—in those things, to wit, which they do not understand.

I have no doubt that had my distinguished friend, the probable President-elect of the next Meeting of the Association, applied his uncommon powers of reasoning, induction, comparison, observation, and invention to the study of mathematical science, he would have become as great a mathematician as he is now a biologist; indeed he has given public evidence of his ability to grapple with the practical side of certain mathematical questions; but he has not made a study of mathematical science as such, and the eminence of his position and the weight justly attaching to his name render it only the more imperative that any assertions proceeding from such a quarter, which may appear to me erroneous, or so expressed as to be conducive to error, should not remain unchallenged or be passed over in silence.

He says "mathematical training is almost purely deductive. The mathematician starts with a few simple propositions, the proof of which is so obvious that they are called self-evident, and the rest of his work consists of subtle deductions from them. The teaching of languages, at any rate as ordinarily practised, is of the same general nature—authority and tradition furnish the data, and the mental operations are deductive." It would seem from the above somewhat singularly juxtaposed paragraphs that, according to Prof. Huxley, the business of the mathematical student is from a limited number of propositions (bottled up and labelled ready for future use) to deduce any required result by a process of the same general nature as a student of language employs in declining and conjugating his nouns and verbs —that to make out a mathematical proposition and to construe or parse a sentence are equivalent or identical mental operations. Such an opinion scarcely seems to need serious refutation. The passage is taken from an article in *Macmillan's Magazine* for June last, entitled "Scientific Education — Notes of an After-dinner Speech," and I cannot but think would have been couched in more guarded terms by my distinguished friend had his speech been made *before* dinner instead of *after*.

The notion that mathematical truth rests on the narrow basis of a limited number of elementary propositions from which all others are to be derived by a process of logical inference and verbal deduction, has been stated still more strongly and explicitly by the same eminent writer in an article of even date with the preceding in the *Fortnightly Review*, where we are told that "Mathematics is that study which knows nothing of observation, nothing of experiment, nothing of induction, nothing of causation." I think no statement could have been made more opposite to the undoubted facts of the case, that mathematical analysis is constantly invoking the aid of new principles, new ideas, and new methods, not capable of being defined by any form of words, but springing direct from the inherent powers and activity of the human mind, and from continually renewed introspection of that inner world of thought of which the phenomena are as varied and require as close attention to discern as those of the outer physical world (to which the inner one in each individual man may, I think, be conceived to stand in somewhat the same general relation of correspondence as a shadow to the object from which it is projected, or as the hollow palm of one hand to the closed fist which it grasps of the other), that it is unceasingly calling forth the faculties of observation and comparison, that one of its principal weapons is induction, that it has frequent recourse to experimental trial and verification, and that it affords a boundless scope for the exercise of the highest efforts of imagination and invention.

... Were it not unbecoming to dilate on one's personal

experience, I could tell a story of almost romantic interest about my own latest researches in a field where Geometry, Algebra, and the Theory of Numbers melt in a surprising manner into one another, like sunset tints or the colours of the dying dolphin, "the last still loveliest" (a sketch of which has just appeared in the *Proceedings of the London Mathematical Society**), which would very strikingly illustrate how much observation, divination, induction, experimental trial, and verification, causation, too (if that means, as I suppose it must, mounting from phenomena to their reasons or causes of being), have to do with the work of the mathematician. In the face of these facts, which every analyst in this room or out of it can vouch for out of its own knowledge and personal experience, how can it be maintained, in the words of Professor Huxley, who, in this instance, is speaking of the sciences as they are in themselves and without any reference to scholastic discipline, that Mathematics "is that study which knows nothing of observation, nothing of induction, nothing of experiment, nothing of causation"?

I, of course, am not so absurd as to maintain that the habit of observation of external nature will be best or in any degree cultivated by the study of mathematics, at all events as that study is at present conducted; and no one can desire more earnestly than myself to see natural and experimental science introduced into our schools as a primary and indispensable branch of education: I think that that study and mathematical culture should go on hand in hand together, and that they would greatly influence each other for their mutual good. I should rejoice to see mathematics taught with that life and animation which the presence and example of her young and buoyant sister could not fail to impart, short roads preferred to long ones, Euclid honourably shelved or buried "deeper than did ever plummet sound" out of the schoolboy's reach, morphology introduced into the elements of Algebra—projection, correlation, and motion

* Under the title of "Outline Trace of the Theory of Reducible Cyclodes."

accepted as aids to geometry—the mind of the student quickened and elevated and his faith awakened by early initiation into the ruling ideas of polarity, continuity, infinity, and familiarization with the doctrine of the imaginary and inconceivable.

It is this living interest in the subject which is so wanting in our traditional and mediaeval modes of teaching. In France, Germany, and Italy, everywhere where I have been on the Continent, mind acts direct on mind in a manner unknown to the frozen formality of our academic institutions, schools of thought and centres of real intellectual cooperation exist; the relation of master and pupil is acknowledged as a spiritual and a lifelong tie, connecting successive generations of great thinkers with each other in an unbroken chain, just in the same way as we read, in the catalogue of our French Exhibition, or of the Salon at Paris, of this man or that being the pupil of one great painter or sculptor and the master of another. When followed out in this spirit, there is no study in the world which brings into more harmonious action all the faculties of the mind than the one of which I stand here as the humble representative, there is none other which prepares so many agreeable surprises for its followers, more wonderful than the changes in the transformation-scene of a pantomime, or, like this, seems to raise them, by successive steps of initiation, to higher and higher states of conscious intellectual being.

This accounts, I believe, for the extraordinary longevity of all the greatest masters of the Analytical art, the Dii Majores of the mathematical Pantheon. Leibnitz lived to the age of 70; Euler to 76; Lagrange to 77; Laplace to 78; Gauss to 78; Newton, the crown and glory of his race, to 85; Archimedes, the nearest akin, probably, to Newton in genius, was 75, and might have lived on to be 100, for aught we can guess to the contrary, when he was slain by the impatient and illmannered sergeant, sent to bring him before the Roman general, in the full vigour of his faculties, and in the very act of working out a problem; Pythagoras, in whose school, I believe, the word mathematician (used, however, in a somewhat wider than its present sense) originated, the second founder of geometry, the inventor of the matchless theorem which goes by his name, the precognizer of the undoubtedly mis-called Copernican theory, the discoverer of the regular solids and the musical canon, who stands at the very apex of this pyramid of fame, (if we may credit the tradition) after spending 22 years studying in Egypt, and 12 in Babylon, opened school when 56 or 57 years old in Magna Græcia, married a young wife when past 60, and died, carrying on his work with energy unspent to the last, at the age of 99. The mathematician lives long and lives young; the wings of his soul do not early drop off, nor do its pores become clogged with the earthy particles blown from the dusty highways of vulgar life.

. . . Time was when all the parts of the subject were dissevered, when algebra, geometry, and arithmetic either lived apart or kept up cold relations of acquaintance confined to occasional calls upon one another; but that is now at an end; they are drawn together and are constantly becoming more and more intimately related and connected by a thousand fresh ties, and we may confidently look forward to a time when they shall form but one body with one soul. Geometry formerly was the chief borrower from arithmetic and algebra, but it has since repaid its obligations with abundant usury; and if I were asked to name, in one word, the pole-star round which the mathematical firmament revolves, the central idea which pervades as a hidden spirit the whole corpus of mathematical doctrine, I should point to Continuity as contained in our notions of space, and say, it is this, it is this! Space is the *Grand Continuum* from which, as from an inexhaustible reservoir, all the fertilizing ideas of modern analysis are derived; and as Brindley, the engineer, once allowed before a parliamentary committee that, in his opinion, rivers were made to feed navigable canals, I feel almost tempted to say that one principal reason for the existence of space, or at least one principal function which it discharges, is that of feeding mathematical invention. Everybody knows what a wonderful influence geometry has exercised in the hands of Cauchy, Puiseux, Riemann, and his followers Clebsch, Gordan, and others, over the very form and presentment of the modern calculus, and how it has come to pass that the tracing of curves, which was once to be regarded as a puerile amusement, or at best useful only to the architect or decorator, is now entitled to take rank as a high philosophical exercise, inasmuch as every new curve or surface, or other circumscription of space is capable of being regarded as the embodiment of some specific organized system of continuity.

APPENDIX.

Additional Notes to Prof. Sylvester's Exeter British Association Address

Induction and analogy are the special characteristics of modern mathematics, in which theorems have given place to theories, and no truth is regarded otherwise than as a link in an infinite chain. "Omne exit in infinitum" is their favourite motto and accepted axiom. No mathematician now-a-days sets any store on the discovery of isolated theorems, except as affording hints of an unsuspected new sphere of thought, like meteorites detached from some undiscovered planetary orb of speculation. The form, as well as matter, of mathematical science, as must be the case in any true living organic science, is in a constant state of flux, and the position of its centre of gravity is liable to continual change. At different periods in its history defined, with more or less accuracy, as the science of number or quantity, or extension or operation or arrangement, it appears at present to be passing through a phase in which the development of the notion of Continuity plays the leading part. In exemplification of the generalising tendency of modern mathematics, take so simple a fact as that of two straight lines or two planes being incapable of including "a space." When analysed this statement will be found to resolve itself into the assertion that if two out of the four triads that can be formed with four points lie respectively *in directo,* the same must be true of the remaining two triads; and that if two of the five tetrads that can be formed with five points lie respectively *in plano,* the remaining three tetrads (subject to a certain obvious exception) must each do the same. This, at least, is one way of arriving at the notion of an unlimited rectilinear and planar schema of points. The two statements above made, translated into the language of determinants, immediately suggest as their generalised expression my great "Homaloidal Law," which affirms that the vanishing of a certain specifiable number of minor determinants of a given order of any matrix (i.e. rectangular array of quantities) implies the simultaneous evanescence of all the rest of that order. I made (*inter alia*) a beautiful application of this law (which is, I believe, recorded in Mr. Spottiswoode's valuable treatise on Determinants, but where besides I know not) to the establishment of the well-known relations, wrung out with so much difficulty by Euler, between the cosines of the nine angles, which two sets of rectangular axes in space make with one another. This is done by contriving and constructing a matrix such that the six known equations connecting the nine cosines taken both ways in sets of threes shall be expressed by the evanescence of six of its minors; the simultaneous evanescence of the remaining minors given by the Homaloidal Law will then be found to express the relations in question (which, Euler has put on record, it drove him almost to despair to obtain), but which are thus obtained by a simple process of inspection and reading off, without any labour whatever. The fact that such a law, containing in a latent form so much refined algebra, and capable of such interesting immediate applications, should present itself to the *observation* merely as the extended expression of the ground of the possibility of our most elementary and seemingly intuitive conceptions concerning the right line and plane, has often filled me with amazement to reflect upon.

●

ADDRESS ON COMMEMORATION DAY AT JOHNS HOPKINS UNIVERSITY 22 FEBRUARY, 1877

From *The Collected Papers of James Joseph Sylvester, Vol. III*

It is with unaffected feelings of diffidence that I present myself before you, for, save on rare and exceptional occasions, it has not been my wont to make my voice heard in public assemblies. I know, indeed, and can conceive of no pursuit so antagonistic to the cultivation of the oratorical faculty—that faculty so prevalent in this country that the possession of it is not regarded as a gift, but the want of it as a defect—as the study of Mathematics. An eloquent mathematician must, from the nature of things, ever remain as rare a phenomenon as a talking fish, and it is certain that the more anyone gives himself up to the study of oratorical effect the less will he find himself in a fit state of mind to mathematicize. It is the constant aim of the mathematician to reduce all his expressions to their lowest terms, to retrench every superfluous word and phrase, and to condense the Maximum of meaning into the Minimum of language. He has to turn his eye ever inwards, to see everything in its dryest light, to train and inure himself to a habit of internal and impersonal reflection and elaboration of abstract thought, which makes it most difficult for him to touch or enlarge upon any of those themes which appeal to the emotional nature of his fellow-men. When called upon to speak in public he feels as a man might do who has passed all his life in peering through a microscope, and is suddenly called upon to take charge of an astronomical observatory. He has to go out of himself, as it were, and change the habitual focus of his vision.

One of our great English judges observed on some occasion, when he was outvoted by his brethren on the bench (or, perchance, it may have been the twelfth outstanding juryman, who protested that never before in his life had he been shut up with eleven other such obstinate men) that "opinions ought to count by weight rather than by number," and so I would say that the good done by a university is to be estimated not so much by the mere number of its members as by the spirit which actuates and the work that is done by them. When I hear, as I have heard, of members of this University, only hoping to be enabled to keep body and soul together in order that they may continue to enjoy the advantages which it affords, it may be for a decade of years to come; when I find classes diligently attending lectures on the most abstruse branches of scholarship and science, remote from all the avenues which lead to fortune or public recognition; when I observe the earnestness with which our younger members address themselves to the studies of the place, and the absence of all manifestations of disorder or levity, without the necessity for the exercise of any external restraint, it seems to me that this establishment, even in its cradle, better responds to what its name should import, more fully embodies the true idea of a university, than if its halls and lecture-rooms swarmed with hundreds of idle and indifferent students, or with students, diligent, indeed, but working not from a pure love of knowledge, not even for the chaplet of olive, or the laurel crown, but for high places in examinations, for marks, as we say in England, the counters or vouchers to enable their fortunate possessor to draw large stakes out of the pool of sinecure fellowships or lucrative civil appointments.

At this moment I happen to be engaged in a research of fascinating interest to myself, and which, if the day only responds to the promise of its dawn, will meet, I believe, a sympathetic response from the Professors of our divine Algebraical art wherever scattered through the world.

There are things called Algebraical Forms. Professor Cayley calls them Quantics. These are not, properly speaking, Geometrical Forms, although capable, to some extent, of being embodied in them, but rather schemes of processes, or of operations for forming, for calling into existence, as it were, Algebraic quantities.

To every such Quantic is associated an infinite variety of other forms that may be regarded as engendered from and floating, like an atmosphere, around it—but infinite in number as are these derived existences, these emanations from the parent form, it is found that they admit of being obtained by composition, by mixture, so to say, of a certain limited number of fundamental forms, standard rays, as they might be termed in the Algebraic Spectrum of the Quantic to which they belong. And, as it is a leading pursuit of the Physicists of the present day to ascertain the fixed lines in the spectrum of every chemical substance, so it is the aim and object of a great school of mathematicians to make out the fundamental derived forms, the Covariants and Invariants, as they are called, of these Quantics.

This is the kind of investigation in which I have for the last month or two been immersed, and which I entertain great hopes of bringing to a successful issue. Why do I mention it here? It is to illustrate my opinion as to the invaluable aid of teaching to the teacher, in throwing him back upon his own thoughts and leading him to evolve new results from ideas that would have otherwise remained passive or dormant in his mind.

But for the persistence of a student of this University in urging upon me his desire to study with me the modern Algebra I should never have been led into this investigation; and the new facts and principles which I have discovered in regard to it (important facts, I believe), would, so far as I am concerned, have remained still hidden in the womb of time. In vain I represented to this inquisitive student that he would do better to take up some other subject lying less off the beaten track of study, such as the higher parts of the Calculus or Elliptic Functions, or the theory of Substitutions, or I wot not what besides. He stuck with perfect respectfulness, but with invincible pertinacity, to his point. He would have the New Algebra (Heaven knows where he had heard about it, for it is almost unknown in this continent), that or nothing. I was obliged to yield, and what was the consequence? In trying to throw light upon an obscure explanation in our text-book, my brain took fire, I plunged with re-quickened zeal into a subject which I had for years abandoned, and found food for thoughts which have engaged my attention for a considerable time past, and will probably occupy all my powers of contemplation advantageously for several months to come.

I remember, too, how, in like manner, when a very young professor, fresh from the University of Cambridge, in the act of teaching a private pupil the simpler parts of Algebra, I discovered the principle now generally adopted into the higher text books, which goes by the name of the "Dialytic Method of Elimination." So much for the reaction of the student on the teacher*. May the time never come when the two offices of teaching and researching shall be sundered in this University! So long as man remains a gregarious and sociable being, he cannot cut himself off from the gratification of the instinct of imparting what he is learning, of propagating through others the ideas and impressions seething in his own brain, without stunting and atrophying his moral nature and drying up the surest sources of his future intellectual replenishment.

I should be sorry to suppose that I was to be left for long in sole possession of so vast a field as is occupied

---

* Not to speak of professor on professor. Thus it was in order to be able to meet the threatened interrogatories of my valued colleague, the irrepressible Mr. Rowland, that I was led, on my return passage to England last summer, to look into Prof. Clerk Maxwell's extremely valuable, but ill-digested and somewhat unduly pretentious treatise on Electricity and Magnetism, which led to my theory of the Bipotential, and to my writing the paper published in the *Philosophical Magazine* for October last, which ought to have the effect of causing the author to rewrite one of his leading chapters on Statical Electricity.

I have at present a class of from eight to ten students attending my lectures on the Modern Higher Algebra. One of them, a young engineer, engaged from eight in the morning to six at night in the duties of his office, with an interval of an hour and a half for his dinner or lectures, has furnished me with the best proof, and the best expressed, I have ever seen of what I call the Law of Concomitant Interchange, applicable to permutation systems, *i. e.* the law which affirms that every complete set of permuted elements may be separated into two parts, or if we like to say so, be presented in the form of a diptych with two precisely similar Alæ, such that a single interchange between any two elements is accompanied with a total interchange between the two Alæ. This is the theorem which lies at the basis of the great theory of simple equations, which every school-boy is supposed to understand, but which was not really made out until a bevy of great Mathematicians, including Leibnitz, Leplace and Lagrange, had turned their attention to the subject. Jacobi, I have read somewhere, used to say that if he at all excelled other mathematicians, it was chiefly due to his greater facility in manipulating simple equations that he owed it. The same Jacobi, who, I remember, visited our English Cambridge, and so much relished the Trinity audit ale which he drank there, and who once being asked whether he was brother to the eminent physicist, Professor Jacobi, of St. Petersburg, replied: "Quite the contrary—he is my brother." And *apropos* of the zeal of the student in question, let me mention for the benefit of my English friends, I have been agreeably surprised to find how widely diffused a spirit there exists in this country of disinterested love of learning. Out of Italy, especially Tuscany, where my friend Enrico Betti, as I had the opportunity of observing, and in his own country too, where no man is supposed to be a prophet, the neighborhood of Pistoja, as a Professor is more influential, more honored and courted than he could be if he were a rich Marquis, I believe there is no nation in the world where ability with character counts for so much, and the mere possession of wealth (in spite of all that we hear about the Almighty dollar), for so little as in America, with exception it may be of certain of the Trans-Atlantic cities, which are really only colonies and emporiums for the trading classes of Europe.

by modern mathematics. Mathematics is not a book confined within a cover and bound between brazen clasps, whose contents it needs only patience to ransack; it is not a mine, whose treasures may take long to reduce into possession, but which fill only a limited number of veins and lodes; it is not a soil, whose fertility can be exhausted by the yield of successive harvests; it is not a continent or an ocean, whose area can be mapped out and its contour defined: it is limitless as that space which it finds too narrow for its aspirations; its possibilities are as infinite as the worlds which are forever crowding in and multiplying upon the astronomer's gaze; it is as incapable of being restricted within assigned boundaries or being reduced to definitions of permanent validity, as the consciousness, the life, which seems to slumber in each monad, in every atom of matter, in each leaf and bud and cell, and is forever ready to burst forth into new forms of vegetable and animal existence.

JOHN VENN

(1834—1923)

John Venn, English logician, descended from a Devonshire family long distinguished for its erudition, was born at Drypool, Hull, on August 4, 1834. Representing the eighth generation of his family to study at Cambridge (to be followed by a ninth), he entered Gonville and Caius College in 1853, beginning an association with the College which was to last seventy years. In 1854 he was elected mathematical scholar; he received his degree in January 1857 as Sixth Wrangler and a few months later he was elected Fellow of the College. Ordained a deacon in 1858 and priest in 1859, he served for a short period in parochial work. In 1862 he accepted an appointment as lecturer in moral science at Cambridge. While retaining his sincere religious convictions, Venn resigned his orders in 1883 to devote himself entirely to the study and teaching of logic. In that same year he received his Sc. D. degree at Cambridge and was elected Fellow of the Royal Society. In 1888 he presented to the Cambridge Library the largest private collection of books on logic ever to be brought together. As historian of his College, Venn undertook exhaustive researches which culminated in his three volume publication of the *Biographical History of Gonville and Caius College* (1897). Venn also edited a number of volumes of university archives. Of spare build, even disposition, a devotee of mountain climbing, an excellent linguist, he was loved and admired at home and abroad. Venn died at Cambridge on April 4, 1923. His son, John Archibald, became president of Queens' College, Cambridge, in 1932.

John Venn wrote three important works which became standard texts almost at once: *The Logic of Chance* (1866), *Symbolic Logic* (1881; second edition, revised and rewritten, 1894) and the *Principles of Empirical Logic* (1889). His *Symbolic Logic* contained the *Venn Diagrams,* a system of overlapping circles or ellipses or other figures, for representing given premisses in which shaded regions were used to designate an empty class.

DIAGRAMMATIC REPRESENTATION

Our primary diagram for two terms is thus sketched:

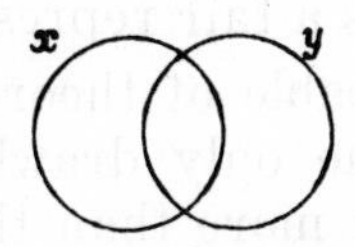

On the common plan this would represent a *proposition,* and is indeed commonly regarded as standing for the proposition 'some x is y'; though (as was mentioned in the first chapter) it equally involves in addition the two independent propositions 'some x is not y', and 'some y is not x', if we want to express all that it undertakes to tell us. With us however it does not as yet represent a proposition at all, but only the framework into which propositions may be fitted; that is, it indicates only the four combinations represented by the letter compounds, xy, $x\bar{y}$, $\bar{x}y$, $\overline{xy}$.

Now suppose that we have to reckon with the presence, and consequently with the absence, of a third term z. We just draw a third circle intersecting the above two, thus:

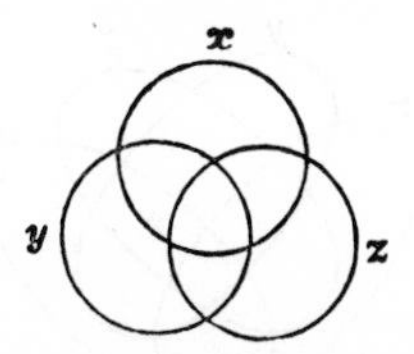

Each circle is thus cut up into four parts, and each common part of two circles into two parts, so that, including what lies outside of all the three, there are eight compartments. These of course correspond precisely to the eight combinations given by the three literal symbols; viz. xyz, $xy\bar{z}$, $x\bar{y}z$, $x\overline{yz}$, $\bar{x}yz$, $\bar{x}y\bar{z}$, $\overline{xy}z$, $\overline{xyz}$. Put a finger upon any compartment, and we have a symbolic name ready provided for it; mention the name, and there can be no doubt as to the compartment thereby referred to.

Both schemes, that of letters and that of areas, agree in their elements being mutually exclusive and collectively exhaustive. No one of the ultimate elements trespasses upon the ground of any other; and, amongst them, they account for all possibilities. Either scheme therefore might be taken as a fair representative of the other.

This process is capable of theoretic extension to any number of terms. The only drawback to its indefinite extension is that with more than three terms we do not find it possible to use such simple figures as circles; for four circles cannot be so drawn as to intersect one another in the way required. With employment of more intricate figures we might go on for ever. All that is requisite is to draw some continuous figure which shall intersect once, and once only, every existing subdivision. The new outline must be so drawn as to cut every one of the previous compartments in two, and so double their number. There is clearly no reason against continuing this process indefinitely.

With four terms in demand the most simple and symmetrical diagram seems to me that produced by making four ellipses intersect one another in the desired manner:—

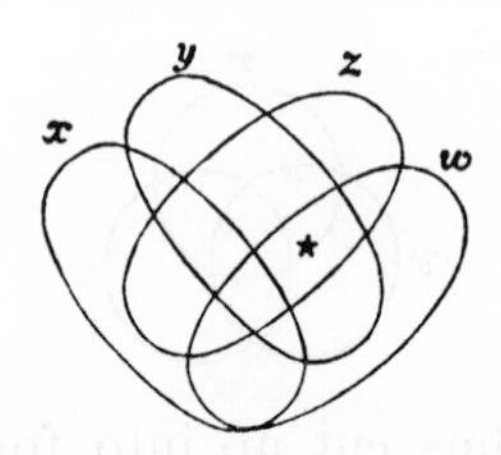

It is obvious that each component class-figure (say y) is thus divided into eight distinct compartments, producing in all 16 partitions; that these partitions are all different from each other in their composition, and are therefore mutually exclusive; and moreover that they leave nothing unaccounted for, and are therefore collectively exhaustive. And this is all that is required to make them a fitting counterpart of the 16 combinations yielded by x, y, z, w, and their negations, in the ordinary tabular statement.

With five terms combined together ellipses fail us, at least in the above simple form. It would not be difficult to sketch out figures of a horse-shoe shape which should answer the purpose, but then any outline which is not very simple and easy to follow fails altogether in its main requirement of being an aid to the eye. What is required is that we should be able to identify any assigned compartment in a moment. Thus it is instantly seen that the compartment marked with an asterisk above is that called $\bar{x}yzw$.

What we do, then, is to ascertain what combinations or classes are negatived by any given proposition, and proceed to put some kind of mark against these in the diagram. For this purpose the most effective means is just to shade them out.

For instance the proposition 'all x is y' is interpreted to mean that there is no such class of things in existence as 'x that is not-y', or $x\bar{y}$. All that we have to do is to scratch out that subdivision in the two-circle figure[1], thus:

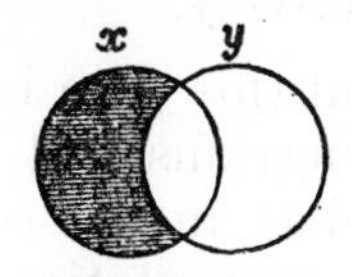

If we want to represent 'all x is all y', we take this as adding on another denial, viz., that of $\bar{x}y$, and proceed to scratch out that division also; thus

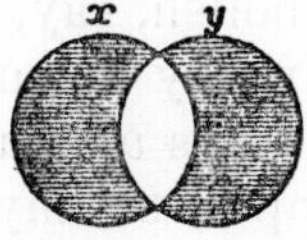

On the common Eulerian plan we should have to begin with a new figure in each of the two cases respectively,

---

[1] Other logicians (*e.g.* Schroder, *Operationskreis*, p. 10; Macfarlane, *Algebra of Logic*, p. 63) have made use of shaded diagrams to direct attention to the compartments under consideration; not, as here, with the view of expressing propositions.

viz., 'all x is y' and 'all y is x'; whereas here we start with the same general outline in each case, merely modifying it in accordance with the varying information given to us.

We postulate at present that every universal proposition may be sufficiently represented by one or more denials, and shall hope to justify this view in its due place. But it will hardly be disputed that every such proposition does in fact negative one or more combinations, and this affords an excellent means of combining two or more propositions together so as to picture their collective import. The first proposition empties out a certain number of compartments. In so far as the next may have covered the same ground it finds its work already done for it, but in so far as it has fresh information to give it displays this by clearing out compartments which the first had left untouched. All that is necessary therefore for a complete diagrammatic illustration is to begin by drawing our figure, as already explained, and then to shade out, or in some way distinguish, the classes which are successively abolished by the various premises. This will set before the eye, at a glance, the whole import of the propositions collectively.

How widely different this plan is from that of the old-fashioned Eulerian diagrams will be readily seen[1]. One great advantage consists in the ready way in which it lends itself to the representation of successive increments of knowledge as one proposition after another is taken into account, instead of demanding that we should endeavour to represent the net result of them all at a stroke. Our first data abolish, say, such and such classes. This is final, for, as already intimated, all the resultant denials must be regarded as absolute and unconditional: This leaves the field open to any similar accession of knowledge from the next data, and so more classes are swept away. Thus we go on till all the data have had

[1] I have not found any previous attempt to represent propositions on this scheme. Scheffler's elaborate *Naturgesetze* (Part III., on Logic) was apparently published about the same time as my paper in the *Phil. Magazine.*

their fire, and the muster-roll at the end will show what classes are, or may be, left surviving. If therefore we simply shade out the compartments in our figure which have thus been successively declared empty, nothing is easier than to continue doing this till all the information furnished by the data is exhausted.

As another very simple illustration of the contrast between the two methods, consider the case of the disjunction, 'All x is either y or z'. It is very seldom even attempted to represent such propositions diagrammatically, (and then, so far as I have seen, only if the alternatives are mutually exclusive), but they are readily enough exhibited when we regard the one in question as merely extinguishing any x that is neither y nor z, thus:—

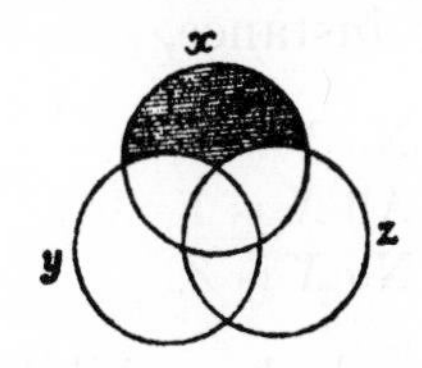

If to this were added the statement that 'none but the x's are either y or z' we should meet this fresh assertion by the further abolition of $\bar{x}y$ and $\bar{x}z$, and thus obtain:—

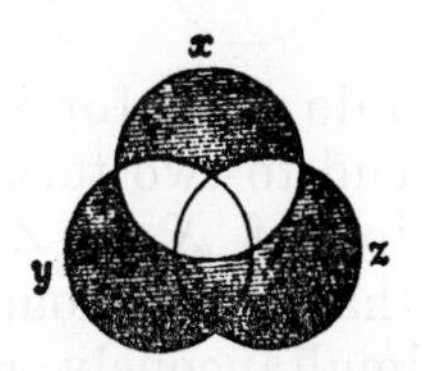

And if, again, we erase the central, or xyz compartment, we have then made our alternatives exclusive; i.e., the x's, and they alone, are either y or z only.

Now if we tried to do this by aid of Eulerian circles we should find at once that we could not do it in the only way in which intricate matters can generally be settled, viz., by breaking them up into details, and taking these step by step, making sure of each as we proceed. The Eulerian figures have to be drawn so as to indicate at once the final outcome of the knowledge furnished. This offers no difficulty in such exceedingly simple cases as those furnished by the various moods of the Syllogism, but it is quite a different matter when we come to handle the complicated results which follow upon the combination of four or five terms. Those who have only looked at the simple diagrams given by Hamilton, Thomson, and most other logicians, in illustration of the Aristotelian Syllogism, have very little conception of the intricate task which would be impressed upon them if they tried, with such resources, to illustrate equations of the type that we must be prepared to take in hand.

As the syllogistic figures are the form of reasoning most familiar to ordinary readers, I will begin with one of these, though they are too simple to serve as effective examples. Take, for instance,

No Y is Z,
All X is Y,
∴ No X is Z.

This would commonly be exhibited thus:

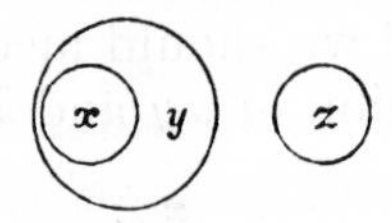

It is easy enough to do this; for in drawing our circles we have only to attend to two terms at a time, and consequently the relation of X to Z is readily detected; there is not any of that troublesome interconnexion of a number of terms simultaneously with each other which gives rise to the main perplexity in complicated problems. Accordingly such a simple example as this is not a very good one for illustrating the method now proposed; but, in order to mark the distinction, the figure to represent it is given, thus:

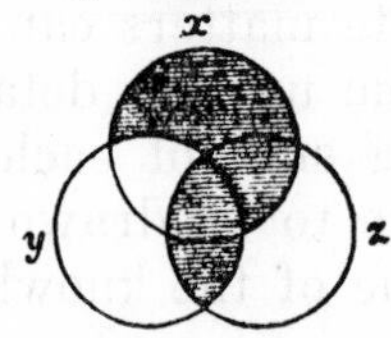

In this case the one particular relation asked for, viz. that of x to Z, it must be admitted, is not made more obvious on our plan than on the old one. The superiority, if any, in such an example must rather be sought in the completeness of the pictorial information in other respects—as, for instance, in the intimation that, of the four kinds of x which originally had to be taken into consideration, one only, viz. the $xy\bar{z}$, or the 'x that is y but is not z', is left surviving. Similarly with the formal possibilities of y and z: the relative number of these, as compared with the resultant actualities permitted by the data, is detected at a glance.

As a more suitable example consider the following—

$$\begin{cases} \text{All } x \text{ is either } y \text{ and } z, \text{ or not } y, \\ \text{If any } xy \text{ is } z, \text{ then it is } w, \\ \text{No } wx \text{ is } yz; \end{cases}$$

and suppose we are asked to exhibit the relation of x and y to each other. The problem is essentially of the same kind as the syllogistic one; but we certainly could not draw the figures in the off-hand way we did there. Since there are four terms, we sketch the appropriate 4-ellipse figure, and then proceed to analyse the premises in order to see what classes are destroyed by them. The reader will readily see that the first premise annihilates all 'xy which is not z', or $xy\bar{z}$; the second destroys 'xyz which is not w', or $xyz\bar{w}$; and the third 'wx which is yz', or $wxyz$. Shade out these three classes, and we see the resultant figure at once, viz.

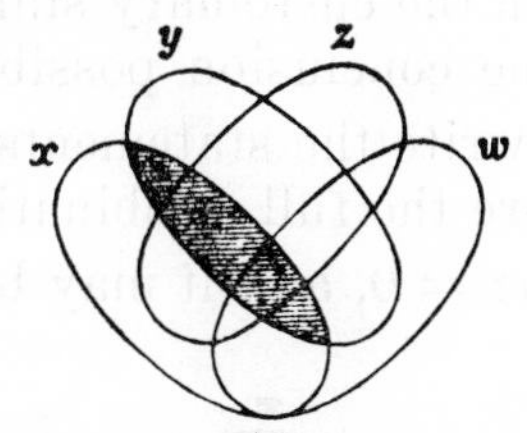

It is then evident that *all xy* has been thus made away with; that is, x and y must be mutually exclusive, or, as it would commonly be thrown into propositional form, 'No x is y.'

LOGICAL STATEMENTS OR EQUATIONS.

Interpretation of Equations in general.

There are few departments of the Symbolic Logic in which acquired views will have to be more completely abandoned than in reference to the interpretation of our equations. In the common Logic we talk of *the* solution as if there were but one; in fact a plurality of possible answers is considered a fatal defect, so that certain syllogistic figures are rejected on this ground alone.

On the symbolic system all this has, at first sight, to be altered. We must be prepared here for an apparent variety of possible answers. In saying this it is not, of course, implied that conflicting answers could be drawn, but rather that the modes of expression are so various that the same substantial answer can assume a variety of forms.

This distinction rests upon two grounds; firstly, the fact that we put a term and its contradictory (x and $\bar{x}$) on exactly the same footing, whereas the common system seeks always to express itself in positive terms, putting the negation into the predicate. Secondly, there is the obvious difference that whereas but two or three terms are commonly admitted into the former, the latter is prepared to welcome any number.

For instance, take the familiar syllogism, 'all x is y; no z is y; therefore no z is x'. Here it would be said, and very correctly from the customary standpoint, that there is one and only one conclusion possible. Now look at it symbolically: We write the statements in the form $x\bar{y} = 0$, $yz = 0$. Therefore the full combination of the two may be written $x\bar{y} + yz = 0$, and it may be represented in a diagram thus:

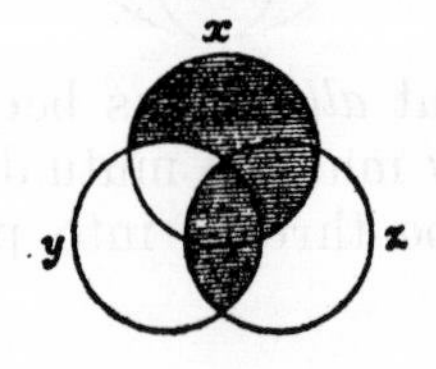

It will be seen at once, even in such a simple case, what a variety of possible solutions are here open to us. First take the fully complete solutions. These fall into the usual distinction offered by the positive and negative interpretation; that is, according as we enumerate all the abolished classes, or all the possible surviving ones. Thus $x\bar{y} + yz = 0$ expanded into its details gives four terms to be destroyed, the remaining four being equated to unity.

$$\begin{cases} x\bar{y}z + x\overline{yz} + xyz + \bar{x}yz = 0 \\ xy\bar{z} + \bar{x}y\bar{z} + \overline{xy}z + \overline{xyz} = 1 \end{cases}$$

These are the complete alternative answers given in detail. The former states, with negative disjunction, that there is nothing which falls into any one of certain four classes; the latter, with affirmative disjunction, that everything does fall into one or other of the remaining four classes.

These ultimate elements we may of course group at will, and thus obtain various simplifications of expression. The former we know will stand as $x\bar{y} + yz = 0$, the latter will stand as $y\bar{z} + \overline{xy} = 1$. They then state respectively that there is nothing which is either yz or $x\bar{y}$, and that everything is either $y\bar{z}$ or $\overline{xy}$.

Our complete scheme comprises two further modifications on anything here indicated. For we may want to determine not merely x and $\bar{x}$, y and $\bar{y}$, z and $\bar{z}$, but any possible combination or function of these; and this we may want to determine not as here in terms of *all* the remaining elements, but in terms of any selection from amongst these, after elimination of the remaining elements. These extensions will be duly discussed in their proper places.

The above example will serve to show how indefinite is the solution of a logical problem, unless some further indications are given as to the sort of information desired. The sum-total of the facts which are left consistent with the data must necessarily be the same, however they may be expressed. But the various ways of expressing those facts, and still more the various ways of expressing selections and combinations of them, are very numerous. Take, for instance, a slightly more complicated example, such as that indicated in the following figure:

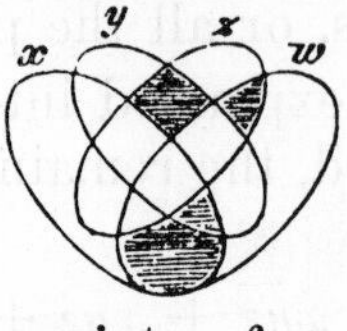

and observe in what a variety of ways the unshaded portion may be described. The figure represents the results of the data;—

$$\begin{cases} \text{All } wx \text{ is } z \\ \text{All } wz \text{ is } x \text{ or } y \\ \text{All } yz \text{ is } w \text{ or } x \end{cases} \quad \text{viz.} \quad \begin{cases} wx\bar{z} = 0 \\ wz\bar{x}\bar{y} = 0 \\ yz\bar{w}\bar{x} = 0. \end{cases}$$

One way of course is to say that the surviving classes are all which are not thus obliterated; these being negatively

$$1 - x\bar{z}w - \bar{x}\bar{y}zw - \bar{x}yz\bar{w}$$

or, slightly grouped,

$$1 - x\bar{z}w - \bar{x}z(\bar{y}w + y\bar{w}).$$

Or again, we may express them all positively thus,

$$x(wz + \bar{w}z + \bar{w}\bar{z}) + \bar{x}z(wy + \bar{w}\bar{y}) + \bar{x}\bar{z}$$

or, less completely positive, but briefer,

$$x(1 - w\bar{z}) + \bar{x}z(wy + \bar{w}\bar{y}) + \bar{x}\bar{z}$$

$$\text{or} \quad x(1 - w\bar{z}) + \bar{x}\{z(wy + \bar{w}\bar{y}) + \bar{z}\},$$

each of these symbolic groupings having of course its suitable verbal description. Thus the last may be read 'All x except what is w but not z; and all not-x, provided it be not-z, or, if z, then both or neither w and y'.

The general nature of the problem thus put before us is easily indicated. Suppose there were four terms involved; then our symbolic apparatus provides 2^4 or 16 compartments or possibilities. The data impose material limits upon these possibilities, leaving only a limited number of actualities. That is, they extinguish a certain number and leave only the remainder surviving. In this case out of the 16 original possibilities 12 are left remaining. The full result then of the data is given by enumerating completely either the extinguished compartments or the remaining ones. Either of these enumerations is only possible in one way, provided we give it in full detail. But when we want to group the results, for more convenience, into compendious statements, we see that this can be done in a variety of ways.

The number of different combinations which can be produced increases with the introduction of every fresh class term in a way which taxes the imagination to follow. Thus three terms yield eight subdivisions. From these we might make eight distinct selections of one only; 28 of a pair; 56 of three together, and so on. The total number of distinct groups which can thus be produced is

$$8 + 28 + 56 + 70 + 56 + 28 + 8 + 1 \text{ or } 255.$$

One case, and only one, is excluded necessarily, namely that in which every compartment is erased, for this corresponds to the one formal impossibility of endeavouring to maintain that every one of our exhaustive divisions is unoccupied: this being, as the reader knows, the symbolic generalization of the Law of Excluded Middle. The arithmetical statement of the total number of cases is readily enough written down. Three terms yield eight sub-classes, viz. 2^3; and these eight sub-classes may be taken as above in $2^8 - 1$ ways: viz. $2^{2^3} - 1$ represents the possible varieties before us. Or expressed generally, if there be n terms we can have 2^n classes, and accordingly $2^{2^n} - 1$ distinct groups of these classes. Of course this expression increases with enormous rapidity as n increases. Four terms thus yield 65,535 possibilities in the way of combination of the elements yielded, and so on.

WAN WANG

(12th cent. B.C.)

Wan Wang (King Wan), Chinese Prince, viceroy of the Chou Province in the 12th century B.C., admired as a model of all that is good, beloved for his wisdom and restraint, is considered the founder of the Chou dynasty, even though he himself never held the throne. Wrongly suspected of disloyalty by Chou Hsin, the last ruler of the Shang dynasty, he was imprisoned by Hsin in 1143 B.C. and in immediate danger of execution. Wan was rescued by a party of his followers led by his son, Wu Wang. Soon afterward, Wu Wang and a coalition of princes drew up a bill of particulars listing their charges of misrule against Hsin. Numerous specific instances of Hsin's unspeakable cruelty were given. In the ensuing war undertaken to overthrow the Shang ruler, the revolt against the Shang succeeded. With the assistance and support of his distinguished brother Chou Kung, the Duke of Chou (Kau), Wu Wang was established as the first emperor of the Chou dynasty.

Wan Wang had been imprisoned for almost a year. During that time he wrote the textual part of the *Yi King,* a book which came to be regarded by the Chinese with great reverence. In the *Yi King* Wang combined the eight *kwa* or trigrams of *Fu-hsi,* by two's into sixty four hexagrams, adding to each his statement of the meaning of the figure. His son the Duke of Chou (Kau) is credited with the explanation of each of the lineal components of each hexagram. Ten *Appendixes* added to the writings of Wan Wang and his son form the latter part of the *Yi King.* The *Appendixes* are attributed to Confucius (c. 550—479 B.C.). Wan Wang and his son, both skilled in divination, intended that their writings be used for divining, and the meanings set forth were deliberately made obscure to avoid abuse by unworthy individuals of the power to be derived from a true knowledge. The *Yi King,* also called the *Book of Changes,* escaped destruction in the general book-burning ordered by the despot of the Ch'in at the end of the third century B.C., as books on divination were expressly exempted from the burning. The interpretation of the text given by Confucius in the *Appendixes* was philosophical. Great pride and respect is felt by the Chinese for the *Yi King* as a fundamental book of their philosophy. A long list of scholars gained distinction as expounders of the meaning of the *Yi King* and its *Appendixes.* The imperial edition of the *Yi King* published in 1718 contained extracts from commentaries on it by more than two hundred writers dating from the second century B.C.

It is stated by some that Wan Wang, the Duke of Chou, and Confucius were all editors, and that Fu-hsi was the original author. Fu-hsi (c. 3020 B.C.), who belonged to the Mythical Period of Chinese history, before the invention of the plow, when men lived mainly by hunting and fishing, is credited with the invention of the practice of divination. The diagrams, contemporary with the invention of writing, became the expression of a philosophy. The first principle to be expressed in the *Yi King* was the philosophy of the dual, involving the strong element and the weak element in nature. As time went on this was contracted into a single antithesis and then expanded into a system containing a number of elements. Rudiments of ancient Chinese mathematics are found in the *Yi King.*

●

THE YI KING

From *The Sacred Books of China*

translated by JAMES LEGGE

INTRODUCTION.

'In (the system of) the Yi there is the Great Extreme, which produced the two I (Elementary Forms). These two Forms produced the four Hsiang (Emblematic Symbols); which again produced the eight Kwa (or Trigrams). The eight Kwa served to determine the good and evil (issues of events), and from this determination there ensued the (prosecution of the) great business of life.'

The two elementary Forms, the four emblematic Symbols, and the eight Trigrams can all be exhibited with what may be deemed certainty. A whole line (——) and a divided (— —) were the two I. These two lines placed over themselves, and each of them over the other, formed the four Hsiang: ⚌; ⚎; ⚍; ⚏. The same two lines placed successively over these Hsiang, formed the eight Kwa, exhibited above.

FU-HSI'S TRIGRAMS.

1	2	3	4	5	6	7	8
*kh*ien	tui	lî	*k*ăn	sun	khân	kăn	khwăn
Heaven, the sky.	Water, collected as in a marsh or lake.	Fire, as in lightning; the sun.	Thunder.	The wind; wood.	Water, as in rain, clouds, springs, streams, and defiles. The moon.	Hills, or mountains.	The earth.
S.	S.E.	E.	N.E.	S.W.	W.	N.W.	N.
Untiring strength; power.	Pleasure; complacent satisfaction.	Brightness; elegance.	Moving, exciting power.	Flexibility; penetration.	Peril; difficulty.	Resting; the act of arresting.	Capaciousness; submission.

KING WĂN'S TRIGRAMS.

1	2	3	4	5	6	7	8
lî	sun	*k*ăn	kăn	khân	*kh*ien	tui	khwăn
Second daughter.	Oldest daughter.	Oldest son.	Youngest son.	Second son.	Father.	Youngest daughter.	Mother.
S.	S.E.	E.	N.E.	N.	N.W.	W.	S.W.

'A strong and a weak line were manipulated together (till there were the 8 trigrams), and those 8 trigrams were added each to itself and to all the others (till the 64 hexagrams were formed).'

PLATE I.

THE HEXAGRAMS, in the order in which they appear in the Yî, and were arranged by king Wăn.

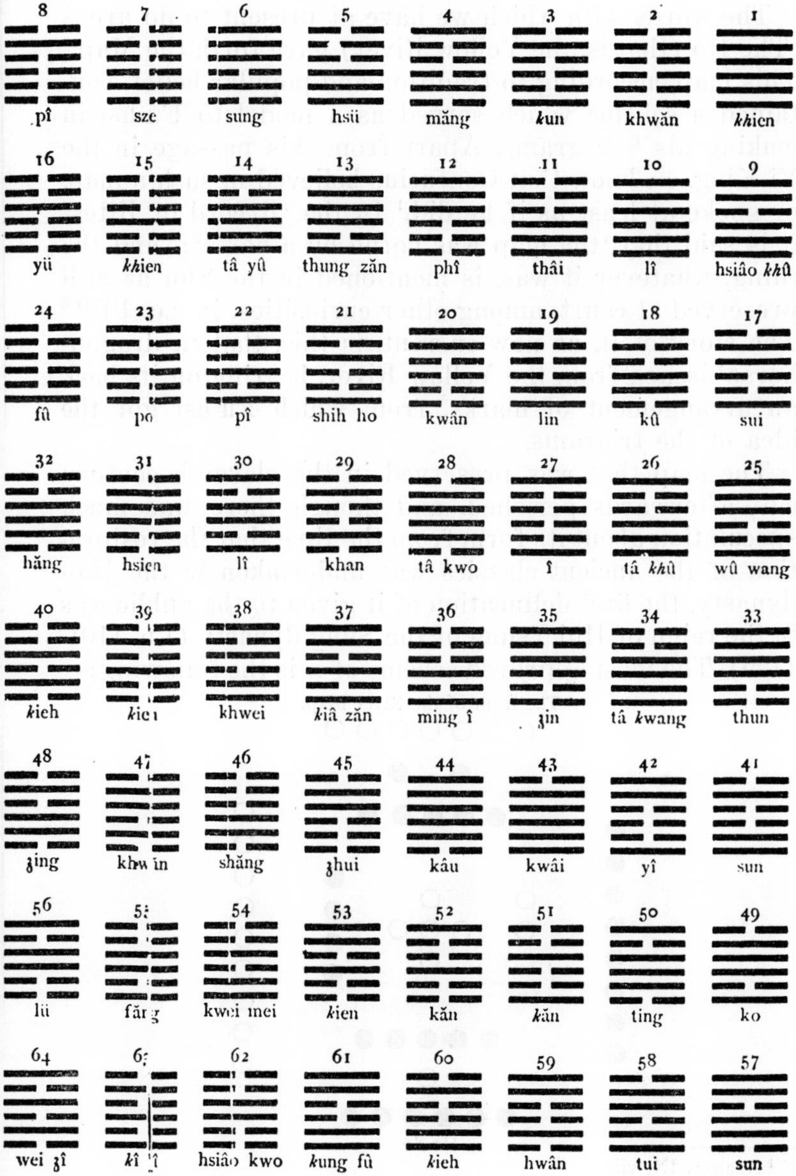

8	7	6	5	4	3	2	1
pî	sze	sung	hsü	măng	*k*un	khwăn	*kh*ien
16	**15**	**14**	**13**	**12**	**11**	**10**	**9**
yü	*kh*ien	tâ yû	thung zăn	phî	thâi	lî	hsiâo *kh*û
24	**23**	**22**	**21**	**20**	**19**	**18**	**17**
fû	po	pî	shih ho	kwân	lin	kû	sui
32	**31**	**30**	**29**	**28**	**27**	**26**	**25**
hăng	hsien	lî	khan	tâ kwo	î	tâ *kh*û	wû wang
40	**39**	**38**	**37**	**36**	**35**	**34**	**33**
*k*ieh	*k*ien	khwei	*k*iâ zăn	ming î	ȝin	tâ *k*wang	thun
48	**47**	**46**	**45**	**44**	**43**	**42**	**41**
ȝing	khwăn	shăng	ȝhui	kâu	kwâi	yî	sun
56	**55**	**54**	**53**	**52**	**51**	**50**	**49**
lü	făng	kwei mei	*k*ien	kăn	*k*ăn	ting	ko
64	**63**	**62**	**61**	**60**	**59**	**58**	**57**
wei ȝî	*k*î ȝî	hsiâo kwo	*k*ung fû	*k*ieh	hwân	tui	sun

'Heaven produced the spirit-like things (the tortoise and the divining plant), and the sages took advantage of them. (The operations of) heaven and earth are marked by so many changes and transformations, and the sages imitated them (by means of the Yi). Heaven hangs out its (brilliant) figures, from which are seen good fortune and bad, and the sages made their emblematic interpretations accordingly. The Ho gave forth the scheme or map, and the Lo gave forth the writing, of (both of) which the sages took advantage.'

The words with which we have at present to do are—'The Ho (that is, the Yellow River) gave forth the Map.' This map, according to tradition and popular belief, contained a scheme which served as a model to Fu-hsi in making his 8 trigrams. Apart from this passage in the Yi King, we know that Confucius believed in such a map, or spoke at least as if he did.[1] In the 'Record of Rites' it is said that 'the map was borne by a horse[2];' and the thing, whatever it was, is mentioned in the Shu as still preserved at court, among other curiosities, in B.C. 1079.[3] The story of it, as now current, is this, that 'a dragon-horse' issued from the Yellow River, bearing on its back an arrangement of marks, from which Fu-hsi got the idea of the trigrams.

The map that was preserved in the eleventh century B.C., afterwards perished, and though there was much speculation about its form from the time that the restoration of the ancient classics was undertaken in the Han dynasty, the first delineation of it given to the public was in the reign of Hui Tsung of the Sung dynasty (A.D. 1101-1125). The most approved scheme of it is the following:—

The form of the River Map.

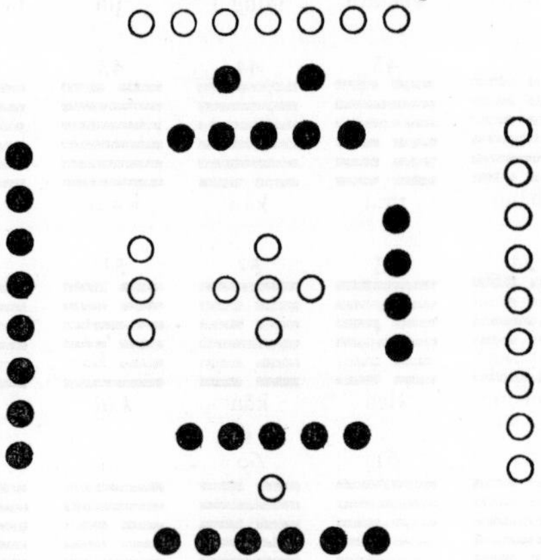

Ho-t'u

[1] Analects IX, viii.
[2] Li *K*i VIII, iv. 16.
[3] Shu V, xxii, 19.

It will be observed that the markings in this scheme are small circles, pretty nearly equally divided into dark and light. All of them whose numbers are odd are light circles,—1, 3, 5, 7, 9; and all of them whose numbers are even are dark,—2, 4, 6, 8, 10. This is given as the origin of the numbers of heaven and earth. The difference in the colour of the circles occasioned the distinction of them and of what they signify into Yin and Yang, the dark and the bright, the moon-like and the sun-like; for the sun is called the Great Brightness (Thai Yang), and the moon the Great Obscurity (Thai Yin). Fu-hsi in making the trigrams, and king Wan, if it was he who first multiplied them to the 64 hexagrams, found it convenient to use lines instead of the circles:—the whole line (——) for the bright circle (O), and the divided line (— —) for the dark (●). The first, the third, and the fifth lines in a hexagram, if they are 'correct' as it is called, should all be whole, and the second, fourth, and sixth lines should all be divided. Yang lines are strong (or hard), and Yin lines are weak (or soft). The former indicate vigour and authority; the latter, feebleness and submission. It is the part of the former to command; of the latter to obey.

'The Lo produced the writing.' This writing was a scheme of the same character as the Ho map, but on the back of a tortoise, which emerged from the river Lo, and showed it to the Great Yu, when he was engaged in his celebrated work of draining off the waters of the flood, as related in the Shu. To the hero sage it suggested 'the Great Plan,' an interesting but mystical document of the same classic, 'a Treatise,' according to Gaubil, 'of Physics, Astrology, Divination, Morals, Politics, and Religion,' the great model for the government of the kingdom. The accepted representation of this writing is the following:—

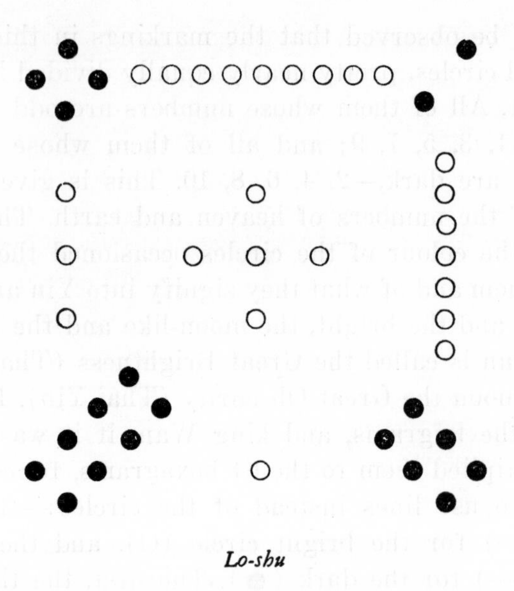

Lo-shu

But substituting numbers for the number of marks, we have

4 9 2

3 5 7

8 1 6

in which the numbers from 1 to 9 are arranged so as to make 15 in whatever way we add them.

TEXT. SECTION I.

I. The *Kh*ien Hexagram.

Explanation of the entire figure by king Wan.

*Kh*ien (represents) what is great and origi
penetrating, advantageous, correct and firm.

Explanation of the separate lines by the duke of *K*au.

1. In the first (or lowest) line, undivided, (we see i
subject as) the dragon lying hid (in the deep). It is nc
the time for active doing.

2. In the second line, undivided, (we see its subject as) the dragon appearing in the field. It will be advantageous to meet with the great man.

3. In the third line, undivided, (we see its subject as) the superior man active and vigilant all the day, and in the evening still careful and apprehensive. (The position is) dangerous, but there will be no mistake.

4. In the fourth line, undivided, (we see its subject as the dragon looking) as if he were leaping up, but still in the deep. There will be no mistake.

5. In the fifth line, undivided, (we see its subject as) the dragon on the wing in the sky. It will be advantageous to meet with the great man.

6. In the sixth (or topmost) line, undivided, (we see its subject as) the dragon exceeding the proper limits. There will be occasion for repentance.

7. (The lines of this hexagram are all strong and undivided, as appears from) the use of the number nine. If the host of dragons (thus) appearing were to divest themselves of their heads, there would be good fortune.

The Text under each hexagram consists of one paragraph by king Wan, explaining the figure as a whole, and of six (in the case of hexagrams 1 and 2, of seven) paragraphs by the duke of *K*au, explaining the individual lines. The explanatory notices introduced above to this effect will not be repeated. A double space will be used to mark off the portion of king Wan from that of his son.

Each hexagram consists of two of the trigrams of Fu-hsi, the lower being called 'the inner,' and the one above 'the outer.' The lines, however, are numbered from one to six, commencing with the lowest. To denote the number of it and of the sixth line, the terms for 'commencing' and 'topmost' are used. The intermediate lines are simply 'second,' 'third,' &c. As the lines must be either whole or divided, technically called strong and weak, yang and yin, this distinction is indicated by the application to them of the numbers nine and six. All whole lines are nine, all divided lines, six.

Two explanations have been proposed of this application of these numbers. The *Khien* trigram, it is said, contains 3 strokes (☰), and the Khwan 6 (☷). But the yang contains the yin in itself, and its representative number will be 3 + 6 = 9, while the yin, not containing the yang, will only have its own number or 6. This explanation, entirely arbitrary, is now deservedly abandoned. The other is based on the use of the 'four Hsiang,' or emblematic figures (⚌ the great or old yang, ⚎ the young yang, ⚏ the old yin, and ⚍ the young yin). To these are assigned (by what process is unimportant for our present purpose) the numbers 9, 8, 7, 6. They were 'the old yang,' represented by 9, and 'the old yin,' represented by 6, that, in the manipulation of the stalks to form new diagrams, determined the changes of figure; and so 9 and 6 came to be used as the names of a yang line and a yin line respectively. This explanation is now universally acquiesced in. The nomenclature of first nine, nine two, &c., or first six, six two, &c., however, is merely a jargon; and I have preferred to use, instead of it, in the translation, in order to describe the lines, the names 'undivided' and 'divided.'

I. Does king Wan ascribe four attributes here to *Kh*ien, or only two? According to Appendix IV, always by Chinese writers assigned to Confucius, he assigns four, corresponding to the principles of benevolence, righteousness, propriety, and knowledge in man's nature. *K*u Hsi held that he assigned only two, and that we should translate, 'greatly penetrating,' and 'requires to be correct and firm,' two responses in divination. Up and down throughout the Text of the 64 hexagrams, we often find the characters thus coupled together. Both interpretations are possible. I have followed what is accepted as the view of Confucius. It would take pages to give a tithe of what has been written in justification of it, and to reconcile it with the other.

'The dragon' is the symbol employed by the duke of *K*au to represent 'the superior man' and especially 'the great man,' exhibiting the virtues or attributes characteristic of heaven. The creature's proper home is in the water, but it can disport itself on the land, and also fly and soar aloft. It has been from the earliest time the emblem with the Chinese of the highest dignity and wisdom, of sovereignty and sagehood, the combination of which constitutes 'the great man.' One emblem runs through the lines of many of the hexagrams as here.

But the dragon appears in the sixth line as going beyond the proper limits. The ruling-sage has gone through all the sphere in which he is called on to display his attributes; it is time for him to relax. The line should not be always pulled tight; the bow should not be always kept drawn. The unchanging use of force will give occasion for repentance. The moral meaning found in the line is that 'the high shall be abased.'

The meaning given to the supernumerary paragraph is the opposite of that of paragraph 6. The 'host of dragons without their heads' would give us the next hexagram, or Khwan, made up of six divided lines. Force would have given place to submission, and haughtiness to humility; and the result would be good fortune. Such at least is the interpretation of the paragraph given in a narrative of the *Tso-Kwan* under B.C. 513.

II. THE KHWAN HEXAGRAM.

Khwan (represents) what is great and originating, penetrating, advantageous, correct and having the firmness of a mare. When the superior man (here intended) has to make any movement, if he take the initiative, he will go astray; if he follow, he will find his (proper) lord. The advantageousness will be seen in his getting friends in the south-west, and losing friends in the north-east. If he rest in correctness and firmness, there will be good fortune.

APPENDIX III.

SECTION I.

Chapter IX. 49. To heaven belongs (the number) 1; to earth, 2; to heaven, 3; to earth, 4; to heaven, 5; to earth, 6; to heaven, 7; to earth, 8; to heaven, 9; to earth, 10.

50. The numbers belonging to heaven are five, and those belonging to earth are (also) five. The numbers of these two series correspond to each other (in their fixed positions), and each one has another that may be considered its mate. The heavenly numbers amount to 25, and the earthly to 30. The numbers of heaven and earth together amount to 55. It is by these that the changes and transformations are effected, and the spirit-like agencies kept in movement.

51. The numbers of the Great Expansion, (multiplied together), make 50, of which (only) 49 are used (in divination). (The stalks representing these) are divided into two heaps to represent the two (emblematic lines, or heaven and earth). One is then taken (from the heap on the right), and placed (between the little finger of

the left hand and the next), that there may thus be symbolised the three (powers of heaven, earth, and man). (The heaps on both sides) are manipulated by fours to represent the four seasons; and then the remainders are returned, and placed (between) the two middle fingers of the left hand, to represent the intercalary month. In five years there are two intercalations, and therefore there are two operations; and afterwards the whole process is repeated.

52. The numbers (required) for *Kh*ien (or the undivided line) amount to 216; those for Khwan (or the divided line), to 144. Together they are 360, corresponding to the days of the year.

In 49 and 50 'heaven' and 'earth' are used as we have seen *Kh*ien and Khwan are in paragraphs 30 and 34. Odd numbers belong to the strong or undivided line, which is symbolical of the active operation in nature, and the even numbers to the weak or divided line, symbolical of its inaction. The phraseology of the paragraphs, however, can only be understood by a reference to 'the river map,' which has been given in the Introduction.

The map, as it appeared on the back of 'the dragon-horse,' consisted of so many circles, and so many dark circular markings, the former, it was assumed, being of the yang character, and the latter of the yin. Fu-hsi for the circle substituted the strong or undivided line (———), and for the dark markings the weak or divided (— —). It will be seen that the yang symbols are the 1, 3, 5, 7 and 9 circles, and the yin are the 2, 4, 6, 8 and 10 circular markings, which is the pictorial delineation of paragraph 49. The only thing to be said upon it is that the arrangement of the five circles and ten circular markings is peculiar, and evidently devised 'for a purpose.' So far, however, as we know, no figure of the map was attempted till after the beginning of our twelfth century.

The same figure is supposed to illustrate what is said in paragraph 50: 'The numbers of the two series correspond to each other in their fixed positions.' 1 and 2, and 3 and 4 certainly front each other, and perhaps 5 and 6; but 7 and 8, and 9 and 10 do not do so in the same way. It is said also that 'each has another that may be considered its mate.' So it is with 1 and 6, 2 and 7, 3 and 8, 4 and 9, but hardly with 5 and 10. Further, $1 + 3 + 5 + 7 + 9 = 25$; $2 + 4 + 6 + 8 + 10 = 30$; and $25 + 30 = 55$; all of which points are stated.

Paragraph 51 is intended to describe the process of divination in manipulating the stalks, but the description is confused by introducing into it the four seasons and the subject of intercalation, so as to be very difficult to understand.

Paragraph 52. The actual number of the undivided and divided lines in the hexagrams is the same, 192 of each. But the representative number of an undivided line is 9, and of a divided line 6. Now 9×4 (the number of the emblematic figures) $\times 6$ (the lines of each hexagram) $= 216$; and $6 \times 4 \times 6 = 144$. The sum of these products is 360, which was assumed, for the purpose of working the intercalation, as the standard length of the year.

53. The number produced by the lines in the two parts (of the Yi) amount to 11,520, corresponding to the number of all things.

54. Therefore by means of the four operations is the Yi completed. It takes 18 changes to form a hexagram.

55. (The formation of) the eight trigrams constitutes the small completion (of the Yi).

56. If we led on the diagrams and expanded them, if we prolonged each by the addition of the proper lines, then all events possible under the sky might have their representation.

57. (The diagrams) make manifest (by their appended explanations), the ways (of good and ill fortune), and show virtuous actions in their spiritual relations. In this way, by consulting them, we may receive an answer (to our doubts), and we may also by means of them assist the spiritual (power in its agency in nature and providence).

58. The Master said:—'He who knows the method of change and transformation may be said to know what is done by that spiritual (power).'

Chapter X. 59. In the Yi there are four things characteristic of the way of the sages. We should set the highest value on its explanations to guide us in speaking; on its changes for (the initiation of) our movements; on its emblematic figures for (definite action as in) the construction of implements; and on its prognostications for our practice of divination.

60. Therefore, when a superior man is about to take action of a more private or of a public character, he asks (the Yi), making his inquiry in words. It receives his order, and the answer comes as the echo's response. Be the subject remote or near, mysterious or deep, he forthwith knows of what kind will be the coming result. (If the Yi) were not the most exquisite thing under heaven, would it be concerned in such an operation as this?

61. (The stalks) are manipulated by threes and fives to determine (one) change; they are laid on opposite

sides, and placed one up, one down, to make sure of their numbers; and the (three necessary) changes are gone through with in this way, till they form the figures pertaining to heaven or to earth. Their numbers are exactly determined, and the emblems of (all things) under the sky are fixed.

SECTION II.

Chapter II. 11. Anciently, when Pao-hsi had come to the rule of all under heaven, looking up, he contemplated the brilliant forms exhibited in the sky, and looking down he surveyed the patterns shown on the earth. He contemplated the ornamental appearances of birds and beasts and the (different) suitabilities of the soil. Near at hand, in his own person, he found things for consideration, and the same at a distance, in things in general. On this he devised the eight trigrams, to show fully the attributes of the spirit-like and intelligent (operations working secretly), and to classify the qualities of the myriads of things.

12. He invented the making of nets of various kinds by knitting strings, both for hunting and fishing. The idea of this was taken, probably, from Li (the third trigram, and thirtieth hexagram).

13. On the death of Pao-hsi, there arose Shannang (in his place). He fashioned wood to form the share, and bent wood to make the plough-handle. The advantages of ploughing and weeding were then taught to all under heaven. The idea of this was taken, probably, from Yi (the forty-second hexagram).

14. He caused markets to be held at midday, thus bringing together all the people, and assembling in one place all their wares. Thy made their exchanges and retired, every one having got what he wanted. The idea of this was taken, probably, from Shih Ho (the twenty-first hexagram).

16. They hollowed out trees to form canoes; they cut others long and thin to make oars. Thus arose the bene-

fit of canoes and oars for the help of those who had no means of intercourse with others. They could now reach the most distant parts, and all under heaven were benefited. The idea of this was taken, probably, from Hwan (the fifty-ninth hexagram).

17. They used oxen (in carts) and yoked horses (to chariots), thus providing for the carriage of what was heavy, and for distant journeys,—thereby benefiting all under the sky. The idea of this was taken, probably, from Sui (the seventeenth hexagram).

18. They made the (defence of the) double gates, and (the warning of) the clapper, as a preparation against the approach of marauding visitors. The idea of this was taken, probably, from Yu (the sixteenth hexagram).

19. They cut wood and fashioned it into pestles; they dug in the ground and formed mortars. Thus the myriads of the people received the benefit arising from the use of the pestle and mortar. The idea of this was taken, probably, from Hsiao Kwo (the sixty-second hexagram).

20. They bent wood by means of string so as to form bows, and sharpened wood so as to make arrows. This gave the benefit of bows and arrows, and served to produce everywhere a feeling of awe. The idea of this was taken, probably, from Khwei (the thirty-eighth hexagram).

23. In the highest antiquity, government was carried on successfully by the use of knotted cords (to preserve the memory of things). In subsequent ages the sages substituted for these written characters and bonds. By means of these (the doings of) all the officers could be regulated, and (the affairs of) all the people accurately examined. The idea of this was taken, probably, from Kwai (the forty-third hexagram).

Chapter II, paragraphs 11-23, treats of the progress of civilisation in China, and how the great men of antiquity who led the way in the various steps of that progress were guided by the Yi.

WANG HS'IAO-T'UNG

(Seventh Century)

Wang Hs'iao-t'ung, Chinese astronomer and mathematician, author of the *Ch'i-ku Suan-ching* ("Arithmetical Classic of Ancient Rules"), which despite its name presented a significant advance over the ancient methods, belonged to the early period of the T'ang dynasty. Few facts of his life are known beyond Wang's service in the T'ang government as an expert on the Astronomical Board. It was his duty in 623, 626, and so on, as a Doctor of Arithmetic to subject to critical examination, the contents of the calendar composed by Fu Jen-Chun in 618. We know something of his personality from his writing which reveals a vast self assurance and supreme confidence in his work.

Wang Hs'iao-t'ung's mathematical treatise, *Ch'i-ku Suan-ching,* has come down to us in very nearly complete form. Only a few lines have been lost where part of the last page is torn away. The treatise consists of a set of twenty problems in solid mensuration and Wang's solutions and commentaries on them. The problems were originally intended to illustrate the fifth section of the old "Nine Sections". Many of the solutions are such as involve cubic equations. Attached to the work and forming a kind of preface to it, is a letter of presentation written by Wang to his Emperor stating that the methods used in the solutions were of his own devising. In a challenge to his readers, Wang offered a thousand taels of silver to anyone who could find a single error in his work. The *Ch'i-ku Suan-ching* by Wang Hs'iao-t'ung antedated by about six hundred years the next mention of cubic equations in Chinese mathematical writings.

CH'I-KU SUAN-CHING

From *The Development of Mathematics in China and Japan*

by Yoshio Mikami

"There is a right triangle, the product of whose two sides is 706-1/50, and whose hypotenuse is greater than the first side by 30-9/60. It is required to know the lengths of the three sides."

Wang gives the answer of this problem to be 14-7/20, 49-1/5 and 51-1/4. He then proceeds to give the rule:

"The product (P) being squared and being divided by twice the surplus (S), make the result the *shih* or the constant class. Halve the surplus, and make it the *lien-fa* or the second degree class. And carry out the operation of evolution according to the extraction of cube root. The result gives the first side. Adding the surplus to it, one gets the hypotenuse. Divide the product with the first side and the quotient is the second side."

The rule is the same as to construct the cubic equation

$$x^3 + \frac{S}{2} x^2 - \frac{P^2}{2S} = 0,$$

or the arrangement as annexed, and to solve it in a process similar to the extraction of a cube root. It is

$-\frac{P^2}{2S}$	0^0
0	1^0
$\frac{S}{2}$	2^0
1	3^0

very evident that the way of solving an equation of the third degree in this way applies only to numerical equations.

"In a right triangle, the product of the first side and the hypotenuse is 397-3/4, and the difference of the hypotenuse and the second side is 1/10; what is the length of this second side?

"Answer. 92-2/5.

"Rule. The (given) product (P) being squared and divided by twice the (given) difference (D), we call the result the 'solid volume'. Again cube the (given) difference, and halve it, when the difference of this quantity and the 'solid volume' should be taken for the *shih* or the constant class. Again square the (given) difference and take its twice as the *fang-fa* or the 1st degree class. Again take 5/2 of the (given) difference as the *lien-fa* or the 2nd degree class. Then (making 1 the 3rd degree class) divide according to the rule of the cubic root extraction. The root gives the length required."

This rule is equivalent to the construction of the cubic equation,

$$x^3 + \frac{5}{2} Dx^2 + 2D^2x = \frac{P^2}{2D} - \frac{D^3}{2}$$

"In a store-house shaped like a truncated square pyramid, the difference of whose upper and lower sides is 6 feet (D) and whose height is 9 feet (G) greater than the upper side, there is contained 187·2 measures of corn, of which 50·4 measures are carried out. What will be the lengths of the upper and lower sides of the store-house, its height, and the depth and a side of the upper end of the remaining corn?

"Answer. Upper side is 3 feet; lower side is 9 feet; height 12 feet; depth and upper side of the remainder are each 6 feet."

To find the upper side of the store-house in this problem, Wang Hs'iao-t'ung applies the equation,

$$x^3 + (D + G)\,x^2 + \left(DG + \frac{D^2}{3}\right)x = P - \frac{D^2 G}{3},$$

where P represents the volume of the store-house expressed in cubic feet. This is the very equation to which we are led by eliminating y and z from

$$y - x = D, \quad z - x = G, \quad \frac{1}{3}\,z\,(xy + x^2 + y^2) = P,$$

where y and z represent the lower side and the height respectively, and the last equation is in accordance with the formula that appears in the "Arithmetic in Nine Sections".

Wang Hs'iao-t'ung gives in the *Ch'i-ku Suan-ching* only his rules for the arrangement of the equations; he does not give the particulars of the procedure for arriving at such equations.

CASPAR WESSEL

(1745—1818)

The first clear, scientific exposition of the modern geometrical method of representing $\sqrt{-1}$ was given in a paper entitled *On the Analytic Representation of Direction* before the Royal Academy of Sciences and Letters of Denmark in 1797 by a Norwegian surveyor, Caspar Wessel. The treatise contained a complete development of the laws governing operations with directed line segments as representations of numbers in the form $a + b\sqrt{-1}$ and their applications, as well as a partial theory of rotation.

Caspar Wessel was born in Jonsrud, Norway, on June 8, 1745. His father was a pastor in that town and Caspar was one of a bustling household of thirteen children. He received an excellent education, begun at Jonsrud and continued in 1757 at the high school in Christiania. In 1763 Wessel went to Copenhagen for further study. The following year he was engaged by the Danish Academy of Sciences as an assistant in the preparation of a map of Denmark. He remained in the employ of the Academy from that time, uninterruptedly until 1805. Possessing broad interests and a versatile turn of mind, Wessel also studied Roman law, passing an examination in this field in 1778. Wessel received many marks of appreciation of his distinguished services in Denmark. For a special assignment performed for the Academy after his retirement, he was awarded the Academy's silver medal and a complete set of its memoirs. He was made Knight of the Danebrog in 1815. The high place Wessel held in the estimation of his contemporaries was sustained in 1819 when many of the maps of Denmark were declared out of date, while Wessel's trigonometric calculations were retained, being specifically excluded from the general discard.

It speaks well for the Academy that they received Wessel's paper sympathetically, since he was neither a member of the Academy nor was he considered a mathematician. Sponsored and encouraged by Tetens, Councillor-of-state, Wessel's presentation of his work in 1797 was followed by its publication in 1798 and its appearance in Vol. V of the Memoirs of the Academy in 1799. Written in Danish, it failed to achieve wide accessibility to the mathematicians of other countries with the result that this excellent and significant work did not become generally known until a French translation of it was published in 1897.

ON THE ANALYTICAL REPRESENTATION OF DIRECTION

AN ATTEMPT[1]

APPLIED CHIEFLY TO THE SOLUTION OF PLANE AND SPHERICAL POLYGONS (BY CASPAR WESSEL, SURVEYOR.)

(Translated from the Danish by Professor Martin A Nordgaard, St. Olaf College, Northfield, Minnesota.)

This present attempt deals with the question, how may we represent direction analytically; that is, how shall we express right lines so that in a single equation involving one unknown line and others known, both the length and the direction of the unknown line may be expressed.

To help answer this question I base my work on two propositions which to me seem undeniable. The first one is: changes in direction which can be effected by algebraic operations shall be indicated by their signs. And the second: direction is not a subject for algebra except in so far as it can be changed by algebraic operations. But since these cannot change direction (at least, as commonly explained) except to its opposite, that is, from positive to negative, or *vice versa,* these two are the only directions it should be possible to designate, by present methods; for the other directions the problem should be unsolvabe. And I suppose this is the reason no one has taken up the matter.[2] It has undoubtedly been considered impermissible to change anything in the accepted explanation of these operations.

And to this we do not object so long as the explana-

[1] [In recent histories of mathematics, there have come about very misleading translations into English of Wessel's title word "forsog" as "essay on, etc." This possibility comes from the word "essai" used in the French translation of Wessel's memoir, the French word meaning both an attempt or endeavor, and a treatise (essay). Wessel's word "forsog" can only mean *attempt* or *endeavor.*]

[2] Unless it be Magister Gilbert, in Halle, whose prize memoir on *Calculus Situs* possibly contains an explanation of this subject.

tion deals only with quantities in general. But when in certain cases the nature of the quantities dealt with seems to call for more precise definitions of these operations and these can be used to advantage, it ought not to be considered impermissible to offer modifications. For as we pass from arithmetic to geometric analysis, or from operations with abstract numbers to those with right lines, we meet with quantities that have the same relations to one another as numbers, surely; but they also have many more. If we now give these operations a wider meaning, and do not as hitherto limit their use to right lines of the same or opposite direction; but if we extend somewhat our hitherto narrow concept of them so that it becomes applicable not only to the same cases as before, but also to infinitely many more; I say, if we take this liberty, but do not violate the accepted rules of operations, we shall not contravene the first law of numbers. We only extend it, adapt it to the nature of the quantities considered, and observe the rule of method which demands that we by degrees make a difficult principle intelligible.

It is not an unreasonable demand that operations used in geometry be taken in a wider meaning than that given to them in arithmetic. And one will readily admit that in this way it should be possible to produce an infinite number of variations in the directions of lines. Doing this we shall accomplish, as will be proved later, not only that all impossible operations can be avoided—and we shall have light on the paradoxical statement that at times the possible must be tried by impossible means—, but also that the direction of all lines in the same plane can be expressed as analytically as their lengths without burdening the mind with new signs or new rules. There is no question that the general validity of geometric propositions is frequently seen with greater ease if direction can be indicated analytically and governed by algebraic rules than when it is represented by a figure, and that only in certain cases. Therefore it seems not only permissible, but actually profitable, to make use of operations that apply to other lines than the equal (those of the same direction) and the opposite. On that account my aim in the following chapters will be:

I. First, to define the rules for such operations;

II. Next, to demonstrate their application when the lines are in the same plane, by two examples;

III. To define the direction of lines lying in different planes by a new method of operation, which is not algebraic;

IV. By means of this method to solve plane and spherical polygons;

V. Finally, to derive in the same manner the ordinary formulas of spherical trigonometry.

These will be the chief topics of this treatise. The occasion for its being was my seeking a method whereby I could avoid the impossible operations; and when I had found this, I applied it to convince myself of the universality of certain well-known formulas. The Honorable Mr. Tetens, Councillor-of-state, was kind enough to read through these first investigations. It is due to the encouragement, counsel, and guidance of this distinguished savant that this paper is minus some of its first imperfections and that it has been deemed worthy to be included among the publications of the Royal Academy.

A Method Whereby from Given Right Lines to Form Other Right Lines by Algebraic Operations; and How to Designate Their Directions and Signs

---

Certain homogeneous quantities have the property that if they are placed together, they increase or diminish one another only as increments or decrements.

There are others which in the same situation effect changes in one another in innumerable other ways. To this class belong right lines.

Thus the distance of a point from a plane may be changed in innumerable ways by the point describing a more or less inclined right line outside the plane.

For, if this line is perpendicular to the axis of the plane, that is, if the path of the point makes a right angle with the axis, the point remains in a plane parallel to the given plane, and its path has no effect on its distance from the plane.

If the described line is indirect, that is, if it makes an oblique angle with the axis of the plane, it will add to or subtract from the distance by a length less than its own; it can increase or diminish the distance in innumerable ways.

If it is direct, that is, in line with the distance, it will increase or diminish the same by its whole length; in the first case it is positive, in the second, negative.

Thus, all the right lines which can be described by a point are, in respect to their effects upon the distance of a given point from a plane outside the point, either direct or indirect or perpendicular[1] according as they add to or subtract from the distance the whole, a part, or nothing, of their own lengths.

Since a quantity is called absolute if its value is given as immediate and not in relation to another quantity, we may in the preceding definitions call the distance the absolute line; and the share of the relative line in lengthening or shortening the absolute line may be called the "effect" of the relative line.

There are other quantities besides right lines among which such relations exist. It would therefore not be a valueless task to explain these relations in general, and to incorporate their general concept in an explanation on operations. But I have accepted the advice of men of judgment, that in this paper both the nature of the contents and plainness of exposition demand that the reader be not burdened here with concepts so abstract. I shall consequently make use of geometric explanation only. These follow.

§1

Two right lines are added if we unite them in such a

[1] "Indifferent" would be a more fitting name were it not so unfamiliar to our ears.

way that the second line begins where the first one ends, and then pass a right line from the first to the last point of the united lines. This line is the sum of the united lines.

For example, if a point moves forward three feet and backward two feet, the sum of these two paths is not the first three and the last two feet combined; the sum is one foot forward. For this path, described by the same point, gives the same effect as both the other paths.

Similarly, if one side of a triangle extends from a to b and the other from b to c, the third one from a to c shall be called the sum. We shall represent it by $ab + bc$, so that ac and $ab + bc$ have the same meaning; or $ac = ab + bc = -ba + bc$, if ba is the opposite of ab. If the added lines are direct, this definition is in complete agreement with the one ordinarily given. If they are indirect, we do not contravene the analogy by calling a right line the sum of two other right lines united, as it gives the same effect as these. Nor is the meaning I have attached to the symbol + so very unusual; for in the expression $ab + \frac{ba}{2} = \frac{1}{2}ab$ it is seen that $\frac{ba}{2}$ is not a part of the sum. We may therefore set $ab + bc = ac$ without, on that account, thinking of bc as a part of ac; $ab + bc$ is only the symbol representing ac.

§2

If we wish to add more than two right lines we follow the same procedure. They are united by attaching the terminal point of the first to the initial point of the second and the terminal point of this one to the initial point of the third, etc. Then we pass a right line from the point where the first one begins to the point where the last one ends; and this we call their sum.

The order in which these lines are taken is immaterial; for no matter where a point describes a right line within three planes at right angles to one another, this line has the same effect on the distances of the point from each of the planes. Consequently any one of the added lines contributes equally much to the determination of the position of the last point of the sum whether it have first, last, or any other place in the sequence. Consequently, too, the order in the addition of right lines is immaterial. The sum will always be the same; for the first point is supposed to be given and the last point always assumes the same position.

So that in this case, too, the sum may be represented by the added lines connected with one another by the symbol +. In a quadrilateral, for example, if the first side is drawn from a to b, the second from b to c, the third from c to d, but the fourth from a to d, then we may write: $ad = ab + bc + cd$.

§3

If the sum of several lengths, breadths and heights is equal to zero, then is the sum of the lengths, the sum of the breadths, and the sum of the heights each equal to zero.

§4

It shall be possible in every case to form the product of two right lines from one of its factors in the same manner as the other factor is formed from the positive or absolute line set equal to unity. That is:

Firstly, the factors shall have such a direction that they both can be placed in the same plane with the positive unit.

Secondly, as regards length, the product shall be to one factor as the other factor is to the unit. And,

Finally, if we give the positive unit, the factors, and the product a common origin, the product shall, as regards its direction, lie in the plane of the unit and the factors and diverge from the one factor as many degrees, and on the same side, as the other factor diverges from the unit, so that the direction angle of the product, or its divergence from the positive unit, becomes equal to the sum of the direction angles of the factors.

§5

Let $+1$ designate the positive rectilinear unit and $+\epsilon$ a certain other unit perpendicular to the positive unit and having the same origin; then the direction angle of $+1$ will be equal to 0°, that of -1 to 180°, that of $+\epsilon$ to 90°, and that of $-\epsilon$ to $-90°$ or 270°. By the rule that the direction angle of the product shall equal the sum of the angles of the factors, we have: $(+1)(+1) = +1$; $(+1)(-1) = -1$; $(-1)(-1) = +1$; $(+1)(+\epsilon) = +\epsilon$; $(+1)(-\epsilon) = -\epsilon$; $(-1)(+\epsilon) = -\epsilon$; $(-1)(-\epsilon) = +\epsilon$; $(+\epsilon)(+\epsilon) = -1$; $(+\epsilon)(-\epsilon) = +1$; $(-\epsilon)(-\epsilon) = -1$.

From this it is seen that ϵ is equal to $\sqrt{-1}$; and the divergence of the product is determined such that not any of the common rules of operation are contravened.

§6

The cosine of a circle arc beginning at the terminal point of the radius $+1$ is that part of the radius, or of its opposite, which begins at the center and ends in the perpendicular dropped from the terminal point of the arc. The sine of the arc is drawn perpendicular to the cosine from its end point to the end point of the arc.

Thus, according to §5, the sine of a right angle is equal to $\sqrt{-1}$. Set $\sqrt{-1} = \epsilon$. Let v be any angle, and let $\sin v$ represent a right line of the same length as the sine of the angle v, positive, if the measure of the angle terminates in the first semi-circumference, but negative, if in the second. Then it follows from §§4 and 5 that $\epsilon \sin v$ expresses the sine of the angle v in respect to both direction and extent. . . .

§7

In agreement with §§1 and 6, the radius which begins at the center and diverges from the absolute or positive unit by angle v is equal to $\cos v + \epsilon \sin v$. But, according to §4, the product of the two factors, of which one diverges from the unit by angle v and the other by angle u, shall diverge from the unit by angle $v + u$. So that if the right line $\cos v + \epsilon \sin v$ is multiplied by the right line $\cos u + \epsilon \sin u$, the product is a right line whose direction angle is $v + u$. Therefore, by §§1 and 6, we may represent the product by $\cos (v + u) + \epsilon \sin (v + u)$.

§8

The product $(\cos v + \epsilon \sin v) (\cos u + \epsilon \sin u)$, or $\cos (v + u) + \epsilon \sin (v + u)$, can be expressed in still another way, namely, by adding into one sum the partial products that result when each of the added lines whose sum constitutes one factor is multiplied by each of those whose sum constitutes the other. Thus, if we use the known trigonometric formulas.

$$\cos (v + u) = \cos v \cos u - \sin v \sin u,$$
$$\sin (v + u) = \cos v \sin u + \cos u \sin v,$$

we shall have this form:

$$(\cos v + \epsilon \sin v) (\cos u + \epsilon \sin u) = \cos v \cos u - \sin v \sin u + \epsilon (\cos v \sin u + \cos u \sin v).$$

For the above two formulas can be shown, without great difficulty, to hold good for all cases,—be one or both of the angles acute or obtuse, positive or negative. In consequence, the propositions derived from these two formulas also possess universality.

§9

By §7 $\cos v + \epsilon \sin v$ is the radius of a circle whose length is equal to unity and whose divergence from $\cos 0°$ is the angle v. It follows that $r \cos v + r\epsilon \sin v$ represents a right line whose length is r and whose direction angle is v. For if the sides of a right angled triangle increase in length r times, the hypotenuse increases r times; but the angle remains the same. However, by §1, the sum of the sides is equal to the hypotenuse; hence,

$$r \cos v + r\epsilon \sin v = r(\cos v + \epsilon \sin v).$$

This is therefore a general expression for every right

line which lies in the same plane with the lines cos 0° and ϵ sin 90°, has the length r, and diverges from cos 0° by v degrees.

§10

If a, b, c denote direct lines of any length, positive or negative, and the two indirect lines $a + \epsilon b$ and $c + \epsilon d$ lie in the same plane with the absolute unit, their product can be found, even when their divergences from the absolute unit are unknown. For we need only to multiply each of the added lines that constitute one sum by each of the lines of the other and add these products; this sum is the required product both in respect to extent and direction: so that $(a + \epsilon b)(c + \epsilon d) = ac - bd + \epsilon(ad + bc)$.

Proof.—Let the length of the line $a + \epsilon b$ be A, and its divergence from the absolute unit be v degrees, also let the length of $c + \epsilon d$ be C, and its divergence be u. Then, by §9, $a + \epsilon b = A \cos v + A\epsilon \sin v$, and $c + \epsilon d = C \cos u + C\epsilon \sin u$. Thus $a = A \cos v$, $b = A \sin v$, $c = C \cos u$, $d = C \sin u$ (§3). But, by §4, $(a + \epsilon b)(c + \epsilon d) = AC [\cos (v + u) + \epsilon \mathit{sin} (v + u)] = AC [\cos v \cos u - \sin v \sin u + \epsilon(\cos v \sin u + \cos u \sin v)]$ (§8). Consequently, if instead of $A\ C \cos v \cos u$ we write ac, and for $A\ C \sin v \sin u$ write bd, etc., we shall derive the relation we set out to prove.

It follows that, although the added lines of the sum are not all direct, we need make no exception in the known rule on which the theory of equations and the theory of integral functions and their simple divisors are based, namely, that if two sums are to be multiplied, then must each of the added quantities in one be multiplied by each of the added quantities in the other. It is, therefore, certain that if an equation deals with right lines and its root has the form $a + \epsilon b$, then an indirect line is represented. Now, if we should want to multiply together right lines which do not both lie in the same plane with the absolute unit, this rule would have to be put aside. That is the reason why the multiplication of such lines is omitted here. Another way of representing changes of direction is taken up later, in §§24-35.

The quotient multiplied by the divisor shall equal the dividend. We need no proof that these lines must lie in the same plane with the absolute unit, as that follows directly from the definition in §4. It is easily seen also that the quotient must diverge from the absolute unit by angle $v - u$, if the dividend diverges from the same unit by angle v and the divisor by angle u.

Suppose, for example, that we are to divide $A(\cos v + \epsilon \sin v)$ by $B(\cos u + \epsilon \sin u)$. The quotient is

$$\frac{A}{B}[\cos(v - u) + \epsilon \sin(v - u)] \text{ since}$$

$$\frac{A}{B}[\cos(v - u) + \epsilon \sin(v - u)] \times B(\cos u + \epsilon \sin u) = A(\cos v + \epsilon \sin v),$$

by §7. That is, since $\frac{A}{B}[\cos(v - u) + \epsilon \sin(v - u)]$ multiplied by the divisor $B(\cos u + \epsilon \sin u)$ equals the dividend $A(\cos v + \epsilon \sin v)$, then $\frac{A}{B}[\cos(v - u) + \epsilon \sin(v - u)]$ must be that required quotient. . . .

YANG HUI

(c. 1275)

Yang Hui, the greatest Chinese arithmetician and algebraist of his period, flourished under the Sung Monarchy in China in the latter part of the thirteenth century. A skillful and prolific writer, he was the author of many works, several of which have been preserved to our time. In 1261 Yang Hui wrote his *Hsiang-chieh Chiu-chang Suan-fa* "The Analysis of the Arithmetical Rules of the Nine Sections", containing an explanation of the last five sections of the old "Nine Sections" as well as a classified arrangement of the ancient text. This was followed by his "Supplement to the Analysis" where the computations clearly indicated that in a period of transition in the development of mathematics, when the use of computing rods was still prevalent and reckoning on the suan-pan was rising in favor, Yang Hui was far ahead of his time in his possession of arithmetical methods employing decimal fractions. Five of his other works were grouped together by the celebrated biographer and historian Yuan Yuan (1764-1849) under the title *Song Yang Hoei Soan fa* (or Sung Yang Hui Suan-fa), "Treatise on Arithmetic by Yang Hoei (Yang Hui) of the Sung Dynasty." This treatise contained methods for calculating land areas, a geometrical representation of an arithmetic progression and the arithmetical rule for its sum. Yang Hui's *Suan-fa T'ung-pien Pen-mo* gave rules for summing other series including the sum of the squares of the first n natural numbers. In his *Ch'ong-ch'u T'ung-pien Suan-pong,* Yang Hui solved problems with the aid of a division table of a type used in later times with the suan-pan, including among his problems a case involving the solution of a biquadratic equation. Great interest was maintained in Yang Hui's work to a very late date. His *Hsio-ku-tse-ch'i Suan-fa,* "A Remarkable Arithmetic Adapted from the Ancients", presenting both the ancient rules and the rules of his day, was printed from blocks in the *mi shu* (Statistical Bureau) in 1804.

YANG HUI'S MATHEMATICAL WORKS

From *The Development of Mathematics in China and Japan*

by YOSHIO MIKAMI

In the "Analysis of the Nine Sections" Yang Hui illustrates the summation of an arithmetical progression. To find the total distance traversed in fifteen days by a steed who goes 193 Chinese miles (*li*) on the first day and who increases his speed 15 miles every day, Yang takes the product of the number of days and half the sum of the first day's speed and that of the last day, which is found by adding to the former 14 times one day's increase of speed. Here he adds a diagram as shown annexed.

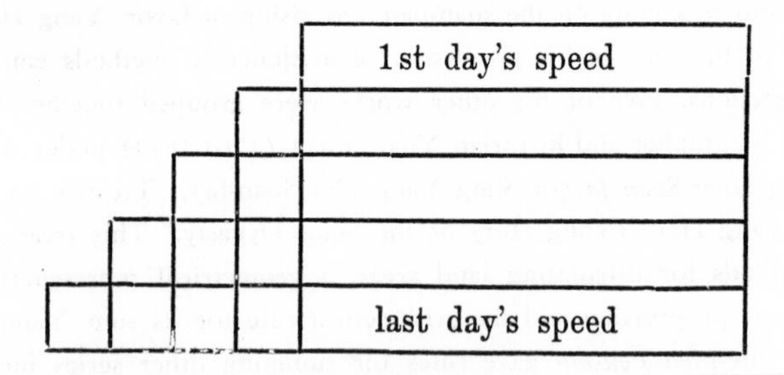

It is obvious that Yang intends to show that the required answer is obtained by taking a quantity corresponding to the area of the rectangle composed by twice this figure, and halving the result.

In the *Suan-fa T'ung-pien Pen-mo* Yang Hui further gives the formulae for the sums of the progressions he calls the triangular and the square, which are

$$1 + (1 + 2) + (1 + 2 + 3) + \cdots + (1 + 2 + 3 + 4 \cdots + n) = \frac{n(n+1)(n+2)}{6},$$

$$1^2 + 2^2 + 3^2 + \cdots + n^2 = \frac{1}{3}n\left(n + \frac{1}{2}\right)(n + 1).$$

About these progressions the formulae, or rather rules

that lead to these formulae, alone are given; no explanation is tried.

Yang Hui considers in the "Supplement" problems in simple proportion, one of which is this: "A runs 100 paces (a), while B runs 60 paces (b). If now B starts 100 paces (c) ahead of A, in how many paces will the latter overtake the former?"

This problem may be obviously solved by the formula of proportion:

$$a : a - b = c : x,$$

which is the very formula Yang Hui employs. He only writes it in the form as annexed and cross multiplies

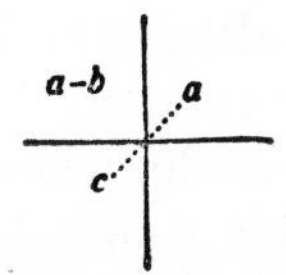

two of the elements and divides the result by the remaining element.

Problems in proportion were considered in the "Nine Sections" but this scheme of expressing a proportion was given for the first time by Yang Hui, so far as our limited knowledge goes. He calls proportion by the name *hu-huan,* which means literally "alternate exchange". He considers in his *Hsu Ku-chai-ch'i Suan-fa* also problems in compound proportion, which he calls *chung hu-huan* or "doubled alternate exchanges".

In linear equations Yang considers problems where four or five unknown quantities come in.

In the "Supplement to the Analysis" Yang considers the problem: "There is a rectangular field whose breadth is 24 paces and 3·4 feet and whose length is 36 paces and 2·8 feet. What will be its area?" In this problem there is of course nothing that is worthy of notice, but Yang's consideration of it is full of interest. He first treats it expressing the two lengths in terms of the tenth of a foot, but he also tries to carry out the multiplication in this way: When expressed by the decimal parts of the pace, the breadth becomes 24·68 and the length 36·56 paces. If we multiply these together we get

$$24{\cdot}68 \times 36{\cdot}56 = 902{\cdot}3008$$

This shows very well that Yang Hui had been in possession of a way of manipulating directly decimal fractions.

Yang Hui describes in his *Ch'ong-ch'u T'ung-pien Suan-pong* division by the employment of the division-table which is made like the multiplication-table. This table is a part of what has been employed in later years in the arithmetic with the *suan-pan* or the *soroban* of the Japanese.

In the old "Nine Sections" we find the problem: "There is a door whose height is 6·8 feet greater than its breadth and whose diagonal length is 10 feet. What will be the length and breadth?" This is just to find the two sides of a right triangle, whose hypotenuse c and the difference d of two sides a and b are given. To solve it Yang Hui makes use of the relation

$$c^2 = 2a^2 + 4 \times \left(\frac{d}{2}\right)^2 + 4\left(\frac{d}{2} \times a\right),$$

which may be easily verified. This is capable of being represented graphically as annexed. If we subtract

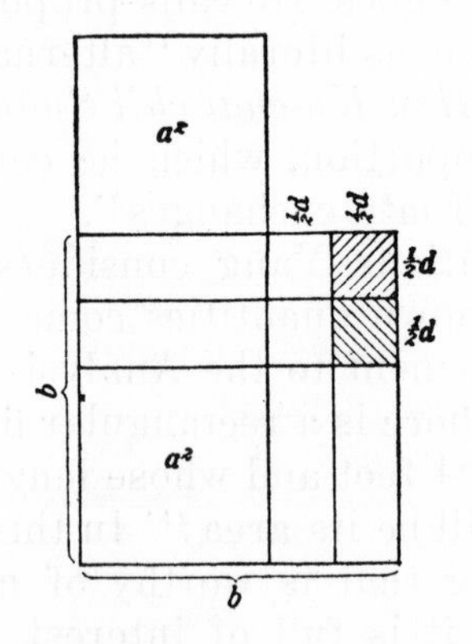

$2 \times (\frac{1}{2}d)^2$ from the whole and take the half of the remainder, the result is the square of $a + \frac{1}{2}d$. We have

therefore

$$a = \sqrt{\frac{1}{2}\left\{c^2 - 2\left(\frac{1}{2}d\right)^2\right\}} - \frac{d}{2}.$$

For this problem Yang Hui tries a second mode of solution. Thus from the relation $c^2 = 2a^2 + 2\,da + d^2$ follows

$$c^2 - d^2 = 2\,(a^2 + d\,a) \quad \text{or} \quad a^2 + d\,a = \frac{1}{2}(c^2 - d^2),$$

to which the method of evolution with an additive term applies, i. e., the approximate solution of the numerical equation of the second degree can be employed to obtain the value of a.

This method of evolution is explained graphically in the "Supplement to the Analysis" for the case of a quadratic equation, being referred to as taken from Liu I's *I-ku Kon-yuan*. Yang employs several problems for that purpose and considers several cases separately; but we shall give only one of these cases.

"There is a rectangular field, 864 square paces in area, whose breadth is 12 paces less than the length. It is required to find the breadth."

Here we have $A = lb = (b + d)b$, where the meanings of the letters employed will be obvious. Consequently b = breadth is to be obtained from

$$-864 + 12\,x + x^2 = 0.$$

A method had indeed existed from old times for the solution of such an equation as this, as we have already observed. But Yang Hui explains how such a way is to be followed. Namely, if we know beforehand that $b = 24$ and $l = 36$ paces, the area of the rectangle will consist of such parts as shown in the left of the figures. Suppose therefore we take $x = 20$ and operate as in the case of the extraction of a square root, then we shall see that the area may be divided as in the right-hand figure. If we subtract therefrom 20^2 and 20×12, the remainder will be $= 2 \times (20 \times 4) + 12 \times 4 + 4^2$. Hence trying to divide roughly the remainder by $(20 \times 2 + 12)$, we see that the next figure in the evolved root should be 4. If we now subtract 4^2, there is no remainder for the

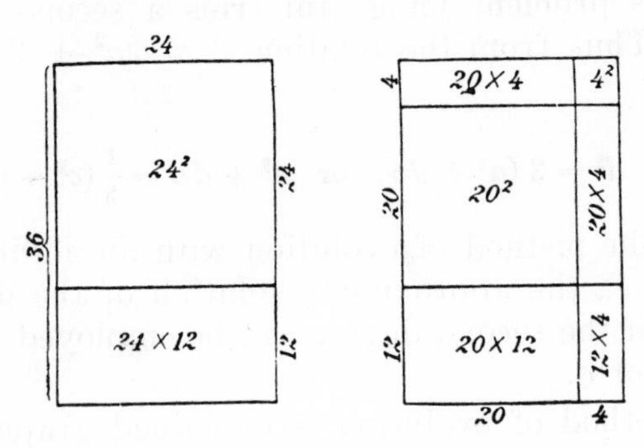

present case, and we find the breadth to be 24. If how ever there still is a remainder, the same process may be continued further.

Yang Hui also gives a case of a bi-quadratic equation. In the problem of finding the chord and altitude of a circular segment whose area (a) is 32 and whose diameter (d) is 13 he gives the equation

$$-(2a)^2 + 4ax^2 + 4dx^3 - 5x^4 = 0,$$

or

$$-4096 + 128x^2 + 52x^3 - 5x^4 = 0$$

for the determination of the altitude. The solution of this equation is briefly explained and the root is given to be $x = 4$.